McGraw-Hill Electrical and Electronic Engineering Series
FREDERICK EMMONS TERMAN, *Consulting Editor*

# Analysis of Alternating-current Circuits

# McGraw-Hill Electrical and Electronic Engineering Series

FREDERICK EMMONS TERMAN, *Consulting Editor*

---

BAILEY AND GAULT · Alternating-current Machinery
CAGE · Theory and Application of Industrial Electronics
CUCCIA · Harmonics, Sidebands, and Transients in Communication Engineering
EASTMAN · Fundamentals of Vacuum Tubes
FITZGERALD AND KINGSLEY · Electric Machinery
GEPPERT · Basic Electron Tubes
HESSLER AND CAREY · Fundamentals of Electrical Engineering
HILL · Electronics in Engineering
JOHNSON · Transmission Lines and Networks
KRAUS · Antennas
KRAUS · Electromagnetics
LEPAGE · Analysis of Alternating-current Circuits
LEPAGE AND SEELY · General Network Analysis
MILLMAN AND SEELY · Electronics
RÜDENBERG · Transient Performance of Electric Power Systems
SEELY · Electron-tube Circuits
SISKIND · Direct-current Machinery
SKILLING · Electric Transmission Lines
SKILLING · Transient Electric Currents
SPANGENBERG · Vacuum Tubes
TERMAN · Radio Engineering
TERMAN AND PETTIT · Electronic Measurements
THALER AND BROWN · Servomechanism Analysis

# ANALYSIS OF ALTERNATING-CURRENT CIRCUITS

W. R. LePage, Ph.D.
Professor of Electrical Engineering
Syracuse University

FIRST EDITION

New York Toronto London
McGRAW-HILL BOOK COMPANY, INC.
1952

ANALYSIS OF ALTERNATING-CURRENT CIRCUITS



*Library of Congress Catalog Card Number:* 51-12626

THE MAPLE PRESS COMPANY, YORK, PA.

# PREFACE

In the development of this text the goal always has been to impart understanding of fundamental principles to the student, rather than merely to have him acquire a dexterity in working problems. The first draft gave analytical discussions for most of the questions that had ever troubled the author. It soon became evident that the student readers did not have the necessary perspective to appreciate so much philosophy, and so, in the course of successive mimeographed editions, the language has been simplified and extraneous discussions have been removed, while compromises with the above stated objective have been avoided as much as possible.

The study of a-c circuits is a well-defined branch of electrical engineering. It is largely divorced from the general theory of electricity and magnetism, borrowing from it only the basic concepts of circuit theory and notation. On the foundation of these fundamentals is built a structure of special techniques based on the properties of the trigonometric functions. As a result, the material in a course on alternating currents is largely mathematical. This statement is not to be misinterpreted and taken to mean that the subject is a formidable one. The necessary mathematics is actually quite simple, being little more than trigonometry, algebra, and a bit of the calculus. The statement is intended, rather, to emphasize that the fundamental electrical ideas are assumed to have been established in previous studies and that it is the application of the mathematics of trigonometric functions to known electrical quantities that is new.

Adherence to the above-mentioned objectives resulted in four features worth noting:

1. In order to avoid an overly abstract treatment, simple problems are solved as early as possible. In many instances the exercise problems are drawn from devices which the reader is likely to meet in his everyday life.

2. Much attention has been given to the problem of communication between the author and the reader. To this end, an attempt has been made to state definitions clearly and to adhere to them rigidly. In a few instances unusual interpretations are given to old terms or new terms are introduced, because otherwise ambiguities could arise.

3. An attempt has been made to keep the development logical and to

have the technical level rise gradually with progress through the book. Every precaution has been taken to avoid peaks of difficulty which could plunge the reader into a topic without sufficient preparation.

4. The reader is taken "behind the scenes" to show him the meaning of the algebraic processes whereby physical entities are represented by algebraic quantities. An understanding of this process is particularly important in the subject of alternating currents.

A few of the more unusual practices in this text are mentioned below, as illustrations of these points.

The discussion of sources is made broad enough to include common devices, such as the phonograph pickup. As soon as simple circuits can be solved, the phenomenon of resonance is introduced, so that practical illustration can be drawn from the tuned circuits of radio receivers.

The treatment of sine and cosine functions of time may be mentioned as an example of the attempt to obtain a logical development. In the introductory work the geometrical concept is given strong emphasis over complex numbers. The technique of using complex numbers therefore appears very late. Another aspect of the attempt at a logical development is the emphasis on duality. Potential and current sources, and both Kirchhoff's laws, are placed on an equal footing. The author finds that students have little difficulty in understanding and using the ideas of duality, if they are introduced early.

The treatment given to the directed lines used in a-c theory illustrates the attempt at adequate definition of terms. Directed lines are used in a-c theory in two ways, each of which differs in certain respects from the use of three-dimensional vectors. To clarify the distinctions, the terms *sinor* and *phasor* are used for the directed lines used in circuit analysis.

Stress is placed on the terms *reference polarity* and *reference current direction*, rather than *positive polarity* and *positive current direction*. It is felt that this practice reduces confusion arising from the conflicting use of the "positive" and "negative" to describe types of electric charge and also to describe conditions of algebraic quantities.

The system adopted for potential-difference (voltage) notation requires some comment. At this writing there is little unanimity among engineers; thus it is literally impossible to adopt a system that will please everyone. However, it is felt that the system employed is adequate, and that it is simple. It seems to lead to no confusion in the mind of the unbiased reader. The question of notation for potential difference has been approached on the principle that it should be as simple and free of ambiguity as the notation for currents. *Potential difference* is used in place of the commonly used *voltage* in agreement with the recommendation of the latest standards of the American Standards Association and the American Institute of Electrical Engineers.

In order to avoid repeated definitions, standardized notation is used as much as possible. This standardization is not necessarily applicable outside the bounds of this book. Neither should it be considered binding even when working within the limits of the text. Symbols should be servants of the reader, and there must always be freedom to give a new definition to an old symbol, if to do so serves the purpose best. Boldface characters are used for symbols which represent directed lines, whether or not they are treated as complex quantities. There is perhaps a slight disadvantage in doing this, because it is impossible to write boldface script. In writing, the author recommends some such system of marking as the placing of a bar above the symbol. As comprehension grows, these marks can be dropped where they are not needed and retained where there would otherwise be ambiguities.

The author's aims have been retained in writing the exercise problems. The problems should provide an adequate amount of drill, but many of them are more than drill problems. Most of them are quite comprehensive, and an attempt has been made to make their results meaningful. In general, the degree of difficulty increases toward the end of each set, and so the problems should be assigned with care. Sets of questions are also included at the end of each chapter.

The subject of electric circuits ties in with other branches of electrical engineering through the various types of sources which excite the circuits and the circuit elements themselves (resistors, inductors, and capacitors). A considerable amount of space is devoted to discussions of the circuit viewpoint of sources. However, to go into the details of the sources themselves involves many related subjects: machinery, acoustics, radiation phenomena, and electronics. These details are by-passed in a study of circuits by postulating that the current and potential difference at the terminals of a source obey specific laws. A brief survey of how the $R$, $L$, and $C$ parameters of circuit elements are related to physical properties is given in Appendix A. Rationalized mks units are used throughout the text.

Some teachers feel that the general techniques of circuit analysis should be taught thoroughly for d-c circuits first. In order to make such a procedure possible a comprehensive treatment of d-c circuit analysis is given in Appendix B. This is a highly concentrated treatment which should be useful either for review or for an initial presentation if it is preceded by an introductory course in electrical engineering.

A list of representative texts on circuit analysis is given at the end. This list does not necessarily represent the author's sources of information, which could not possibly be acknowledged specifically. Actual developments are original, but they are of course based on knowledge and ideas gained from the author's teachers, the general literature, and, not the least, from his colleagues who have made many helpful suggestions. For many refinements the author is indebted to B. James Ley for his thorough review of the original manuscript and constructive criticisms. Acknowledgment is also made to E. L. Harder for his letter to the editor in the May, 1948, issue of *Electrical Engineering*, which initiated in the author's mind the idea of defining "reference conditions," and to M. B. Reed and W. A. Lewis for certain ideas about notation presented in their paper "Voltage Notation Conventions" in the January, 1948, issue of *Electrical Engineering*.

The author wishes to express his appreciation to the many members of the teaching staff of the Electrical Engineering Department of Syracuse University for their patience in using the early mimeographed editions. Particular thanks are due to H. F. Cooke, who read the original manuscript, to W. H. Thayer and R. P. Lett for their assistance in reading galley proof, to L. E. Lingo for reading page proof, to P. A. Dodge and W. A. Lombard for checking many of the exercise problems, and to Miss Phyllis Booher for her proficiency in typing the manuscript and for her help in preparing many of the figures. Finally, the author expresses appreciation to his wife, Eveline, for her constant willingness to subordinate her own activities to the heavy demands on the author's time during the preparation of the book.

WILBUR R. LEPAGE

SYRACUSE, N. Y.
*March*, 1952

CONTENTS

# CHAPTER 1

# ALTERNATING-CURRENT SYSTEMS

**1-1. Introduction.** In many electrical devices and their connected circuits, potentials and currents vary with time. When this variation follows a repeating pattern, the system is called an a-c circuit.* Because of the variation of the potentials and currents, a-c systems are more difficult to analyze than d-c systems. In spite of this they are widely used because they can perform services which cannot be provided by direct currents.

In most electrical applications, even in communication usage, it is necessary to transmit power. It is therefore important to understand how it is possible to transmit power continuously in one direction, while currents and potentials are continuously reversing. As an aid in understanding this it is helpful to note the similarity with many commonly encountered mechanical systems. For example, a crank mechanism is analogous to an a-c electrical system.

**1-2. Mechanical Transmission of Power.** The reciprocating steam engine illustrated in Fig. 1-1 provides mechanical analogues of both a-c

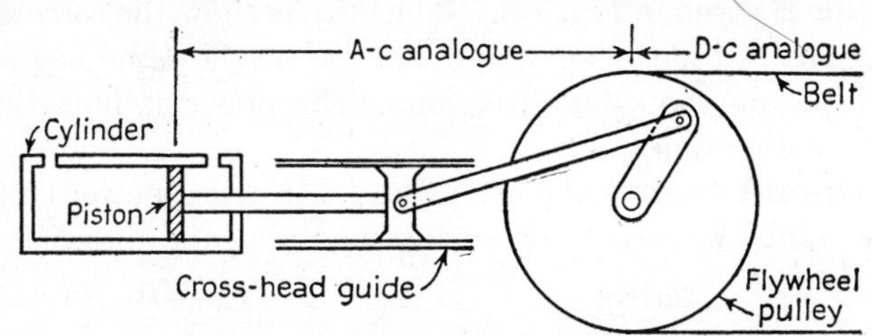


FIG. 1-1. Mechanical analogues of d-c and a-c electrical power transmission.

and d-c systems. The transmission of power from the flywheel, by means of a belt, is a mechanical analogue of d-c electrical transmission. The velocity of the belt (analogue of current) is always in the same direction, and the force exerted on the belt by the pulley (analogue of potential difference) is always in the same direction. Power is the product of force and velocity, so it is always in the same direction.

* It is common usage to employ the symbols a-c and d-c as adjectives. Thus, although a-c is an abbreviation for "alternating current," it is proper to speak of an a-c potential difference between two points, even though there actually may be no current flowing between the points.

The power transmitted by the pulley comes originally from the piston. The mechanical linkage between the piston and the pulley is analogous to an a-c electrical system. Power is transmitted from piston to flywheel no matter which way the piston is moving, because the force and velocity both reverse simultaneously.

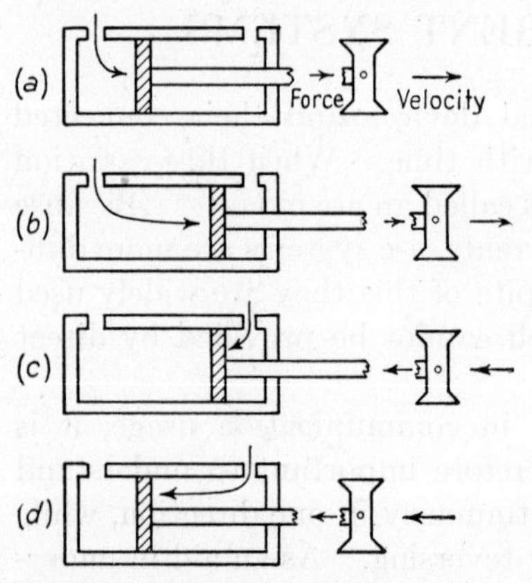


FIG. 1-2. Force and velocity at various positions of the piston.

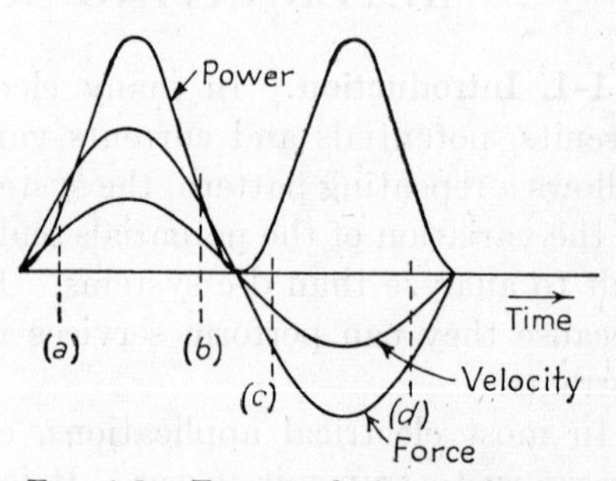


FIG. 1-3. Force, velocity, and power diagrams, showing how force and velocity both reverse simultaneously so that power does not reverse. Above the axis, force and velocity are to the right. Below the axis, they are to the left.

This is explained by Fig. 1-2. It shows the factors determining the power flow at the crosshead, at four different instants of time. In each case, force and velocity are both in the same direction. A more complete representation is given in Fig. 1-3. The graphs show the force and velocity as functions of time. They both reverse at the same instant, so the power is always in the same direction. The power is pulsating, but it never reverses direction.

**1-3. Electrical Transmission of Power.** Electrical power transmission in an a-c system can be considered by imagining the rate of reversal of

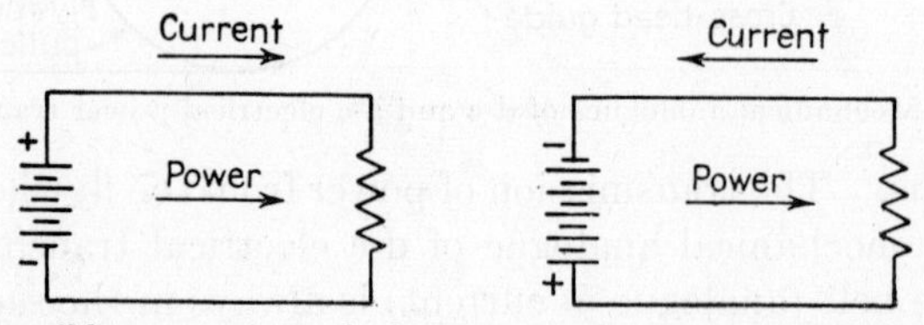


FIG. 1-4. Two possible connections of a battery to a d-c system. In either case the power flows in the same direction.

potential and current to be slowed down to the point where it can be visualized. Figure 1-4 shows two possible connections of a d-c source. An a-c system is simulated by imagining a repeating reversal of connections at the source. When the source polarity reverses, the current reverses also, and so the power continues to flow in the same direction.

In the simplest possible a-c system the battery is replaced by an a-c generator. Such an a-c circuit is shown in Fig. 1-5, in several typical instantaneous conditions. Although the magnitude of the power varies,

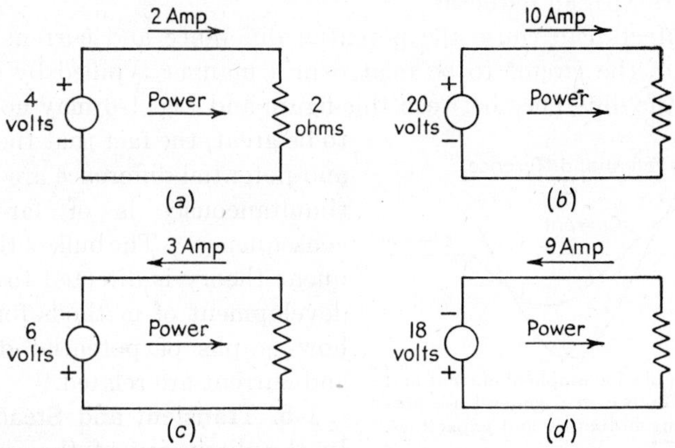


FIG. 1-5. Potential difference and current for various instants of time, in a simple a-c circuit.

it always flows in the same direction. This figure may be compared with Fig. 1-2, to which it is analogous. The analogy is completed by Fig. 1-6, which shows graphs of current and potential difference at the terminals of the generator. As with Fig. 1-3, the simultaneous reversal of potential difference and current explains how it is possible to have transmission of power always in the same direction.

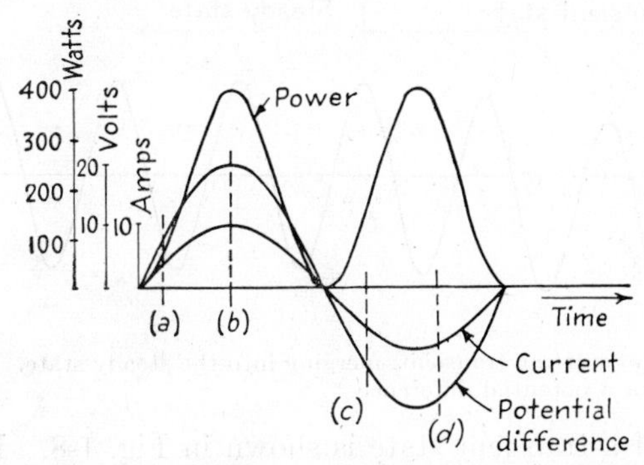


FIG. 1-6. Graphs of potential difference, current, and power. Above the axis potential difference has the polarity shown at (a) and (b) of Fig. 1-5, and current is to the right in the upper conductor. Opposite conditions prevail when the curves are below the axis, but power always flows to the right.

**1-4. A-C Systems.** The analysis of the circuit of Fig. 1-5 is only slightly more difficult than the d-c circuit of Fig. 1-4. However, few a-c circuits are as simple as this because capacitors and inductors have effects on the circuit. For example, in a d-c circuit a capacitor is an open circuit and has no effect, but in an a-c circuit the capacitor periodically charges and discharges, making an a-c current appear in its leads. A similar situation occurs with an inductor.

These effects can cause the potential difference and current at various parts of the circuit to be related in a manner typified by Fig. 1-7. Although the difference between this figure and Fig. 1-6 may not appear to be great, the fact that the current and potential difference are not zero simultaneously is of far-reaching consequence. The bulk of the subsequent theory is directed toward the development of methods for finding how graphs of potential difference and current are related.

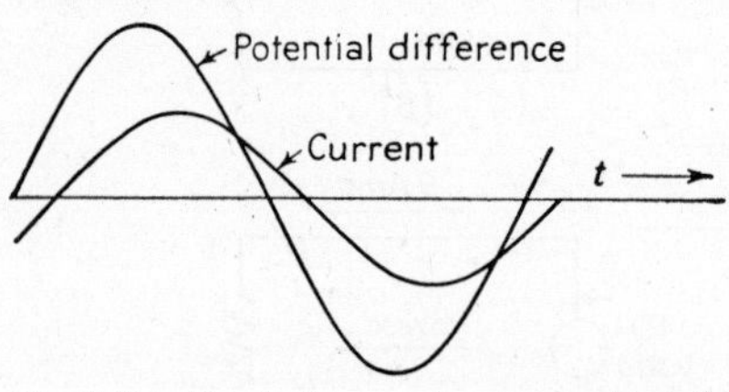


FIG. 1-7. Typical example of current and potential difference in a general a-c network including inductors and capacitors.

**1-5. Transient and Steady State.** In the discussion of the a-c system it is assumed that each cycle of operation is exactly like the preceding one. This condition is called the *steady state*. In any system there must be a starting-up period during which there is a nonrepeating disturbance called a *transient*. Whenever an a-c circuit is brought from rest to a steady-state condition, or if it is brought from one steady state to another, a transient is involved. Under very special conditions, the transient can be zero.

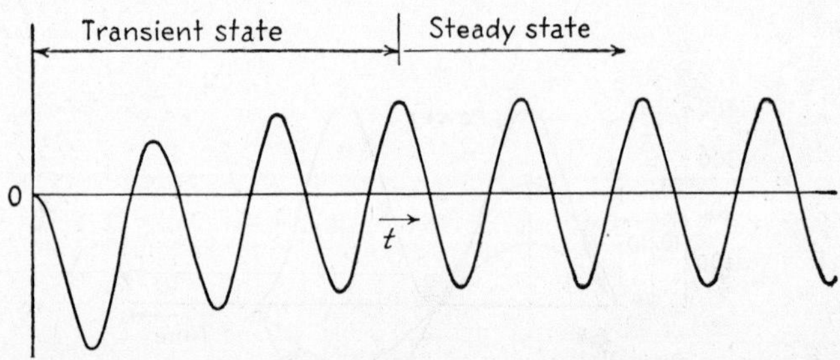


FIG. 1-8. Example of starting transient, merging into the steady state. The graph could represent a current or a potential difference.

An example of a transient state is shown in Fig. 1-8. No attempt is made here to derive the equation for the transient. It is sufficient to realize that a transient must appear at one time in the history of the circuit and that it dies out, leaving the steady-state condition to prevail.

In subsequent discussions the transient is neglected. This does not mean that the results are invalid or approximations. It means that the results apply only after sufficient time has elapsed for the transient to die out. There is a large class of situations for which this is true, and it is to these that the text applies.

**1-6. Applications of A-C Systems.** It is logical to ask why a-c systems are used, when d-c systems are simpler. There are a number of reasons. In the transmission of large amounts of power over great distances it is important to have high potentials and low currents, to give efficient transmission. However, generation and utilization of the power must be at lower potentials. It is therefore necessary to have simple and efficient means of changing potential and current levels. The a-c transformer is such a device. Another advantage of an a-c power system, for some applications, is the possibility of having constant-speed motors.

When intelligence is to be transmitted electrically, some sort of a-c system is mandatory. The signals which represent the intelligence are themselves represented by a-c functions of time. It follows that a knowledge of the principles of circuit behavior under a-c conditions is essential for the understanding of communication systems.

**1-7. Summary.** In spite of the alternating nature of currents and potentials in an a-c system, it is possible to attain a net flow of power in one direction. In the analysis of an a-c system, it is necessary to include the effects of capacitors and inductors. They have very significant influences on the distribution of potentials and currents throughout a system, and consequently on the amount of power which can be transmitted.

The problem of circuit analysis, under a-c steady-state conditions, is to find the expressions for currents and potential differences at pertinent points in the circuit. The solutions usually include the finding of the power absorption in various parts of the circuit.

## PROBLEMS

**1-1.** The idea of an alternating current and potential, and the associated flow of power, is conveyed by the circuit of Fig. P1-1. Plot graphs of the potential $v$,

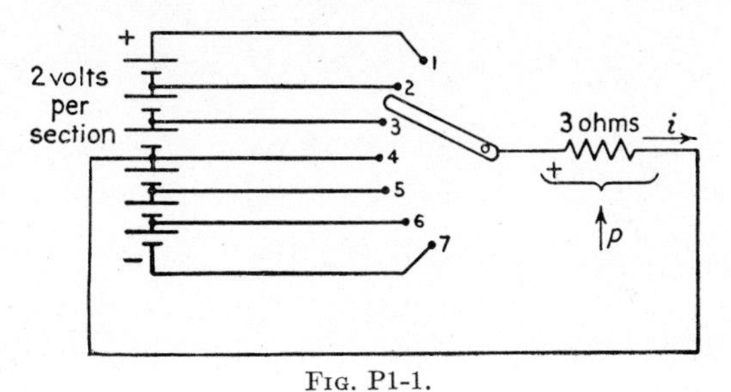


FIG. P1-1.

the current $i$, and the power $p$, as functions of numbered position of the contact arm. Note that if the polarity is opposite to the polarity shown, the graph becomes negative. Similarly, if the current is opposite to the arrow, its graph is then negative. Show graphs starting with point 1, going through point 7 and back to point 1.

**1-2.** This problem offers a comparison of the cost of conductor material for a low-potential and a high-potential transmission system. It is required that 5,000 kw be delivered to a load at a distance of 50 miles with a power loss of not more than 10 per cent of the sending-end power. For each of the following cases, determine the weight of copper needed in the entire transmission system, assuming two wires in each case:

*a.* A d-c system operating with 800 volts at the receiving end.

*b.* An a-c system operating with 100,000 volts at the receiving end.

NOTE: Of course, the conductor material is not the only expense. The a-c system requires transformers and other equipment that is not needed in the d-c system, so the above comparison is somewhat more favorable to the a-c system than a complete analysis would be.

## QUESTIONS

**1-1.** Why is it necessary to use, and therefore to study, a-c circuits?

**1-2.** How is it possible that an a-c system can transmit power, although the potentials and currents are continually reversing?

**1-3.** What is meant by the transient and steady state of an a-c circuit?

**1-4.** When potentials and currents at a given point in a circuit reverse at different instants, what happens to the power flow at each reversal? What happens at each reversal of potential and current when they occur simultaneously?

# CHAPTER 2
# INTRODUCTORY CONCEPTS

*If you wish to converse with me,*
*define your terms.*

*Voltaire*

**2-1. Introduction.** Electric circuits (or networks) consist of interconnected systems of devices which are capable of causing currents to flow (sources), and devices which are not capable of causing currents by themselves (passive elements). In most cases the passive elements are resistors, inductors, and capacitors; but sometimes they are vacuum tubes or other electronic devices. In analyzing a network the usual objectives are to find expressions for currents in the elements and potential differences across them. It is assumed that the reader understands the concepts of *current* and *potential difference* (abbreviated to *potential* in this text wherever it seems permissible to do so).*

We shall be studying *steady-state* conditions, which means that all currents and potentials vary periodically with time. For the term "steady state" to apply there is no restriction on the law of variation, except that it repeat itself periodically with advancing time. The type of variation depends on the sources that excite the circuit and on the passive elements. The primary objective of this text is to derive and explain these relationships, for the most general steady-state cases.

This chapter deals with a collection of ideas that must be established before the real work can begin. Much of it is given to establishing ideas that are used later. In particular, much emphasis is placed on the meaning of algebraic symbols when they are applied to currents and potentials that are continuously reversing, explaining what it means to speak of a current in a given direction, when it actually reverses direction repeatedly.

**2-2. Sources.** In the literature on circuit analysis the term "source" is used in a number of ways. The following usage is employed in this text.

*Source:*† A device which is capable of supplying energy to a circuit (but

* Potential difference is used in this text, rather than *voltage*, in compliance with the preference of the American Standards Association, as given in its 1950 publication of recommended electrical terminology.

† This usage of the term "source" may be somewhat at variance with the reader's experience. In some texts "source" may be used to mean "energy source."

does not necessarily do so) is a source. Another viewpoint of a source is that it is capable of maintaining a potential across its terminals when they are on open circuit or is capable of maintaining a current in its terminals when they are on short circuit. The open-circuit potential or short-circuit current may be functions of time. A source may be further classified as follows:

*Energy Source:* A source which is actually supplying energy to a circuit is called an energy source. It is often called a generator.

*Potential Source:* A potential source is a source for which the potential difference across its terminals follows a prescribed law of variation with time regardless of the current. This law is a characteristic of the source. In d-c circuits the potential difference is constant, and in a-c circuits it is a function of time. A potential source is a hypothetical source used in analysis. It is closely approximated by some practical sources.

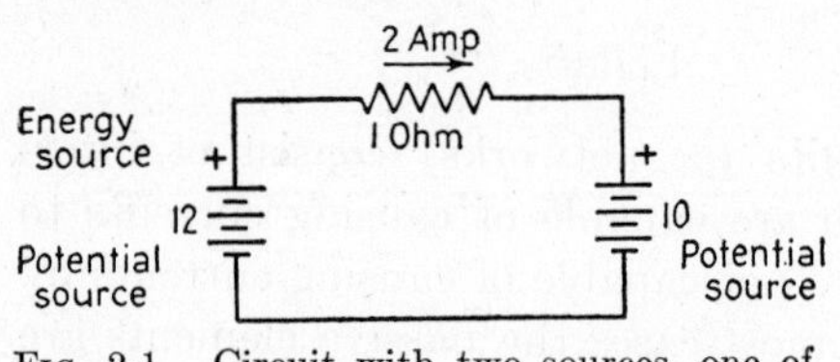


FIG. 2-1. Circuit with two sources, one of which is an energy source.

*Current Source:* A current source is a source for which the current in its terminals follows a prescribed law of variation with time regardless of the potential between them. As with the above case, the law is a characteristic of the source: it may be constant, or it may be a varying function. A current source is a hypothetical device which is closely approximated by some practical sources.

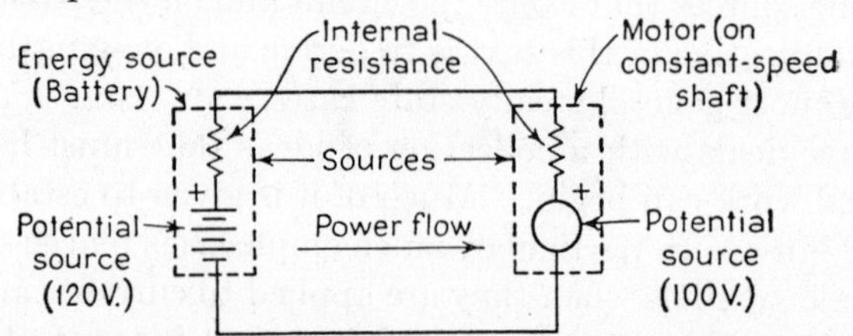


FIG. 2-2. Illustration of various types of sources in a d-c circuit.

The circuit of Fig. 2-1 illustrates two d-c sources. Each battery is assumed to have no internal resistance, so they are both potential sources. The 12-volt battery is also an energy source. Additional illustrations are given in Fig. 2-2. The battery is shown replaced by a potential source and a resistor. It is an energy source in this case, but it would not necessarily be an energy source (if it were charging, for example). The motor on the right is a source, if its shaft is connected to a driving machine that will keep it rotating when electrical energy is no longer fed to it.

Some devices closely approximate a potential source, and others closely approximate a current source. A storage battery and many devices based on electromagnetic induction are approximate potential sources. Approximate current sources are somewhat less common, and so a brief description of several types is given in Sec. 2-5. Even with devices which are not inherently nearly potential or current sources, sometimes regulators are connected to them to improve the degree of approximation.

When a source is not a potential or current source, a circuit employing it is analyzed by first replacing the source by an equivalent circuit which includes a current or potential source and some associated network, like the resistors inside the dotted rectangles in Fig. 2-2. The details of such substitutions are considered in Chap. 9. The ability to make such changes makes the concepts of current and potential sources important in circuit analysis.

In this text a circle on a circuit diagram represents a source; the only exception is the battery, for which the standard symbol is used. If the source is a potential source, the symbol $v$ is placed by the circle, and a + symbol is placed at one terminal; and if it is a current source, the symbol $i$ and an arrow are placed by the circle. The meanings of the + sign and the arrow are explained in Sec. 2-6. It is sometimes convenient to include a symbol within the circle to indicate the law of variation of the source. In this text the most usual symbol is ~, indicating a sinusoidal (see Sec. 2-3) wave shape.

**2-3. Rotating A-C Sources.** Sources for power purposes operate on the principle of electromagnetic induction. Figure 2-3 shows the usual arrangement of conductors and magnet. Other arrangements are possible. The conductors are stationary, the induction taking place as the magnetic poles sweep by. The rotor is magnetized by a direct current. The stator is of iron, to provide a low-reluctance path for the magnetic flux. The portion of the conductor lying in the slot is the active part. In Fig. 2-3 two such conductors are connected in series, but in an actual machine many such conductors are bunched together in a slot. Taken with their end connections, they form a coil. Many such coils are placed in slots spaced around the periphery.

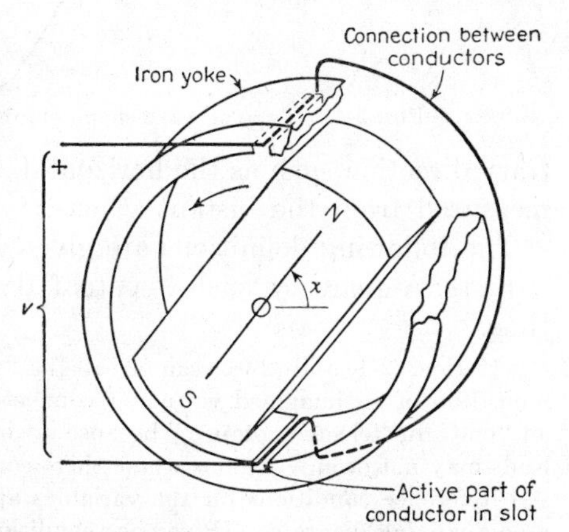


FIG. 2-3. Arrangement of rotating magnet and stationary conductors, as used in one common type of a-c source.

The potential difference between the ends of each conductor on open circuit (the induced potential*) is

$$v = Blu \qquad \text{volts} \tag{2-1}†$$

where $B$ is the flux density in webers per square meter, $l$ is the length of the conductor in meters, and $u$ is the relative velocity between flux and conductor, in meters per second.

Figure 2-4 shows a typical plot of the induced potential of a coil. The shape of the graph is determined by the distribution of flux around the periphery of the air gap. The waves are flat-topped because the flux is nearly uniform over the pole face. The curve goes below as well as above the axis because the polarity reverses in going from an N to an S pole.

The horizontal axis of Fig. 2-4 is labeled with two variables, $x$ and $t$. The former is the angular position of the rotor, measured from some arbi-

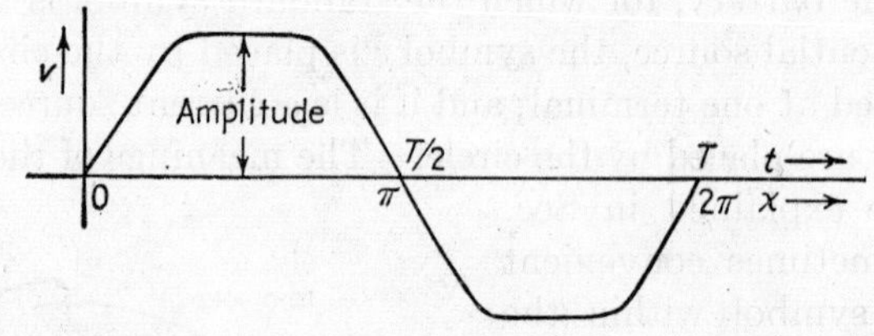


FIG. 2-4. Type of wave shape obtained from a source like Fig. 2-3.

trary direction such as the horizontal, and the latter is the elapsed time, measured from the instant when $x = 0$.

The following definitions are given in terms of the graph of Fig. 2-4.

*Wave:* A quantity, such as potential or current, plotted as a function of time.

* In Eqs. (2-1) and (2-9) $v$ can be called a "potential difference" (meaning a unique indication of an imagined voltmeter connected between the terminals), rather than an "emf" or "electromotance," because in circuit analysis it is agreed that voltmeter leads may not occupy regions where there can be electromagnetic induction.

† Reference conditions for the variables appearing in Eq. (2-1) are given by the accompanying diagram. (Reference conditions are discussed further in Sec. 2-6.)

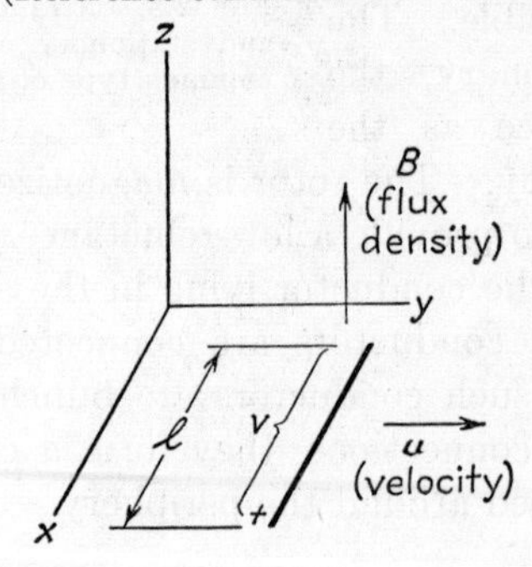

*Periodic Wave (or Periodic Function):* A wave which repeats itself at uniform intervals of time.

*Period:* The time interval after which a periodic wave repeats.

*Cycle:* That part of a wave embracing one period of time.

*Frequency:* The number of cycles occurring in 1 sec.

*Time Angle:* The variable $x$.

From the definitions of period and frequency, it follows that

$$f = \frac{1}{T} \tag{2-2}$$

where $f$ is the frequency in cycles per second and $T$ is the period in seconds. The time angle is proportional to time. This relationship may be written

$$x = \omega t \tag{2-3}$$

where $\omega$ is a constant of proportionality. When $x = 2\pi$, $t = T$. Therefore

$$\omega = \frac{2\pi}{T} = 2\pi f \qquad \text{rad/sec} \tag{2-4}$$

For this case $\omega$ is the angular velocity of the rotating magnet. It is also called the *angular frequency* of the wave.

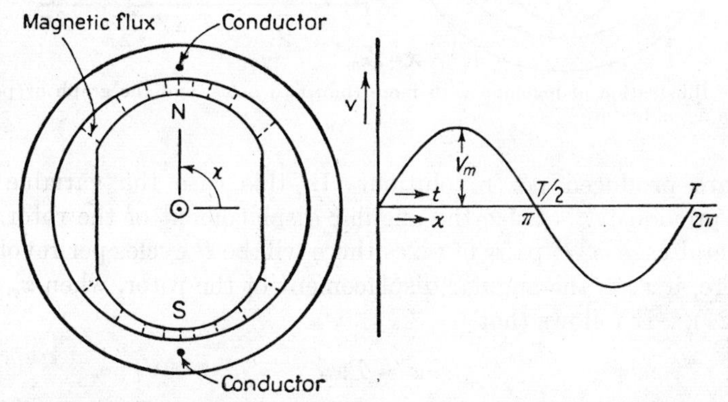


FIG. 2-5. A sinusoidal wave of potential difference; with an end view of a machine showing shaping of pole ends to make the potential induced in a conductor approximate the sinusoidal shape.

The wave shown in Fig. 2-4 does not have a satisfactory shape for most a-c applications. The shape shown in Fig. 2-5 is preferable, for reasons to become apparent later. It is called a wave of *sinusoidal shape,* or a *sinusoid.* Its equation is

$$v = V_m \sin x = V_m \sin \omega t \tag{2-5}$$

$V_m$ is called the *amplitude* (or *peak value*) of the wave. In Chaps. 15 and

16 it is shown that, when waves are not sinusoidal, solutions can be built up by adding together a number of sinusoidal components having different frequencies.

The generator can be modified to give a sinusoidal wave by adjusting the distribution of magnetic flux in the air gap. One way to do this is shown in Fig. 2-5. The air gap is made shorter in the center of the pole face and longer at the pole edges. This concentrates the flux at the center of each pole. In some cases the d-c winding on the magnet is distributed in such a way as to accomplish the same result.

In many cases a machine has more than two poles. Figure 2-6 shows one having four poles, and the wave it generates in one revolution. Two

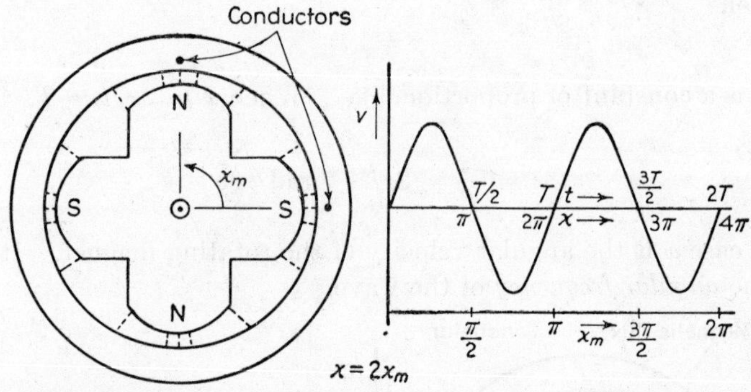


FIG. 2-6. Illustration of machine with more than two poles, and the graph of potential induced in a conductor.

cycles are produced per revolution. In this case the variable $x$, as defined previously, is twice the angular displacement of the rotor. For the general case of $P$ pairs of poles there will be $P$ cycles per revolution. Therefore, if $x_m$ is the angular displacement of the rotor, when $x_m = 2\pi$, $x = P(2\pi)$. It follows that

$$x = Px_m \tag{2-6}$$

and also

$$\omega = P\omega_m \tag{2-7}$$

where $\omega_m$ is the angular velocity of the rotor, and $\omega$ continues to be $2\pi f$.

Suppose S is the rotational speed of the rotor, in revolutions per minute. There are $P$ cycles per revolution and S rpm. Therefore the frequency of the wave is

$$f = \frac{PS}{60} \quad \text{cps} \tag{2-8}$$

This shows that the frequency of an a-c generator is rigidly related to the number of poles and its speed of rotation.

Waves generated by the machines described above are limited to frequencies lower than a few hundred cycles per second. Higher frequencies can be generated by the scheme illustrated in Fig. 2-7. A potential is induced in the coil by a changing flux. The flux is caused to vary by

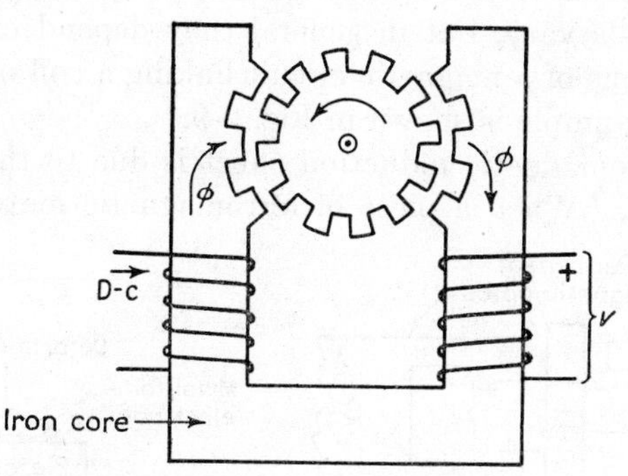


FIG. 2-7. A type of a-c source employing electromagnetic induction, but capable of producing higher frequencies than machines of the type of Fig. 2-6.

a variation of the reluctance of the air gap as the teeth move by one another. The potential goes through one cycle for each tooth on the wheel. Therefore, Eq. (2-8) relates the speed of rotation with the frequency, if $P$ is taken as the total number of teeth on the wheel. Frequencies up to 50,000 cps have been generated by such a device.

**2-4. Nonrotating Sources.** *Electromagnetic Induction Devices.* Any coil linked with a varying magnetic flux *not caused by its own current* may

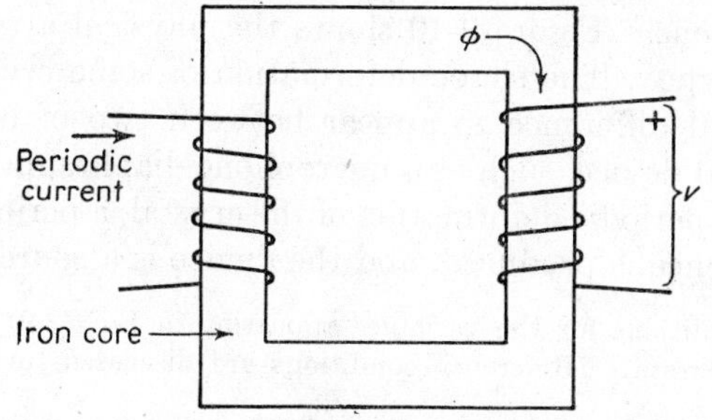


FIG. 2-8. The transformer: a type of a-c source.

be considered a source. When the varying flux is due to a varying current in another coil, the combination is called a transformer. An illustration is given in Fig. 2-8. On open circuit the potential difference between the coil ends (the induced potential) is given by

$$v = N\frac{d\phi}{dt} \tag{2-9}$$ *

where $N$ is the number of turns on the coil and $\phi$ is the flux linking the coil. This equation also applies to Fig. 2-7.

Other electromagnetic induction devices are used in communication applications. Certain types of microphones and phonograph pickups are examples. Details vary, but in general they depend on small periodic motions of portions of a magnetic circuit linking a coil or motions of the coil itself. An example is shown in Fig. 2-9.

Another electromagnetic induction effect is due to the phenomena of magnetostriction. When a piece of ferromagnetic material is distorted

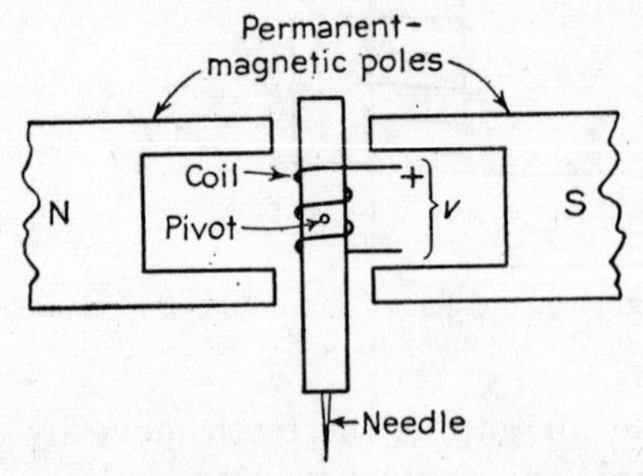


FIG. 2-9. One possible arrangement of the magnetic circuit of a magnetic phonograph pickup.

Deforming force
Metal foil electrode
+
v
Piezoelectric crystal
Conducting support

FIG. 2-10. The piezoelectric crystal as a source.

in shape, its magnetic properties are changed. If it is included as part of a magnetic circuit linking a coil and if the distortion takes place periodically, the result is a source.

*Piezoelectric Devices.* Piezoelectric devices are important in communication applications. Figure 2-10 shows the physical arrangement for a source of this type. The shape deformation of some crystals causes an electric potential difference to appear between two of its surfaces. If some mechanical device, such as a microphone diaphragm or phonograph needle, causes a periodic deformation of the crystal, a periodically varying potential difference is produced, and the device is a source.

* Reference conditions for the variables appearing in Eq. (2-9) are given by the accompanying diagram. (Reference conditions are discussed further in Sec. 2-6.)

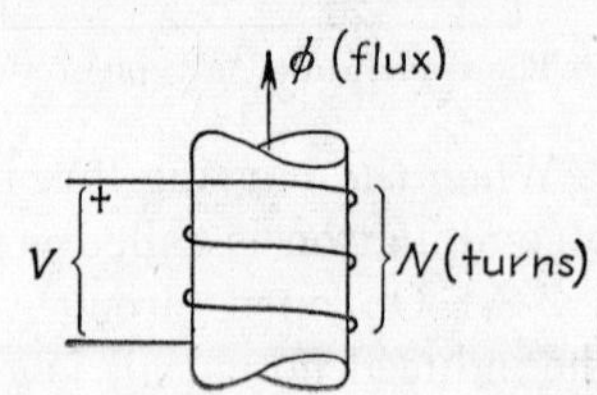

*Commutation Devices.* A switching device, such as the vibrating contacts of Fig. 2-11, can be used to provide a periodic source. A d-c source is switched into the circuit, with alternate polarities. A rectangular wave shape is obtained. The shape of the current wave can be made

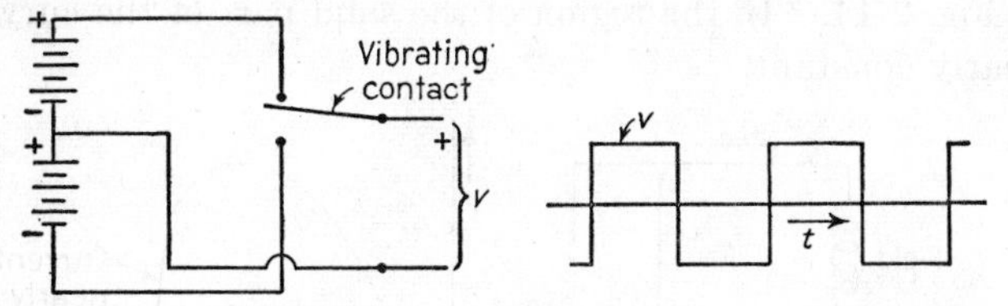


FIG. 2-11. Use of vibrating contacts to obtain a square wave.

nearly sinusoidal by attaching a suitable filtering network, like the one shown in Fig. 2-12, in which $L$ and $C$ are chosen to fit the formula

$$f = \frac{1}{2\pi\sqrt{LC}} \tag{2-10}$$

*Electronic Devices.* Electronic tubes (vacuum, or gas-filled) can be used as parts of a source. For example, one or more tubes can be substituted for the vibrating contacts of Fig. 2-11. The result is called a vacuum-tube oscillator. Other applications combine tubes with piezoelectric or magnetostriction devices.

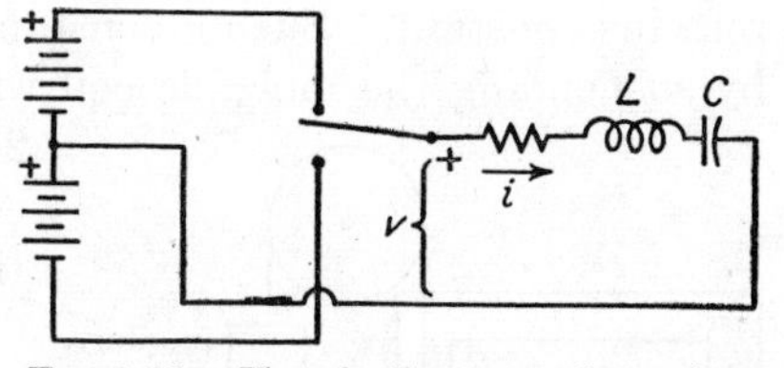


FIG. 2-12. Use of a "resonant" circuit to obtain a sinusoidal wave of current from a square wave of potential difference.

*Variable Circuit Elements.* Another method of exciting an a-c circuit is to use a d-c source and to vary one of the circuit elements periodically. The common telephone transmitter, shown in Fig. 2-13, is an example. The motion of a diaphragm causes a variation of a resistance element and

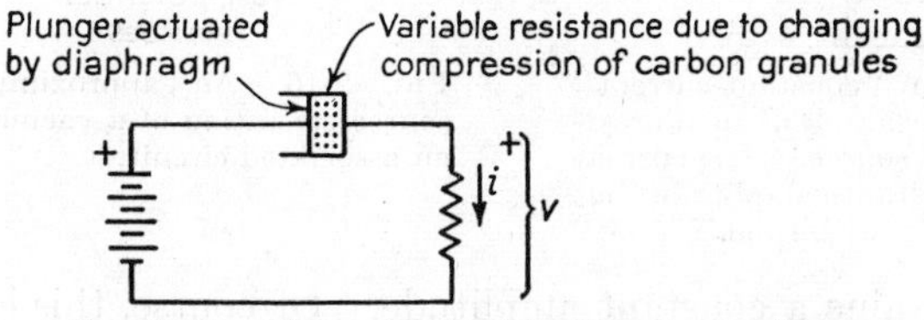


FIG. 2-13. Elements of a telephone transmitter.

a resulting current fluctuation. The condenser microphone is similar, except that the moving diaphragm causes a change of capacitance.

**2-5. Some Approximate Current Sources.** Many familiar devices, such as batteries and electromagnetic sources, closely approximate potential sources. Other devices, which are not so well known, are close approximations for current sources. A brief description of some of them follows.

A series-connected d-c machine can be operated as an approximate d-c current source. The potential-current curve of such a machine is shown in Fig. 2-14. In the region of the solid part of the curve the current is nearly constant.

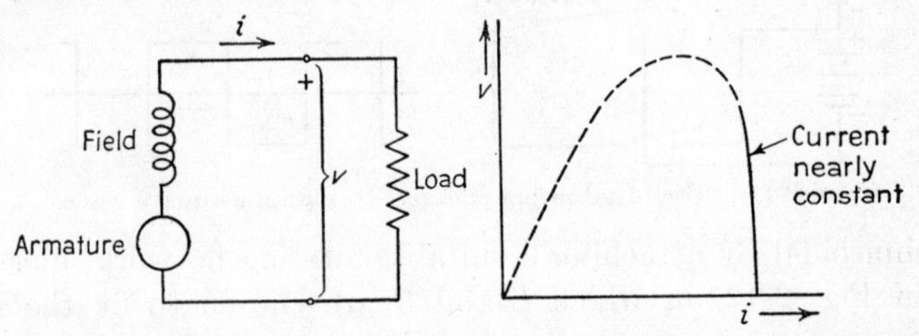


FIG. 2-14. Example of an approximate d-c current source: the series generator.

A transformer with one movable winding can be an approximate a-c current source. If the current in the coil remains of constant amplitude, the average mechanical force between the movable and stationary coils remains constant. Such a constant mechanical force can be maintained by suspending the movable coil with a counterweight as shown in Fig. 2-15. As the demands of the load connected to the coil change, the position of the coil changes but the a-c current maintains a constant amplitude. Of course, this is true only so long as the secondary remains within the limits of its range of travel.

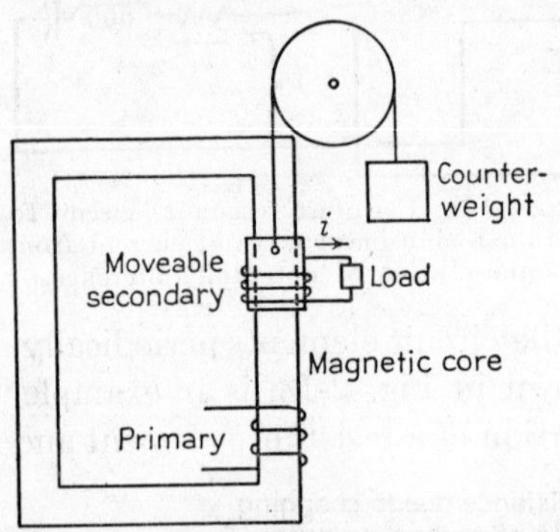


FIG. 2-15. The "constant-current" transformer: an example of an approximate a-c current source. The current has nearly constant amplitude but varies sinusoidally with time.

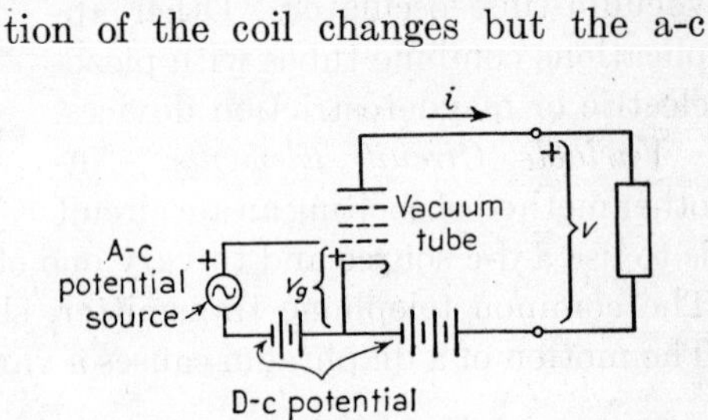


FIG. 2-16. An approximate current source consisting of a vacuum tube and an associated circuit.

Vacuum electronic tubes can sometimes be incorporated with other circuit elements to give a *combination* which will operate as an approximate current source. It may be an a-c or a d-c source, or a combination of the two. Figure 2-16 is an illustration. The arrangements of the "grids" within the tube are such that the current $i$ is almost completely a linear function of the potential $v_g$. Therefore, if $v_g$ is a potential source, the combination is an approximate current source.

**2-6. Algebraic Representation.** The quantitative analysis of any physical system (of which an electric circuit is a typical example) requires the representation of *physical entities* by *algebraic symbols*. Velocity, displacement, current, potential, etc., are examples of physical entities. An algebraic quantity is a symbol which can take on positive or negative numerical values.

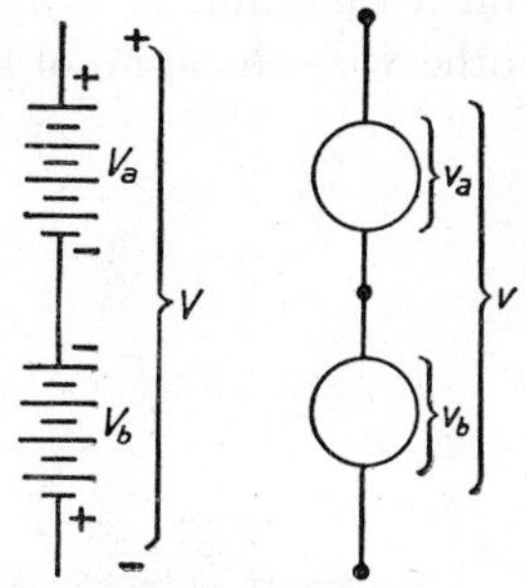

FIG. 2-17. Possible ambiguity in combination of a-c potential differences, indicating need of reference polarities.

The two examples shown in Fig. 2-17 illustrate the need for this discussion. When the two batteries are connected in series, their potentials combine by the equation

$$V = V_a - V_b \tag{2-11}$$

The polarity markings determine what sign should be placed between $V_a$ and $V_b$. Now consider two a-c potential sources connected in series, as shown at the right of Fig. 2-17. They no longer have unidirectional polarity, so it is impossible to decide from Fig. 2-17 whether

$$v = v_a + v_b$$

or

$$v = v_a - v_b \tag{2-12}$$

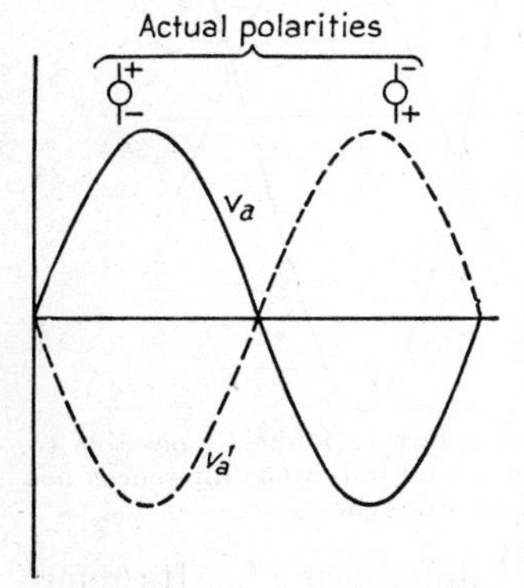

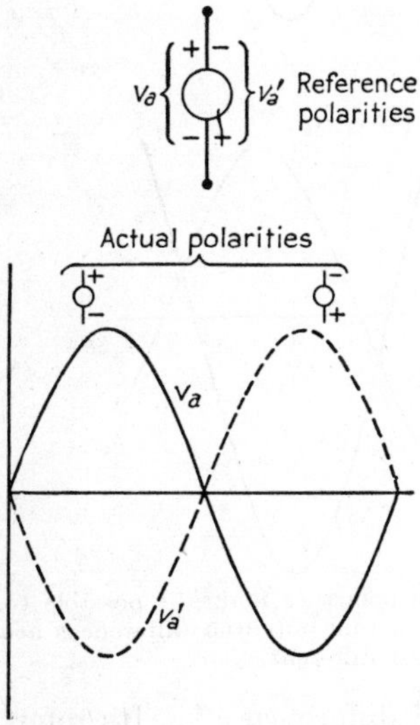

FIG. 2-18. Meaning of reference polarity. Actual polarities are shown above portions of the graph for which they apply.

Only one of these can be correct in a given case, and so it is necessary to define $v_a$ and $v_b$ in such a way as to be able to decide which equation applies.

The ambiguity is removed by introducing the idea of a *reference polarity*. To understand how the ambiguity is removed, consider the graphs of Fig. 2-18. Consider $v_a$ first. It is an algebraic symbol. It is positive when the curve is above the axis, and it is negative when the curve is below the axis.* As the curve changes from positive to negative, the actual electric polarity changes, as indicated by the

* Owing to an unfortunate historical accident, + and − signs are used to designate polarity as well as for labels on a graph. The two usages are entirely different. Acknowledgment of this fact will help eliminate confusion.

polarity symbols labeled "actual polarities" above the graph. *The actual polarity which exists at the time when the curve is positive is defined as the reference polarity of the potential difference $v_a$.* When $v_a$ is placed on a diagram, as a label, this reference polarity must also be shown; otherwise the symbol has no meaning.

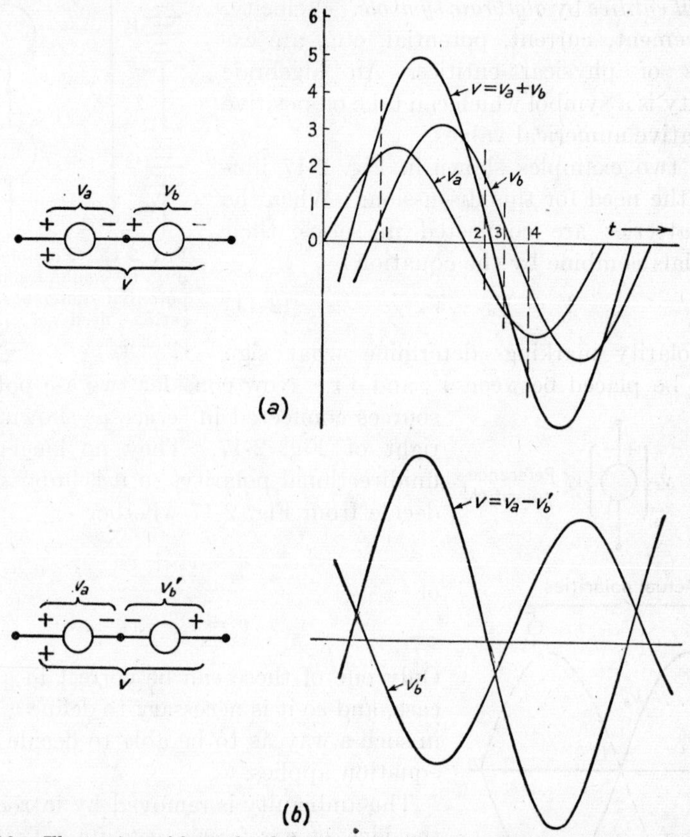


Fig. 2-19. Illustration of how the definition of reference polarities makes it possible to apply the Kirchhoff law for potential differences. The actual potential differences are identical in parts (a) and (b), only the reference polarities are different.

A similar discussion applies to the potential difference $v_a'$. Its reference polarity is the opposite of that for $v_a$. Accordingly, $v_a' = -v_a$, and its graph is the negative of the graph for $v_a$.

Reference polarities are used in the manner shown in Fig. 2-19. *Kirchhoff's law for potential differences is applied as if each potential difference were like its reference polarity.* For example, for Fig. 2-19*a* the reference polarities are such that

$$v = v_a + v_b \tag{2-13}$$

and for Fig. 2-19*b* the potentials combine in accordance with the equation

$$v = v_a - v_b' \qquad (2\text{-}14)$$

Any number of potentials can be combined in this way by repeating the process. Any doubt as to the validity of Eqs. (2-13) and (2-14) can be dispelled by considering them for several numerical cases. Take Eq. (2-13), for example, and consider it for the instants labeled (1), (2), (3), and (4) in Fig. 2-19*a*. The information is presented in the following table:

| Instant | $v_a$ | $v_b$ | $v = v_a + v_b$ |
|---|---|---|---|
| (1) | 2.4 | 0.7 | 3.1 |
| (2) | −1.0 | 1.8 | 0.8 |
| (3) | −1.8 | 0.6 | −1.2 |
| (4) | −2.5 | −1.2 | −3.7 |

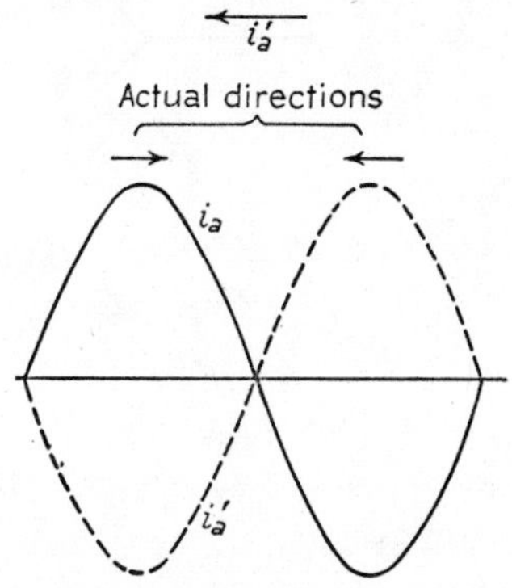


FIG. 2-20. Meaning of reference direction for current. The line at the top represents a current carrying conductor. Actual directions are shown above portions of the graph for which they apply.

Emphasis is on the fact that the one equation $v = v_a + v_b$ applies at all times and that it is obtained by applying Kirchhoff's potential law to the *reference polarities.* Without the reference polarities the equation could not be written.

In the case of currents which are continually reversing direction a *reference direction* is defined. This concept is illustrated in Fig. 2-20. *The reference direction of $i_a$ is the actual direction at those instants when the curve is positive.* When $i_a$ is placed on a diagram, as a label, an arrow must show the reference direction; otherwise the symbol has no meaning.

With the aid of reference directions it is possible to apply Kirchhoff's current law at a junction. *The equation is written as if each current direction were actually in its reference direction.* For Fig. 2-21*a* all possible conditions are satisfied by the one equation

$$i = i_a + i_b \qquad (2\text{-}15)$$

Similarly, the alternate situation in Fig. 2-21*b* is represented by the one equation

$$i = i_a - i_b' \qquad (2\text{-}16)$$

Any number of currents can be combined by repeating the process.

This preliminary discussion of potential reference polarity and current reference direction, and their use in Kirchhoff's laws, is not carried to completion here. Nothing has been said so far about how reference directions and polarities are chosen. In many cases they are arbitrary, and in other cases they are not. A more general and more complete discussion of this whole subject is given in Chap. 9.

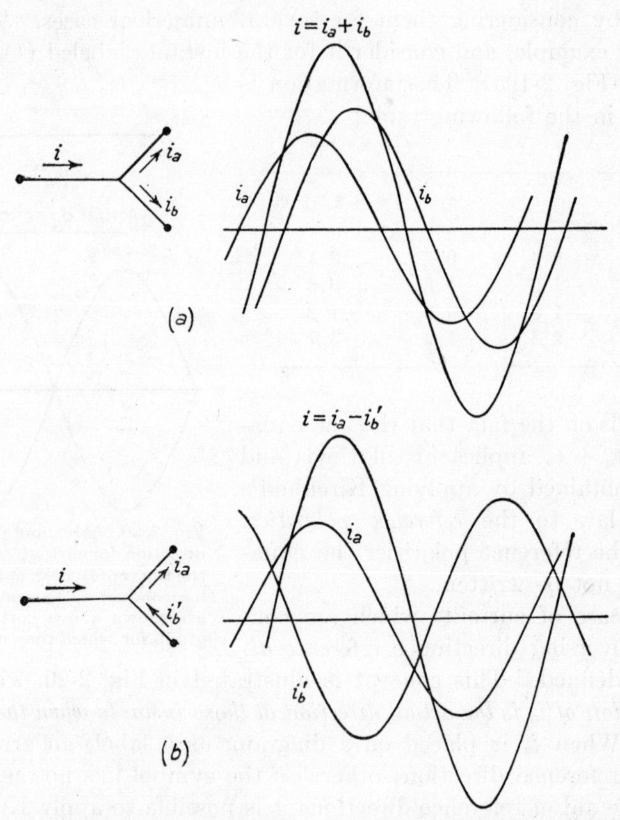


FIG. 2-21. Illustration of how the definition of reference directions makes it possible to apply the Kirchhoff law for currents. The actual currents are identical in parts (*a*) and (*b*), only the reference directions are different.

Potential reference polarities and current reference directions are grouped together under the name "*reference conditions.*" In summary, two facts are to be noted about reference conditions. A reversal of a reference condition causes a change in sign of the corresponding variable quantity. Also, the reference condition serves to give the variable its name, for example, a potential *drop in a certain direction*, or a current *in a certain direction.* The meaning of such a statement as "$i$ is the current to the right" is clarified when it is understood to mean that the reference direction is to the right and that part of the time the current can actually be in the opposite direction.

Reference conditions have been explained in terms of potentials and currents. The same concept applies for any situations where algebraic quantities are employed, even when they are not varying rapidly with time. In subsequent parts of the text reference conditions are defined for other quantities, a number of which are angular measure, magnetic flux, electric charge, and power flow.

**2-7. Reference Conditions for Potentials and Currents.** For each symbol used to represent a potential or current it is necessary to indicate on a circuit diagram:

1. The quantity represented.
2. The reference condition.

Without the inclusion of these two facts, a symbol is meaningless.

Two systems of notation are in common use. One of them uses a letter, with possibly one identifying subscript ($v_a$, $v_1$, $i_a$, $i_1$, etc.). The other system employs two subscripts on the symbol ($v_{12}$, $i_{ab}$, etc.).

*Single-subscript System.* In this system, subscripts are used only when it is necessary to use a single letter to represent more than one quantity. The symbol is placed on the circuit diagram in a suitable position to indicate what potential difference or current it represents.

A current is localized in a conductor, so it is necessary only to place the symbol alongside the conductor. A potential difference exists between *two* points in a circuit, so it is necessary to indicate these points. This may be done by one of the schemes shown in Fig. 2-22.

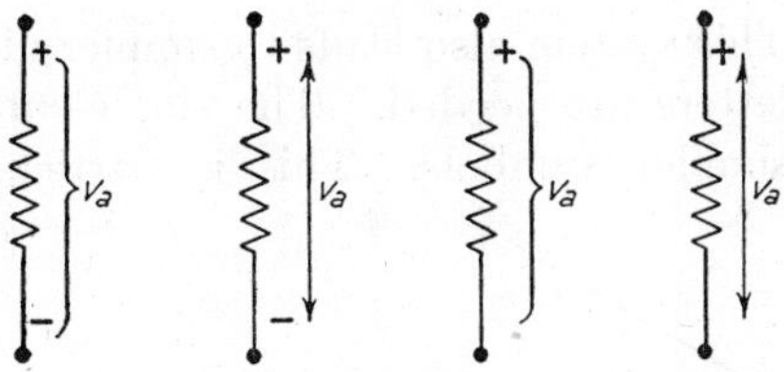

FIG. 2-22. Various equivalent methods for specifying the reference polarity for a varying potential difference.

The reference condition is given by additional markings. For a potential, + and − signs are placed at the points between which the potential difference exists. In practice it is sufficient to use only the + sign, the other sign being implied. The reference direction of a current is indicated by an arrow. Figures 2-17 to 2-21 are illustrations of the single-subscript system.

*Double-subscript System.* In a double-subscript system the circuit diagram is labeled with a system of letters or numbers placed at appropriate points in the circuit. In the example of Fig. 2-23 the symbol $v_{12}$ means the following: It is the potential between points 1 and 2, with a + sign implied at the position of the first subscript. The potential $v_{12}$ is alternatively called the potential of 1 with respect to 2, or the potential drop from 1 to 2.

Figure 2-24 shows the meaning of a double subscript on a current symbol. The reference direction for $i_{12}$ is from point 1 to point 2.

Figures 2-23 and 2-24 include single-subscript symbols to show how the two systems are related. In many cases there is freedom of choice of system, so it is worth while to consider their relative merits. The double-

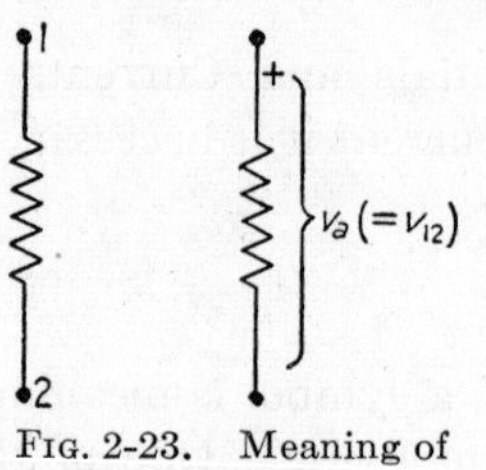


FIG. 2-23. Meaning of double subscripts for potential difference.

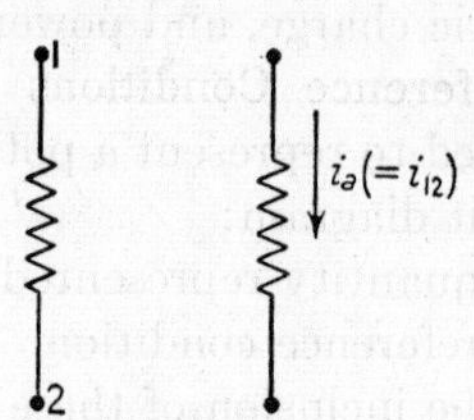


FIG. 2-24. Meaning of double subscripts for current.

subscript system eliminates many negative signs because a reversal of subscripts is equivalent to a change of sign. For example,

$$\begin{aligned} v_{12} &= -v_{21} \\ i_{12} &= -i_{21} \end{aligned} \tag{2-17}$$

This system also leads to simpler diagrams, because only the identifying letters are needed. The single-subscript system has the advantage of simpler symbols. This is particularly important when the symbols appear in extensive formulas. The choice of system is left to individual cases, so it is necessary to become familiar with both.

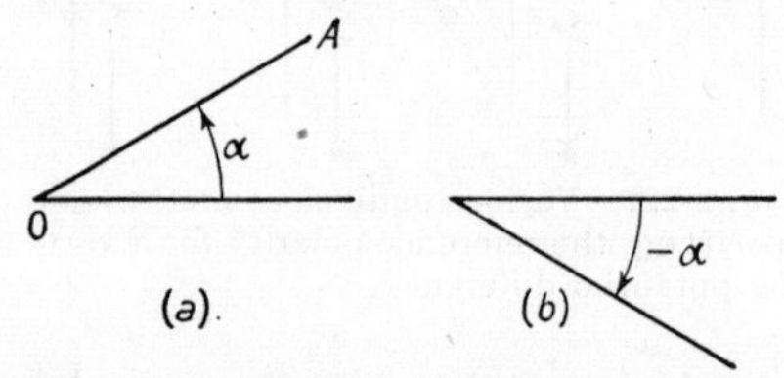


FIG. 2-25. Meaning of reference direction for angular measure.

**2-8. Geometric Reference Conditions.** The concept of a reference direction applies to the algebraic representation of geometric quantities. Figure 2-25 is an example. At (*a*) the quantity $\alpha$ is shown as the angular position of line $OA$, measured from the horizontal line. The reference direction is counterclockwise. It may be said that $\alpha$ is the counterclockwise angular position of line $OA$. The arrow on the diagram conveys this information. It points in the reference direction, and it is directed from the datum line (horizontal) toward the variable line.

In some cases it is necessary to label a diagram when the variable is not positioned in its reference direction. An example is shown in Fig. 2-25*b*. The arrow is drawn from the fixed to the variable line, but then it opposes the reference direction. To compensate, it is labeled by placing a negative sign on the symbol.

Both figures define $\alpha$ as the angle by which the line $OA$ is counterclockwise from the horizontal line. The numerical values of the figure may be cited as examples: in Fig. 2-25*a* the line is $+30°$ counterclockwise, and in Fig. 2-25*b* it is counterclockwise by $-30°$ (clockwise by 30°).

**2-9. Nonsinusoidal Waves.** In some a-c circuits nonsinusoidal wave shapes are encountered. Some of these are mentioned in the section on sources. When a wave is nonsinusoidal, several attributes are defined, in addition to the ones given in Sec. 2-3.

An example of a nonsinusoidal periodic wave is shown in Fig. 2-26. To represent a general condition, a case was chosen where the area below

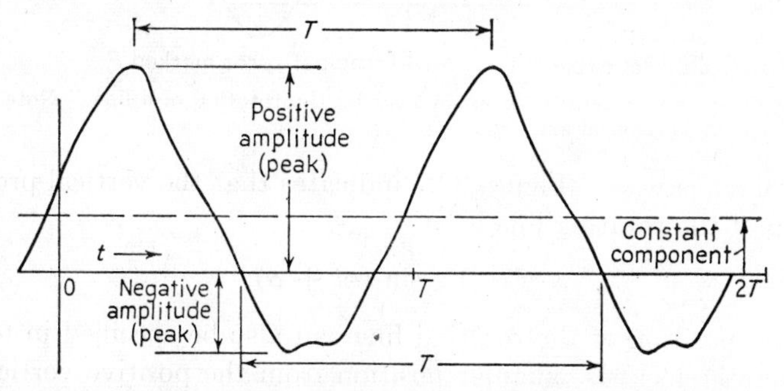


Fig. 2-26. Graph of a nonsinusoidal periodic function.

the axis is less than the area above the axis. The horizontal dotted line is positioned so that the curve has the same area above and below it. The following properties of the wave are defined:

*Constant Component (D-C Component):* The distance of the horizontal dotted line above the horizontal axis. If the dotted line is below, the constant component is negative.

*Alternating Component:* The wave obtained by considering the dotted line as the horizontal axis.

*Positive Amplitude (Positive Peak):* The magnitude of the largest displacement in the positive direction. If the function is everywhere negative, it has no positive amplitude. The positive amplitude is always a positive number.

*Negative Amplitude (Negative Peak):* The magnitude of the largest displacement in the negative direction. If the function is everywhere positive, it has no negative amplitude. The negative amplitude is always a positive number.

**2-10. Sinusoidal Waves.** The equation for a sinusoid given by Eq. (2-5) lacks generality because it requires that the curve go through zero at $t = 0$. The general case is shown in Fig. 2-27. It is convenient to think of the wave as a plot of the vertical projection of the tip of a line, as it rotates with constant angular velocity $\omega$. At $t = 0$ the line makes an angle $\alpha$ with the positive horizontal axis. The reference direction of

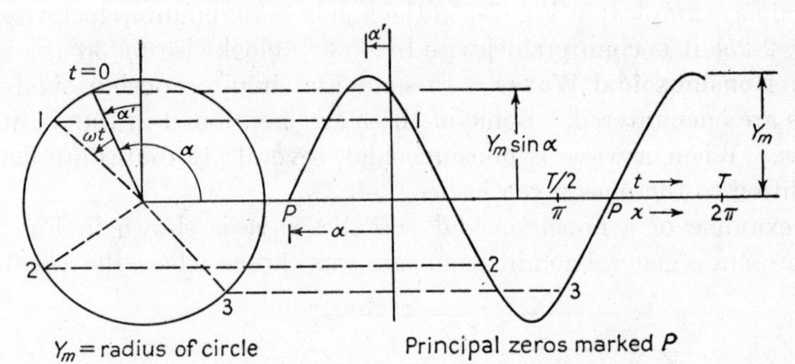


Fig. 2-27. Geometric generation of a sinusoid by the rotation of a line. Note that $x$ is used for $\omega t$ on the horizontal axis.

$\alpha$ is counterclockwise. Figure 2-27 indicates that the vertical projection of the tip of the rotating line is

$$y = Y_m \sin (\omega t + \alpha) \tag{2-18}$$

The initial position of the rotating line can also be specified in terms of $\alpha'$, its counterclockwise angular position from the positive vertical axis. The vertical projection of the rotating line then becomes

$$y = Y_m \cos (\omega t + \alpha') \tag{2-19}$$

Either Eq. (2-18) or (2-19) can be used in all cases, by a proper choice of $\alpha$ or $\alpha'$. From the figure it is seen that

$$\alpha = \alpha' + \frac{\pi}{2} \tag{2-20}$$

The choice of whether to use a sine or cosine function is arbitrary. Rather than to carry both, the sine form is chosen for this text. In some developments cosine forms may appear, but Eq. (2-20) can always be used to convert to the sine form. The term "sinusoid" always applies, no matter which trigonometric function is used.

The angular position of the rotating line for any instant of time is called the *phase angle* of the wave at that instant. Because the wave is periodic, the phase angle is always less than $2\pi$ rad. In terms of Eq. (2-18) the quantity $\omega t + \alpha$ may be called the phase angle when it is less than $2\pi$.

The quantities $Y_m$ and $\alpha$ completely specify a sinusoid when it is plotted on the $x = \omega t$ scale. $Y_m$ has been defined as the amplitude.

The angle $\alpha$ is called the *initial phase angle* (abbreviated to *initial angle*). The initial position of the rotating line is given as one possible graphical interpretation of the initial angle. It also has meaning on the plot of the sinusoidal wave. A point where the wave goes through zero, with a positive slope, is called a *principal zero*. The initial angle is the position of a principal zero with respect to the origin on the $\omega t$ scale. The reference direction of $\alpha$ is toward the left, as indicated in Fig. 2-27.

The initial angle is an algebraic quantity and may therefore have negative values. Negative values are obtained when measurement is made to a principal zero to the right of the origin. In all cases, two initial

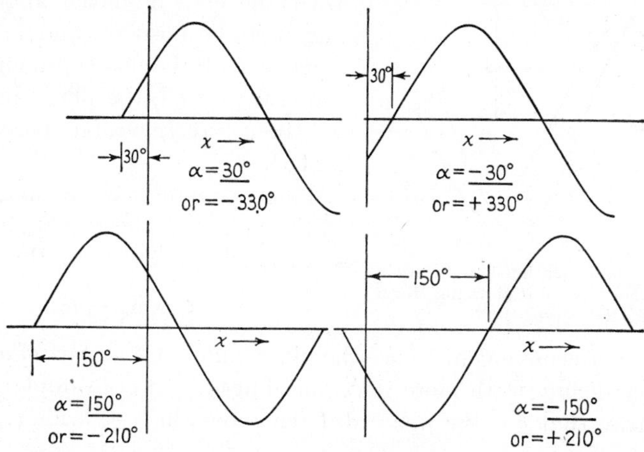


FIG. 2-28. Examples of various values of initial angle. Principal values are underlined.

angles can be specified for a wave, one positive and one negative, since there always will be a principal zero on each side of the origin. Examples are shown in Fig. 2-28. If the nearest principal zero is always chosen, values of $\alpha$ will always be between $-\pi$ and $\pi$. Such values are called *principal values* of the initial angle.

The amplitude of a sinusoidal wave is always a positive number. However, a negative sign can appear before the equation. Suppose the initial angle of the wave of Fig. 2-27 is increased or decreased by $\pi$ rad, causing a half period horizontal shift. At all points the shifted wave is the negative of its former self, so

$$y = -Y_m \sin(\omega t + \alpha \pm \pi) \tag{2-21}$$

This is a useful relation because developments sometimes lead to expressions with negative signs. Equation (2-21) shows that a negative sign before a sine function can be removed by adding or subtracting $\pi$ radians. The same property applies to a cosine function.

**2-11. Phase-angle Difference (Phase Difference).*** Consider two waves *of the same frequency*, as shown in Fig. 2-29. Time progresses from left to right. Therefore, a principal zero of $y_a$ occurs earlier than the nearest principal zero of $y_b$. Wave (*a*) is said to *lead* wave (*b*) by the angle $\theta$. It may also be said that wave (*b*) *lags* wave (*a*) by the angle $\theta$. The angle $\theta$ is called the *phase-angle difference* (or *phase difference*) between the waves. Phase difference is an algebraic quantity, and so it can be said that $y_a$ lags $y_b$ by $-\theta$. It is also noted that $y_a$ lags $y_b$ by the large angle $\phi$. This is a typical situation. It shows that two angles of lead or lag can be given, in similarity with the case of initial angle. One angle will be positive, and one will be negative. If the closest principal zeros are always used, the phase difference will be a *principal value* (between $-\pi$ and $\pi$).

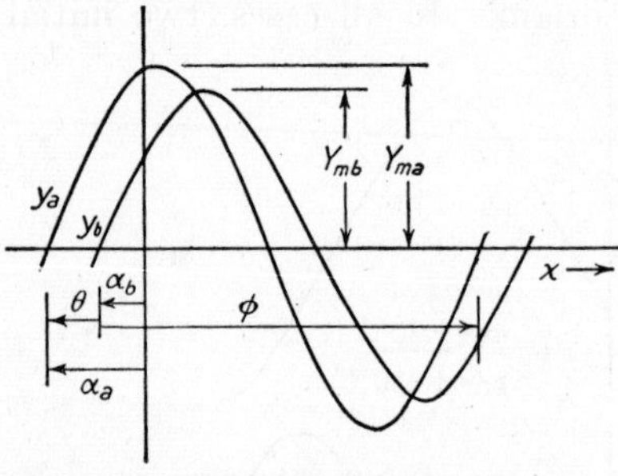


FIG. 2-29. The relationship between phase difference and initial angles, for a pair of sinusoidal waves.

Phase difference is related to the initial angles of the two waves. For example, Fig. 2-29 shows that

$$\theta = \alpha_a - \alpha_b \tag{2-22}$$

It is sometimes convenient to use the phase difference as part of an initial angle when dealing with more than one sinusoid. For example, in order to emphasize that $\theta$ is the phase difference by which $y_a$ leads $y_b$, we can write

$$\begin{aligned} y_a &= Y_{ma} \sin (\omega t + \alpha_b + \theta) \\ y_b &= Y_{mb} \sin (\omega t + \alpha_b) \end{aligned} \tag{2-23}$$

Phase differences of 0°, 90°, and 180° are particularly important in circuit analysis, and so distinctive adjectives are used to describe these three special cases. When the phase difference between two waves is zero, the waves are said to be *in phase;* when the absolute value of the angle is 90°, the waves are said to be *in quadrature;* and when the angle is 180°, the waves are said to be 180° *out of phase.*

**2-12. Simple A-C Circuits with Sinusoidal Currents and Potentials.** The simplest possible a-c electric circuits are shown in Fig. 2-30. They can be used to illustrate the basic characteristics of all a-c circuit problems; the finding of currents if known variations of potentials are given, or vice versa. Strict heed should be given to the reference condi-

* In electrical-engineering literature it is quite common to find the term *phase* used to mean either initial angle or phase-angle difference. There is no objection to this so long as it leads to no ambiguities.

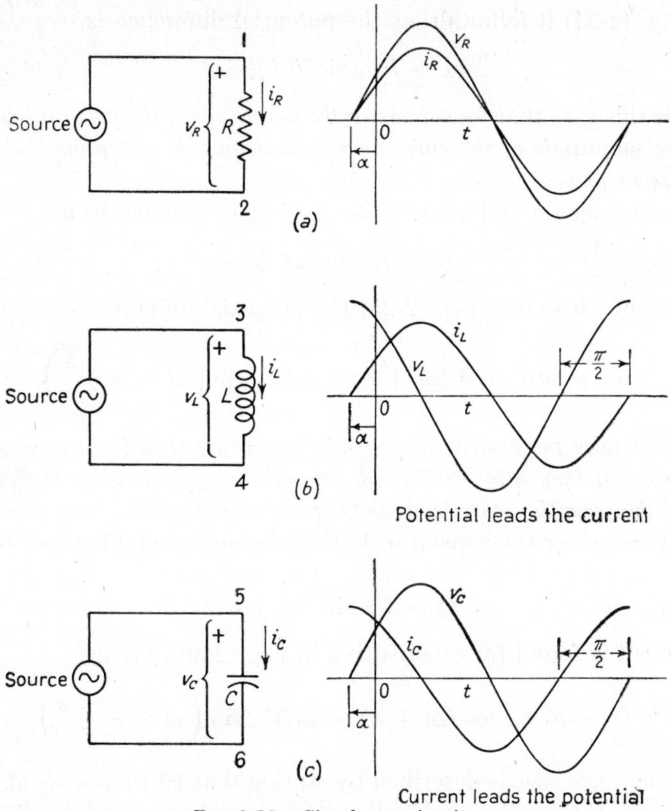


FIG. 2-30. Simple a-c circuits.

tions. Equations are given twice, once using the single-subscript system, and once using the double subscript system.

We are beginning a study of ideal linear circuits, for which resistors, inductors, and capacitors, respectively, obey the three following laws:

$$v_R = Ri_R \quad \text{or} \quad v_{12} = Ri_{12} \quad \text{for a resistor} \tag{2-24}$$

$$v_L = L\frac{di_L}{dt} \quad \text{or} \quad v_{34} = L\frac{di_{34}}{dt} \quad \text{for an inductor} \tag{2-25}$$

$$i_C = C\frac{dv_C}{dt} \quad \text{or} \quad i_{56} = C\frac{dv_{56}}{dt} \quad \text{for a capacitor} \tag{2-26}$$

They are called *linear elements* because the factors $R$, $L$, and $C$ are constants. Formulas for computing $R$, $L$, and $C$ are given in Appendix A.

Let us consider the case of sinusoidal waves in the examples of Fig. 2-30. For the resistor, suppose the current is

$$i_R = I_m \sin (\omega t + \alpha) \tag{2-27}$$

From Eq. (2-24) it follows that the potential difference is

$$v_R = RI_m \sin (\omega t + \alpha) \tag{2-28}$$

In words this says that for a resistor *the amplitude of the potential wave is R times the amplitude of the current wave and that the potential and current waves are in phase.*

Now consider the inductor. The current is assumed to be

$$i_L = I_m \sin (\omega t + \alpha) \tag{2-29}$$

If this is substituted in Eq. (2-25) the potential difference is found to be

$$v_L = \omega L I_m \cos (\omega t + \alpha) = \omega L I_m \sin \left( \omega t + \alpha + \frac{\pi}{2} \right) \tag{2-30}$$

This result may be described in words by saying that for an inductor *the amplitude of the potential wave is* $\omega L$ *times the amplitude of the current wave, and that the potential wave leads the current wave by* 90°.

Finally consider the capacitor, letting the potential difference be given by*

$$v_c = V_m \sin (\omega t + \alpha) \tag{2-31}$$

The current is found by substituting in Eq. (2-26), giving

$$i_C = \omega C V_m \cos (\omega t + \alpha) = \omega C V_m \sin \left( \omega t + \alpha + \frac{\pi}{2} \right) \tag{2-32}$$

The capacitance case is described by stating that *the amplitude of the current wave is* $\omega C$ *times the amplitude of the potential wave, and that the current wave leads the potential wave by* 90°.

**Example 2-1.** In Fig. 2-31*a* let the current $i$ be

$$i = 2 \sin 377t$$

and find the equation for $v$.

*Solution.* First $v_R$ and $v_C$ are found independently, noting that $i = i_R = i_C$. Thus, using the principles enunciated above,

$$v_R = (20)(2) \sin 377t$$

$$v_C = \frac{2}{(377)(80 \times 10^{-6})} \sin \left( 377t - \frac{\pi}{2} \right)$$

$$= 65.1 \sin \left( 377t - \frac{\pi}{2} \right)$$

* It is to be emphasized that the *relationship* between potential and current is the goal of this development. Therefore, it makes no difference whether the potential difference or the current is the initially assumed function.

Finally, the equation for $v$ is

$$v = v_R + v_C$$
$$= 40 \sin (377t) + 65.1 \sin \left(377t - \frac{\pi}{2}\right)$$

Ultimately these can be combined further than this, by techniques discussed in Chap. 4. The graphs are shown at (b) in Fig. 2-31.

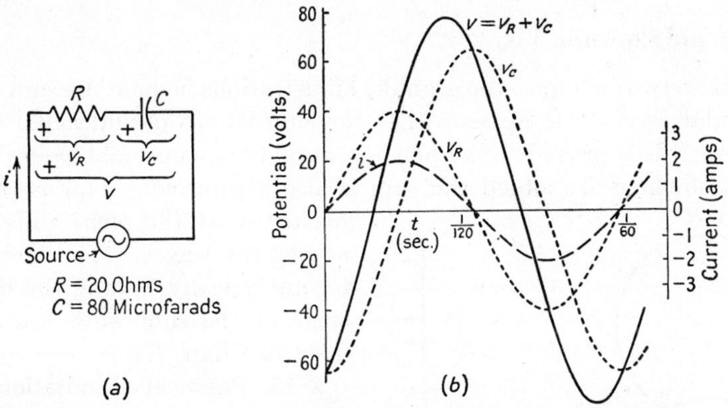


Fig. 2-31. Analysis of a series circuit under sinusoidal conditions.

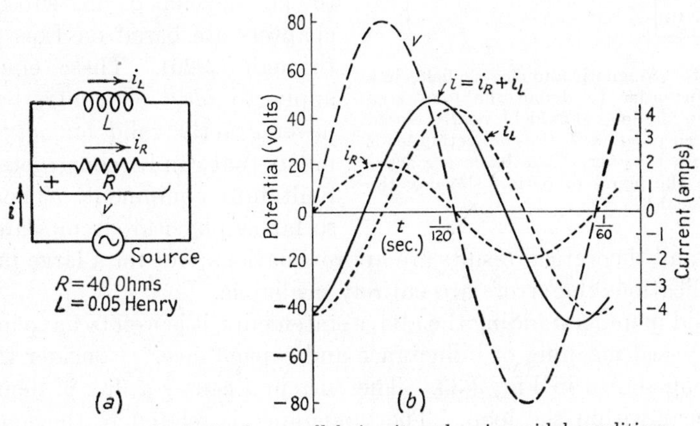


Fig. 2-32. Analysis of a parallel circuit under sinusoidal conditions.

**Example 2-2.** In Fig. 2-32*a* let the potential difference be

$$v = 80 \sin 377t$$

Find the equation for the current $i$.

*Solution.* First the individual currents $i_R$ and $i_L$ are found as follows:

$$i_R = 80/40 \sin 377t$$

$$i_L = \frac{80}{18.8} \sin\left(377t - \frac{\pi}{2}\right) = 4.24 \sin\left(377 - \frac{\pi}{2}\right)$$

The reference directions for the current are such that

$$i = i_R + i_L$$
$$= 2 \sin 377t + 4.24 \sin\left(377t - \frac{\pi}{2}\right)$$

Graphs are shown in Fig. 2-32*b*.

In these two examples the graphical illustrations include the sum of two sinusoidal waves. It appears that the sum is also of sinusoidal shape. In Chap. 4 it is proved that when any number of sinusoidal waves of the same frequency are added the sum is also a sinusoid. This is true no matter what the phase differences among the waves. The technique for analytically finding the dimensions of the sum wave are developed in Chap. 4.

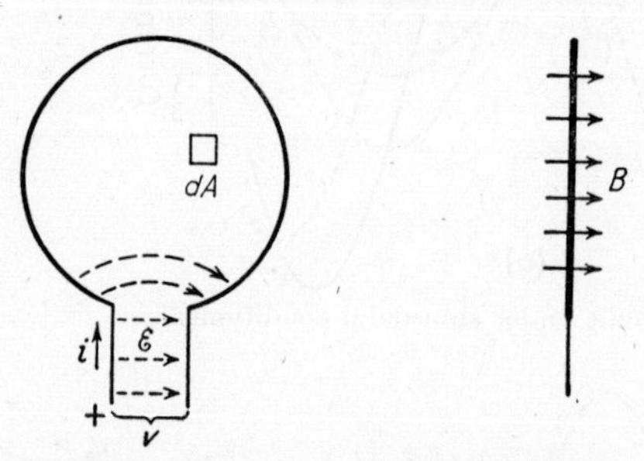


FIG. 2-33. Magnetic and electric fields in a loop. In order to define the loop area uniquely, the loop should be nearly closed at the feed point, with the connecting leads very close together. The leads are separated in the figure to permit showing the electric field ℰ.

**2-13. Practical Limitations on Circuit Elements.** The techniques to be developed in subsequent chapters are based on Eqs. (2-24) through (2-26). These equations apply to *ideal* elements, but are never exactly valid for actual elements that can be constructed and built into equipment. Therefore, so far as physical circuits are concerned, all theoretical results are approximations; but for a large number of applications the errors are entirely negligible.

To aid in understanding the above statements, it is well to have in mind the physical meaning of inductance and capacitance. Consider the flat wire loop shown in Fig. 2-33. The current $i$ causes a flux of density $B$ to appear within the loop. The inductance is related to the magnetic field by the formula

$$L = \frac{1}{i} \int B \, dA \qquad (2\text{-}33)$$

where $i$ is a d-c current in amperes, $B$ is the flux density in webers per square meter, and $A$ is area in square meters. The integration is over the area of the loop, in its plane. This equation emphasizes the relationship between the concepts of inductance and magnetic field. If the wire is assumed to have zero resistance, there is no potential gradient along the wire and so the electric field shown by the dotted lines in Fig. 2-33 is absent.

Now consider the parallel-plate capacitor in Fig. 2-34. The potential difference $v$ has associated with it an electric field $\mathcal{E}$. In terms of the field, the capacitance can be given by

$$C = k_e \frac{8.85 \times 10^{-12}}{v} \int \mathcal{E}\, dA \tag{2-34}$$

in which $v$ is a d-c potential in volts, $\mathcal{E}$ is the field strength in volts per meter, $k_e$ is the dielectric constant, and $A$ is area in square meters. Assuming no fringing of field at the edges, the integration is over the area of one plate. This equation emphasizes that capacitive effects are associated with an electric field. When the potential is constant and if the insulation between the plates is perfect, there will be no current in the leads and so the magnetic field indicated by the dotted arrows will be zero.

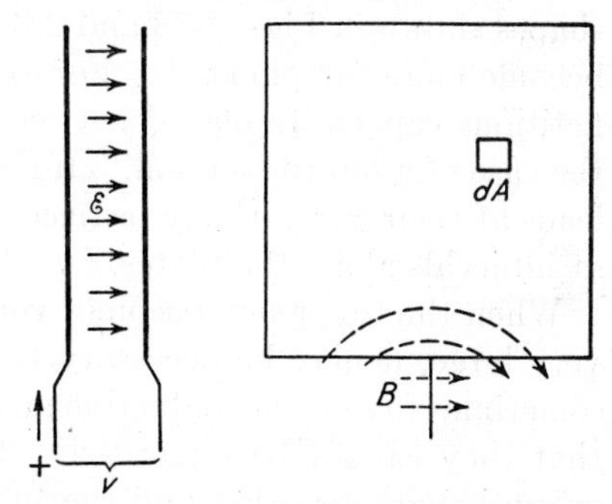

FIG. 2-34. Electric and magnetic fields between two parallel plates, showing how inductive effects can occur in a capacitor.

Up to this point the current in the inductor and the potential difference across the capacitor are assumed to be constant. The potential difference and current will now be allowed to vary.

Consider the inductive loop when the current $i$ is increasing. We know that a potential difference $v = L\, di/dt$ will appear between the terminals. The result will be an electric field, as indicated by the dotted arrows in Fig. 2-33. The resultant effect can be approximately represented by imagining a capacitor connected across the terminals. The loop is like an inductor in parallel with a capacitor.

This does not mean that the capacitive effect must always be included. It must be considered only when the time *rate of change* of the electric field is so great that the charge accumulation near the terminals (which is proportional to the electric field) causes the current in the loop to be appreciably different from the current in the terminals. Under sinusoidal conditions this means that there will be an upper frequency limit above which the electrical behavior of the loop cannot be described by the simple equation $v = L\, di/dt$.

A similar situation exists for the capacitor of Fig. 2-34. Suppose the potential difference $v$ is increasing. There will be a current $i$, as charge flows into the plates; and the current will produce a magnetic field $B$. This field will extend somewhat into the area between the plates. The effect of the magnetic field can be represented approximately by imagining an inductor inserted in one of the connecting wires.

If the time *rate of change* of the magnetic field is low enough, its effect may be negligible. The magnetic effect comes into play when the potential difference between the plates is appreciably different from the potential difference between the terminals. In the sinusoidal case this establishes an upper frequency limit, beyond which the equation $i = C\,dv/dt$ does not apply.

If the elements have more complexity than the simple geometrical shapes shown in Figs. 2-33 and 2-34, then the effects described above can become more complicated. For example, it may be necessary to imagine fictitious capacitors placed between turns of a coil, or between layers in the case of a multilayer coil. If a capacitor has long narrow plates, with leads at their ends, it may be necessary to intermingle fictitious inductors at intervals along the plates.

When the frequency becomes very high or the circuit element becomes very large, it may be necessary to change the viewpoint entirely. It is sometimes found that inductive and capacitive effects are so intermingled that they cannot be separated. The element is then said to have *distributed* characteristics, and the solution takes this into account. Exact solutions are possible for a limited number of distributed elements of simple geometrical shapes. The familiar transmission lines used for power transmission, and for communications, are examples of distributed elements. A network that does not include distributed elements is said to be *lumped*. This text is confined to the study of lumped networks.

It is not possible to specify a clear-cut limiting frequency beyond which an inductor or capacitor no longer obeys one of the simple equations. The transition is a gradual one. The range of frequencies over which the transition occurs depends on the physical size and arrangement of the inductor or capacitor. The frequency at which a wavelength of electromagnetic radiation is about 100 times the largest linear dimension of the element can be used as a fairly conservative estimate of a limit. Frequency is the velocity of propagation (the velocity of light $= 3 \times 10^{10}$ cm/sec) divided by the wavelength. Thus, a coil 10 cm long may be expected to obey the $L\,di/dt$ law up to a frequency of $(3 \times 10^{10})1{,}000 = 3 \times 10^{7}$ cps.

The effect of resistance in an inductor or capacitor has been neglected. In general the effect of the resistance of a coil can be approximated by imagining an equivalent resistor in series with an ideal resistanceless coil. For low frequencies the equivalent series resistance is approximately the same as the d-c resistance of the coil. A capacitor can usually be approximated by an equivalent circuit consisting of an ideal capacitor in parallel with an ideal resistor.

Mention should be made of the difficulty of making a resistor which will obey Eq. (2-24) at high frequencies. A physical resistor will exhibit effects which can be represented by inductance in series with it and capacitance across it. If the resistance wire is wound on a form, as in Fig. 2-35*a*, it will have both inductance and capacitance. The bifilar winding shown at (*b*) reduces the inductance but increases the capacitance. The inductance is reduced because opposing currents in adjacent wires nearly cancel one another magnetically. Another arrangement, which minimizes both $L$ and $C$, is shown in Fig. 2-35*c*. The current travels in two paths from one end to the other. The paths travel in opposite directions around the core, so they cancel magnetically. Capacitive effects are minimized because adjacent turns of the two paths are at the same potential.

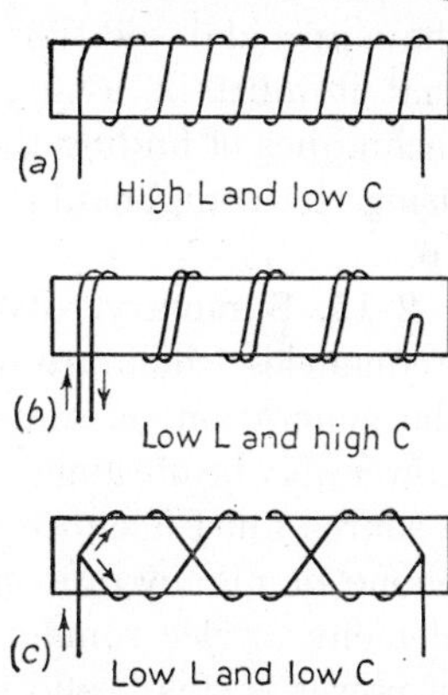

FIG. 2-35. Methods of constructing a resistor with various amounts of inductance and capacitance.

It is not the intention to give an exhaustive discussion of these limitations. The purpose in mentioning them is to emphasize that there are frequency limits beyond which actual circuit elements cannot be replaced by simple ideal equivalents for purposes of analysis. In spite of this fact, the subject of circuit analysis is developed in terms of ideal elements. This does not limit the usefulness of the techniques to be developed because, when necessary, an element can be replaced by an equivalent *network* of ideal elements. A considerable amount of study may be necessary to determine what that equivalent network is; but such a study is not within the scope of introductory circuit analysis and so is not pursued further.

**2-14. Fourier's Theorem.** The fact that many sources have sinusoidal outputs has been given as one reason for the importance of studying circuits under sinusoidal conditions. A second reason is the simplicity of the analysis.

There is still a third reason. It is a consequence of a theorem due to a French mathematician, Fourier. A detailed statement of the theorem would be out of place here, but its implications can be presented. The theorem states that any periodic function may be represented by the sum of an infinite number of sinusoidal components, of frequencies which are integral multiples of the frequency of the given wave. A finite number of these sinusoidal harmonic components is sufficient for reasonable accuracy. For practical purposes the theorem of Fourier states that an excitation source of nonsinusoidal wave shape of frequency $f$ may be replaced, for purposes of calculation, by a number of sinusoidal sources of frequencies $f$, $2f$, $3f$, etc. They all are considered to act on the circuit simultaneously. There is a known technique for finding the amplitudes and initial angles of these components, from the properties of the given wave. This is of no concern at this stage, the important observation being that the sinusoidal solution is useful even for nonsinusoidal conditions and that it must be available for a number of different frequencies. The techniques of finding the harmonic components of a periodic wave and of using the components in circuit analysis are discussed in Chaps. 15 and 16.

**2-15. Summary.** When large amounts of power are required, at frequencies which are not too high, electromagnetic induction is used in the generation of sinusoidal potentials. Reasonably large amounts of power may be obtained at higher frequencies by electronic means. Where a source must accurately follow some mechanical motion, as in a microphone or phonograph pickup, the piezoelectric effect, a variable circuit element, or electromagnetic induction is used. In such cases the amount of power is small, and accurate reproduction of wave shape is of greater importance than the conversion of power.

Many electrical devices generate or employ potentials or currents which are periodic functions of time. This fact necessitates the extension of the idea of current direction and potential polarity, from the constants encountered in d-c analysis, to the varying quantities encountered in a-c analysis. Even though a current may be continually changing direction, it is said to flow in one direction, which is defined as the reference direction. A similar situation defines reference polarity. The concept of a reference condition is very important.

The sinusoid is a periodic function of great importance. It has been defined as the curve generated by the vertical projection of the end of a rotating line. The function can be expressed mathematically by the trigonometric sine or cosine functions.

When the amplitude and initial angle of a sinusoid are known, the wave is completely specified on the time-angle scale. If the frequency is also known, the wave is then also specified as a function of time.

When two sinusoids of the same frequency are compared, it is said that one wave leads (or lags) the other by an angle called the phase difference. Phase difference has meaning for nonsinusoidal waves as long as their shapes are the same. However, initial angles apply only to sinusoidal waves.

The sinusoidal function is of basic importance for the analysis of linear circuits. It is possible to generate potentials and currents which are very nearly sinusoidal. The analysis is simplest for this form, and, through the Fourier theorem, it is possible to analyze other periodic shapes in terms of the sinusoid. These are the reasons for emphasizing the solution of circuits under sinusoidal conditions.

For a resistor, inductor, or capacitor, if the potential difference is a sinusoid, the current is also a sinusoid; and the ratio of the amplitude of the potential wave to the amplitude of the current wave is, respectively, $R$, $\omega L$, and $1/\omega C$. Furthermore, *if reference conditions are as shown in Fig.* 2-27, for the resistor the potential and current waves are in phase, for the inductor the potential wave leads the current wave by 90°, and for the capacitor the current wave leads the potential wave by 90°.

## PROBLEMS

**2-1.** *a.* In the circuit of Fig. P2-1*a* are four d-c sources of various types, labeled $A$, $B$, $C$, and $D$. Classify each of them.

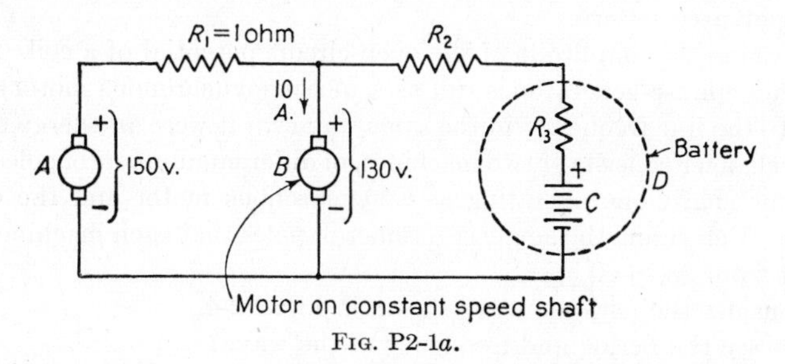


Fig. P2-1*a*.

*b.* A vacuum photocell is a device consisting of two electrodes, as shown at $A$ in Fig. P2-1*b*. Electrons are emitted from the large electrode at a rate proportional to the light intensity. Assuming constant light intensity, classify $B$ and $C$ as to types of sources. What would be your answer if the light should vary periodically with time?

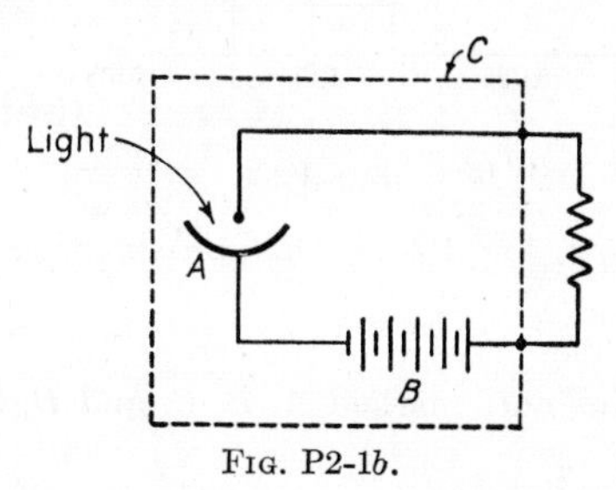


Fig. P2-1*b*.

**2-2.** A two-pole a-c generator has an air-gap flux density which is related to angular distance from the point halfway between the poles by the following tabulated function:

| *Angular position, deg* | *Flux density, weber/sq m* |
|---|---|
| 0 | 0.00 |
| 10 | 0.11 |
| 20 | 0.20 |
| 30 | 0.44 |
| 40 | 0.65 |
| 50 | 0.79 |
| 60 | 0.91 |
| 70 | 0.98 |
| 80 | 1.00 |
| 90 | 1.00 |

The flux is distributed symmetrically with respect to a pole center. The machine is to operate at a frequency of 60 cps. Each of the stator coils has eight turns, and the diameter of the machine at the coil sides is 0.8 m. The axial length of each active coil side is 1.3 m.

*a.* Plot a graph of the potential induced in a single active conductor (*i.e.*, one conductor on a coil side) as a function of the angular position of the rotor.

*b.* Include on this graph a time scale, measuring zero time from the instant when the potential is zero.

*c.* Determine the amplitude of the open-circuit potential of a coil.

**2-3.** When an a-c generator is run as a motor (synchronous motor), its speed is related to the line frequency in the same way as if it were an energy source. A frequency changer consists of two machines, of different numbers of poles, mounted on the same shaft, one operating as a synchronous motor and the other as a generator. Determine the smallest number of poles that each machine can have, to convert from 25 to 60 cps.

**2-4.** Consider the periodic wave shown in Fig. P2-4.

*a.* What are the period and frequency of the wave?

*b.* What values does the time angle have at points (*a*) and (*b*)?

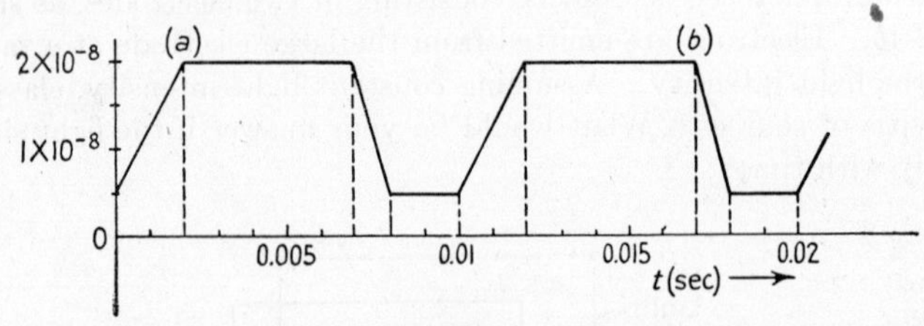


FIG. P2-4.

**2-5.** The wave shown in Fig. P2-5 is an approximation of a typical wave generated in a single conductor of a rotating machine.

*a.* Tabulate the angular position of the center line of one of the poles of the machine rotor, at the instants marked *A*, *B*, *C*, and *D*, if the machine has two, four, and six poles.

*b.* If the machine has 36 poles, at what speed must it operate?

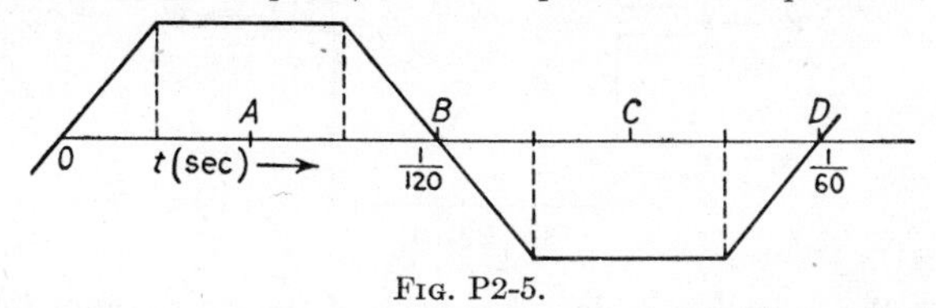


FIG. P2-5.

**2-6.** Suppose the d-c magnetizing windings on the rotor of a six-pole machine are connected incorrectly. Sketch the approximate wave of the potential induced in one conductor, as a function of time, for one revolution of the rotor:

*a.* If successive poles are N, N, N, S, S, S.

*b.* If successive poles are N, N, S, N, N, S.

*c.* If successive poles are N, N, N, N, S, S.

NOTE: Only the approximate relative heights and durations of various parts of the wave are of interest. Neglect saturation effects in the iron, and assume that the entire reluctance of the magnetic circuit is due to air gaps.

**2-7.** Assume that the permeance of the magnetic circuit of Fig. 2-7 is variable in accordance with the law shown in Fig. P2-4, for which the vertical-axis scale is permeance, in henrys. The d-c coil provides an mmf of 5,000 amp turns. Plot graphs of

*a.* The flux through the magnetic circuit.

*b.* The potential induced in the right-hand winding, if it has 600 turns.

**2-8.** *a.* The tones of a Hammond organ are generated by a rotating system similar to Fig. 2-7. Suppose the note middle A (frequency 440 cps) is to be generated by a wheel having 12 teeth. At what speed must it rotate, in revolutions per minute?

*b.* Suppose a-c energy is to be generated at high frequency by a device such as shown in Fig. 2-12. The vibrating contact is to complete 1 cycle of operation for each 100 cycles of the current. (Actually the current wave will die down slightly during each of these sets of 100 cycles.) The associated circuit has an inductance of 0.002 henry and a capacitance of 0.008 $\mu$f. How many cycles of operation does the vibrator undergo per second?

**2-9.** A phonograph pickup of the magnetic type, as illustrated in Fig. 2-9, is actuated by a constant-tone record. Suitable measurements show that the induced potential is 0.3 sin 5,480$t$. The record turntable rotates at 33⅓ rpm.

*a.* How many complete cycles are obtained from one revolution of the record?

*b.* Obtain an equation for the time variation of the flux in the magnetic circuit if there are 500 turns on the coil. Take the flux reference direction downward through the coil.

**2-10.** This problem is intended to emphasize the difference between the algebraic and arithmetic concepts. Figure P2-10, illustrates a water tank with four pipe connections. The arrows show reference directions for velocities of water in the pipes.

*a.* Write the algebraic equilibrium equation, expressing the condition that the tank is always full of water. Use the velocity reference directions shown.

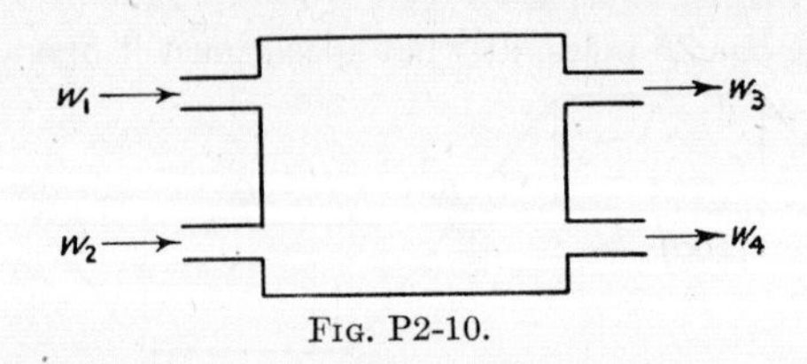


FIG. P2-10.

*b.* Construct the following table. For each of the rows complete the tabulation of $w_1$, $w_2$, $w_3$, and $w_4$, and tabulate in the appropriate column on the right the *algebraic* sum of the velocity of water entering and leaving the tank. Also tabulate the *actual* sum of the velocities of water entering and leaving. See the sample case included in the table.

| $w_1$ | $w_2$ | $w_3$ | $w_4$ | Algebraic sum entering | Algebraic sum leaving | Actual sum entering | Actual sum leaving |
|---|---|---|---|---|---|---|---|
| 5 | 10 | 2 | | | | | |
| 3 | −4 | −2 | 1 | −1 | −1 | 5 | 5 |
| −2 | −8 | | 17 | | | | |
| −10 | | 37 | −21 | | | | |
| −5 | 10 | | 3 | | | | |
| 8 | −2 | | −5 | | | | |

**2-11.** Refer to Fig. P2-11, which shows an isolated resistor. It is part of a circuit which is not shown. Various situations are shown in the three parts of the figure.

*a.* In Fig. P2-11*a* let $i_1$ be given by the equation

$$i_1 = 4.5 \sin 377t$$

Write equations for $v_1$ and $v_2$.

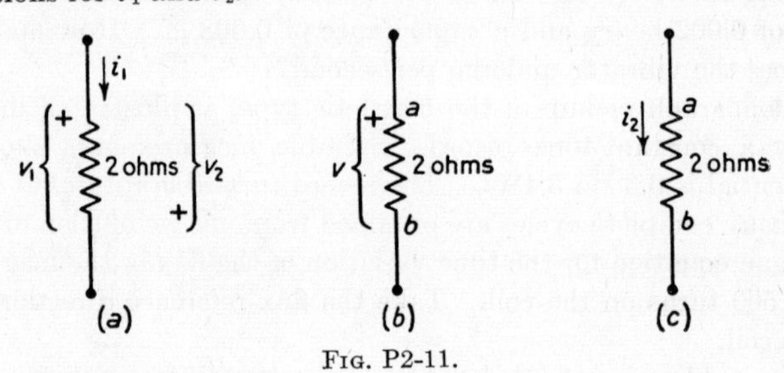


FIG. P2-11.

*b.* In Fig. P2-11*b* let $v$ be given by

$$v = 25 \cos 377t$$

Write equations for $i_{ab}$ and $i_{ba}$.

*c.* In Fig. P2-11*c* let $i_2$ be $-6 \sin 377t$. Write equations for $v_{ab}$ and $v_{ba}$.

**2-12.** Consider the arrangement shown in Fig. P2-12. The conductor is carried at the end of a pendulum which swings with a sinusoidal (simple harmonic) motion. The conductor remains within the air gap throughout its swing, and the radius of the arc is so great that the arc may be considered a straight line. Using a reference direction to the right, a plot of the velocity $w$ is shown.

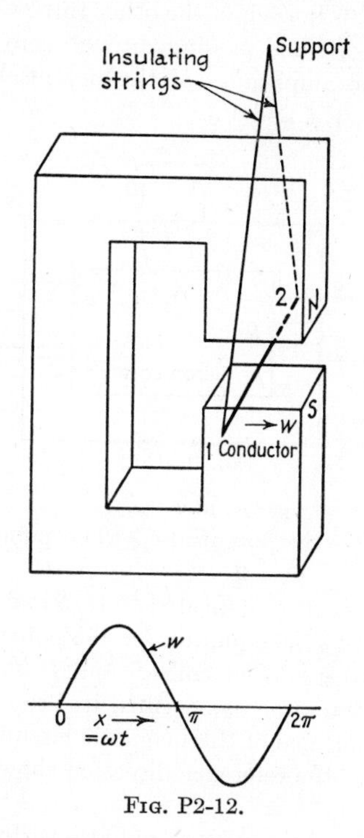


FIG. P2-12.

*a.* Draw graphs of the potentials $v_{12}$ and $v_{21}$, properly related to the velocity graph. Numerical amplitudes are not required.

*b.* Write the equation for $v_{12}$ and $v_{21}$, leaving the amplitude undetermined.

**2-13.** Use tables of trigonometric functions to plot the functions:

*a.* $y_a = \sin x$.

*b.* $y_b = \cos x$.

*c.* $y_c = \sin (x + 20°)$.

*d.* $y_d = \sin (x - 50°)$.

Plot each wave for one complete cycle, starting from the first intercept on the $x$ axis to the left of the origin.

**2-14.** Plot the following sinusoidal waves, using the projections of successive positions of a rotating line to obtain the ordinates. In each case clearly indicate the initial position of the rotating line, and extend the graph to the left of the origin as far as the first intercept with the horizontal axis. Plot on a horizontal scale of $\omega t$, in degrees.

*a.* $v = 20 \sin (\omega t + 30°)$.
*b.* $i = 1.5 \cos \omega t$.
*c.* $v = 35 \sin (\omega t - 140°)$.

**2-15.** A flux $\phi$ is produced in the core of Fig. P2-15 by a current in coil $D$. This flux is the same throughout the magnetic circuit, and it changes with time, inducing sinusoidal potentials in each of the other three windings. The potential $v_{12}$ is assumed to be increasing and passing through zero at zero time. The frequency is 60 cps. Let the amplitudes of the potentials induced in coils $A$, $B$, and $C$ be, respectively, $V_A$, $V_B$, and $V_C$.

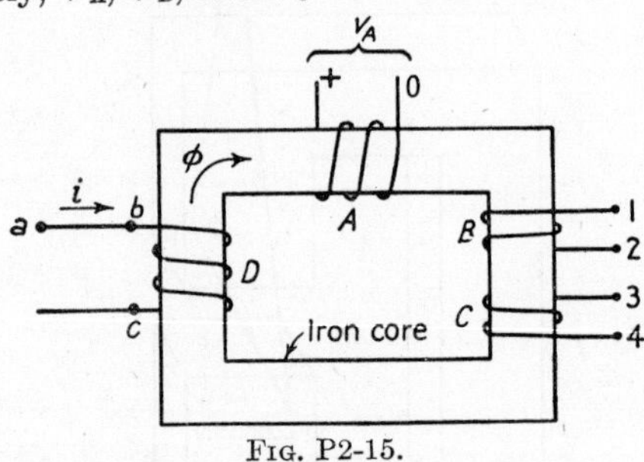


FIG. P2-15.

*a.* Write the expressions for $v_A$, $v_{12}$, and $v_{34}$.

*b.* Write an expression for the potential $v_{14}$ when points 2 and 3 are connected together.

*c.* The + terminal of coil $A$ is connected to terminal 2, and terminal 1 is connected to terminal 3. Write the equation for the potential $v_{04}$.

**2-16.** Refer to Fig. P2-15, and let coils $B$ and $D$ have 5,000 and 400 turns, respectively. Let $v_{12}$ be the same as specified in Prob. 2-15, with a peak value $V_B = 50$ volts. The permeance of the magnetic circuit is $6 \times 10^{-6}$ henry.

*a.* If flux in the core has the reference direction shown in the figure, write the equation for this flux.

*b.* Write the equation for the current $i$, and also write the equation for the current $i_{cb}$.

**2-17.** The three coils shown in perspective view in Fig. P2-17 rotate in a uniform horizontal magnetic field. The maximum potential induced in each is 0.2 volt. Let the time zero be so chosen that $v_{aa'}$ is a sine wave with zero initial angle and frequency of 1,000 cps.

*a.* Write the equations for $v_{aa'}$, $v_{bb'}$, and $v_{cc'}$.

*b.* Connect $a'$ to $b$ and $b'$ to $c'$, and write an expression for $v_{ac}$.

*c.* Connect $a'$ to $b$ and $b'$ to $c$, and write an expression for $v_{ac'}$.

*d.* Connect $a$ to $b$ and $b'$ to $c$, and write an expression for $v_{a'c'}$.

*e.* Connect $a$ to $c'$ and $c$ to $b'$, and write an expression for $v_{a'b}$.

NOTE: In parts $b$ and $d$ do not try to simplify the expressions; the sum of two trigonometric terms will appear in each, and they should be left in that form. In each case when coils are connected together, assume the connecting wires do not cut any flux, which can be the case if they are always either radial or along the axis of rotation.

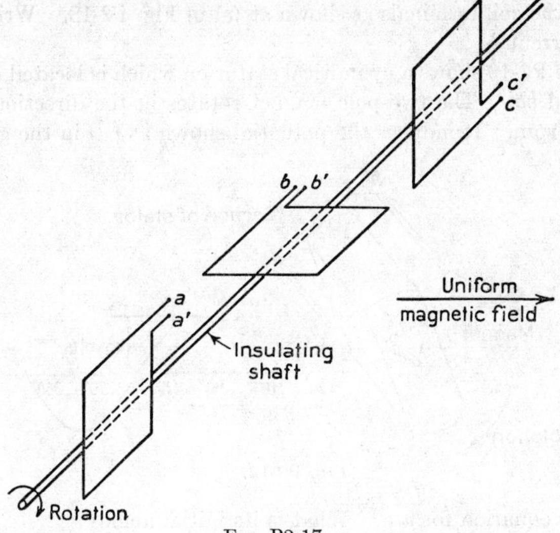


FIG. P2-17.

**2-18.** Figure P2-18 shows three identical "constant-current" transformers with their primaries connected in parallel to a common source. This ensures

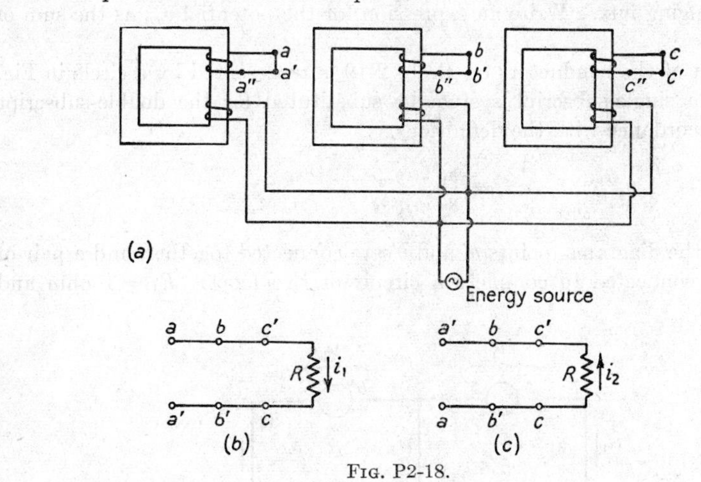


FIG. P2-18.

similar flux conditions in each transformer. Let the current $i_{aa'}$ through the short circuit on the secondary of transformer $A$ be

$$i_{aa'} = 10 \sin 377t$$

*a*. Write equations for $i_{bb'}$ and $i_{c'c}$.

*b*. Connect the coil terminals as shown at (*b*) in Fig. P2-18. Write an expression for the current $i_1$.

*c.* Connect the coil terminals as shown at (*c*) in Fig. P2-18. Write an expression for the current $i_2$.

**2-19.** Figure P2-19 shows a cylindrical stator on which is located a pair of conductors $aa'$ and $bb'$. The two-pole magnet rotates in the direction shown at a speed of 4,000 rpm. It induces the potential shown as $v_{aa'}$ in the graph.

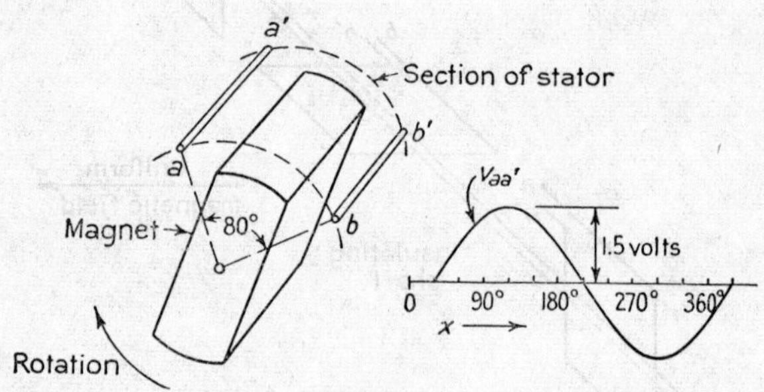


FIG. P2-19.

*a.* Write the equation for $v_{aa'}$. What is its initial angle?

*b.* Write the equation for $v_{bb'}$, and show it on a sketch, along with $v_{aa'}$. What is the phase angle by which $v_{bb'}$ leads $v_{aa'}$?

*c.* Terminals $a'$ and $b'$ are connected together by a connection which is not cut by a changing flux. Write an expression for the potential $v_{ab}$, as the sum of two sinusoids.

**2-20.** Each of the conductors on Prob. 2-19 is represented by a circle in Fig. P2-20. Let a single-subscript system be substituted for the double-subscript system, in accordance with the definitions.

$$v_1 = v_{aa'}$$
$$v_2 = v_{b'b}$$

As shown in the diagrams, points $a'$ and $b'$ are connected together, and a pair of resistors are connected to complete a circuit of two loops. $R_1 = 1$ ohm and $R_2 = 2$ ohms.

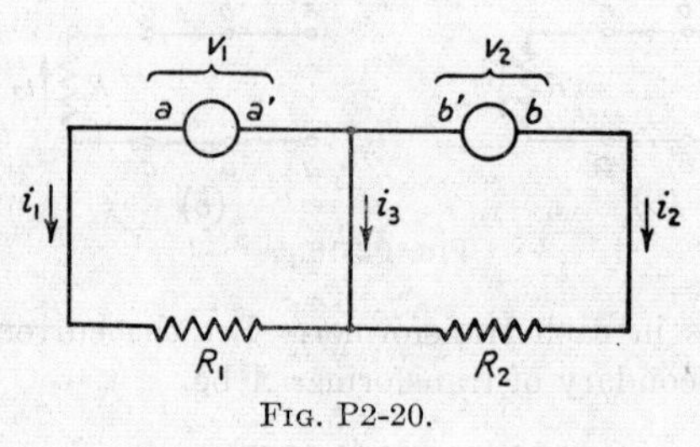


FIG. P2-20.

*a.* Reference polarity designations for $v_1$ and $v_2$ are omitted from Fig. P2-20. Add these to the diagram.

*b.* Write the sinusoidal expression for each of the currents $i_1$ and $i_2$.

*c.* Write the expression for the current $i_3$, as the sum of two sinusoids.

**2-21.** Three sinusoidal waves of frequency 800 cps are shown in Fig. P2-21.

*a.* Using the principal value of initial angle, write the equation for each of the waves, as a function of time.

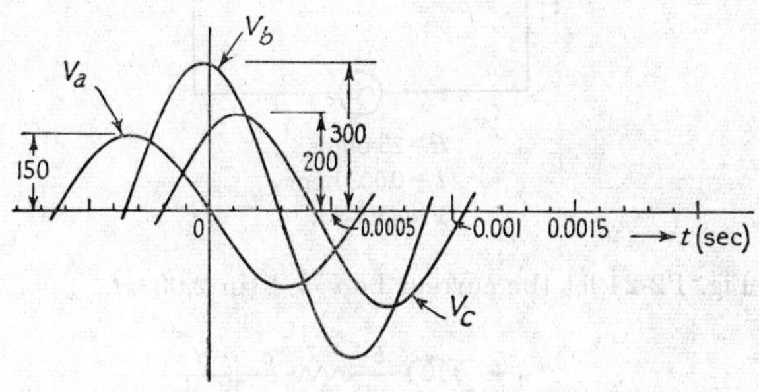


Fig. P2-21.

*b.* Write two expressions for each of the waves shown, (1) using positive initial angles in each case, and (2) using negative initial angles in each case.

*c.* Give the principal values of the angles by which $v_a$ leads $v_b$, $v_a$ leads $v_c$, and $v_c$ leads $v_b$.

*d.* Give the principal values of the angles by which $v_a$ lags $v_b$, $v_a$ lags $v_c$, and $v_c$ lags $v_b$.

*e.* Specify the angles mentioned in part *c*, but give positive values in each case, rather than always adhering to principal values.

**2-22.** Two sinusoidal functions are represented by the curves in Fig. P2-22. Determine, including the proper sign,

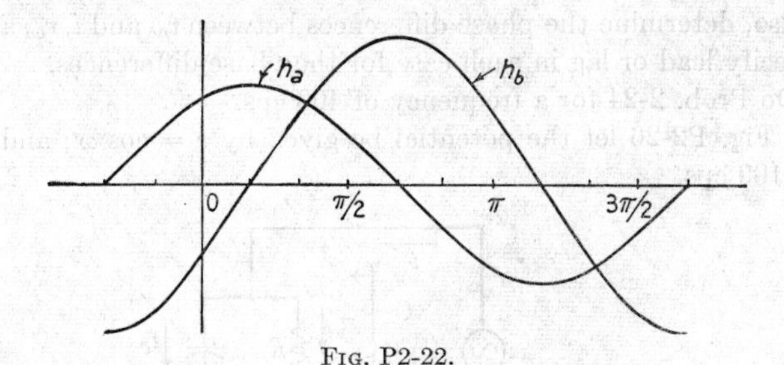


Fig. P2-22.

*a.* The initial angle of $h_a$, when it is expressed as a sine function.

*b.* The angle by which $h_b$ leads $h_a$.

*c.* The angle by which $h_a$ lags $h_b$.

**2-23.** In Fig. P2-23 the current is $i = \sin \omega t$ and the frequency is 1,000 cps.

*a.* Obtain equations for the potentials $v_R$, $v_L$, and $v$.

*b.* Plot graphs of the potentials asked for in part *a*.

*c.* From the graphs determine the initial angle of $v$, and determine the phase differences by which $i$ lags $v$ and $v_L$ leads $v_R$.

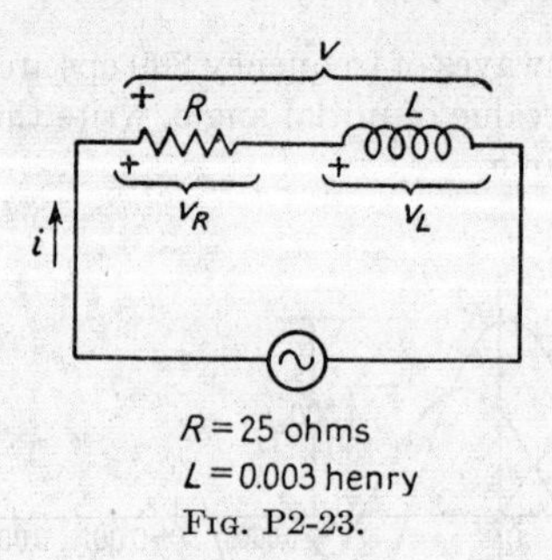

FIG. P2-23.

**2-24.*** In Fig. P2-24 let the current be $i = 4 \sin 2{,}000\pi t$.

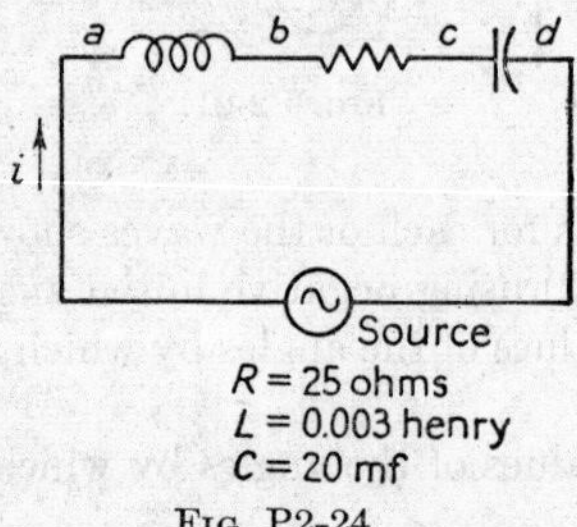

FIG. P2-24.

*a.* Obtain equations for the potentials $v_{ab}$, $v_{bc}$, and $v_{cd}$.
*b.* Obtain equations for the potentials $v_{ac}$, $v_{db}$, and $v_{ad}$.
*c.* Plot graphs of the potentials asked for in parts *a* and *b*.
*d.* From the graphs determine the initial angles of the potentials asked for in part *b*. Also, determine the phase differences between $v_{ac}$ and $i$, $v_{bd}$ and $i$, and $v_{ad}$ and $i$. Specify lead or lag in each case for the phase differences.

**2-25.*** Do Prob. 2-24 for a frequency of 400 cps.

**2-26.** In Fig. P2-26 let the potential be given by $v = \cos \omega t$, and let the frequency be 100 cps.

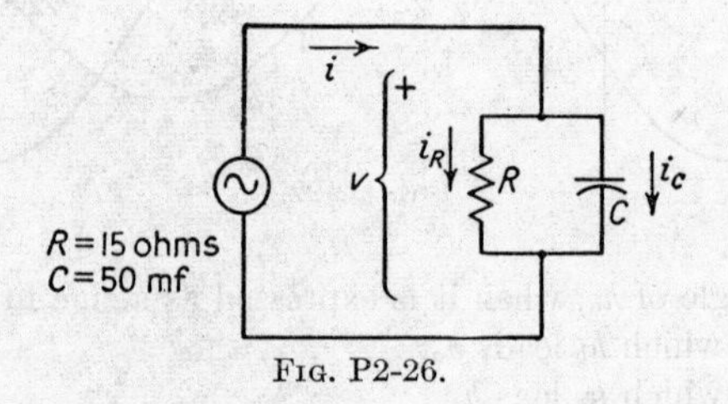

FIG. P2-26.

*a.* Obtain equations for the currents $i_R$, $i_C$, and $i$.
*b.* Plot graphs of the currents asked for in part *a*.

* In expressions involving the sum of two sinusoidal functions it is not necessary to combine the functions into a single expression.

*c*. From the graphs determine the initial angle of $i$, and determine the phase differences by which $v$ lags $i$ and $i_C$ leads $i_R$.

**2-27.*** Let the potential $v$ in Fig. P2-27 be the same as in Prob. 2-26.

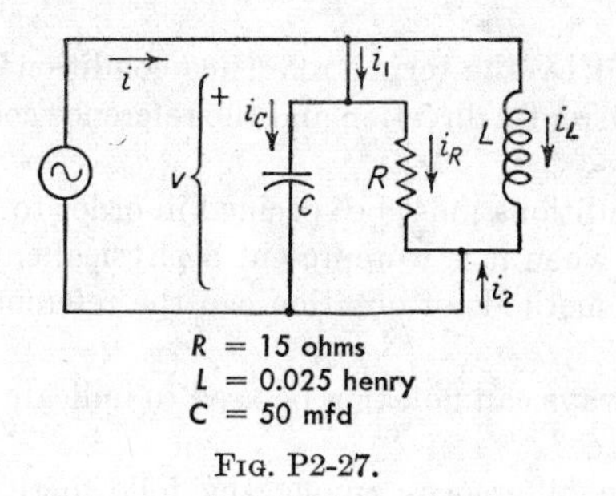


FIG. P2-27.

*a*. Obtain equations for the currents $i_C$, $i_R$, and $i_L$.

*b*. Obtain equations for the currents $i_1$, $i_2$, and $i$.

*c*. Plot graphs of the currents asked for in parts *a* and *b*.

*d*. From the graphs determine the initial angles of the currents asked for in part *b*. Also, determine the phase differences between $i_1$ and $v$, $i_2$ and $v$, and $i$ and $v$. Specify lead or lag in each case for the phase differences.

**2-28.*** Do Prob. 2-27 with the frequency changed to 200 cps.

## QUESTIONS

**2-1.** Would it be appropriate to call an *energy* source a *power* source?

**2-2.** What are the distinctions among source, potential source, and current source?

**2-3.** In a potential source is the potential difference across its terminals necessarily a constant? In a current source is the current in its terminals necessarily a constant?

**2-4.** According to the definition given, would the motor of Fig. 2-2 be a source if its shaft were not connected to a machine that would keep it going if the electrical connections were removed?

**2-5.** Why is it necessary for an a-c generator of the type described in Fig. 2-6 to have an even number of magnetic poles?

**2-6.** What is the distinguishing feature of a periodic wave?

**2-7.** What advantage is there to changing the time variable of a periodic wave to the variable $x$?

**2-8.** Is there any difference in meaning of the words "period" and "cycle"?

**2-9.** In Fig. 2-9 the armature is pictured in its equilibrium position. Explain how the polarity of the induced potential varies as the pivoted armature oscillates about the equilibrium position.

**2-10.** Why is it more necessary to pay attention to algebraic representation in a-c circuits than in d-c circuits?

* In expressions involving the sum of two sinusoidal functions it is not necessary to combine the functions into a single expression.

**2-11.** In a d-c circuit, what does it mean to say that current flows in a certain direction?

**2-12.** In a d-c circuit, what does it mean to say that a potential has a certain polarity?

**2-13.** What is meant by the term "reference condition"? Why is the reference condition for a current a direction and the reference condition for a potential a polarity?

**2-14.** What two conditions must be specified in order to unambiguously define an algebraic variable, when it is to represent a physical entity?

**2-15.** By what two methods of notation can the reference direction for a current be indicated?

**2-16.** In what two ways can notation be used to indicate the reference polarity for a potential difference?

**2-17.** What are the differences among the following: sinusoidal wave, sine wave, cosine wave?

**2-18.** Can all sinusoidal waves be expressed mathematically as either sine or cosine functions?

**2-19.** Two lines are rotating about a common center. If one line geometrically generates a sine wave and the other a cosine wave, of the same frequency, how are the lines related to each other?

**2-20.** What is meant by the principal value of an initial angle? Is it always positive?

**2-21.** In this text is the concept of initial angle defined for any type of wave or only for sinusoidal waves?

**2-22.** What is the difference between initial angle and phase-angle difference?

**2-23.** How are the initial angles of two sinusoidal waves related to their phase-angle difference?

**2-24.** Would it be possible to express all possible phase-angle differences with only the concept of lead (or only lag) rather than to have both lead and lag used?

**2-25.** In the expression $v_{--} = -L\, di_{ab}/dt$ replace the dashes following the $v$ by letters that will make the expression true.

**2-26.** Show reference conditions on an inductor which would lead to the equation $v = -L\, di/dt$.

**2-27.** A resistor is connected in series with either an inductor or a capacitor. For each case tell whether the potential across the combination leads or lags the current. Use the reference conditions as they are shown in Fig. 2-31.

**2-28.** A resistor is connected in parallel with either an inductor or a capacitor. For each case tell whether the potential across the combination leads or lags the current. Use the reference conditions as they are shown in Fig. 2-32.

**2-29.** What is the fundamental idea of the Fourier theorem?

**2-30.** To what sort of varying quantities does the Fourier theorem apply?

# CHAPTER 3

# METERING AND EFFECTIVE VALUE

**3-1. Introduction.** The quantitative discussion of any physical system requires measurability of the physical entities involved. This introduces the metering problem. In a-c systems, the matter is more complicated than for d-c systems, because currents and potentials are continually changing. This variable nature of currents and potentials makes it necessary to exert care in defining what is to be measured. The technique of measuring the defined quantity may then be discussed.

**3-2. Pictorial Representation.** For certain situations the ideal measurement is one which gives a complete picture of a wave. An instrument for accomplishing this is called an oscilloscope. Oscilloscopes appear in many forms, but the cathode-ray type is most frequently encountered. Its essential features are shown in Fig. 3-1.

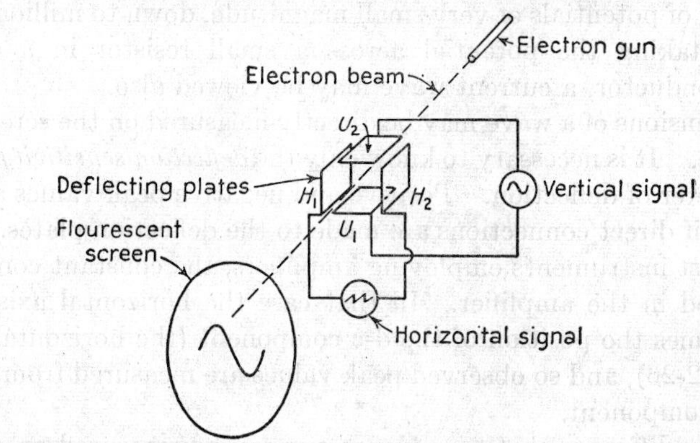


FIG. 3-1. Essential features of one type of cathode-ray oscilloscope.

Electrons are directed from an electron gun toward a fluorescent screen. A luminous spot is produced where the stream of electrons hits the screen. On their way to the screen, the electrons pass between two pairs of deflection plates. When a potential difference is applied between plates $U_1$ and $U_2$, the stream of electrons is deflected vertically. Similarly, a potential difference between plates $H_1$ and $H_2$ causes a horizontal deflection. The polarity of the potential difference determines the sense of the deflection, and the deflection is proportional to the potential difference. The electron beam can follow variations of potential up to millions of cycles per second.

The oscilloscope will show a wave plotted on a horizontal time axis if the electron beam is deflected horizontally at uniform velocity. This type of horizontal deflection is called a linear sweep. It is produced by a saw-tooth wave, as shown in Fig. 3-1. The potential rises linearly and then very suddenly returns to zero, again to repeat.

Such an oscilloscope system is useful for viewing periodic functions. The period of the saw-tooth wave must be the same as (or an integral multiple of) the period of the wave to be viewed. Otherwise, the wave will not stand still on the screen. In most cases the wave is traced out at a sufficiently high repetition rate to make a stationary wave appear, rather than a moving spot. If the sweep frequency is adjustable to known values, an oscilloscope can be used to measure frequency by adjusting the sweep until the wave is stationary.

A cathode-ray oscilloscope is a potential-sensitive device. Potentials in hundreds of volts are required for reasonable deflections. For this reason it is customary to include an amplifier in its case. This permits the viewing of potentials of very small magnitude, down to millionths of a volt. By taking the potential across a small resistor in a current-carrying conductor, a current wave may be viewed also.

The dimensions of a wave may be directly measured on the screen of an oscilloscope. It is necessary to know only the *deflection sensitivity* in volts per centimeter of deflection. Positive and negative peak values are both observable if direct connections are made to the deflection plates. However, in most instruments employing amplifiers, the constant component is eliminated in the amplifier. In that case the horizontal axis on the screen assumes the position of the d-c component (the horizontal dotted line of Fig. 2-26), and so observed peak values are measured from the line of the d-c component.

The phase difference between two waves can be measured on an oscilloscope. If the waves can be viewed simultaneously on a common time axis the phase difference can be obtained by direct measurement on the screen. The phase difference is the separation between them. However, a single-gun cathode-ray oscilloscope is not readily adapted to viewing two waves simultaneously on a common time axis. It can be done, but it is necessary to use a special switching device to present the two waves alternately, or to have a special tube with two electron streams and two deflection systems. In the absence of such a special device, if the waves are sinusoidal, phase difference can be measured by applying one wave to the horizontal system and the other to the vertical system.

**3-3. Lissajous Figures.** A Lissajous figure is obtained when two waves of the same frequency and shape are separately applied to the horizontal and vertical deflection systems. If both waves are sinusoidal, the figure obtained is an ellipse. The dimensions of the ellipse can be used to find the phase difference between the waves.

The details of this application may be considered by letting the vertical and horizontal potentials be, respectively,

$$\begin{aligned} u &= A \sin (\omega t + \theta) \\ h &= B \sin \omega t \end{aligned} \tag{3-1}$$

Wave $u$ leads wave $h$ by the angle $\theta$.

A typical case is illustrated in Fig. 3-2. Various instants of time are correspondingly numbered on the two axes and on the ellipse. At each

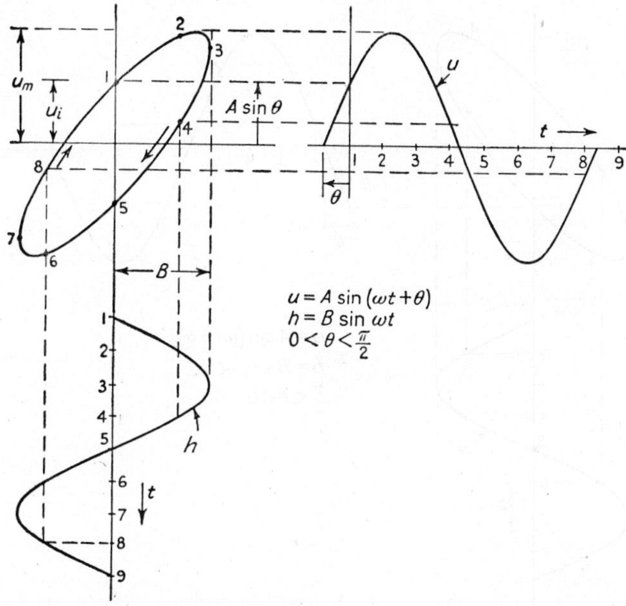


FIG. 3-2. The generation of a Lissajous figure when the vertical wave leads the horizontal wave by a positive angle smaller than 90°.

instant the two waves have a particular pair of values, which determine the position of the luminous spot. As time progresses, each wave takes on different values, resulting in the tracing of the ellipse. Constructions are shown for points 4 and 8, showing how the spot position is determined by the two sinusoids. For this case the spot travels around the ellipse in a clockwise direction.

The phase difference can be determined from the dimensions $u_i$ and $u_m$ of the ellipse, which can be measured on the screen and so may be assumed known. From the figure,

$$u_i = A \sin \theta$$
$$u_m = A \tag{3-2}$$

Hence,

$$\theta = \sin^{-1} \frac{u_i}{u_m} \tag{3-3}$$

For the example shown in Fig. 3-2 the intercepts are

$$u_i = 1.7 \qquad u_m = 3.0$$

It follows that $\theta = \sin^{-1} 0.566 = 34.5°$.

A similar ellipse is shown in Fig. 3-3, but for $\theta = -34.5°$. The only difference from Fig. 3-2 is that the point travels in the opposite direction

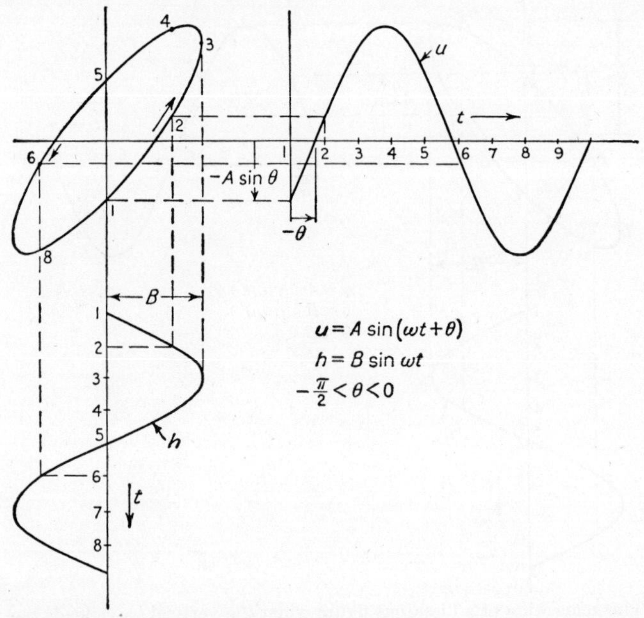


FIG. 3-3. The generation of a Lissajous figure when the vertical wave lags the horizontal wave by a positive angle smaller than 90°.

in tracing out the ellipse. Since this direction can not be determined from an ordinary observation, the sign of $\theta$ is not known from the ellipse alone. Accordingly, for an ellipse that looks like Fig. 3-2 or 3-3, only the absolute value of $\theta$ is given by the formula

$$|\theta| = \sin^{-1} \frac{u_i}{u_m} \tag{3-4}*$$

* In Eq. (3-4) the $\sin^{-1}$ function is to be the smallest value. That is, although $\sin^{-1} 0.566 = 34.5°$ or 145.5, the former is used.

When $|\theta|$ is greater than $\pi/2$, the ellipse takes the form shown in Fig. 3-4. For this case the smallest value of $\sin^{-1}(u_i/u_m)$ represents $\pi - |\theta|$ instead of $|\theta|$. Therefore, when the ellipse has its main axis in the second and fourth quadrants the formula for $|\theta|$ is

$$|\theta| = \pi - \sin^{-1}\frac{u_i}{u_m} \tag{3-5}*$$

For Fig. 3-4 the numerical value of $|\theta|$ is

$$|\theta| = 180° - \sin^{-1} 0.566 = 145.5°$$

It is to be noted, by way of caution, that the pairing of Eqs. (3-4) and (3-5) with ellipses slanted, respectively, as in Figs. 3-3 and 3-4 depends on having the positive directions to the right on the horizontal axis and

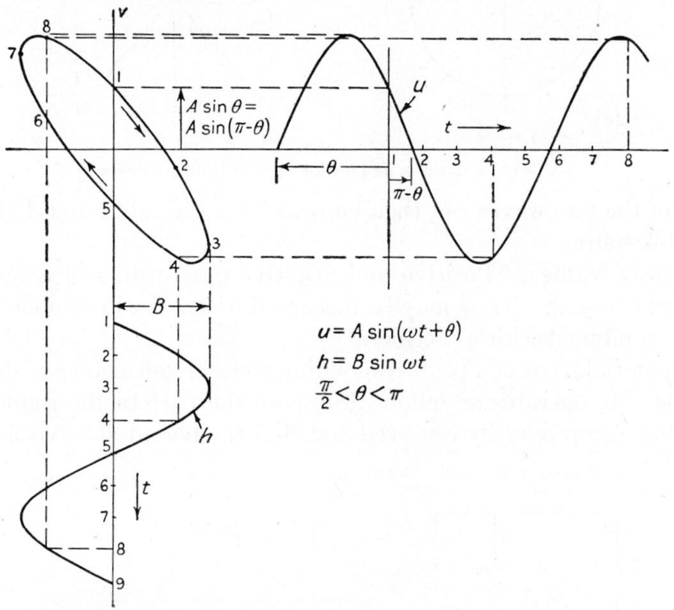


Fig. 3-4. Generation of a Lissajous figure when the vertical wave leads the horizontal wave by an angle greater than 90°.

upward on the vertical axis. This may not always be the case, especially if a different number of stages of amplification are used in the two deflection systems.

The special cases of $|\theta| = 0$, $\pi/2$, and $\pi$ are of interest. They are illustrated in Fig. 3-5. The straight lines are special cases of ellipses with minor axes of zero length.

It is important to note that the ratio $u_i/u_m$ is independent of the values

* In Eq. (3-5) the $\sin^{-1}$ function is to be the smallest value. That is, although $\sin^{-1} 0.566 = 34.5°$ or 145.5, the former is used.

of $A$ and $B$. However, $A$ and $B$ should each be large enough to permit an accurate determination of $u_i$ and $u_m$.

It is worth mentioning that a Lissajous figure can be used to measure frequency if a calibrated source of adjustable frequency is available. The wave of unknown frequency is applied to one deflection system and the wave of adjustable frequency is applied to the other deflection system and is then adjusted to make the figure stand still. The common fre-

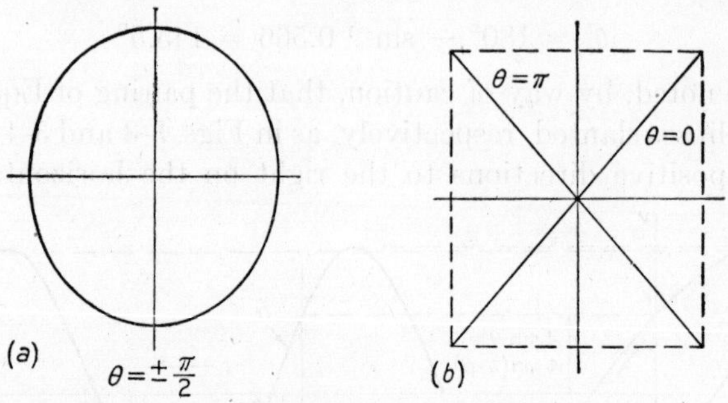


FIG. 3-5. Lissajous figures for special limiting cases.

quency of the two waves can then be read from the calibrated dial of the adjustable source.

**3-4. Peak Values.** Positive and negative peak values of a wave are defined in Chap. 2. They may be measured with a d-c instrument if it is suitably combined with a rectifier.

The essential parts of a peak-responding rectifier voltmeter are shown in Fig. 3-6*a*. It operates as follows: Suppose the part to the right of the dotted line is temporarily removed and that the potential wave shown in

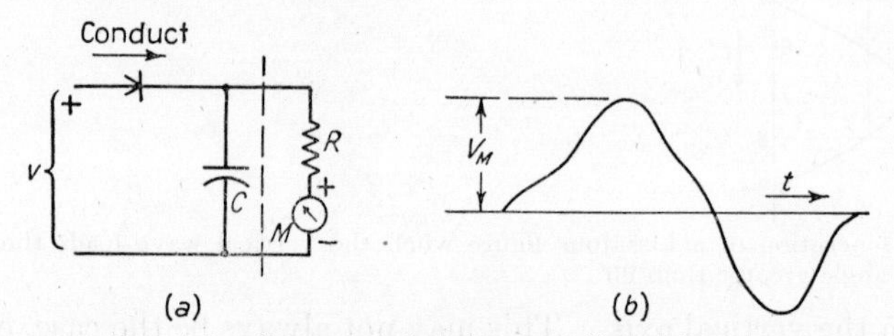


FIG. 3-6. One type of peak-responding voltmeter.

Fig. 3-6*b* is applied. The rectifier can conduct in the direction of the arrow, so the capacitor can charge up to the potential $V_m$. It will remain at that potential because the rectifier will not conduct in the discharge direction. In the absence of the resistor-voltmeter part of the circuit, the capacitor would remain charged to the largest positive value of $v$.

When the meter is added, the capacitor can discharge through it. This effect is negligible if $R$ is so large that the capacitor cannot appreciably discharge during one cycle. This is true if the product $RC$ is much larger than one period of the applied wave. Since only a small discharge current is allowed, $M$ must be a sensitive meter. The important function of the capacitor is to store energy which it can feed to the meter during the time intervals when the rectifier is not conducting.

The peak-responding meter circuit may require an appreciable time to follow a sudden reduction of amplitude of the wave being measured because it takes time for the charge to leak off through the meter circuit. Several seconds' delay in the response is not uncommon.

The negative peak of the wave may be measured by interchanging the connections. The wave shape has no effect on the indication of the meter. Only the peak value is important. For example, all the waves of Fig. 3-7 give the same indication on a peak-responding voltmeter, when connected to indicate positive peaks. It should be mentioned that

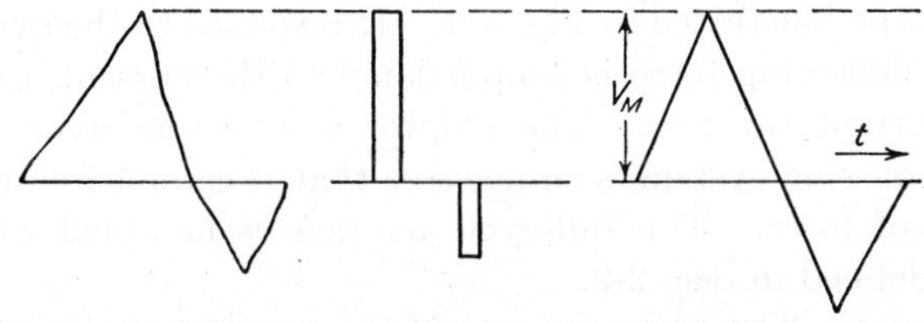


FIG. 3-7. Several waves having the same positive peaks.

in many peak-responding meters the capacitor and rectifier are interchanged. Such an arrangement causes the d-c component to be removed so that the meter indicates peak values from the line of the d-c component. Such a meter would not show the same response on all the waves of Fig. 3-7.

The meter of Fig. 3-6 is essentially a potential-measuring device. In some instruments an amplifier is included between the input terminals and the rectifying circuit, to increase its sensitivity. If it is to be used to measure current, it is necessary to place a resistor of low value in the current circuit, to create a potential difference which may then be measured. It is possible to construct a peak-current meter, using an inductor for energy storage, instead of a capacitor.

**3-5. Average Values.** A periodic wave may be averaged in several ways. The average may be taken for the whole cycle, giving the *full-cycle average.* It may be obtained for either the positive or the negative portions of the wave, to give the *positive* or *negative pulse average.* Finally, the average may be taken without regard for the algebraic sign of the portions of the wave, to give the *absolute average.* Meters for responding to averages are usually current-sensitive, so the explanation will be based on the measurement of current.

*Full-cycle Average.* In Fig. 3-8 is shown the plot of a periodic wave. Let it be called $i(t)$, a function of the time $t$. Its average, over a complete cycle, is the area divided by the base, which is $T$. The area is obtained by integration. Thus, the full-cycle average is

$$I_{av} = \frac{1}{T}\int_0^T i(t)\,dt \tag{3-6}$$

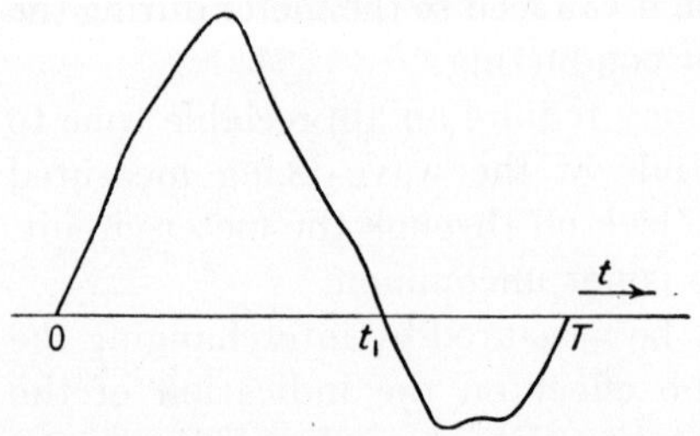


Fig. 3-8. A periodic wave having a nonzero full-cycle average.

It is noted that the area below the axis counts negatively. A wave having equal areas above and below, such as a sinusoid, has zero full-cycle average value.

The full-cycle average is measured by an ordinary d-c meter of the d'Arsonval type illustrated in Fig. 3-9. It responds to the average value because the deflecting force is proportional to the current, and reverses when the current reverses. The pointer assumes an average position because the moving system is so massive that it cannot follow the rapid fluctuations of force. The full-cycle average is identical with the d-c component defined in Sec. 2-9.

*Pulse Average.* The pulse average is the average of the wave on one side of the axis (positive or negative) taken over a whole cycle. For the example of Fig. 3-8 let $I_+$ and $I_-$ designate, respectively, the positive and negative pulse averages. Then

$$\begin{aligned} I_+ &= \frac{1}{T}\int_0^{t_1} i(t)\,dt \\ I_- &= \frac{-1}{T}\int_{t_1}^{T} i(t)\,dt \end{aligned} \tag{3-7}$$

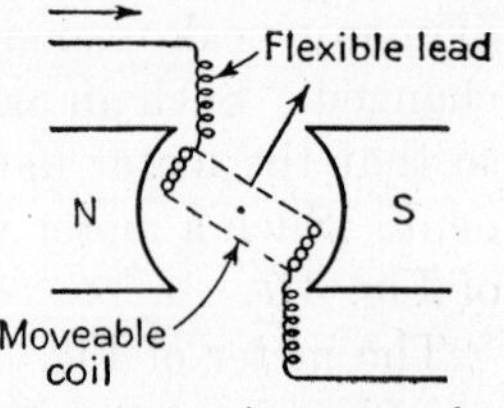


Fig. 3-9. A meter for responding to full-cycle average (d'Arsonval meter movement).

It is possible for a wave to have a number of positive or negative (or both) pulses per cycle, as in Fig. 3-10. In that case each pulse average must include all positive or negative portions of the wave.

Consider the pulse average of a sinuoisdal current,

$$i(x) = I_m \sin x \tag{3-8}$$

The variable can be left as $x$ in the integration. The positive and negative pulse averages are the same, and so

$$I_- = I_+ = \frac{I_m}{2\pi}\int_0^{\pi} \sin x\,dx = \frac{I_m}{2\pi}[-\cos x]_0^{\pi} = \frac{I_m}{\pi} \tag{3-9}$$

This proves that for any sinusoidal wave the pulse average is $1/\pi = 0.318$ times the peak value.

The essential components of a pulse-average ammeter are shown in Fig. 3-11. A d-c meter $M$ is used in conjunction with two rectifiers $R_1$

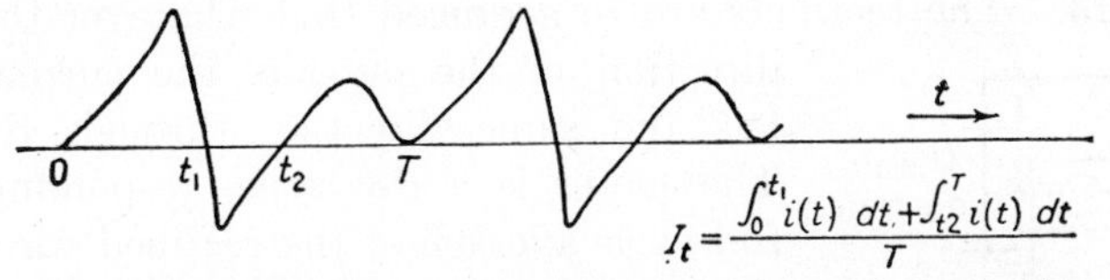


FIG. 3-10. Periodic wave having two positive peaks per cycle.

and $R_2$. The rectifiers conduct in the directions shown by the arrows. Only the positive parts of the wave can flow through $M$, so it measures the positive pulse average. A reversal of the external connections would yield the negative pulse average. Rectifier $R_1$ is needed to provide continuity of the circuit. In a pulse-average voltmeter a series resistor is used with the meter, and $R_1$ is omitted because it is not necessary to maintain a conducting path through a voltmeter for both halves of the cycle.

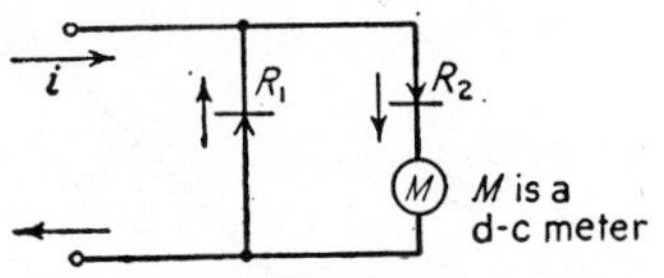


FIG. 3-11. Circuit of a meter responding to the pulse average.

*Absolute Average.* The absolute average is obtained by inverting the negative portions of the wave and then taking the full-cycle average of the result. Accordingly, if $|i(t)|$ is the absolute value of the current,

$$I_{abs} = \frac{1}{T}\int_0^T |i(t)|\,dt \qquad (3\text{-}10)$$

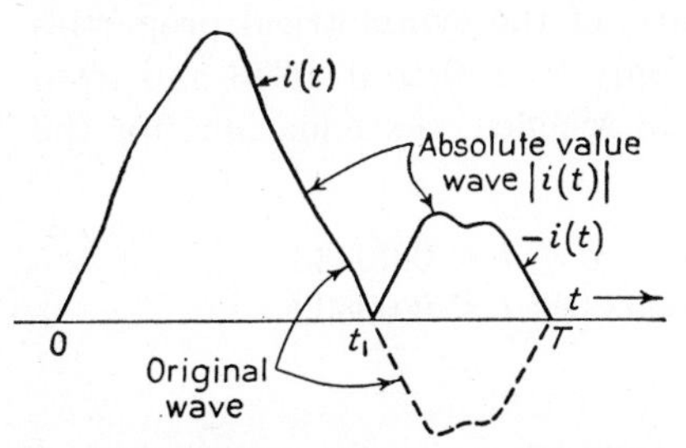


FIG. 3-12. Relationship between absolute-value wave and original wave.

In any numerical example it is necessary to break the integral at the points where the function changes sign. Thus, for the example of Fig. 3-12

$$I_{abs} = \frac{1}{T}\left[\int_0^{t_1} i(t)\,dt - \int_{t_1}^{T} i(t)\,dt\right] \qquad (3\text{-}11)$$

For a sinusoid the absolute average is twice the pulse average, because the positive and negative peaks are equal. Therefore, from the known pulse average, the absolute average is $2/\pi = 0.636$ times the peak value of a sinusoid.

A comparison of Eq. (3-11) with Eqs. (3-7) shows useful relationships among the three types of average values. The absolute average is the sum of the two pulse averages. Furthermore, the full-cycle average is given by the difference between the positive and negative pulse averages. These statements are true no matter how many positive and negative pulses there may be in one cycle.

The absolute average of a current can be measured by the circuit shown in Fig. 3-13. The rectifiers are so arranged that whatever the current direction in the outside, the current always has the same direction through the meter. The meter is a d-c type, responding to the full-cycle average of the rectified wave applied to it.

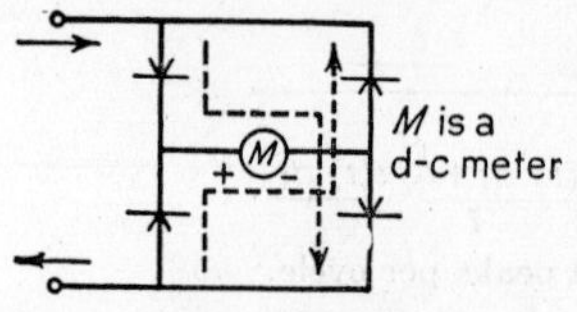


FIG. 3-13. Circuit of a meter for measuring absolute average value. Conduction paths are shown by dashed lines.

**Example 3-1.** Find the various average values for the wave shown in the accompanying graph.

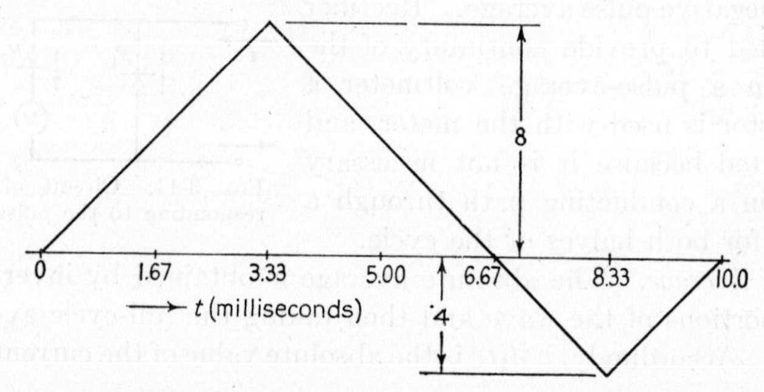


*Solution. Full-cycle Average.* Because of the symmetrical properties of the wave it is sufficient to integrate only from 0 to 0.00333 and from 0.00667 to 0.00833. If $t$ is measured in seconds, the equations for the required portions of the wave are:

$$i(t) = 2{,}400t \qquad 0 \leq t \leq 0.00333$$
$$i(t) = 16 - 2{,}400t \qquad 0.00333 \leq t \leq 0.00833$$

It follows that the full-cycle average is

$$I_{av} = (100)\left[2\int_0^{0.00333} 2{,}400t\,dt + 2\int_{0.00667}^{0.00833} (16 - 2{,}400t)\,dt\right]$$
$$= 200\left[2{,}400\,\frac{t^2}{2}\Bigg|_0^{0.00333} + \left(16t - 2{,}400\,\frac{t^2}{2}\right)\Bigg|_{0.00667}^{0.00833}\right]$$
$$= 2.67 + 26.67 - 21.33 - 16.67 + 10.66 = 40 - 38 = 2 \text{ amp}$$

*Positive-pulse Average.* For the same wave the positive pulse average is

$$I_+ = (100)(2)\int_0^{0.00333} 2{,}400t\,dt = (200)(2{,}400)\,\frac{t^2}{2}\Bigg|_0^{0.00333}$$
$$= 2.67 \text{ amp}$$

and the negative pulse average is

$$I_- = (100)(2)\int_{0.00667}^{0.00833} -(16 - 2{,}400t)\,dt = -200\left(16t - 2{,}400\frac{t^2}{2}\right)\Bigg|_{0.00667}^{0.00833}$$

$$= -26.667 + 21.333 + 16.667 + 10.666 = 0.667 \text{ amp.}$$

*Absolute Average.* As pointed out in the text, the absolute average is the sum of the positive and negative pulse average. Thus

$$I_{abs} = 2.667 + 0.667 = 3.333$$

This illustration is carried out by actually performing the integrations. However, in cases like this, where the wave is made up of simple geometric figures, the area can sometimes be determined by observation. For example, the area of a triangle is half the product of the base times the altitude. Applying this to the positive pulse average, it follows that

$$I_+ = \frac{\text{area positive triangle}}{0.01} = \frac{(0.00333)(8)}{0.01} = 2.67 \text{ amp}$$

which agrees with the previous value.

**3-6. Effective Value.** The various wave dimensions so far discussed are useful under special conditions. For example, peak values are of interest in vacuum-tube applications and in situations involving possible

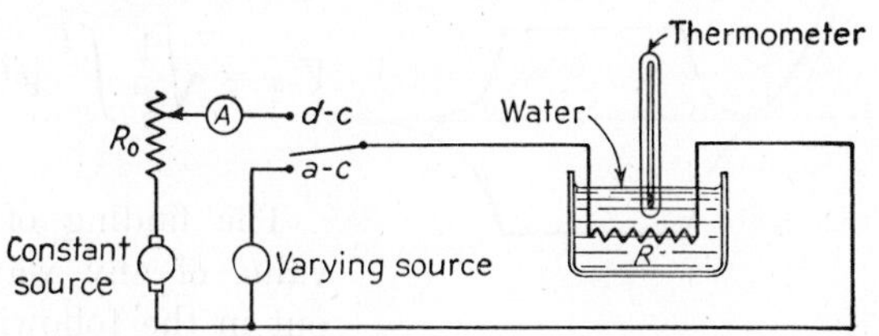


FIG. 3-14. A laboratory experiment illustrating the meaning of "effective value."

breakdown of insulation. Average values are of interest where the transportation of charge is of interest, as in electroplating. However, for many purposes the effective value is used.

The *effective value* of a periodically varying potential (or current) is defined as the magnitude of a constant potential (or current) which would produce heat in a given resistor at the same average rate that it is produced by the varying one. For an explanation of this consider Fig. 3-14. When the switch is in the a-c position, a periodic current wave flows through the resistor $R$. The temperature ultimately attained by the surrounding water is a measure of the average electrical power flow into the resistor. Now suppose the switch is thrown to the d-c position and that $R_0$ is adjusted until the water attains the same steady temperature as before. The electrical power flow is the same as before. The value of this equivalent d-c current is defined to be the effective value of the periodic wave.

A mathematical formula for the effective value may be deduced. The instantaneous power into a resistor is $i^2R$. It is a varying quantity if $i$ is varying. Typical graphs of $i$ and $i^2$ are given in Fig. 3-15. The average power delivered to the resistor is $R$ multiplied by the area under the $i^2$ curve, divided by $T$. The average produced by the constant current is $(I_{\text{eff}})^2R$. These two are equal, by definition, giving

$$(I_{\text{eff}})^2R = \frac{R}{T}\int_0^T [i(t)]^2\,dt \tag{3-12}$$

$$I_{\text{eff}} = \sqrt{\frac{1}{T}\int_0^T [i(t)]^2\,dt} \tag{3-13}$$

A similar treatment can be applied to a potential difference. The power delivered to a resistor is $v^2/R$, so a formula exactly similar to Eq. (3-12) would be obtained, with $R$ in the denominator of both sides. $R$ cancels anyway, so the equation for effective potential difference is

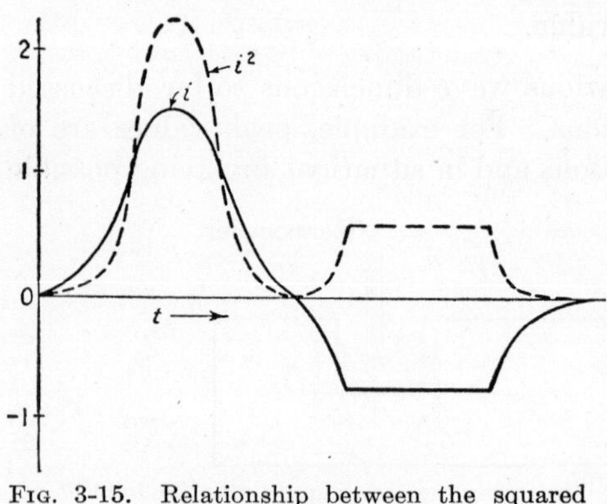


FIG. 3-15. Relationship between the squared wave and the original wave.

$$V_{\text{eff}} = \sqrt{\frac{1}{T}\int_0^T [v(t)]^2\,dt} \tag{3-14}$$

The finding of an effective value of any wave is carried out in the following sequence: (1) the function is squared, (2) the average of the squared function is obtained, and (3) the square root is taken of the average. The process is described by the phrase "root mean square." Thus, an alternate name for effective value is *root-mean-square* value (abbreviated to *rms* value).

**Example 3-2.** Find the effective value of the wave specified in Example 3-1.

*Solution.* As in the previous case it is necessary to integrate over only half of the wave, because of its symmetry. In this case let time be measured in millisecond units. The equations are

$$i(t) = 2.4t \qquad 0 \le t \le 3.33$$
$$i(t) = 16 - 2.4t \qquad 3.33 \le t \le 8.33$$

The effective value is

$$I_{\text{eff}} = \sqrt{2/10 \int_0^{3.33} (2.4t)^2\,dt + 2/10 \int_{6.67}^{8.33} (16 - 2.4t)^2\,dt}$$

$$= \sqrt{0.2\left(\frac{5.76}{3}\right) t^3 \Big|_0^{3.33} + 0.2\left(256t - \frac{76.8}{2}t^2 + \frac{5.76}{3}t^3\right)\Big|_{6.67}^{8.33}}$$

$$= \sqrt{14.22 + 85.33 - 192 + 108.44} = \sqrt{16} = 4 \text{ amp}$$

As an important special case, consider a sinusoidal wave. When $i$ is given by Eq. (3-8),

$$I_{\text{eff}} = \sqrt{\frac{I_m^2}{2\pi}\int_0^{2\pi} \sin^2 x\,dx} = I_m \sqrt{\frac{1}{4\pi}\int_0^{2\pi} (1 - \cos 2x)\,dx}$$

$$= I_m \sqrt{\frac{1}{4\pi}\left(x - \frac{\sin 2x}{2}\right)\Big|_0^{2\pi}} = \frac{I_m}{\sqrt{2}} \tag{3-15}$$

Thus it is shown that the effective value of a sinusoidal wave is 0.707 times the peak value. This is a factor worth remembering, but it is also important to observe that, as a general rule, it is applicable only to a sinusoidal wave.

There are several meter types that theoretically respond to effective value, regardless of the wave shape or frequency.* One of the simplest to describe is the hot-wire ammeter illustrated in Fig. 3-16. The current to be measured, or a known fraction of it, flows through a fine wire. The wire is heated by the current, causing it to stretch slightly and allowing the thread attached to its center to rotate a small drum on the pointer spindle. A spring maintains a tension in the thread at all times. Although the mechanism is simple, the meter is delicate, it is somewhat sensitive to surrounding temperatures, and it lacks electrical sensitivity.

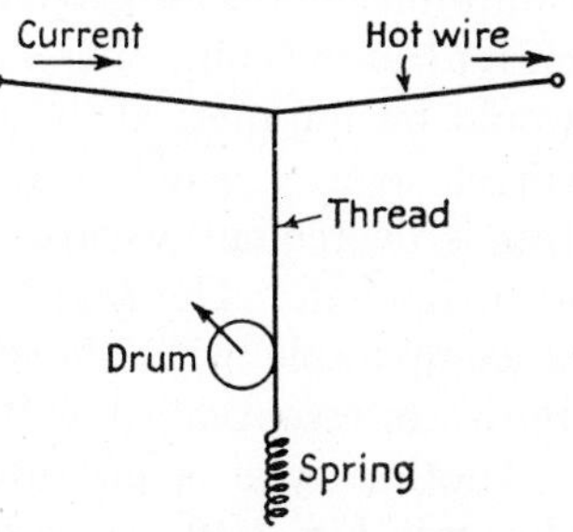


FIG. 3-16. Principle of operation of the "hot-wire" effective-responding meter.

The meter sketched in Fig. 3-17 is called an electrodynomometer type. It is similar to the d'Arsonval d-c instrument, except that the usual permanent magnet is replaced by a pair of stationary coils. All coils, moving and stationary, are connected in series. Therefore, when the

* In practical meters, some effective responding types are restricted in their usable frequency range or do not indicate accurately if the wave has corners which are too sharp. There are a variety of reasons for these restrictions, some of which are due to the frequency limitations of the circuit elements used in construction of the meters. A brief discussion of circuit element limitations is given in Sec. 2-13.

current reverses, it does so in all coils and the mechanical force tending to rotate the movable coil always remains in the same direction. This force is proportional to the product of the current in the movable coil and the magnetic field. But the magnetic field is proportional to the current, so the force is proportional to the current squared. The moving parts are massive enough to make the moving system take a position proportional to the average force, and therefore the deflection is proportional to the average of the current squared. The scale can be marked with numbers which are proportional to the square root of the deflection. The pointer then indicates true effective value on the scale.

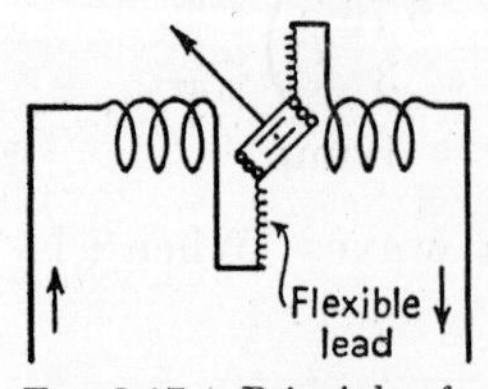


FIG. 3-17. Principle of operation of the electrodynamometer type of effective-responding meter.

A meter having similar utility is shown in Fig. 3-18, in very rudimentary form. It is called a moving iron-vane meter. The general principal of operation is based on the tendency of an elongated piece of iron to orient itself along the direction of a magnetic field. For example, the piece of iron in Fig. 3-18 tends to rotate clockwise no matter what the direction of current in the coil. The simple scheme illustrated would be impractical because the pointer would travel over a small arc. In practical meters this is overcome by variations of the mechanical arrangement. The frequency range of this meter is comparable with the electrodynometer type. Both are essentially low-frequency meters.

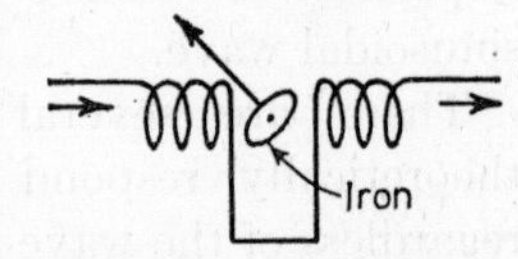


FIG. 3-18. Principle of operation of the moving-iron-vane type of effective-responding meter.

Another type of instrument suitable for measuring effective value is shown in Fig. 3-19. It is similar to the hot-wire instrument to the extent that the indication is dependent on heating effects. The difference between the two is in the method of relating the motion of the pointer to the temperature change. In the meter of Fig. 3-19 a sensitive thermocouple is attached to the heater wire. The output of this thermocouple is measured on a d-c meter. The thermocouple meter is more rugged mechanically than the hot-wire type and shares with it the advantage of being operable at a much higher frequency than the other two types so far discussed.

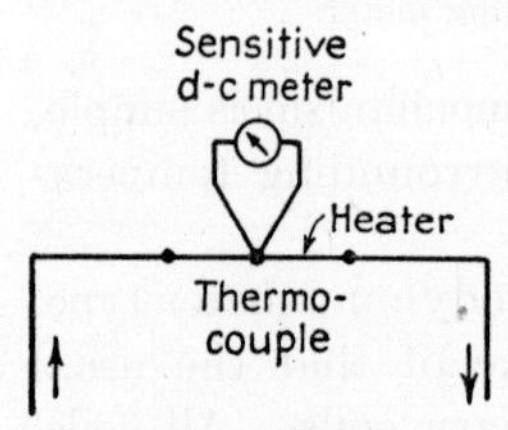


FIG. 3-19. The basic elements of the thermocouple effective-responding meter.

All meters which respond to effective value exhibit a common disadvantage. They do not have a uniform scale. By careful design some uniformity may be achieved, but the scale is basically one in which the deflection is proportional to the square of the current. Such a scale is intolerably crowded at the low end. To compensate for this, it is necessary always to choose a meter of proper range, so it will give an indication well upscale. The scale of a square-law meter is shown in Fig. 3-20*a*. It could not be accurately read below the value ½. The uniform scale of a d-c meter, shown at (*b*) in the figure, does not have this disadvantage.

All of these effective-responding meters indicate correctly on direct current. They may therefore be calibrated against standard d-c meters, in d-c circuits.

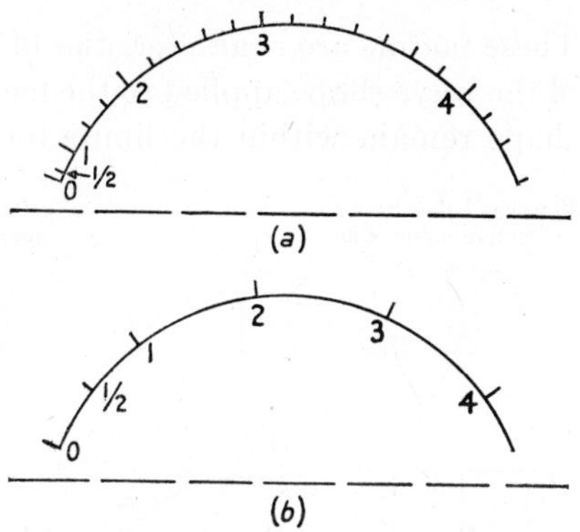

FIG. 3-20. Comparison of linear and nonlinear meter scales.

**3-7. Comparison of Meters Calibrated to Indicate Effective Value of a Sinusoid.** In many cases a meter which responds to an average or peak value is calibrated to indicate effective value *when used on a sinusoid.* Such a meter does not necessarily indicate correctly when actuated by a nonsinusoidal wave shape. However, if the shape is known, the effective value can be deduced from the meter indication.

To explain this, it is convenient to imagine a second scale on the meter. Since it does not actually appear, it is called the *latent scale.* The latent scale would indicate the quantity to which the meter responds—the *response quantity.* For example, suppose a peak-responding meter is

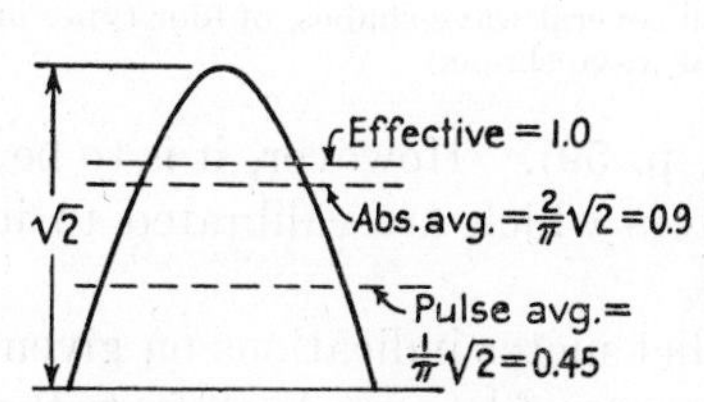


| | Peak | Abs. avg. | Pulse avg. | Eff. |
|---|---|---|---|---|
| Meter indication | 1 | 1 | 1 | 1 |
| Latent scale indication | 1.414 | 0.9 | 0.45 | 1 |

FIG. 3-21. Relationships among values of response quantities (latent scale indications) for meters calibrated to indicate effective values on sinusoidal waves.

calibrated to indicate effective values on sinusoidal waves. If it indicates 1 amp on a sinusoid, the latent scale would indicate the peak value, *viz.*, 1.414 amp. The concept of a latent scale is useful because the latent scale is applicable no matter what the wave shape. Figure 3-21 shows the latent-scale indications for the common meter types, when they are actuated by a sinusoid of unit effective value.

The information given in Fig. 3-21 yields the following set of conversion factors:

| *Meter type* | *Scale factors* | |
|---|---|---|
| Peak | Latent = 1.414 × actual | Actual = 0.707 × latent |
| Absolute average | Latent = 0.90 × actual | Actual = 1.11 × latent |
| Pulse average | Latent = 0.45 × actual | Actual = 2.22 × latent |

These factors are characteristics of the meter types and are not functions of the wave shape applied to the meters as long as the frequency and wave shape remain within the limits for which the meter accurately indicates

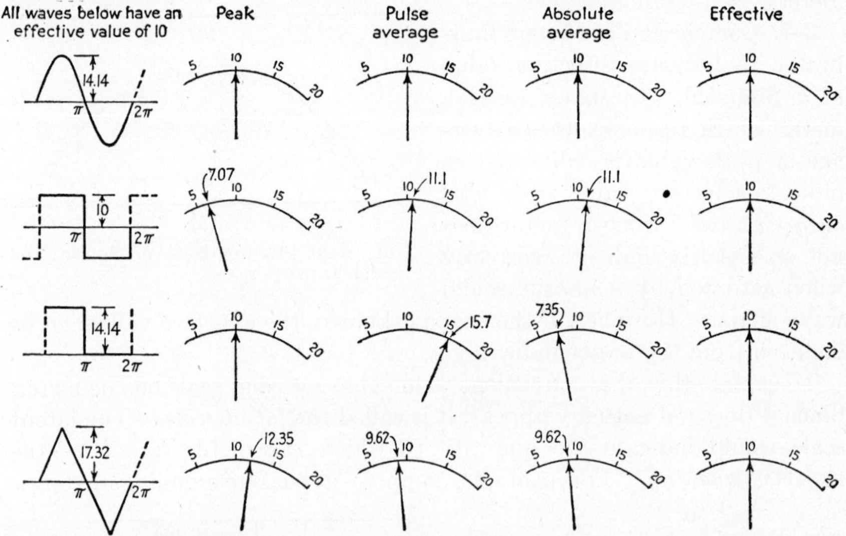


Fig. 3-22. Comparison of the indications, on several wave shapes, of four types of meters, all of which indicate correctly on a sinusoidal wave shape.

its response quantity (see footnote, p. 59). However, it is to be understood that they apply only to meters which are calibrated to indicate effective values on sinusoidal waves.

These factors can be used to predict meter indications on given waves or to determine the dimensions of a wave of known shape from the meter indication. Examples of both these applications are given below, and in Fig. 3-22.

**Example 3-3.** A pulse-average-responding meter, which is calibrated to indicate correctly on a sinusoid, is actuated by the triangular wave of Fig. 3-22. Find the indication of the meter.

*Solution.* The response quantity (latent-scale indication) is the average of one pulse, *viz.*,

$$\text{Latent-scale indication} = \frac{17.32}{4} = 4.33$$

From the above table it is found that for this meter the actual indication is 2.22 times its latent-scale indication. Therefore

$$\text{Actual indication} = (2.22)(4.33) = 9.62 \text{ amp}$$

**Example 3-4.** A peak-responding voltmeter, which indicates effective values on sinusoidal waves, is actuated by a triangular wave similar to the one shown in Fig. 3-22. Find the effective value of the wave if the meter indication is 20 volts.

*Solution.* From the above table it follows that the response quantity for the meter is

$$\text{Latent-scale indication} = (1.414)(20) = 28.28$$

This is the peak value of the wave. From its known shape it is known that its effective value is $1/\sqrt{3}$ times its peak value. Therefore,

$$\text{Effective value of wave} = \frac{28.28}{1{,}732} = 17.32 \text{ volts}$$

**3-8. Form Factor.** A factor relating the absolute average of a wave to its effective value is defined. It is called the form factor and is given by

$$\text{Form factor} = \frac{\text{effective value}}{\text{absolute average}} \tag{3-16}$$

It is obviously a characteristic of the wave shape. The tabulation below shows form factors for the waves of Fig. 3-22.

| *Wave* | *Form factor* |
|---|---|
| Sinusoid | 1.111 |
| Rectangular (symmetrical) | 1.000 |
| Rectangular (single-sided) | 1.414 |
| Triangular | 1.153 |

These factors can be used for finding effective values from the indications of absolute-average-responding meters. Similar factors could be defined for pulse-average and peak values.

**3-9. Summary.** The accurate specification of an a-c wave involves three attributes of the wave:

1. Its shape.
2. Its position on the time (or time-angle) axis, relative to some other wave.
3. Its frequency.

4. Its size, as measured by some characteristic dimension (peak, average, or effective value).

Items 1, 2 and 3 are conveniently measured on an oscilloscope. Items 2 and 3 can also be determined with special meters of various types. However, these meters are of such a special nature as to be omitted from this general discussion.

The measurement of a dimension of a wave requires an instrument which will respond in spite of its alternating nature. A variety of principles are used to obtain such indicating meters. Some cause the meter to respond to the peak value, some respond to the average value on either side of the axis, or to the absolute average, and some respond to the effective value. The effective value is defined in terms of effectiveness in producing heat in a resistor. Because it is the most useful dimension, most meters are calibrated to indicate effective values when actuated by a sinusoidal wave. Such meters do not always indicate correctly on nonsinusoidal wave shapes.

## PROBLEMS

**3-1.** The oscillograph of Fig. P3-1*a* portrays the sinusoidally varying potential appearing across a portion of a circuit. If the sinusoidal potential is replaced by a battery, as shown in Fig. P3-1*b*, it is found that the base line takes a deflection upward. Give a double-subscript designation for the wave shown in Fig. P3-1*a*.

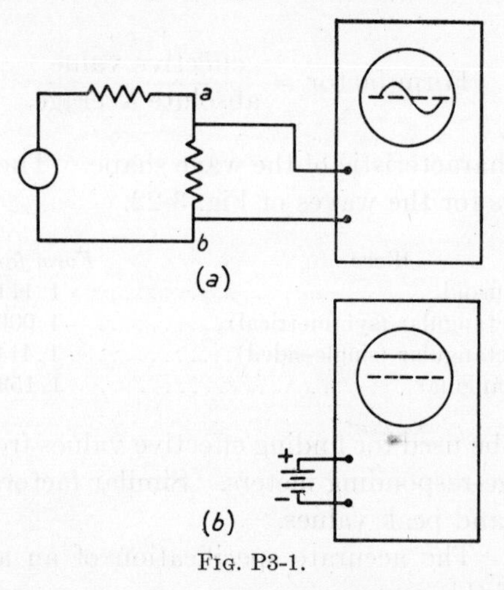


Fig. P3-1.

**3-2.** A particular oscilloscope is operated without an internal sweep. With no potentials applied to the deflection plates the spot is in the center of the tube. Preliminary tests with batteries give the results shown in Fig. P3-2*a*. The oscilloscope is then connected to portions of a circuit which yields sinusoidal waves, as shown in Fig. P3-2*b*. It can then be used to determine the phase-angle difference between the two waves to which its deflection systems are connected. For various conditions of the circuit a Lissajous figure of one of the

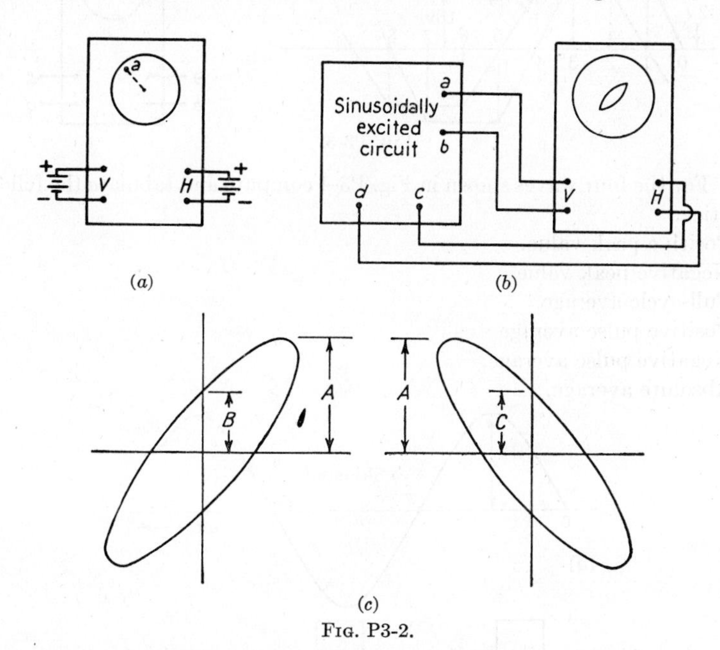

FIG. P3-2.

types shown in Fig. P3-2*c* is obtained. Compute the phase-angle differences between $v_{ab}$ and $v_{cd}$ for the following dimensions of the Lissajous figures:

| | *A* | *B* | *C* |
|---|---|---|---|
| (*a*) | 120 | 120 | |
| (*b*) | 120 | 60 | |
| (*c*) | 60 | 30 | |
| (*d*) | 150 | 0 | |
| (*e*) | 120 | | 60 |
| (*f*) | 60 | | 10 |
| (*g*) | 50 | | 0 |

**3-3.** Set up a set of coordinates to represent the face of a cathode-ray screen. Let the deflection systems have the characteristics described in Prob. 3-2. The device is excited by the waves shown in Fig. P3-3. Each deflection system has a deflection sensitivity of 2 cm/volt.

*a*. Plot the figure traced on the screen.

*b*. Plot the figure traced on the screen if one wave had been labeled $v_{dc}$ rather than $v_{cd}$.

NOTE: In each case mark the position of the spot for the numbered instants on the time axis.

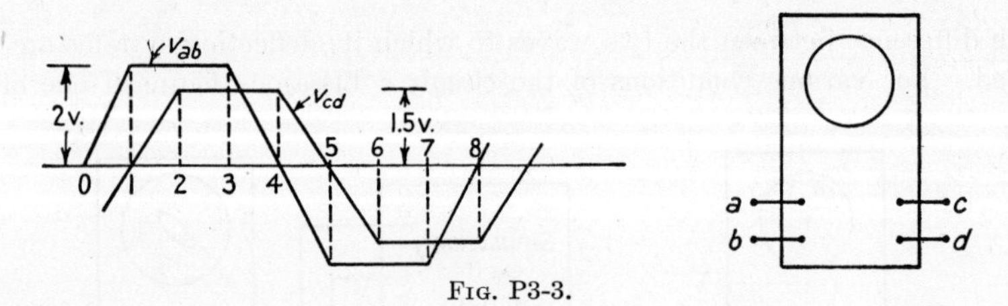


FIG. P3-3.

**3-4.** For the four waves shown in Fig. P3-4 compute and tabulate the following quantities:

*a.* Positive peak value.
*b.* Negative peak value.
*c.* Full-cycle average.
*d.* Positive pulse average.
*e.* Negative pulse average.
*f.* Absolute average.

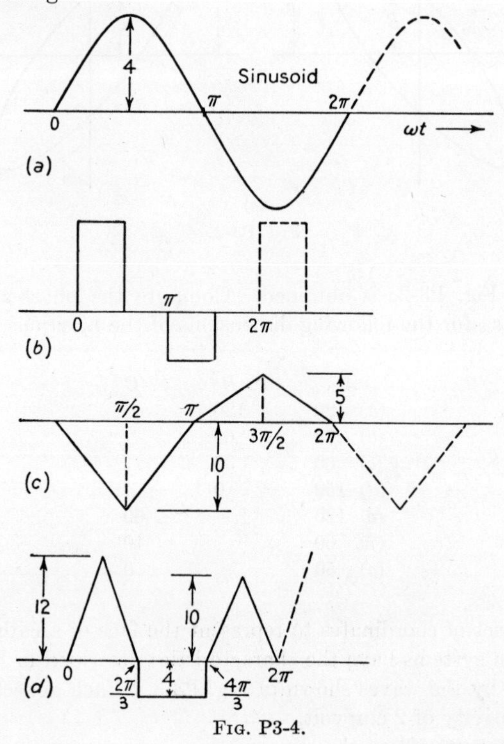


FIG. P3-4.

**3-5.** The circuit of Fig. P3-5 represents an electroplating system in which the cell is represented by the rectangle and the resistance of the connecting wires is indicated by the series resistor. The current in the circuit is always in the direction of the arrow, but it goes through the following sequence of values: For 1 min it is 10 amp; it then drops suddenly to 4 amp, at which value it remains for 2 min. This is followed by an interval of 2 min during which the current is zero, after which there is a 4-min interval during which the current is constant at 6 amp. The cycle then repeats itself.

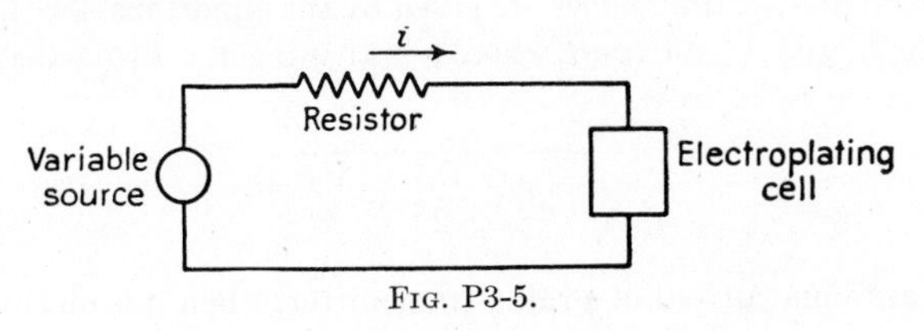


FIG. P3-5.

*a.* What value of constant current would deposit metal at the same average rate as this fluctuating current?

*b.* What value of constant current would produce the same average temperature rise, in the connecting wires, as the varying current?

**3-6.** Compute the effective value of each of the waves given in Fig. P3-4.

**3-7.** Compute the effective value for each of the two current waves shown in Fig. P3-7. Also, show the wave obtained if these two waves are added, and compute the effective value of the sum.

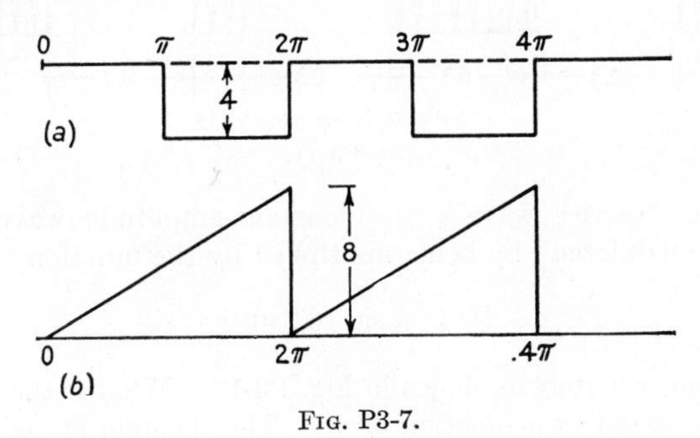


FIG. P3-7.

**3-8.** Suppose the wave (*a*) of Fig. P3-7 is a potential which is added to a constant potential of +1 volt. Sketch the resultant function, and compute its effective value. Repeat for wave (*b*).

**3-9.** A sine-wave source is connected in series with a d-c source. The graphs of the two individual potentials are shown in Fig. P3-9.

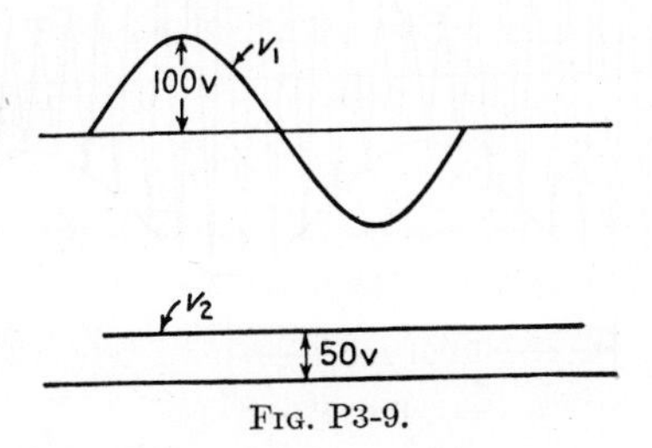


FIG. P3-9.

*a.* What is the effective value of the sinusoidal wave?

*b.* What is the effective value of the d-c component?

*c.* Analytically compute the effective value of the sum of the two waves if it is $v_1 + v_2$.

**3-10.** Three potential differences are given by the equations $v_0 = V_0$, a constant, $v_1 = V_1 \sin 2\pi ft$, $v_2 = V_2 \sin 2\pi nft$, where $n$ is an integer. Prove that the effective value of $v_0 + v_1 + v_2$ is

$$\sqrt{V_0^2 + \frac{V_1^2}{2} + \frac{V_2^2}{2}}$$

**3-11.** The antenna current of a radio transmitter, when it is on continuously, is

$$i = 27 \sin (942 \times 10^6 t)$$

When a succession of dots and dashes is transmitted, the amplitude is varied in accordance with the function shown in Fig. P3-11. What is the effective value of the antenna current? Assume that each pulse of waves starts at a principal zero.

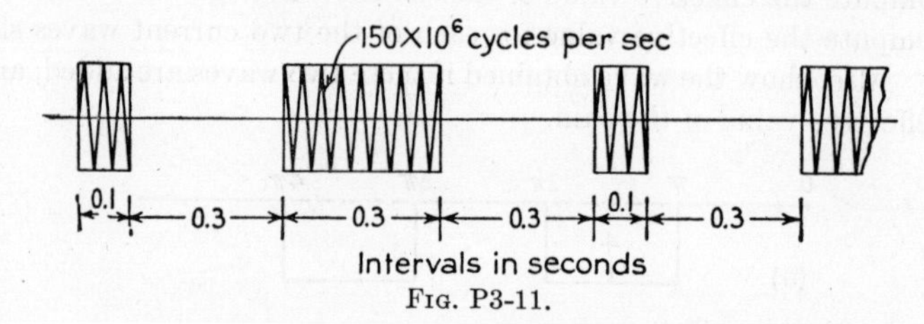


Fig. P3-11.

**3-12.** Let the "carrier wave" (the constant-amplitude wave) specified in Prob. 3-11 be "modulated" by being multiplied by the function

$$[1 + m \sin (6{,}280t)]$$

The result is approximately as shown in Fig. P3-12. What is the effective value of this wave expressed as a function of $m$? The theorem stated in Prob. 3-10 may be used in this problem.

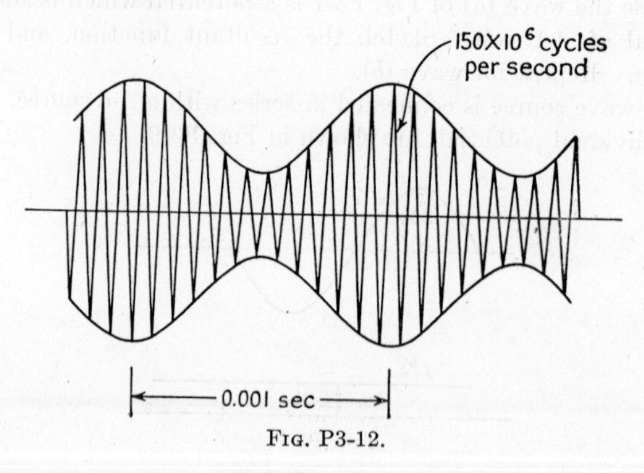


Fig. P3-12.

**3-13.** A battery is being charged in a rectifier circuit as shown in Fig. P3-13. The current $i$ is the top half of a sinusoid, as shown in the figure.

*a.* What is the rate at which energy is stored chemically?

*b.* What is the power loss in the current-limiting resistor?

*c.* What is the total power flowing into the battery at its terminals?

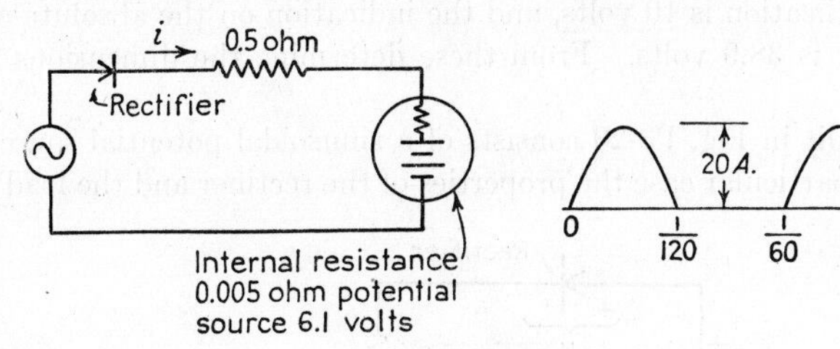


FIG. P3-13.

**3-14.** Four ammeters are connected in series to measure the current $i$ of Fig. P3-13. They are of the following types: effective-responding, positive-pulse-average-responding, absolute-average-responding, and peak-responding. All meters are calibrated to indicate the effective value on a sinusoid. Compute the indication of each meter.

**3-15.** Four voltmeters, one of each of the types described in Prob. 3-14, are connected in parallel. They are successively excited by potential waves of the forms shown in Fig. P3-4. Compute the indication of each meter for each of the four waves.

**3-16.** Find the positive-pulse average, negative-pulse average, positive-peak, negative-peak, full-cycle average, absolute average, and effective values of a wave having the equation

$$v = 15 + 60 \sin x + 30 \cos 3x$$

The wave passes through zero when $x = 2.96$ and 5.87 radians.

**3-17.** The equation of a current wave is

$$i = 25 \sin 1{,}000t + 40 \sin 1{,}500t$$

*a.* What is its frequency?

*b.* What is its effective value?

*c.* What is its pulse-average value?

**3-18.** The wave shown in Fig. P3-18 has undetermined positive and negative peak values, ($a$) and ($b$). A d-c meter (full-cycle-average-responding) gives an

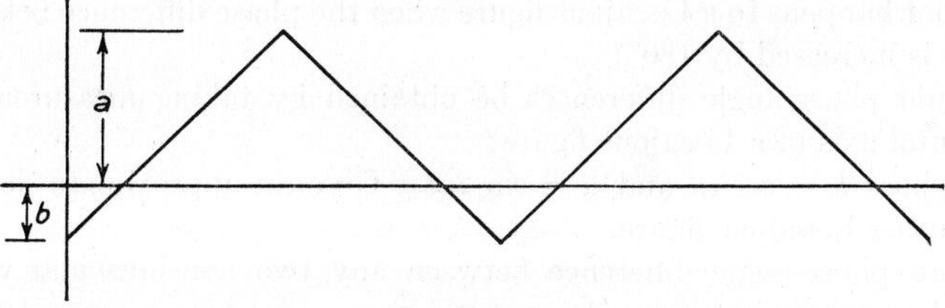


FIG. P3-18.

indication of 0.06 amp, and an effective-responding meter gives an indication of 0.13 amp. From this information determine the two peak values labeled $a$ and $b$.

**3-19.** A wave of the shape shown in Fig. P3-18 is impressed on two meters. One is a d-c meter (responding to full-cycle average) and the other is an absolute-average-responding meter, calibrated to indicate effective values on a sinusoid. The d-c meter indication is 10 volts, and the indication on the absolute-average-responding meter is 38.9 volts. From these determine the dimensions ($a$) and ($b$) of the wave.

**3-20.** The circuit in Fig. P3-20 consists of a sinusoidal potential source and a rectifier. For a particular case the properties of the rectifier and the load resistor

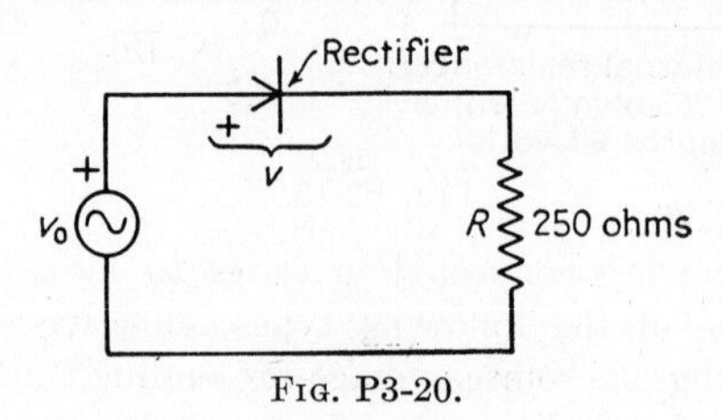


FIG. P3-20.

$R$ are such that the instantaneous current $i$ is given by the formula

$$i = 0.001v^{3/2}$$

when $v$ is positive. When $v$ is negative the current is zero.

*a.* Compute the power dissipation in the resistor if $v_0 = 100 \sin \omega t$.

*b.* What is the effective value of the potential across the resistor?

## QUESTIONS

**3-1.** What law of variation is used for the deflection potential on the horizontal plates of a cathode-ray oscilloscope if it is to portray the true wave shape of a periodic time function?

**3-2.** A signal of frequency $f$ is being viewed on an oscilloscope screen, using a linear horizontal sweep potential of frequency $f$. The sweep frequency is then increased to $2f$; what change will this make in the figure seen on the screen?

**3-3.** How can a cathode-ray oscilloscope be used to show the wave of a current?

**3-4.** What is meant by a Lissajous figure?

**3-5.** Mention two uses of a Lissajous figure.

**3-6.** Why is a Lissajous figure inadequate for differentiating between lead and lag?

**3-7.** What happens to a Lissajous figure when the phase difference between the two waves is increased by 180°?

**3-8.** Could phase-angle differences be obtained by taking measurements on the horizontal axis of a Lissajous figure?

**3-9.** Suppose $h = \cos \omega t$ and $u = \sin 2\omega t$. Give an approximate description of the resulting Lissajous figure.

**3-10.** Can phase-angle difference between any two nonsinusoidal waves be determined on a Lissajous figure?

**3-11.** Why is the capacitor necessary in Fig. 3-6?

**3-12.** Make up two waves having the same peak values but different average values.

**3-13.** Why is the full-cycle average of a wave called the constant component?

**3-14.** Suppose the axis of a wave is placed so that its full-cycle average value is zero. Will the positive and negative peak values be the same for periodic waves of all shapes?

**3-15.** How can the absolute and full-cycle averages of a wave be found from a knowledge of positive and negative pulse averages?

**3-16.** How are the pulse averages related to the absolute average for a sinusoid?

**3-17.** Is the absolute average of a wave always less than its effective value?

**3-18.** How is it possible for a wave to have zero full-cycle average and a non-zero effective value?

**3-19.** What wave shape has peak, absolute average, and effective values which are all the same?

**3-20.** A voltmeter responds to peak values but is calibrated to indicate effective values on a sinusoid. Will it indicate high or low on a symmetrical triangular wave? On a symmetrical square wave?

**3-21.** A voltmeter responds to the absolute average but is calibrated to indicate effective values on a sinusoid. Will it indicate high or low on a symmetrical triangular wave? On a symmetrical square wave?

# CHAPTER 4
# SYMBOLIC TREATMENT OF SINUSOIDS

**4-1. Introduction.** The solution of electrical networks, under conditions of sinusoidal variations of currents and potentials, includes the addition of sinusoidal waves. If many waves are involved, this process can become very complicated when carried out on the sinusoidal waves themselves. Fortunately, it is possible to represent sinusoidal waves by directed lines in a plane. Addition can be carried out more simply by using these lines than by using the waves themselves. The techniques of addition are so closely related to the idea of symbolic representation by directed lines that the two topics are combined in this chapter.

**4-2. Directed-line Symbolism.** In Chap. 2 it is shown that a sinusoidal wave can be graphed by plotting the vertical projection of a

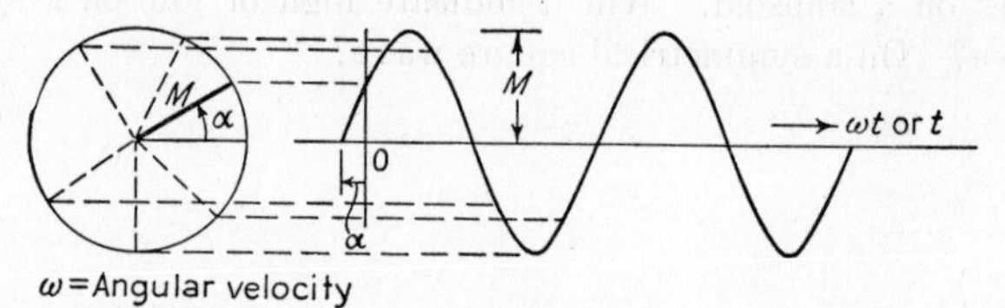


Fig. 4-1. A rotating line geometrically generating a sinusoidal wave. The heavy radial line is at the $t = 0$ position.

rotating line. The angular velocity of the line is constant, and the vertical projection is plotted against time (or time angle), to give a sinusoidal wave, as illustrated in Fig. 4-1. If the position of the line is known as a function of time, the sinusoid can always be constructed. Therefore, a knowledge of the motion of the line is equivalent to a knowledge of the sinusoid. This is the central idea behind the practice of symbolically representing sinusoids by directed lines.

The motion of a rotating line is completely determined by (1) its angular velocity, (2) its center of rotation, (3) its position at some known instant, and (4) its length. The last three items can be specified by drawing the line itself. The center of rotation can be implied by placing an arrowhead on the moving end, the line can be shown in its position when $t = 0$, and its length can be drawn to scale. When necessary, the angular velocity, or frequency, can be added, as a label. However, this is usually not necessary, because when directed lines are used for addition *all waves must be of the same frequency.*

The above discussion emphasizes that the heavy line of Fig. 4-1 gives all the pertinent information about the sinusoidal wave. The line need not be shown in its $t = 0$ position as long as it is given for a known instant of time, but the $t = 0$ position is a convenient one to use.

**4-3. Sinors and Phasors.** The scheme of symbolically representing a sinusoid by a directed line is used in circuit analysis to represent potentials, currents, and other electrical quantities. The fact that electrical quantities are symbolized influences the use of the lines in two ways: their lengths are modified, and a precise system of notation is used.

From the standpoint of appearance, the amplitude of a sinusoidal wave is more apparent than the effective value. However, when the waves are potentials or currents, the effective value is important. Therefore, when symbolically representing a sinusoid by a directed line plotted to scale, it is convenient to scale the length to equal the effective value. If a line is not plotted to scale, it is conveniently labeled with the effective value. A directed line having a length scaled to the effective value of the wave and making an angle with the horizontal equal to the initial angle of the wave, *when it is written as a sine function*, is called a *sinor*. This is a coined term, intended to emphasize the close relationship between a sinusoidal wave and the directed line that symbolically represents it. The term "sinor" is to be interpreted as an abbreviation for the phrase "symbolic representation for a sinusoid."*

Subsequent developments will introduce other directed lines which do not represent sinusoids. All these lines are similar to vectors, but they *lie in one plane*, making them significantly different from three-dimensional vectors. Therefore, a distinctive name is given to the two-dimensional directed lines used in electrical applications. They are called *phasor quantities* or *phasors*.† A sinor is a phasor quantity—a particular one that symbolically represents a sinusoidal wave. Distinctive symbols are used to represent phasor quantities. The practice followed in this text is to print the symbol in boldface type.

Examples of sinors are given in Fig. 4-2. Let typical potential and current waves be given by

$$\begin{aligned} v &= \sqrt{2}\, V \sin (\omega t + \alpha) \\ i &= \sqrt{2}\, I \sin (\omega t + \beta) \end{aligned} \tag{4-1}$$

* A sinor does not represent a sinusoid in the sense that an ordinary variable represents a quantity. The directed line is quite different from a sinusoid. Therefore, the word "symbolic" is important.

† In many textbooks a phasor is called a vector. A discussion of the difference between a phasor and a three-dimensional vector is not possible here because this text does not presuppose a knowledge of vector analysis.

where $V$ and $I$ are the effective values. The fact that $\mathbf{V}$ and $\mathbf{I}$ are the corresponding sinors is indicated by writing

$$\begin{aligned} &\mathbf{V} \text{ symbolizes } v \\ &\mathbf{I} \text{ symbolizes } i \end{aligned} \tag{4-2}$$

The two quantities that determine a sinor (phasor quantity) are its *magnitude* and *angle*. They can be indicated by a composite symbol, as follows:

$$\begin{aligned} \mathbf{V} &= V\underline{/\alpha} \\ \mathbf{I} &= I\underline{/\beta} \end{aligned} \tag{4-3}$$

This notation makes it possible to use numerical values to specify a sinor. For example, $\mathbf{V} = 100\underline{/30°}$ symbolizes $v = 141 \sin(\omega t + 30°)$, and $\mathbf{I} = 5\underline{/60°}$ symbolizes $i = 7.07 \sin(\omega t + 60°)$. Equation (4-3) is said to express a sinor in *polar* form, because it expresses the position of the end of the line in polar coordinates. It is noted that sinors carry the physical dimensions (volts, amperes, etc.) of the quantities they symbolically represent.

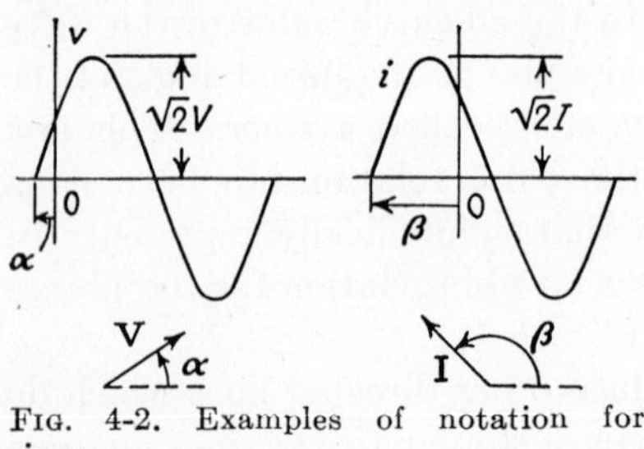


FIG. 4-2. Examples of notation for sinors.

The *magnitudes* $V$ and $I$ are always positive quantities. However, negative signs can appear before them. A rotation through an angle $\pi$ is equivalent to a change of sign. Therefore, a negative sign is interpreted to mean the following:

$$-\mathbf{V} = -V\underline{/\alpha} = V\underline{/\alpha \pm \pi} \tag{4-4}$$

A sinor has been defined in terms of a sine function. However, a sinusoidal wave can also be written as a cosine function, and therefore a cosine function can be represented symbolically by a sinor. For example, a sinor for $\cos \omega t$ would be a vertical line, since $\cos \omega t = \sin(\omega t + 90°)$.

**4-4. Reference Conditions for Sinors.** A sinor does not vary with time, but it symbolically represents a time-varying sinusoid. It was shown in Sec. 2-6 that the meaning of the time variable is indefinite unless a reference condition is specified. It follows that *the reference condition has meaning for the sinor also.* This fact is indicated by adopting the same notation for a sinor as for the sinusoidal function, except that an upper-case boldface letter is used for the sinor and lower-case italic for the sinusoid.

For example, consider the sinusoidal potential difference in Fig. 4-3*a*. Its reference polarity is shown in the usual way, and it is represented by the sinor $\mathbf{V}_a$. The symbol $\mathbf{V}_a$ is meaningless unless the reference polarity is given.

The sinor representation of a current is interpreted similarly. If $i_a$ is the current of Fig. 4-3b, with the reference direction shown, its sinor representation is labeled $\mathbf{I}_a$. The reference direction must be specified for $\mathbf{I}_a$ to have a meaning.

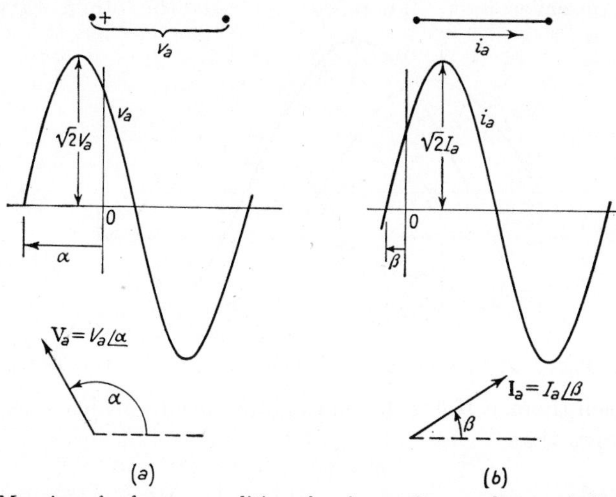


FIG. 4-3. Meaning of reference conditions for sinors when used to symbolically represent potential and current waves.

In each of these examples a sinusoidal wave is intermediate between the reference conditions and the sinor. The sinusoidal wave is needed to tie the notation used for the sinor to the reference condition. The sinusoid may be omitted, but is always implied. When the sinusoid is omitted, it is also customary to use the sinor symbols on the circuit diagram, rather than the symbols for instantaneous values. Accordingly, the notation given in Fig. 4-3 may be reduced to the simpler systems of Fig. 4-4.*

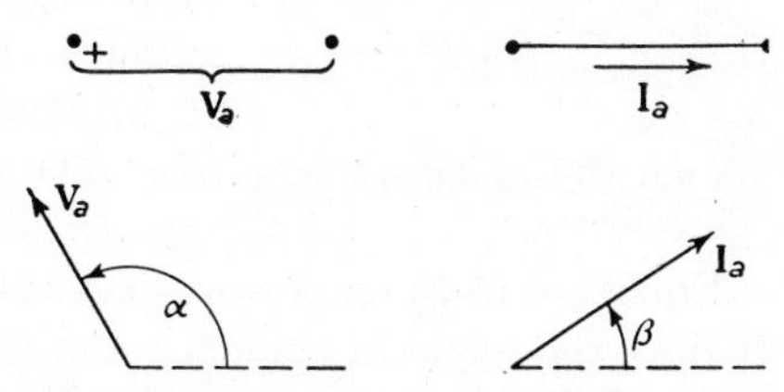


FIG. 4-4. Use of sinor symbols to indicate reference conditions.

Double subscripts may be used with sinors. For example, a sinor $\mathbf{V}_{12}$ symbolically represents a sinusoid $v_{12}$ having the reference-positive point at terminal 1. Similarly, a sinor $\mathbf{I}_{12}$ symbolically represents a

* The magnitude symbol (*i.e.*, not boldface) may be used on the circuit diagram without ambiguity although it has no meaning because reference conditions have no meaning with respect to the amplitude of a sinusoid. When the magnitude symbol is used, the sinor symbol is implied.

sinusoid $i_{12}$ having a reference direction from terminal 1 toward terminal 2.

**4-5. Phase Difference in Terms of Sinors.** Consider the two waves $v_a$ and $v_b$ of Fig. 4-5. They are represented by the sinors of Fig. 4-6. It is recalled that sinors occupy the positions (at $t = 0$) of lines which rotate counterclockwise. The one with the larger angle would pass a stationary observer first. Therefore, it leads the other wave by the

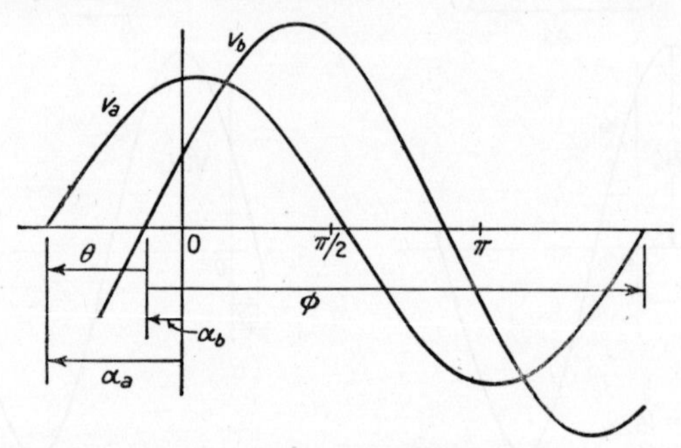


FIG. 4-5. Phase difference, on a plot of sinusoidal waves. (Also see Fig. 2-29.)

angle between them. If $\theta$ is the phase difference by which $v_a$ leads $v_b$, the diagram shows that

$$\theta = \alpha_a - \alpha_b \tag{4-5}$$

which is identical with Eq. (2-22).

Sinor diagrams show that if angles greater than $\pi$ are admitted one sinusoid simultaneously leads and lags another by positive angles. For example, in Fig. 4-6, $v_a$ leads $v_b$ by the positive angle $\theta = 60°$ and $v_a$ lags $v_b$ by the positive angle $\phi = 300°$. Wave $v_a$ also lags $v_b$ by the negative angle $\phi = -60°$ the principal value. Equation (4-5) does not always yield a principal value, but when it does not do so, $2\pi$ (360°) can be added or subtracted, as needed, to obtain the principal value.

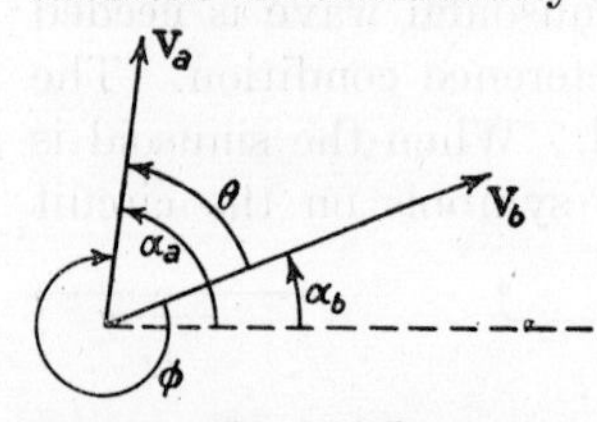


FIG. 4-6. Phase difference, on a sinor diagram.

Equation (4-5) emphasizes the usefulness of the polar form for a sinor. It puts the angle in evidence and therefore makes it possible to find the phase difference between two sinusoids with a minimum of effort. For example, if $\mathbf{V}_a = 50\underline{/60°}$ and $\mathbf{V}_b = 60\underline{/25°}$, $\mathbf{V}_a$ leads $\mathbf{V}_b$ by $60 - 25 = 35°$. As another example, let $\mathbf{V}_a$ be the same as above, but let $\mathbf{V}_b = 60\underline{/-135°}$. According to Eq. (4-5), $\mathbf{V}_a$ leads $\mathbf{V}_b$ by $60 - (-135) = 195°$, which is not a principal value. The principal value is $195 - 360 = -165°$.

It will be noted that the terms "lead" and "lag" are applied to sinors. In so doing it is understood that the sinors symbolically represent sinusoids and that it is really the corresponding sinusoids $v_a$ and $v_b$ that are being compared.

**4-6. Addition of Sinusoidal Waves.** In the application of Kirchhoff's laws to circuits, it becomes necessary to add sinusoidal waves of the *same frequency*. It is also sometimes necessary to add waves of different frequencies, *but this cannot be done by the methods now under discussion*. Any number of waves can be added, but it is sufficient to consider two. The potential waves

$$v_a = \sqrt{2}\, V_a \sin(\omega t + \alpha_a)$$
$$v_b = \sqrt{2}\, V_b \sin(\omega t + \alpha_b) \tag{4-6}$$

will serve as examples. Their graphs and their generating lines are shown in Fig. 4-7. The generating lines are drawn slightly differently than

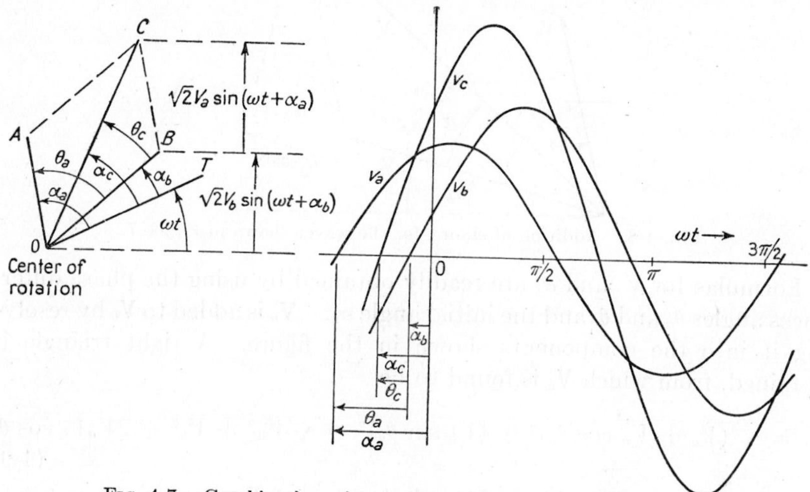


FIG. 4-7. Combination of two sinusoidal waves by addition.

in Fig. 2-27, to show that the time angle $\omega t$ is shared by each wave. At each instant the sum

$$v_c = v_a + v_b \tag{4-7}$$

is the sum of the vertical projections of lines $AO$ and $BO$. This sum may be visualized by drawing the line $CB$ parallel to $AO$ and taking the sum of the vertical projections of lines $CB$ and $BO$. From the figure it is seen that the required sum is always equal to the vertical projection of line $CO$. It follows that the wave $v_c = v_a + v_b$ is generated by the rotating line $CO$. The fact that the new wave is generated by a rotating line proves that it is a sinusoid. The line $OC$ rotates with the same angular velocity as the others, so the frequency of the resultant sinusoid is the same as the frequency of the original waves.

knowledge that the new wave is a sinusoid of angular frequency ...an be written

$$v_c = \sqrt{2}\, V_c \sin(\omega t + \alpha_c) \tag{4-8}$$

where $V_c$ and $\alpha_c$ are tentatively unknown. The amplitude $\sqrt{2}\, V_c$ and initial angle $\alpha_c$ can be determined from triangle $OBC$ in Fig. 4-7, but the usual practice is to use a diagram of sinors. A sinor diagram is equivalent because sinors are similar to the generating lines except for being stationary and having their lengths scaled to the effective values. The sinor diagram for the waves under consideration is given in Fig. 4-8.

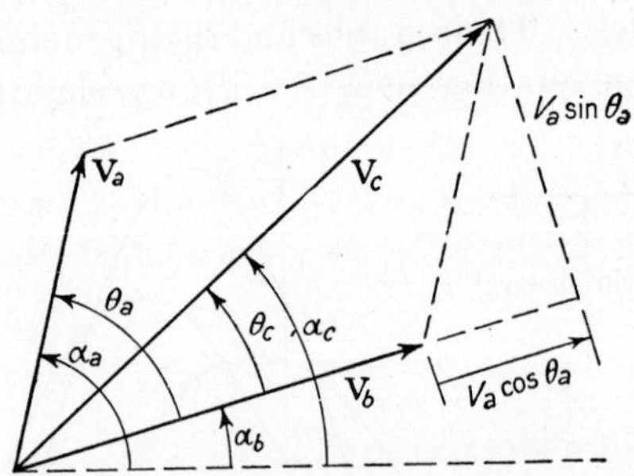


FIG. 4-8. Addition of sinors, for the waves shown in Fig. 4-7.

Formulas for $V_c$ and $\alpha_c$ are readily obtained by using the phase differences angles $\theta_a$ and $\theta_c$ and the initial angle $\alpha_b$. $\mathbf{V}_a$ is added to $\mathbf{V}_b$ by resolving it into the components shown in the figure. A right triangle is obtained, from which $\mathbf{V}_c$ is found to be

$$\mathbf{V}_c = \sqrt{(V_b + V_a \cos\theta_a)^2 + (V_a \sin\theta_a)^2} = \sqrt{V_a{}^2 + V_b{}^2 + 2V_aV_b\cos\theta_a} \tag{4-9}$$

The diagram also provides a formula for $\theta_c$, as follows:

$$\theta_c = \tan^{-1}\frac{V_a \sin\theta_a}{V_b + V_a\cos\theta_a} \tag{4-10}$$

The initial angle of $\mathbf{V}_c$ is

$$\alpha_c = \alpha_b + \theta_c \tag{4-11}$$

The result is summarized by writing

$$\mathbf{V}_c = V_c\underline{/\alpha_c} = V_c\underline{/\alpha_b + \theta_c} \tag{4-12}$$

where $V_c$ and $\theta_c$ are given by the above formulas.

In the above procedure sinor $\mathbf{V}_b$ is used as the datum for angle measurement. Similar results are obtainable if sinor $\mathbf{V}_a$ is used as the datum. In that case phase-difference angles would be measured from $\mathbf{V}_a$. Finally, it is noted that if three sinusoids are to be added, two can first be combined and the result combined with the third. In this way it is concluded that the sum of any number of sinusoids, all having the same frequency, is a sinusoid also of the same frequency.

**4-7. Addition in Sinor Notation.** The process described in Sec. 4-6 is symbolically represented by the equation

$$\mathbf{V}_c = \mathbf{V}_a + \mathbf{V}_b \tag{4-13}$$

This equation replaces Eq. (4-7) when sinor notation is used. Similar equations are written for any number of sinors and for currents as well as potentials. Equation (4-13) is not an ordinary algebraic equation because its terms are phasor (*i.e.*, two-dimensional) quantities. In Chap. 8 further mathematical significance is given to such equations, but for the present they are intended to be symbolic representations for sinor diagrams. That is, Eq. (4-13) is a set of instructions for combining sinors in the manner shown in Fig. 4-8.

It is important to understand the implications of the use of sinors to represent sinusoids in the process of addition. Consider the following numerical examples as illustrations.

**Example 4-1.** Let it be required to find $v_c = v_a + v_b$ when

$$v_a = \sqrt{2}\,(100) \sin (\omega t + 60^\circ)$$
$$v_b = \sqrt{2}\,(50) \sin (\omega t + 15^\circ)$$

*Solution.* Sinors are defined as follows:

$$\mathbf{V}_a = 100\underline{/60^\circ} \text{ symbolizes } v_a$$
$$\mathbf{V}_b = 50\underline{/15^\circ} \text{ symbolizes } v_c$$

and are shown in the accompanying diagram. $\mathbf{V}_c$ is given by Eqs. (4-9) and (4-10), as follows:

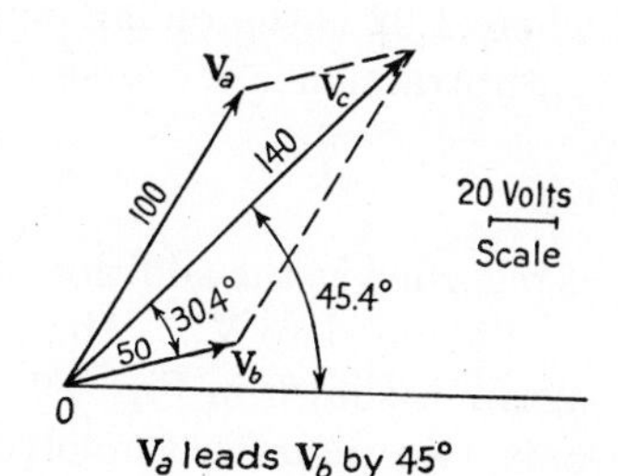

$\mathbf{V}_a$ leads $\mathbf{V}_b$ by 45°

$$V_c = \sqrt{(100)^2 + (50)^2 + 2(100)(50)(\cos 45^\circ)} = 140 \text{ volts}$$

$$\theta_c = \tan^{-1} \frac{100 \sin 45^\circ}{50 + 100 \cos 45^\circ} = 30.4^\circ \qquad \text{and} \qquad \alpha_c = 45.4^\circ$$

Thus,

$$140\underline{/45.4^\circ} \text{ symbolizes } v_c$$

and as a time function

$$v_c = \sqrt{2}\,(140) \sin (\omega t + 45.4^\circ)$$

The result could also be obtained graphically, as shown in the diagram.

**Example 4-2.** As another example consider the sum $v = v_R + v_C$ as it is found in Example 2-1 on page 28. Equations for $v_R$ and $v_C$ are

$$v_R = \sqrt{2}\, 28.2 \sin 377t$$

$$v_C = \sqrt{2}\, 46 \sin\left(377t - \frac{\pi}{2}\right)$$

*Solution.* The required sinors are

$$\mathbf{V}_R = 28.2\underline{/0^\circ} \text{ symbolizes } v_R$$
$$\mathbf{V}_C = 46\underline{/-90^\circ} \text{ symbolizes } v_C$$

as shown on the accompanying diagram. The summation $\mathbf{V} = \mathbf{V}_R + \mathbf{V}_C$ is to be found. From Eqs. (4-9) and (4-10), or from the diagram,

$$\mathbf{V} = \sqrt{(28.2)^2 + (46)^2}\ \underline{/\tan^{-1} \frac{-46}{28.2}}$$
$$= 54\underline{/-58.6^\circ}$$

It follows that the equation for $v$ is

$$v = \sqrt{2}\, 54 \sin (377t - 1.02)$$

where 1.02 is the radian equivalent of 58.6°.

Subtraction is of course a special case of addition. The operation

$$\mathbf{V}_d = \mathbf{V}_a - \mathbf{V}_b \tag{4-14}$$

is regarded as the addition of $\mathbf{V}_a$ and $-\mathbf{V}_b$. That is, $\mathbf{V}_b$ is reversed and the result added to $\mathbf{V}_a$. The sinor diagram is shown in Fig. 4-9. When only two sinors are involved, subtraction can be accomplished in a particular way, as illustrated in Fig. 4-10. If sinors $\mathbf{V}_a$ and $\mathbf{V}_b$ have a common origin, the sinor $\mathbf{V}_a - \mathbf{V}_b$ can be constructed by drawing an arrow from the head end of $\mathbf{V}_b$ to the head end of $\mathbf{V}_a$. The validity of this procedure can be checked by comparing with Fig. 4-9.

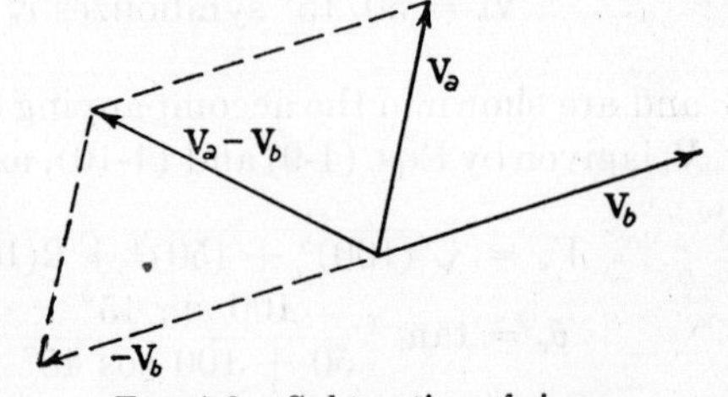


FIG. 4-9. Subtraction of sinors.

Numerical results for the addition of two sinusoidal waves can be computed by the formulas of Sec. 4-6. In some cases it is convenient to use a graphical construction. The sinors are plotted accurately to scale, and the result is obtained by measuring the angle and length of the resultant sinor. This method is useful when many sinors are to be added, particularly when extreme accuracy is not needed.

When more than two sinors are combined graphically, it is convenient to place them end to end, as in Fig. 4-11. The addition of the three

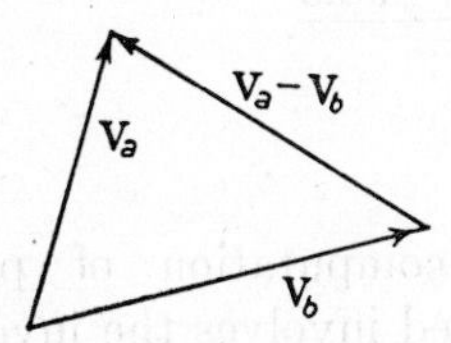


FIG. 4-10. Alternate method of subtracting sinors by constructing a triangle.

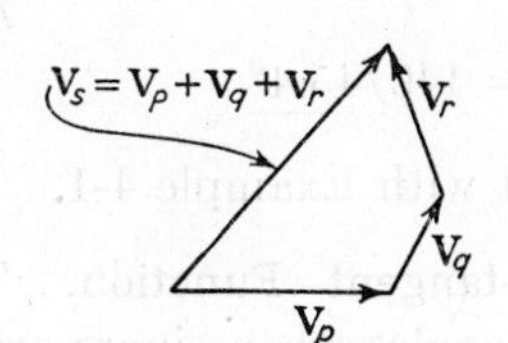


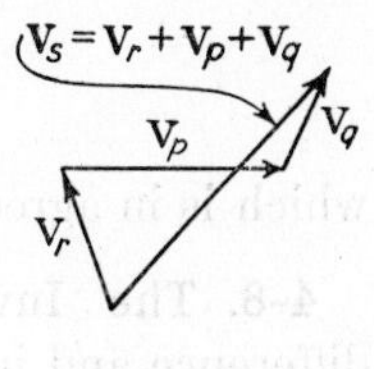


FIG. 4-11. Polygon method of adding more than two sinors.

sinors $\mathbf{V}_p$, $\mathbf{V}_q$, and $\mathbf{V}_r$ is given in two forms to show that the result is independent of the order in which the sinors are taken.

Figure 4-12 suggests a method of analytically adding sinors which is simpler than the application of Eqs. (4-9) and (4-10). Each sinor is resolved into a pair of components along a set of rectangular axes. For

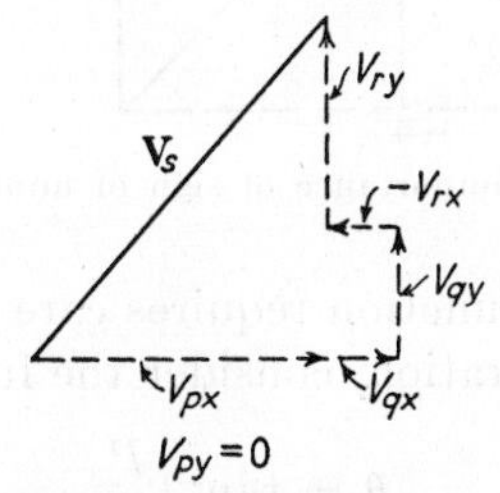


FIG. 4-12. Summation of the sinors shown in Fig. 4-11, by using horizontal and vertical components. (Drawn to a different scale than Fig. 4-11.)

example, $\mathbf{V}_q$ has two components, $V_{qx}$ and $V_{qy}$, along the respective $x$ and $y$ axes. From Fig. 4-12 it is apparent that

$$V_s = \sqrt{(V_{px} + V_{qx} + V_{rx})^2 + (V_{py} + V_{qy} + V_{ry})^2} \qquad (4\text{-}15)^*$$

and

$$\alpha_s = \tan^{-1} \frac{V_{py} + V_{qy} + V_{ry}}{V_{px} + V_{qx} + V_{rx}} \qquad (4\text{-}16)$$

**Example 4-3.** Find the sinor $\mathbf{V}_c$ as it is specified in Example 4-1.

*Solution.* It is given that $\mathbf{V}_c = \mathbf{V}_a + \mathbf{V}_b$ and that $\mathbf{V}_a = 100\underline{/60°}$ and $\mathbf{V}_b = 50\underline{/15°}$. Their components are

* The addition of the $x$ and $y$ subscripts does not make this a double-subscript system of notation of the type described in Sec. 2-7.

$$\begin{array}{llll} V_{ax} = 100 \cos 60° = 50.0 & & V_{ay} = 100 \sin 60° = 86.6 \\ V_{bx} = \phantom{0}50 \cos 15° = 48.3 & & V_{by} = \phantom{0}50 \sin 15° = 12.9 \\ \hline V_{cx} = \qquad\qquad\quad 98.3 & & V_{cy} = \qquad\qquad\quad 99.5 \end{array}$$

$$\mathbf{V}_c = \sqrt{(98.3)^2 + (99.5)^2} \Big/ \tan^{-1} \frac{99.5}{98.3}$$

$$= 140/45.4°$$

which is in agreement with Example 4-1.

**4-8. The Inverse-tangent Function.** The computation of phase difference and initial angles when sinors are added involves the inverse-

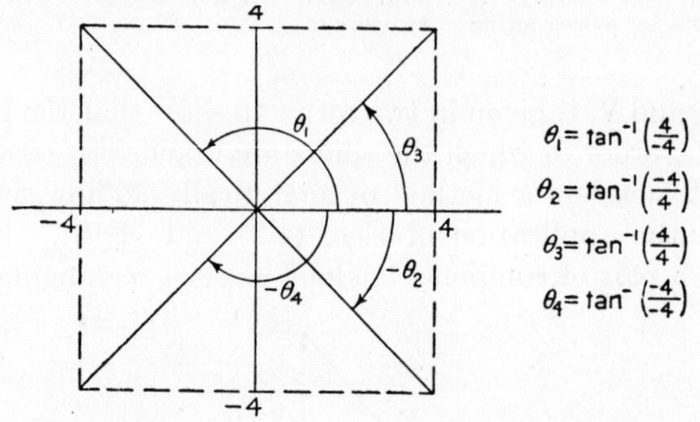


FIG. 4-13. Illustration of the importance of sign of numerator and denominator of the inverse-tangent function.

tangent function. This function requires care in its use, to avoid incorrect results. As an illustration, consider the function

$$\theta = \tan^{-1} \frac{P}{Q} \tag{4-17}$$

where $P$ and $Q$ represent quantities such as the numerator and denominator of Eqs. (4-10) and (4-16). In specific cases, $P$, $Q$, or both, may be negative numbers. The significance of these signs is under consideration.

As an example, consider the various situations portrayed in Fig. 4-13. Without the insight provided by the diagram it might be construed that $\theta_1$ and $\theta_2$ are each $\tan^{-1}(-1)$ and that $\theta_3$ and $\theta_4$ are each $\tan^{-1}(1)$ and hence that $\theta_1 = \theta_2$ and that $\theta_3 = \theta_4$. However, as the diagram shows, this is not true. There is a difference between $\tan^{-1}(-1/1)$ and $\tan^{-1}(1/-1)$ and between $\tan^{-1}(-1/-1)$ and $\tan^{-1}(1/1)$.

This peculiarity arises because the inverse-tangent function is *multi-valued.* For a given value of $P/Q$, $\tan^{-1}(P/Q)$ has an infinite number of values. However, if $\tan^{-1}(P/Q)$ is restricted to principal values, the function is only double-valued, as illustrated by the graph in Fig. 4-14. The labels on the various parts of the curve show the signs of numerator and denominator to be associated with the various branches of the function.

When an inverse-tangent function is evaluated in a numerical case, a diagram like Fig. 4-13 or 4-14 is a help. Figure 4-13 is convenient because it can be sketched readily when needed.

**4-9. Summary.** Nearly all problems arising in an a-c-circuit analysis involve the addition of sinusoidal waves. This process is complicated when carried out with sinusoidal waves themselves. In spite of this, the basic laws are quite simple, and this simplicity is retained by the introduction of quantities called sinors.

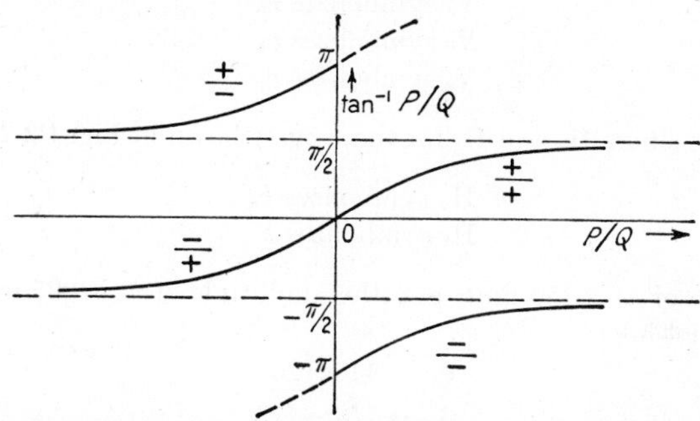


FIG. 4-14. Illustration of the multivalued property of the inverse-tangent function.

Sinors can be used in place of sinusoidal waves because sinors are related to the rotating lines which generate sinusoids. These lines are inherently simpler than the waves they generate. Sinors offer complete representations for sinusoidal waves, except that the frequency must be specified separately. A sinor is characterized by two parts, the magnitude ($1/\sqrt{2}$ times the amplitude of the wave), and an angle (the initial angle of the wave). When sinors represent electrical quantities, it is necessary to specify reference conditions for them and to adopt a system of notation similar to that used for the waves they represent.

The sum of two or more sinusoidal waves of the same frequency is also a sinusoidal wave. Its dimensions can be found by adding sinors. This eventually leads to a system of analysis in which sinors are used exclusively. However, it must always be understood that a sinor is a symbolic representation of a sinusoidal wave.

## PROBLEMS

**4-1.** Let the following sinusoidal waves be generated from the vertical projections of a rotating line, as in Fig. 4-1. Specify the angular position of the line at the values of $t$ for which $\omega t = 0°, 45°, 90°, 130°, 280°$, and $300°$. The waves are

*a.* $v = 140 \sin (\omega t - 45°)$.
*b.* $i = 60 \cos (\omega t + 60°)$.

**4-2.** Draw the sinors for each of the waves of Prob. 4-1. Specify the scales to which they are drawn. Also specify the sinors numerically.

**4-3.** The potential across part of a circuit is represented by the sinor $120\underline{/0°}$, and the current through it is represented by the sinor $35\underline{/-70°}$. Write the equations for the potential and current, as functions of time.

**4-4.** *a.* Specify the sinors $\mathbf{V}_{aa'}$, $\mathbf{V}_{a'a}$, $\mathbf{V}_{bb'}$, and $\mathbf{V}_{b'b}$ for the arrangement shown in Fig. P2-19, where

$$\mathbf{V}_{aa'} \text{ symbolizes } v_{aa'}$$
$$\mathbf{V}_{bb'} \text{ symbolizes } v_{bb'}$$

*b.* Specify the sinors $V_a$, $V_b$, and $V_c$ for the waves shown in Fig. P2-21, where

$$\mathbf{V}_a \text{ symbolizes } v_a$$
$$\mathbf{V}_b \text{ symbolizes } v_b$$
$$\mathbf{V}_c \text{ symbolizes } v_c$$

*c.* Specify the sinors $\mathbf{H}_a$ and $\mathbf{H}_b$ for the waves shown in Fig. P2-22, where

$$\mathbf{H}_a \text{ symbolizes } h_a$$
$$\mathbf{H}_b \text{ symbolizes } h_b$$

if the amplitude of $h_a$ is 150 units and the amplitude of $h_b$ is 225 units.

**4-5.** In Fig. P4-5 let

$$\mathbf{V}_a = 440\underline{/120°}$$
$$\mathbf{I}_a = 75\underline{/-175°}$$

Write equations for $v_{21}$ and $i_{21}$ as functions of $\omega t$.

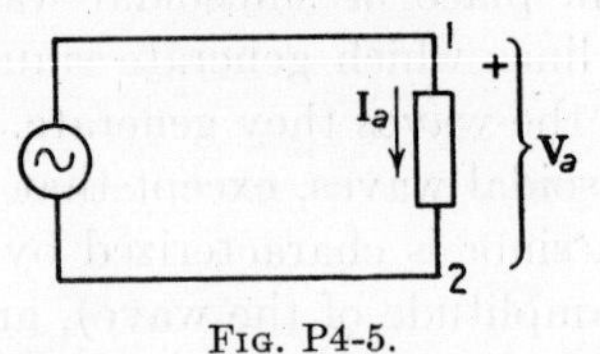


FIG. P4-5.

**4-6.** In Fig. P4-5, let

$$\mathbf{V}_{12} = V\underline{/\alpha} \text{ symbolize } v_{12}$$
$$\mathbf{I}_{12} = I\underline{/\beta} \text{ symbolize } i_{12}$$

In each of the following cases draw the sinors, and determine the principal value of the angle by which $v_{12}$ leads $i_{12}$ and also the principal value of the angle by which $v_{12}$ lags $i_{12}$.

| | $\alpha$ | $\beta$ |
|---|---|---|
| (*a*) | 0° | −30° |
| (*b*) | −110° | 120° |
| (*c*) | −180° | −75° |
| (*d*) | 55° | −170° |
| (*e*) | 80° | 165° |

**4-7.** In each of the situations specified in Prob. 4-6 determine whether power is flowing into the device or out of it at the instant when $t = 0$.

**4-8.** Given the two sinusoids

$$v_1 = A \sin x$$
$$v_2 = B \sin (x + \theta)$$

prove that

$$v_1 + v_2 = \sqrt{A^2 + B^2 + 2AB \cos \theta} \sin \left( x + \theta - \tan^{-1} \frac{A \sin \theta}{B + A \cos \theta} \right)$$

**4-9.** Two sinusoidal functions having a frequency of 60 cps are given by the equations

$$h_a = 50 \sin (\omega t + 20°)$$
$$h_b = 100 \sin (\omega t + 130°)$$

*a.* Plot these curves as functions of time, and combine them graphically point by point in accordance with the equation

$$h_c = h_a + h_b$$

*b.* From the resulting curve of part (*a*), specify the analytical expression for $h_c$.

**4-10.** Repeat parts *a* and *b* of Prob. 4-9, but use the law of combination

$$h_d = h_a - h_b$$

to obtain the sinusoidal function $h_d$.

**4-11.** Three sinusoidal functions are given by the following expressions:

$$h_a = 50 \sin (\omega t + 20°)$$
$$h_b = 100 \sin (\omega t + 40°)$$
$$h_c = -60 \sin (\omega t - 20°)$$

*a.* Obtain the equation for the combination $h_a + h_b + h_c$ by using sinors.

*b.* Obtain the equation for the combination $h_a + h_b - h_c$ by using sinors.

**4-12.** The two generators in Fig. P4-12 are attached to the same shaft, which rotates at 1800 rpm. Each machine has a four-pole rotor. The stators are

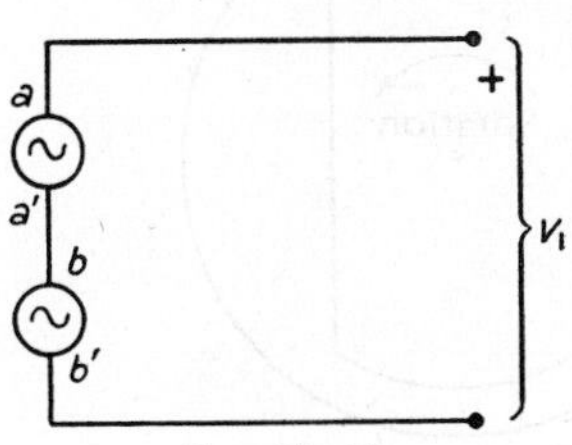


FIG. P4-12.

oriented similarly, but the rotor of machine *A* is displaced 20° ahead of the rotor of *B*. The terminals marked *a* and *b* occupy similar positions with respect to the windings of each machine. Let zero time be the instant at which the potential $v_{aa'}$ is passing through zero with a positive slope (a principal zero). The potential $v_{aa'}$ has an effective value of 2,500 volts, and the effective value of $v_{bb'}$ is 1,800 volts. Use sinors to determine the equation for the potential $v_1$ as a function of time. Compute the numerical values analytically, from the sinors.

**4-13.** The generators specified in Prob. 4-12 are assumed to retain their terminal potentials, as specified, when current flows in their terminals. They are connected in a circuit as shown in Fig. P4-13. Use sinor methods to obtain an equation for the current $i_2$ as a function of time.

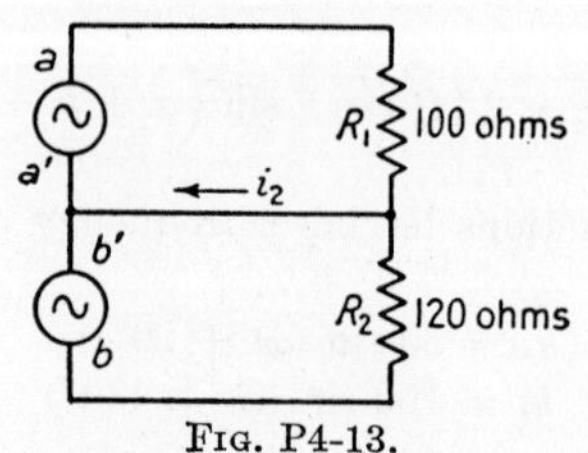


FIG. P4-13.

**4-14.** In most rotating a-c generators, coil sides are spaced around an arc of the periphery of the rotor, as indicated in Fig. P4-14. For this particular case the spacing is 10°. Assume the potential induced in each coil side is a sinusoid of 500 volts effective value and that the rotor rotates at a speed of 3,600 rpm. For the rotor position shown, $v_{33'}$ is going through a positive maximum.

*a.* Graphically construct the necessary sinors to obtain the potential $v_{15'}$, for the connections shown in Fig. P4-14*a*. The dotted lines are interconnections which are substantially out of the magnetic field.

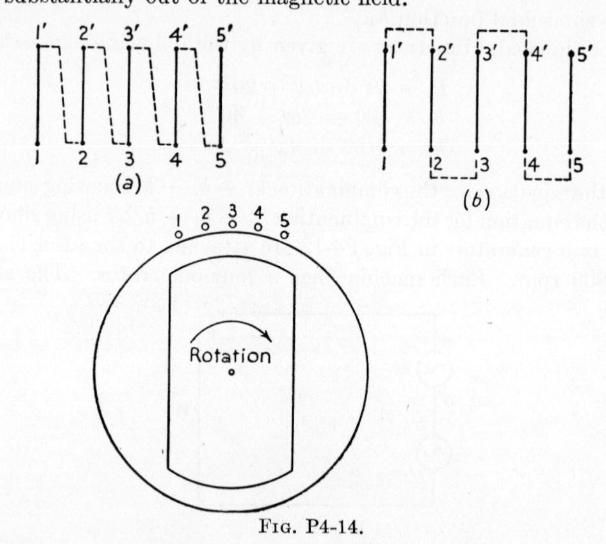


FIG. P4-14.

*b.* Graphically construct the necessary sinors to obtain the potential $v_{15'}$ for the connections shown in Fig. P4-14*b*.

**4-15.** In radio transmission sinusoidal waves are transmitted in space. It can be shown that at a large distance $S$ m from the transmitter the strength of the electric field of the radiation is given by

$$E_m \sin \omega \left(t - \frac{S}{c}\right)$$

where $c$ is the velocity of propagation, *viz.*, $3 \times 10^8$ m/sec. This is known as the equation of a *traveling wave*. Consider a television antenna a distance of 2.5 km from a transmitter, with a reflecting metal object on the side of the receiver away from a transmitter, as shown in Fig. P4-15. The strength of the signal is such that if the reflector were absent 1 volt effective value would appear across the antenna terminals. Assume that the reflected signal has three-fourths the strength of the direct signal. The reflected signal goes a greater distance than the direct signal, and furthermore it undergoes a phase reversal at the reflector. For a

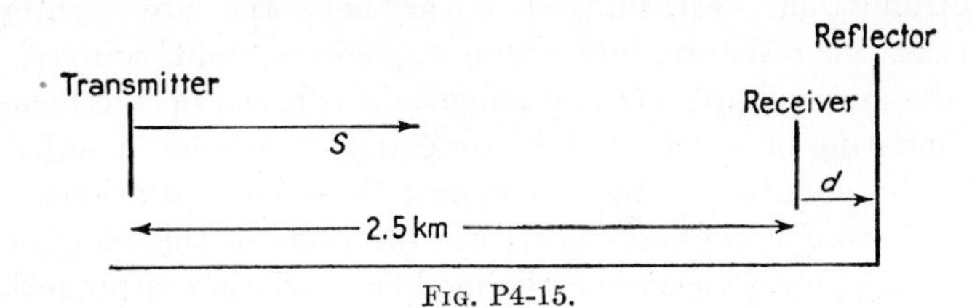


FIG. P4-15.

frequency of $200 \times 10^6$ cps determine the resultant signal induced in the antenna as a function of the distance $d$ from the antenna to the reflector. Do this for the values $d$ = 4.5, 4.65, 4.8, 4.95, 5.10, and 5.25 m. Use sinor diagrams, and obtain the numerical results graphically. Plot a graph of resultant signal as a function of $d$.

## QUESTIONS

**4-1.** What are two differences between a rotating line which generates a sinusoid, and a sinor?

**4-2.** Could a sinor be defined using the cosine equation rather than the sine equation for a sinusoidal wave?

**4-3.** What is the geometrical characteristic of a phasor quantity?

**4-4.** What information about a sinusoid is not included with the specifying parameters of a sinor?

**4-5.** Why is it necessary to consider the sinusoids themselves in order to understand the meaning of reference conditions for sinors?

**4-6.** How is phase difference between two waves obtained if the sinor symbols for them are known?

**4-7.** Is the sum of two sinusoids a sinusoid if their frequencies are different?

**4-8.** When two sinusoids of the same frequency are added, is the amplitude of the sum always greater than the amplitude of each of the original waves?

**4-9.** Why does the instant of zero time have no effect on the amplitude of the sum of two sinusoidal waves?

**4-10.** The addition of any number of sinusoids may be required. Explain how the consideration of the addition of only two sinusoids is sufficiently general to do for all possible cases.

**4-11.** A sinusoid is to be subtracted from another. How could a modification be made so that addition could be used?

**4-12.** In the inverse-tangent function what is the effect of moving a minus sign from the numerator to the denominator of the independent variable?

# CHAPTER 5
# BASIC INTEGRODIFFERENTIAL EQUATIONS

**5-1. Introduction.** All lumped linear networks are composed of combinations of resistors, inductors, capacitors, and sources. Later study of the more complicated combinations is based on the behavior of circuits consisting of resistors, inductors, and capacitors in series and in parallel. The equations which represent these configurations, as they are obtained from Kirchhoff's laws, are the topic of this chapter. The treatment puts no restriction on the mode of variation of potentials and currents, except that time derivatives of the potential and current functions must exist, except possibly at isolated points.

**5-2. Kirchhoff's Laws.** In Sec. 2-5 Kirchhoff's laws are mentioned, to demonstrate the meaning of reference conditions. The basic circuit equations are obtained from Kirchhoff's laws, so a summary of these laws, for instantaneous quantities, is given as an introduction.

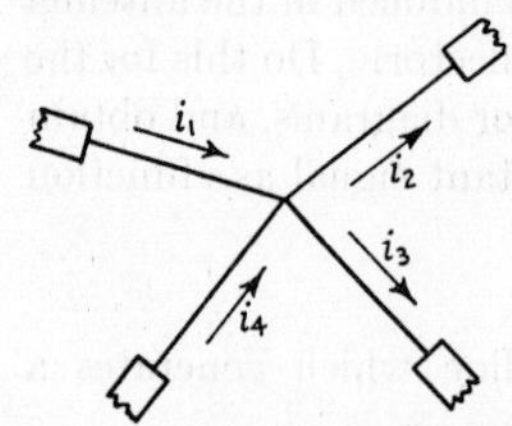

FIG. 5-1. Typical network node (junction).

*The Law for Currents.* In the typical junction of Fig. 5-1 reference directions for current are chosen arbitrarily. Conditions at this junction can be expressed by either of two statements of Kirchhoff's current law. These are:

1. The *actual* current entering a junction is equal to the *actual* current leaving the junction.

2. The sum of the currents (meaning *algebraic* currents) entering a junction is equal to the sum of the currents (meaning *algebraic* currents) leaving the junction.

The difference between these statements is clarified by a numerical example. In Fig. 5-1 let $i_1 = -2$, $i_2 = -5$, $i_3 = 7$, and $i_4 = 4$ at some particular instant. For this example these two statements of the law are, respectively,

$$\underset{\text{entering}}{\text{Actual current}} = -i_2 + i_4 = -i_1 + i_3 = \underset{\text{leaving}}{\text{actual current}} \tag{5-1}$$

$$5 + 4 = 2 + 7$$

$$\underset{\text{entering}}{\text{Algebraic current}} = i_1 + i_4 = i_2 + i_3 = \underset{\text{leaving}}{\text{algebraic current}} \tag{5-2}$$

$$-2 + 4 = -5 + 7$$

The first statement is perhaps more closely related to actuality. It represents the facts as they would be indicated by an instantaneous experiment. However, if the various currents change direction, the terms appearing on the two sides of Eqs. (5-1) would change. This is an inconvenience. However, whenever a current reversal occurs, causing a term to change from one side to the other in Eq. (5-1), a sign change occurs also, so that the literal equation could always be written as in Eqs. (5-2). The literal parts of Eqs. (5-1) and (5-2) are identical, except for a transposition. Conditions at the junction of Fig. 5-1 can be represented by any one of the equations

$$i_1 + i_4 = i_2 + i_3 \tag{5-3}$$

$$i_1 - i_2 - i_3 + i_4 = 0 \tag{5-4}$$

$$-i_1 + i_2 + i_3 - i_4 = 0 \tag{5-5}$$

all of which are mathematical expressions of the second form of the Kirchhoff current law. Equation (5-3) follows directly from statement 2. To make statement 2 fit Eq. (5-4), it is noted that the currents $-i_2$ and $-i_3$ have reference directions toward the junction, and to make it fit Eq. (5-5), it is noted that currents $-i_1$ and $-i_4$ have reference directions away from the junction.

The Kirchhoff law for currents is actually an expression of the law of conservation of electric charge, stating that the rate of charge flow into a junction equals the rate of charge flow out of the junction. The law is accurately true only for junctions which are physically small, so that they have no appreciable capacity to store charge. When an actual circuit has massive junctions, it is replaced on paper by an imagined equivalent circuit having negligibly small junctions, with the effect of the massive junctions replaced by one or more fictitious capacitances and current sources.* Kirchhoff's current law applies to the junctions in this equivalent network.

*The Law for Potential Differences.* A typical network loop is shown in Fig. 5-2, in which the reference polarities have been chosen at random. The Kirchhoff law for potential differences can be expressed by either of the statements:

1. In traveling around a loop, the sum of the *actual* potential rises is equal to the sum of the *actual* potential drops.

2. In traveling around a loop, the sum of the potential rises (meaning *algebraic* rises) is equal to the sum of the potential drops (meaning *algebraic* drops).

* The fictitious current sources are due to any varying electric fields arising from moving charges external to the network.

These two statements could be illustrated by the numerical example given for currents. As with the currents, statement 1 would lead to inconvenient transpositions as various quantities change sign. Taking a clockwise direction of travel, statement 2 leads to any one of the equations

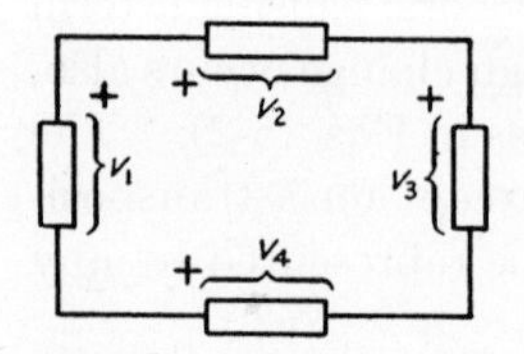

FIG. 5-2. Typical network loop (mesh).

$$v_1 + v_4 = v_2 + v_3 \tag{5-6}$$
$$v_1 - v_2 - v_3 + v_4 = 0 \tag{5-7}$$
$$-v_1 + v_2 + v_3 - v_4 = 0 \tag{5-8}$$

which are all valid no matter what the actual polarities. Statement 2 leads to Eq. (5-6) directly. Statement 2 also gives Eq. (5-7) by regarding $-v_2$ and $-v_3$ as algebraic potential rises, and it leads to Eq. (5-8) if $-v_1$ and $-v_4$ are considered as drops, when traveling in the clockwise direction in all cases.

Kirchhoff's law for potential differences is a form of the law of conservation of energy, stating that zero work is done in carrying an electrical charge around a closed loop if the loop is not linked by a varying magnetic field. The law is accurately true only for a loop of small area, so that it can not be linked by an appreciable varying magnetic flux. When a network has loops that are too large, it is replaced on paper by an imagined equivalent circuit with small loops, with the effects of the magnetic flux replaced by one or more fictitious inductances and potential sources.* The Kirchhoff potential law can be applied to each loop of the equivalent circuit.

**5-3. Reference Conditions for Elements.** In this chapter various circuit components are connected in series and parallel, and Kirchhoff's laws are applied to the combinations. To simplify the discussions, a standard set of reference conditions is used as shown in Fig. 5-3. They are the same as originally given in Fig. 2-30. The rectangle represents a resistor, an inductor, or a capacitor, or some combination thereof. It *does not include sources*. The important feature is that in the lead wire the reference current direction is toward the reference-positive terminal.

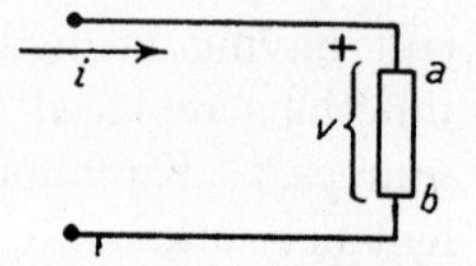

FIG. 5-3. Reference conditions to be used for passive elements.

At least two advantages can be given for this set of universal reference conditions. For one thing, they eliminate many minus signs that would otherwise arise in the equations. Also, they lead to convenient notation when double subscripts are used because then

* The fictitious potential sources are due to any varying magnetic fields arising from currents external to the network.

$$\begin{aligned} i &= i_{ab} \\ v &= v_{ab} \end{aligned} \tag{5-9}$$

This is convenient because the subscripts on the potential and the current appear in the same order.

It is emphasized that this standard set of reference conditions is to be universally used only if the circuit branch does not include a source. If it does include a source, there is no fixed arrangement of references, as will become apparent at a later time.

**5-4. Current-Potential Relations in Basic Circuit Elements.** For the present, it is assumed that the inductors are wound with wire of zero resistivity and that the insulation of the capacitor has infinite resistivity. It is also assumed that the inductance and capacitance are true constants. This implies that there is no magnetic saturation in the inductor, and no dielectric saturation in the capacitor, and that none of the elements

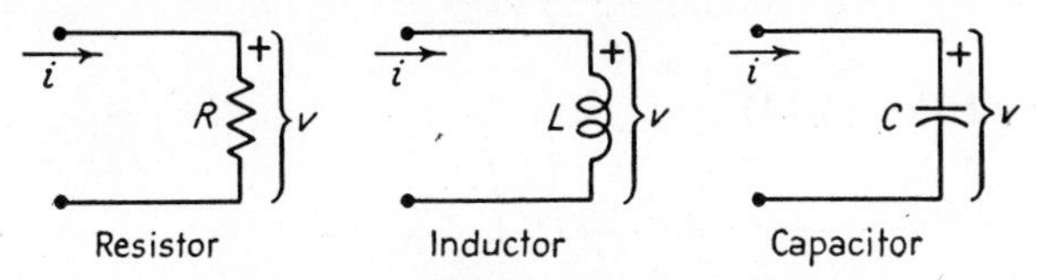


FIG. 5-4. Basic circuit elements.

(resistance, inductance, or capacitance) are distributed or vary with time.

The potential-current relations for the three basic types of circuit elements are given in Sec. 2-12. Each relation is repeated here, but this time two forms are given for each. In one form the current is the independent variable, and in the other the potential is the independent variable. It is important to understand that the potential and current are functions of time and might rightfully be written $v(t)$ and $i(t)$. For the sake of simplicity, when small letters are used the time variable will usually be omitted. Reference conditions are given in Fig. 5-4.

The potential-current relationship for the resistor can be given in either of the two forms

$$v = Ri \tag{5-10}$$

or

$$i = Gv \tag{5-11}$$

which define the mathematical quantities of resistance $R$ and conductance $G$, $(G = 1/R)$. $R$ is the resistance in ohms and $G$ is the conductance in mhos. There is a fundamental difference between these two equations, beyond the obvious difference in form. In Eq. (5-10) the current is the independent variable, while in Eq. (5-11) the potential is the independent variable.

For the inductor the mathematical quantity called inductance is defined so that

$$v = L\frac{di}{dt} \tag{5-12}$$

giving the potential in terms of the independent variable $i$. The inverse of this is

$$i = \frac{1}{L}\int v\,dt \tag{5-13}$$

It will later be pointed out that the integral in Eq. (5-13) is really the flux linkage of the coil.

For the capacitor a mathematical quantity $C$ called capacitance is defined by the equation

$$i = C\frac{dv}{dt} \qquad (5\text{-}14)^*$$

The inverse of Eq. (5-14) is

$$v = \frac{1}{C}\int i\,dt \tag{5-15}$$

In this case the integral gives the charge on the capacitor.

This completes the presentation of the basic equations for the three types of circuit elements. Each was presented as relating the two variables $v$ and $i$, always using $v$ for potential and $i$ for current. In subsequent applications it will be necessary to apply identifying subscripts such as $v_L$, $v_R$, $i_C$, $i_R$, etc.

**5-5. Basic Integrodifferential Equations.** All network analysis procedures stem from the behavior of the two basic circuits shown in Figs. 5-5 and 5-6. There is a similarity between them which makes it possible

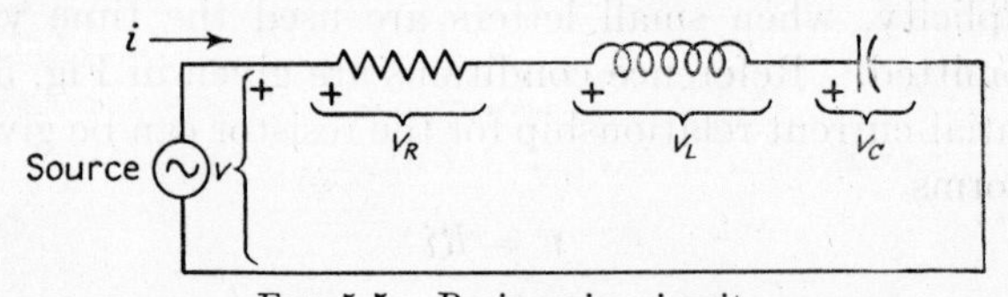


FIG. 5-5. Basic series circuit.

to consider them simultaneously. In each case the mathematical relationship between the terminal potential $v$ and the terminal current $i$ is required. Each circuit is excited by a sinusoidal source.

Consider the series circuit of Fig. 5-5. The potentials across the

* Capacitance is sometimes defined by Eq. (5-15), as the ratio of charge to potential. However, it is more in keeping with subsequent developments to define the capacitance by the same sort of equation (*i.e.*, differential) as is used for inductance.

various elements are designated by subscripts, as indicated. The reference conditions for all potentials and the current are clearly shown. The

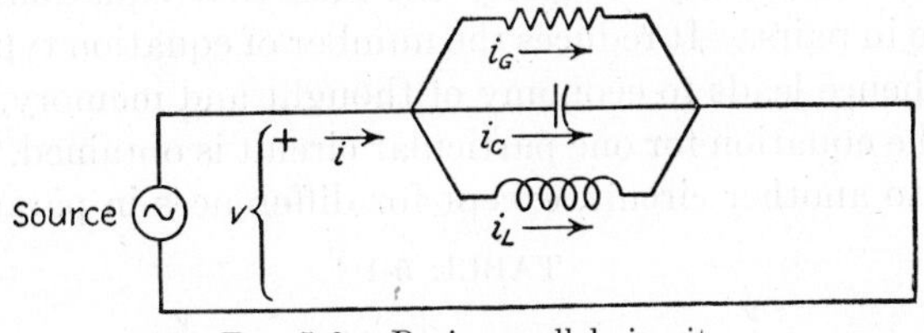


FIG. 5-6. Basic parallel circuit.

Kirchhoff potential equation is

$$v = v_R + v_L + v_C \tag{5-16}$$

Equations (5-10), (5-12), and (5-15) are used, respectively, for $v_R$, $v_L$, and $v_C$, to give

$$v = Ri + L\frac{di}{dt} + \frac{1}{C}\int i\,dt \tag{5-17}$$

The parallel circuit of Fig. 5-6 is treated by applying the Kirchhoff current law, giving

$$i = i_G + i_C + i_L \tag{5-18}$$

Equations (5-11), (5-13), and (5-14), respectively, give $i_G$, $i_C$, and $i_L$. Therefore

$$i = Gv + C\frac{dv}{dt} + \frac{1}{L}\int v\,dt \tag{5-19}$$

**5-6. Duality.** Equations (5-17) and (5-19) are of similar form. One can be obtained from the other by systematically interchanging $v$ and $i$, $R$ and $G$, and $L$ and $C$. Two equations which are related like this are said to be *duals*. The idea of considering them together is the concept of *duality*. The basic ideas of duality are contained in Table 5-1. On each line a pair of relations is given between $v$ and $i$. In each equation the form is the same, but the interchanges are made as mentioned above.

The foregoing statements may be interpreted in detail. Table 5-1 includes the general case in row (5-23) and also the various single element cases in the other rows. On the left the equations explicitly give $v$, and on the right they give $i$. In row (5-20), $v$ and $i$ are interchanged, and $R$ is interchanged with $G$. The situation in the second and third rows is somewhat different because different types of circuit elements are compared. Thus, one equation of a pair is obtained from the other by interchanging $v$ and $i$, and also by interchanging $L$ and $C$. All these types of interchange are found in the general case of row (5-23).

The concept of duality is merely the idea that equations for electric circuits come in pairs. It reduces the number of equation types to be considered and hence leads to economy of thought and memory, because if a solution of the equation for one particular circuit is obtained, this solution also applies to another circuit, except for differences in parameters.

TABLE 5-1

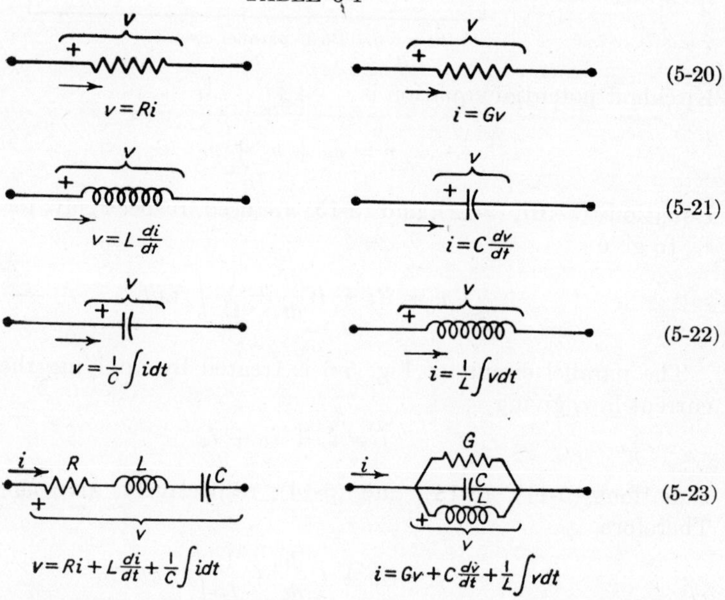

| | | |
|---|---|---|
| $v = Ri$ | $i = Gv$ | (5-20) |
| $v = L\frac{di}{dt}$ | $i = C\frac{dv}{dt}$ | (5-21) |
| $v = \frac{1}{C}\int i\,dt$ | $i = \frac{1}{L}\int v\,dt$ | (5-22) |
| $v = Ri + L\frac{di}{dt} + \frac{1}{C}\int i\,dt$ | $i = Gv + C\frac{dv}{dt} + \frac{1}{L}\int v\,dt$ | (5-23) |

In an introduction to the subject of duality, there is danger that the ideas will be misinterpreted. There is no stipulation of numerical values. That is, in comparing two dual equations expressing the behavior of a pair of dual circuits, there is no need to have the numerical coefficients the same. Thus, in line (5-20) it is not necessary that the $R$ on the left be numerically the same as the $G$ on the right. Similarly, in lines (5-21) and (5-22), $L$ and $C$ in each of the two cases need not have identical numerical values.* Emphasis is on the form of the equations, not on an identity of numerical coefficients. Also, it is to be noted that dual circuits are not equivalent.

The idea of duality may be extended far beyond the point to which it is carried in this section. For example, it is seen from the previous discussions that the two basic laws of Kirchhoff are dually related. Therefore,

* In some circuit-design procedures it is convenient to have a dual in which numerical values are preserved. Such dually related circuits are called *dual analogues*.

it follows also that a circuit junction and a loop are dually related, since the equations which pertain to them are duals. In thinking about the extension of the ideas of duality it should be again emphasized that only the *form* of the equations is the important consideration.

**5-7. Charge and Flux Linkage.** In an elementary introduction to the subject of electricity, it is customary first to define charge; and from charge the concept of current is obtained as a derivative of charge with respect to time. For circuit work it is more convenient to define charge as an integral of current with respect to time. A similar situation pertains to the concept of flux linkage. It is usually defined in terms of the flux within the turns of a coil and the number of turns of the coil. However, for purposes of circuit analysis, it is more convenient to define flux linkage as an integral with respect to time of potential difference across an ideal (zero-resistance) coil. These definitions put into evidence a dual relationship between charge and flux linkage. This relationship will be discussed briefly.

The two quantities to be considered are

$$q = \int i \, dt \tag{5-24}$$

$$\psi = \int v \, dt \tag{5-25}$$

which are, respectively, charge and flux linkage. They are duals because they are the same in form but involve an interchange of the quantities $v$ and $i$.

In order completely to define these quantities, it is necessary to specify reference conditions for them. These will be stated without the steps of reasoning from which they are derived. They are the usual reference conditions tacitly assumed for these quantities, although the quantities are not themselves always defined by Eqs. (5-24) and (5-25). The reference condition for charge is defined in terms of an associated capacitor, and the reference condition for flux linkage is defined in terms of an associated inductor. The pertinent diagrams and reference conditions for $i$ and $v$ are shown in Figs. 5-7 and 5-8.

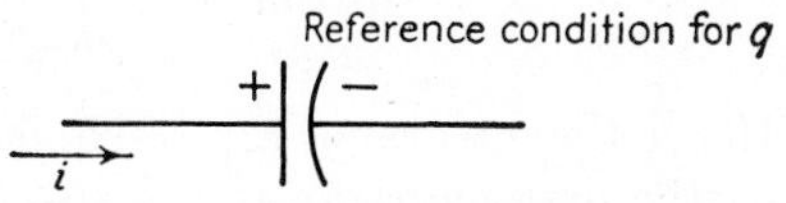

Reference condition for $q$
+ −
$i$

FIG. 5-7. Definition of charge reference condition.

Consider the capacitor of Fig. 5-7, for which $i$ is the current of Eq. (5-24). The associated reference condition for charge is the charge distribution shown on the figure. It is perhaps unfortunate that it looks like a potential polarity reference marking—a regrettable consequence of the overworking of the + and − signs.

The concept of flux linkage is usually introduced as the product of number of turns on a coil and the average flux through the coil. It is to be shown that this is equivalent to Eq. (5-25). The coil of Fig. 5-8 is assumed to be wound with zero-resistance wire. The only way in which $v$ can be different from zero is to have a changing flux in the coil. Then $v$ is given by the equation

$$v = N\frac{d\phi}{dt} \tag{5-26}$$

where $N$ is the number of turns and $\phi$ the flux. The algebraic quantity $\phi$ has a reference direction. Lenz's law can be used to show that $v$ is positive at any instant when $\phi$ has the direction shown in Fig. 5-8 and is increasing (which means $d\phi/dt$ is then positive). Therefore the reference direction for $\phi$ is the direction shown in Fig. 5-8. Since we are interested in relating flux with potential, rather than flux with current, a rule for finding the reference direction for flux can be given in terms of the reference polarity of the potential.* Allow an imaginary screw to turn in the direction the coil encircles the core, when starting at the reference-positive terminal. The direction of axial motion of the screw is the flux reference direction. Equation (5-26) may be used for $v$ in Eq. (5-25), giving

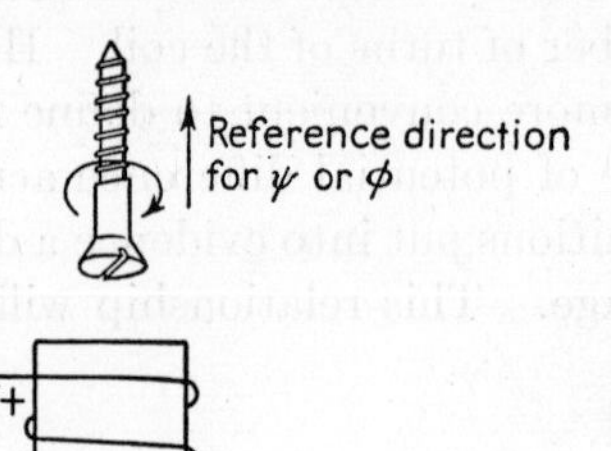

FIG. 5-8. Definition of flux or flux-linkage reference direction.

$$\int v\,dt = N\int\frac{d\phi}{dt}\,dt = N\int d\phi = N\phi \tag{5-27}$$

Hence the integral of Eq. (5-25) is a flux linkage. In writing the equality on the extreme right of Eq. (5-27) the constant of integration has been taken as zero.

**5-8. Interpretation of the Integrals for Charge and Flux Linkage.** The reader will probably interpret the integrals in Eqs. (5-24) and (5-25) as antiderivative functions (indefinite integrals), to be obtained from tables of integration or by analytical methods of integration, with the constant of integration suitably evaluated. This interpretation is applicable as long as $i(t)$ or $v(t)$ can be written as a single formula for which a single expression for the antiderivative can be found. However, in

* The reference direction of flux is sometimes related to the current reference direction by the familiar right-hand rule. There is no inconsistency in the two methods of defining reference directions for flux *if the current reference direction inside the coil is away from the reference-positive terminal.* The advantage in relating flux direction with potential rather than current is that it is consistent with the dual relationship between flux linkage and charge.

many cases $i(t)$ or $v(t)$ may be specified graphically, or by a sequence of different formulas which are valid for different ranges of $t$. A general interpretation for the integrals of Eqs. (5-24) and (5-25), which is valid for all cases, is the following:

$$\int i\,dt = Q_0 + \int_{t_0}^{t} i(t')\,dt' \tag{5-28*}$$

$$\int v\,dt = \Psi_0 + \int_{t_0}^{t} v(t')\,dt' \tag{5-29*}$$

where $Q_0$ and $\Psi_0$ are values of $q$ and $\psi$, respectively, at a particular value of time $t = t_0$.

If an antiderivative formula is available, these expressions lead to the same result as would normally be obtained by properly evaluating the integration constant. For example, suppose $q_1(t)$ is an antiderivative of $i(t)$. Then Eq. (5-28) gives

$$q(t) = Q_0 - q_1(t_0) + q_1(t) \tag{5-30}$$

in which $Q_0 - q_1(t_0)$ assumes the role of the evaluated constant of integration. When a formula for $q_1(t)$ cannot be written, the integral in Eq. (5-28) is regarded as an area under the curve of $i$, between the limits $t_0$ and $t$, which can be found by a suitable method: analytically, graphically, or by the use of a planimeter or other integrating machine.

**5-9. Summary.** There are three basic types of mathematical relations that apply to individual circuit elements, for expressing the relationship between current and potential. These are a linear proportionality, a first-order derivative, or a first order integration. The linear relation always applies to a resistor. Which of the other two applies in a given case depends both on the circuit element in question and on whether the current is required in terms of the potential, or vice versa. There are really six relationships for the three basic types of circuit elements, but there are only three that are different. The ideas of duality are employed to allow these six relations to be analyzed as only three. Each analysis then applies to two cases.

The three basic equations may combine into a single equation embodying all three. This is called an integrodifferential equation, because it embodies both a derivative and an integral. It is the basic equation relating the terminal current and potential for either a series or a parallel connection of a resistor, inductor, and capacitor.

Special cases of this equation also apply to circuits having less than the

* In Eqs. (5-28) and (5-29) an integration variable $t'$, which is different from the upper limit $t$, is necessary because a single variable cannot serve as a limit and at the same time also take on other values less than the limit.

three elements mentioned, by omitting the appropriate terms. The solution of this equation embodies the essential theory of circuit analysis. It is given detailed consideration in Chap. 6.

In the course of the derivation of the basic integrodifferential equations the two quantities, charge and flux linkage, were defined in a way which befits their use in circuit analysis. Charge and flux linkage are found to be dually related, a fact that would not be so readily apparent from their usual definitions.

## PROBLEMS

NOTE: In the problems in Chap. 5 it is possible to borrow results obtained in one problem for application to other problems. This is to be done wherever possible, with the inclusion of adequate explanation.

**5-1.** The current through an inductor of 0.015 henry varies in accordance with the wave shape shown in Fig. P5-1. The frequency is 1,250 cps, and the wave is divided into four portions of equal duration. The peak value is 2 amp.

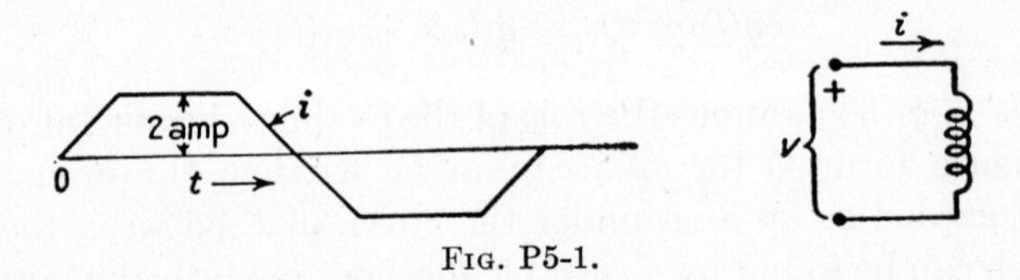


FIG. P5-1.

From these data determine the mode of variation of the potential across the inductor, and plot the result for a complete cycle. This potential is to have the reference polarity shown. The curve should be plotted with sufficient accuracy to give quantitative information.

**5-2.** Let the wave of Fig. P5-2 be the potential across a capacitor of 2 $\mu$f. The wave shape and frequency are the same as in Prob. 5-1, the only difference being that in Prob. 5-2 the wave is a potential with a peak value of 150 volts. The reference polarity is shown in the diagram.

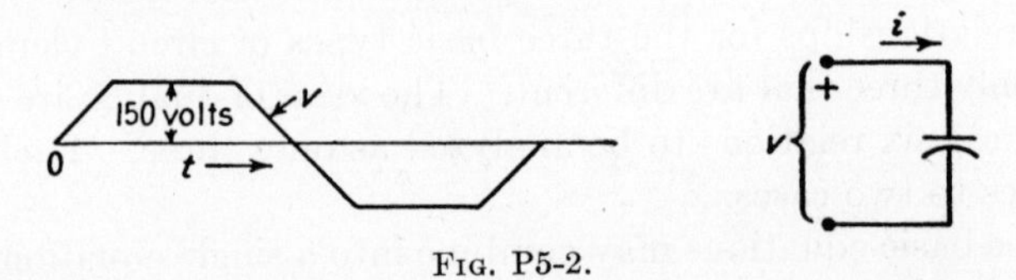


FIG. P5-2.

Plot an accurate curve of the variable current $i$. Use the reference direction shown in the diagram.

**5-3.** Let the current specified in Prob. 5-1 be the current in the capacitor of Prob. 5-2. Furthermore, let the capacitor be uncharged at time $t = 0$. Using the same reference conditions as in Fig. P5-2, plot a graph of the potential $v$ across the capacitor, or a function of time, for a complete cycle.

**5-4.** Let the potential wave of Prob. 5-2 be the potential across the inductor of Prob. 5-1. Also, let the current through the coil be zero when $t = 0$. Plot an accurate graph of the variation of the current $i$ through the inductor, as a function of time for a complete cycle. Use the reference conditions given in Fig. P5-1.

**5-5.** The capacitor and inductor of Probs. 5-1 and 5-2 are connected in series, and also included is a resistor of 20 ohms. Using the reference conditions shown

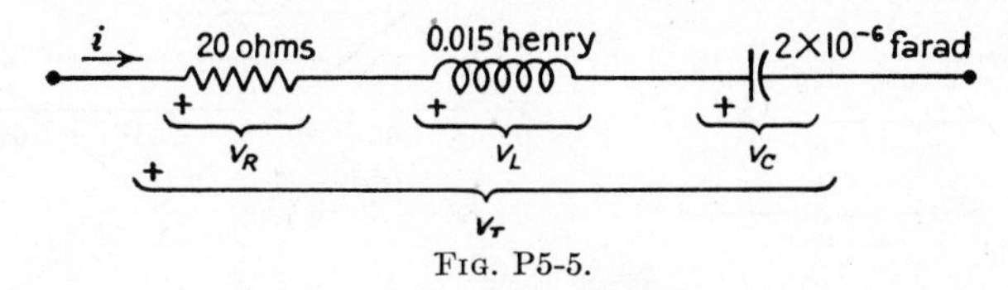


FIG. P5-5.

in Fig. P5-5, draw upon the results of the preceding problems to plot a graph of the total potential difference $v_T$. This is to be done assuming that the current through the circuit is the wave of Prob. 5-1 and that the potential across the capacitor is zero when $t = 0$. Show all steps involved in arriving at the result.

**5-6.** The capacitor and inductor of Probs. 5-1 and 5-2 and a 50-ohm resistor are connected in parallel. The potential across the combination varies in accordance with the wave shape given in Prob. 5-2. The current through the inductor is assumed to be zero when $t = 0$. Use any pertinent results of the preceding problems to obtain the graph of the variation of the total current $I_T$, as a function of time for a complete cycle. Use the reference conditions shown in Fig. P5-6. Show all steps leading to the result.

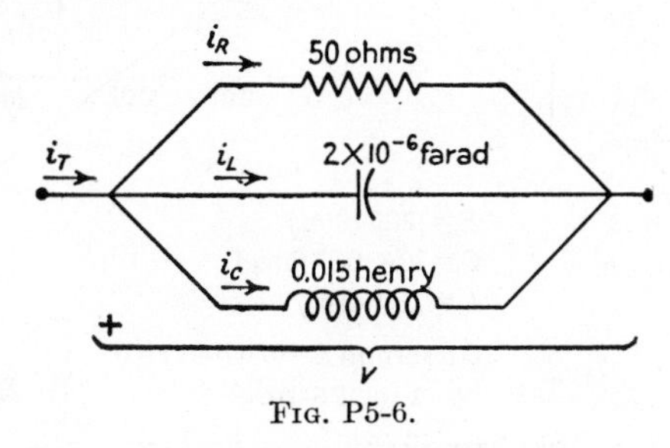


FIG. P5-6.

**5-7.** In a series circuit similar to that of Fig. P5-5 let the current be given by

$$i = t - \frac{t^2}{4} + \frac{t^3}{100}$$

The values of the circuit elements are $R = 5$ ohms, $L = 10$ henrys, and $C = 0.125$ farad. When $t = 0$, the capacitor is unchanged. Obtain the equation for the potential $v_T$.

**5-8.** In a parallel circuit like that of Fig. P5-6 let the potential be given by the equation

$$v = 150\epsilon^{-5000t}$$

The values of the circuit elements are $R = 80$ ohms, $C = 2 \times 10^{-6}$ farad, and $L = 0.015$ henry. When $t = 0$, the current in the inductor is zero. Obtain the expression for the current $i$.

**5-9.** The current in the series circuit of Fig. P5-9 varies as shown.

*a.* Plot curves of the potentials $v_R$, $v_L$, and $v_C$ as functions of time, showing them for a complete cycle.

*b.* Plot a curve of $v_T$ as a function of time, showing it for a complete cycle.

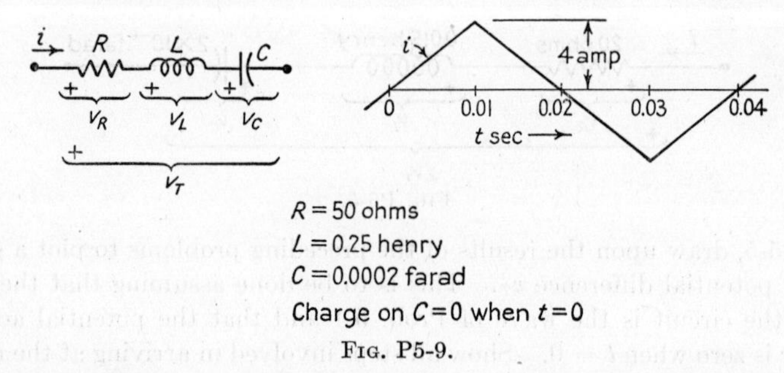


$R = 50$ ohms
$L = 0.25$ henry
$C = 0.0002$ farad
Charge on $C = 0$ when $t = 0$

FIG. P5-9.

**5-10.** The potential across the parallel circuit of Fig. P5-10 varies as shown.

*a.* Plot curves of the currents $i_R$ $i_L$, and $i_C$ as functions of time, showing them for a complete cycle.

*b.* Plot a curve of $i_T$ as a function of time, showing it for a complete cycle.

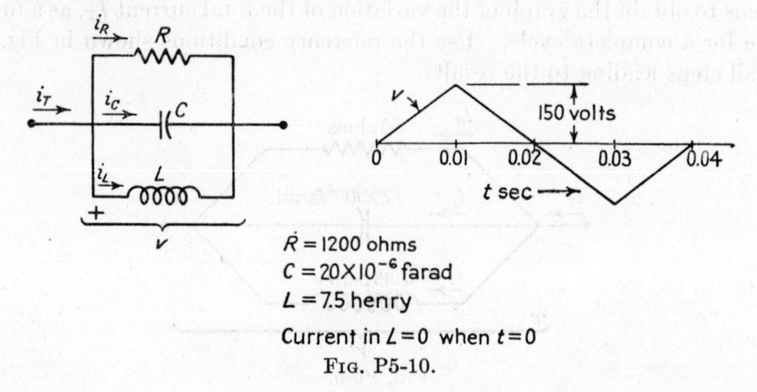


$R = 1200$ ohms
$C = 20 \times 10^{-6}$ farad
$L = 7.5$ henry
Current in $L = 0$ when $t = 0$

FIG. P5-10.

**5-11.** The current in Fig. P5-11 is a series of positive pulses, as shown. If the capacitor is uncharged at $t = 0$, plot a graph of the potential $v$ for the duration of three cycles of current.

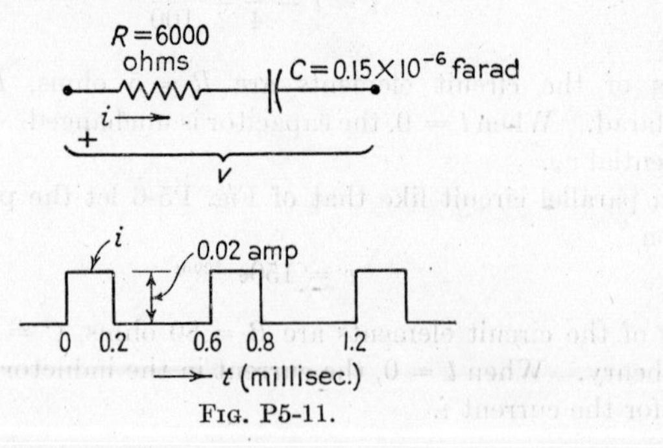


FIG. P5-11.

**5-12.** The parallel circuit shown in Fig. P5-12 is excited by the potential wave shown. If the current in the inductor is initially zero, plot a graph of the current $i$ over the range of $t$ from 0 to 2.5 msec.

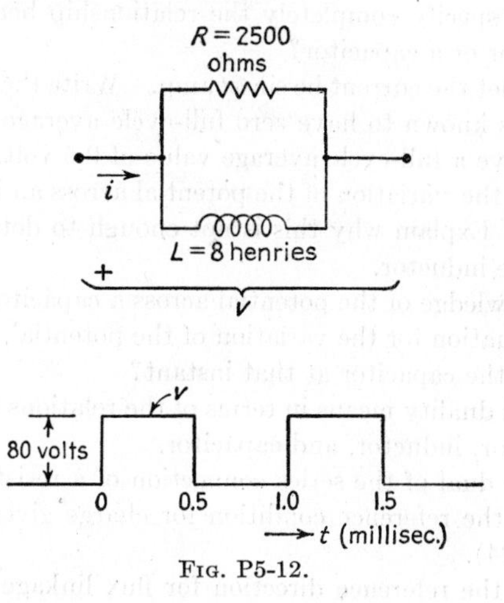


FIG. P5-12.

**5-13.** In Fig. P5-11 let the current wave be shifted vertically so that it has zero average value, and assume that the current is zero up to $t = 0$. Again assume that the capacitor is uncharged at $t = 0$.

*a.* Obtain the graph of the potential $v$.

*b.* Determine the average and effective values of the wave obtained in part *a*.

**5-14.** Consider the circuit specified in Fig. P5-12, but let the potential wave be shifted vertically to make it have zero average value. The current in the inductor is assumed to be zero when $t = 0$, and the potential wave is zero up to time $t = 0$.

*a.* Plot a graph of the current $i$.

*b.* Compute the average and effective values of the wave for $i$.

**5-15.** Do Prob. 5-11, but for the condition that the capacitor is charged to a potential of 120 volts with the right-hand plate positive.

**5-16.** Do Prob. 5-12, but for the condition that at $t = 0$ there is a current of 0.025 amp in the inductor, flowing toward the left.

## QUESTIONS

**5-1.** Why is it not possible to write the Kirchhoff equations when the reference conditions are not known?

**5-2.** Why is it more convenient to write Kirchhoff's laws in terms of reference conditions, rather than in terms of the actual conditions that exist at any particular instant?

**5-3.** Why is it necessary to specify reference conditions for potential and current in a circuit element?

**5-4.** In this text do the standard reference conditions shown in Fig. 5-3 always apply to any two-terminal network, even though it includes a source, or do they apply just to networks of resistors, inductors, and capacitors (passive networks)?

**5-5.** Is it necessary to express the integral relationships, as well as the differential relationships, to specify completely the relationship between potential and current in an inductor or a capacitor?

**5-6.** In Eq. (5-15) let the current be $\sin \omega t$ amp. Write the equation for $v$; (*a*) if the potential wave is known to have zero full-cycle average, (*b*) if the potential wave is known to have a full-cycle average value of 0.5 volt.

**5-7.** Assume that the variation of the potential across an inductor is known as a function of time. Explain why this is not enough to determine the equation for the current in the inductor.

**5-8.** Does the knowledge of the potential across a capacitor at some instant of time, but not the equation for the variation of the potential, suffice to determine the current through the capacitor at that instant?

**5-9.** Explain what duality means in terms of the relations between current and potential for a resistor, inductor, and capacitor.

**5-10.** What is the dual of the series connection of a resistor and a capacitor?

**5-11.** Prove that the reference condition for charge given in Fig. 5-7 is consistent with Eq. (5-24).

**5-12.** Prove that the reference direction for flux linkage given in Fig. 5-8 is consistent with Eq. (5-25).

# CHAPTER 6

# SINUSOIDAL EXCITATIONS

**6-1. Introduction.** The basic integrodifferential equations of network analysis are given in Chap. 5. The next step is to consider their behavior when potentials and currents vary sinusoidally. Other laws of variation may be encountered in a circuit, but the sinusoidal law is of importance in a large number of applications. Eventually, the solutions will be extended to circuits of considerable complexity, but the present chapter is confined to the simple series and parallel circuits discussed in Chap. 5.

To obviate repeated definitions, a standardized notation is employed for potentials and currents. $V$ and $I$ are the effective values, and their respective initial angles are $\alpha$ and $\beta$. Angular frequency is indicated by $\omega$. In some cases it is assumed that $V$ and $\alpha$ are initially known, and $I$ and $\beta$ are found from an analysis of the circuit. In other cases the reverse procedure is followed. The notation

$$v = \sqrt{2}\, V \sin(\omega t + \alpha) \tag{6-1}$$

$$i = \sqrt{2}\, I \sin(\omega t + \beta) \tag{6-2}$$

is employed throughout the chapter. Subscripts are included to differentiate among various potentials and currents, when needed.

It is recalled that initial angle depends on the position of zero on the time-angle scale. When there are two or more related waves, this zero point can be chosen once. This amounts to a choice of the initial angle of *one* of the waves of the group. The initial angles of the others are then not arbitrary. It is customary to choose the initial angle of the originally given function as zero, but this is not always the case. Accordingly, the two general initial angles $\alpha$ and $\beta$ are retained in the notation, although one or the other may be zero in actual cases.

**6-2. Individual Circuit Elements.** An introductory discussion of the relationship between potential and current for a resistor, an inductor, and a capacitor under sinusoidal conditions, is given in Sec. 2-12. A more general treatment is now given, including symbolic representation by sinors.

*Linear Algebraic Relation.* Assume that the current in the resistor of Fig. 6-1 is given by Eq. (6-2). Then, since the equation is

$$v = Ri \tag{6-3}$$

it follows that

$$v = \sqrt{2}\, RI \sin (\omega t + \beta) \tag{6-4}$$

The sinusoidal waves are shown in Fig. 6-1, and the corresponding sinors are shown in Fig. 6-2. The ratio of effective values of potential difference to current is $R$, and the waves are in phase.

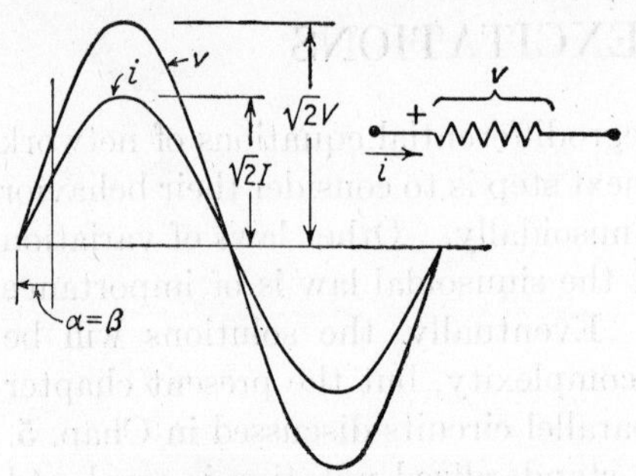


Fig. 6-1. Sinusoidal waves of current and potential difference for a resistor.

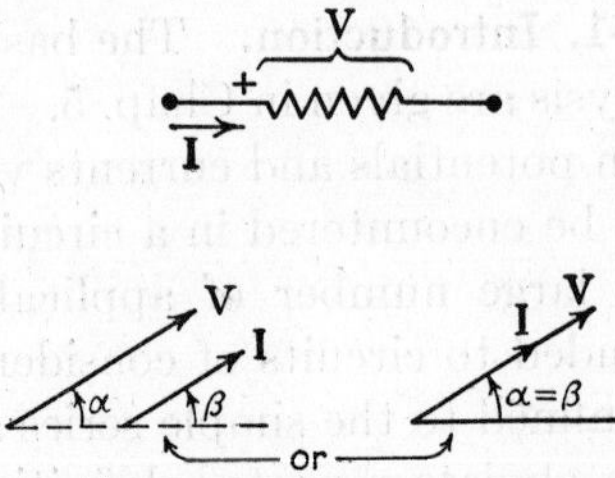

Fig. 6-2. Sinors for current and potential difference for a resistor.

*Linear Derivative Relation.* For Fig. 6-3 the equation is

$$v = L\frac{di}{dt} \tag{6-5}$$

Again taking Eq. (6-2) for the current, it is found by differentiation that

$$v = \sqrt{2}\, \omega LI \cos (\omega t + \beta) = \sqrt{2}\, \omega LI \sin \left( \omega t + \beta + \frac{\pi}{2} \right) \tag{6-6}$$

The sinor diagram is shown in Fig. 6-4. In this case the ratio of effective values of potential difference to current is $\omega L$, and the potential wave leads the current wave by $\pi/2$ rad.

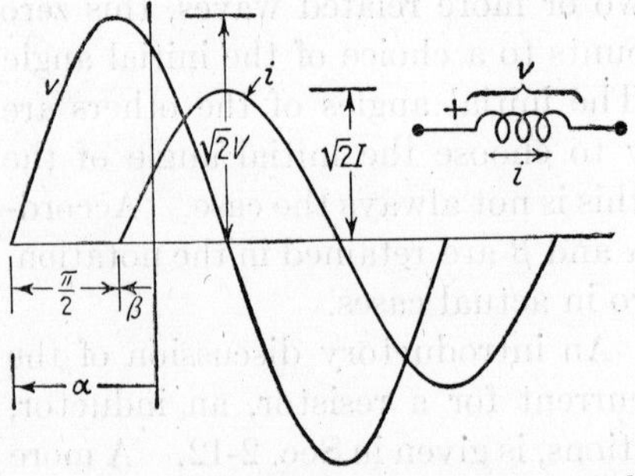


Fig. 6-3. Sinusoidal waves of potential difference and current for an inductor.

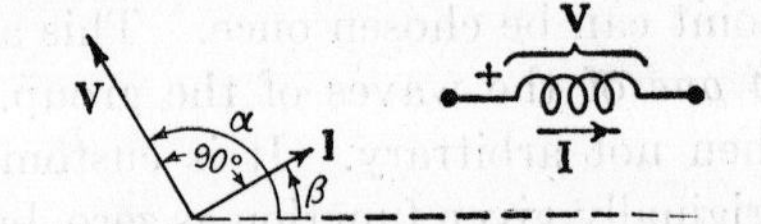


Fig. 6-4. Sinors for potential difference and current for an inductor.

The linear derivative relationship also describes a capacitor when its equation is written

$$i = C\frac{dv}{dt} \tag{6-7}$$

Taking Eq. (6-1) as the potential difference, the equation for $i$ is

$$i = \sqrt{2}\, \omega CV \cos (\omega t + \alpha) = \sqrt{2}\, \omega CV \sin \left( \omega t + \alpha + \frac{\pi}{2} \right) \tag{6-8}$$

Figures 6-5 and 6-6 demonstrate these relationships. In a capacitor, the ratio of effective values of current to potential difference is $\omega C$, and the current wave leads the potential wave by $\pi/2$ rad.

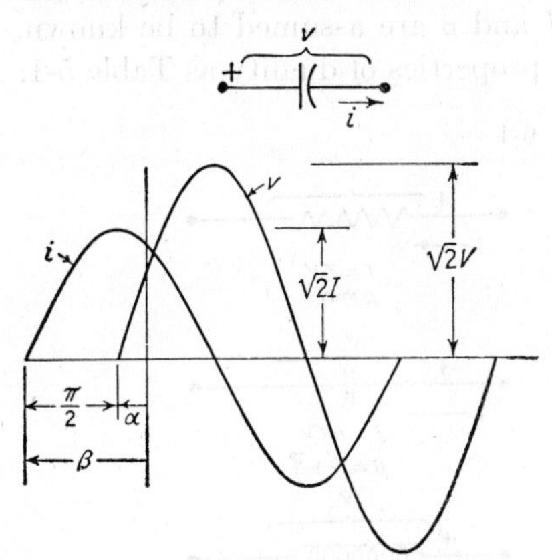


FIG. 6-5. Sinusoidal waves of current and potential difference for a capacitor.

*Linear Integral Relation.* In the sinusoidal case under consideration, the integral relationship is really superfluous. It is necessary only to point out that the above results can be derived from the integral relations,

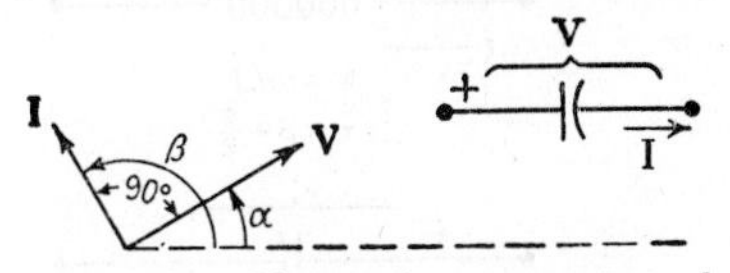


FIG. 6-6. Sinors for current and potential difference for a capacitor.

also. In the case of Fig. 6-3, the potential-current relationship can be written

$$i = \frac{1}{L} \int v \, dt \tag{6-9}$$

Taking Eq. (6-1) for $v$, the current is

$$i = -\sqrt{2} \frac{V}{\omega L} \cos (\omega t + \alpha) = \sqrt{2} \frac{V}{\omega L} \sin \left( \omega t + \alpha - \frac{\pi}{2} \right) \tag{6-10}$$

This result gives the same information as Eq. (6-6).

The capacitor is treated similarly. Its equation can be written

$$v = \frac{1}{C} \int i \, dt \tag{6-11}$$

Equation (6-2) is used for the current, giving

$$v = -\sqrt{2} \frac{I}{\omega C} \cos (\omega t + \beta) = \sqrt{2} \frac{I}{\omega C} \sin \left( \omega t + \beta - \frac{\pi}{2} \right) \tag{6-12}$$

for the potential. Equations (6-12) and (6-8) give equivalent information.

It is noted that in each case the integration constant is taken as zero. This is not necessarily the case in actual circuits. When the integration constant is not zero, it represents a d-c component. In linear circuits the d-c part of a solution can be obtained separately and added to the sinusoidal solution. Therefore, for an a-c analysis, there is no loss of generality in taking the integration constants as zero.

The results so far obtained are tabulated in Table 6-1. In each case the known quantity is written on the right side of the equation. For example, for the left hand column, $I$ and $\beta$ are assumed to be known. Note that this table exhibits the same properties of duality as Table 5-1.

TABLE 6-1

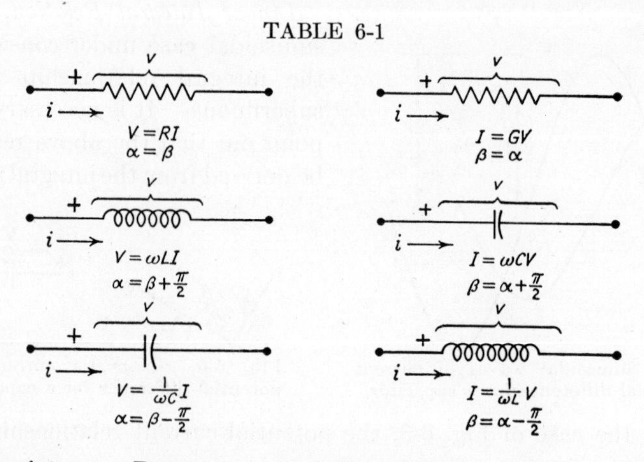


**6-3. Resistance, Reactance, and Susceptance.** For a resistor, the terms *resistance* and *conductance* are retained in a-c circuit analysis. For an inductor or capacitor, the ratio of the effective value of potential difference to the effective value of current is called *reactance* and given the symbol $X$. For an inductor the potential leads the current, and for a capacitor the potential lags the current. In defining reactance this difference can be taken into account by including an algebraic sign. If the potential leads the current, the reactance is *arbitrarily defined* as positive. Thus, for an inductor

$$X_L = \omega L \tag{6-13}$$

and for a capacitor

$$X_C = -\frac{1}{\omega C} \tag{6-14}$$

Reactance is a measure of the degree to which the element "reacts" to prevent current flow. Just as with resistance, a high reactance means a low current.

For an inductor or capacitor a quantity called *susceptance* is also defined. Susceptance is a measure of the degree to which the element is susceptible to current flow. It is represented by the symbol $B$. As with conductance, a high susceptance means a large current. Susceptance is the ratio of the effective value of current to the effective value of potential difference. The susceptance of a capacitor is *arbitrarily defined* as positive. Thus

$$B_C = \omega C \tag{6-15}$$

$$B_L = -\frac{1}{\omega L} \tag{6-16}$$

With this sign convention, current leads potential in a positive susceptance. This is convenient because it makes an inductive reactance the dual of a capacitive susceptance and a capacitive reactance the dual of an inductive susceptance.* When obtaining a reactance from a susceptance, or vice versa, the sign is reversed in taking the reciprocal.

**6-4. Series-connected Elements.** The relation between potential difference and current is to be determined for Fig. 6-7. From Chap. 5 it is known that the equation

$$v = v_R + v_L + v_C \tag{6-17}$$

or

$$v = Ri + L\frac{di}{dt} + \frac{1}{C}\int i\,dt \tag{6-18}$$

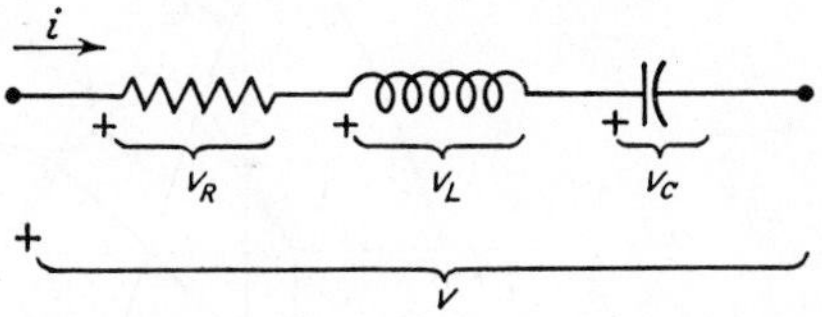

FIG. 6-7. Reference conditions for the basic series circuit.

applies. Equation (6-2) is used for $i$, and the potential $v$ is to be found.

From the summary in Table 6-1 it follows that

$$v = \sqrt{2}\,I\left[R\sin(\omega t + \beta) + \omega L\cos(\omega t + \beta) - \frac{1}{\omega C}\cos(\omega t + \beta)\right] \tag{6-19}$$

Graphs of these three sinusoids are given in Fig. 6-8. However, the actual combination is preferably done in terms of their corresponding sinors. Thus

$\mathbf{V}$ symbolizes $v$
$\mathbf{V}_R$ symbolizes $v_R$
$\mathbf{V}_L$ symbolizes $v_L$
$\mathbf{V}_C$ symbolizes $v_C$
$\mathbf{I}$ symbolizes $i$

From the sinor diagram of Fig. 6-9 it is found that

$$\mathbf{V} = Z_s I \underline{/\beta + \zeta_s} \tag{6-20†}$$

where

$$Z_s = \sqrt{R^2 + \left(\omega L - \frac{1}{\omega C}\right)^2} \tag{6-21}$$

* Further insight as to the reason for the sign conventions is gained in Chap. 8.

† Note that two operations are implied here: the multiplication of magnitudes, and the addition of angles. In Chap. 8 this idea is extended by the introduction of complex algebra.

and

$$\zeta_s = \tan^{-1} \frac{\omega L - (1/\omega C)}{R} \tag{6-22}$$

The time function corresponding to Eq. (6-20) is

$$v = \sqrt{2}\, Z_s I \sin (\omega t + \beta + \zeta_s) \tag{6-23}$$

The quantity $Z_s$ is called the *impedance* of the circuit. It is a measure of the extent to which the circuit "impedes" the current. Resistance and reactance are special cases of impedance.

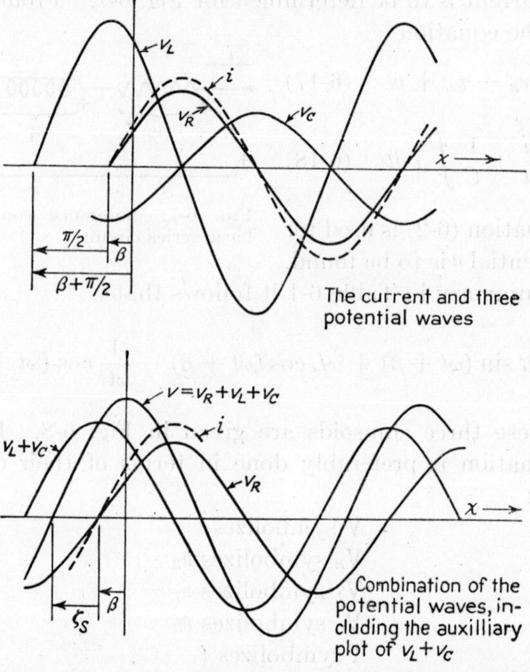


FIG. 6-8. Sinusoidal waves of current and potential difference in the basic series circuit of Fig. 6-7.

The concept of impedance can be carried further than Eq. (6-21) to make it include the phase-angle difference between potential and current waves. To do this the impedance is defined as a phasor quantity (*i.e.*, a two-dimensional directed line) as follows:

$$\mathbf{Z}_s = Z_s \underline{/\zeta_s} \tag{6-24}$$

The various components that go into making up this directed line are shown on an *impedance diagram*. Such an impedance diagram is illustrated in Fig. 6-10.

The impedance diagram is nearly the same as the sinor di
potentials. In fact, they would become identical geometrica
current were unity. That is, $\mathbf{V}_R$ would become $R$, etc. There
tial differences, however, which may be appreciated by comparing
Figs. 6-9 and 6-10. In Fig. 6-9 the potential $\mathbf{V}_R$ is always in phase with

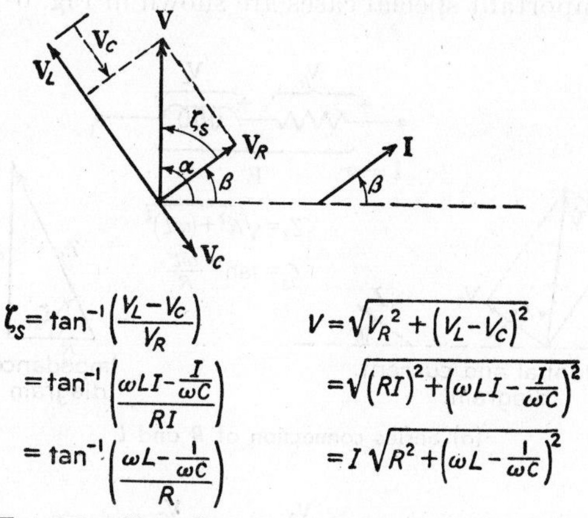

V
$V_C$
$V_L$
$\zeta_s$
$V_R$
I
$\alpha$
$\beta$
$\beta$
$V_C$
$\zeta_s = \tan^{-1}\left(\frac{V_L - V_C}{V_R}\right)$
$= \tan^{-1}\left(\frac{\omega L I - \frac{I}{\omega C}}{RI}\right)$
$= \tan^{-1}\left(\frac{\omega L - \frac{1}{\omega C}}{R}\right)$
$V = \sqrt{V_R^2 + (V_L - V_C)^2}$
$= \sqrt{(RI)^2 + \left(\omega L I - \frac{I}{\omega C}\right)^2}$
$= I\sqrt{R^2 + \left(\omega L - \frac{1}{\omega C}\right)^2}$


FIG. 6-9. Sinor diagram for the basic series circuit.

the current; it is not necessarily horizontal. However, by convention (the reason for which is found in Chap. 8) the line $R$ is always horizontal in the impedance diagram. Also, the components $R$, $X_L$, and $X_C$ of Fig. 6-10 do not represent sinusoidal functions. These are the reasons for making the distinction and calling the lines of the impedance diagram phasors rather than sinors. (It is recalled that a sinor is a special type of phasor, which symbolically represents a sinusoid.)

$$Z_s = \sqrt{R^2 + \left(\omega L - \frac{1}{\omega C}\right)^2} \qquad \zeta_s = \tan^{-1}\frac{\omega L - \frac{1}{\omega C}}{R}$$

FIG. 6-10. Impedance diagram for the basic series circuit.

It is to be understood that for this discussion the current was assumed to be given. However, using the above results, it is possible to find the current if the potential is given. For example, if the potential is specified by Eq. (6-1), from Fig. 6-9 it is seen that the current is symbolically represented by

$$\mathbf{I} = \frac{V}{Z_s} \underline{/\alpha - \zeta_s} \qquad (6\text{-}25)^*$$

* Note that two operations are implied here: the division of magnitudes, and the subtraction of angles. In Chap. 8 this idea is extended by the introduction of complex algebra.

or

$$i = \sqrt{2}\frac{V}{Z_s}\sin(\omega t + \alpha - \zeta_s) \tag{6-26}$$

Any one of the three elements of the basic series circuit may be absent. Two important special cases are shown in Fig. 6-11.

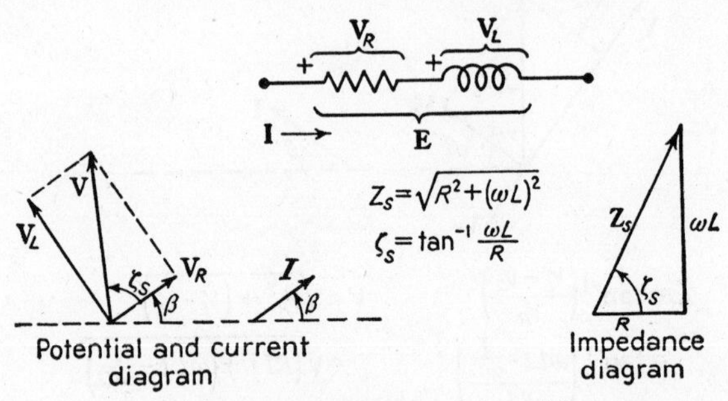


(a) Series connection of $R$ and $L$

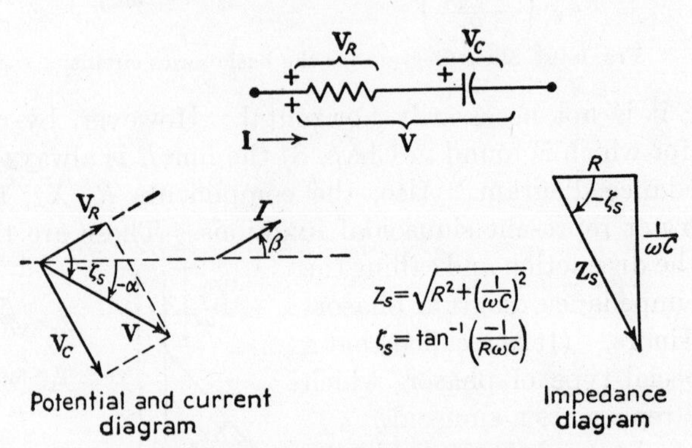


(b) Series connection of $R$ and $C$

FIG. 6-11. Special cases of the basic series circuit.

**Example 6-1.** A resistor of 180 ohms and an inductor of 0.75 henry are connected in series to a source. The current is known to be $i = 3.11 \sin(377t + \pi/6)$ amp. Find the equation for $v$.

*Solution.* *a.* Solution using a sinor diagram of potentials and currents: Adopt the notation

**I** symbolizes $i$
**V** symbolizes $v$
$\mathbf{V}_R$ symbolizes $v_R$
$\mathbf{V}_L$ symbolizes $v_L$

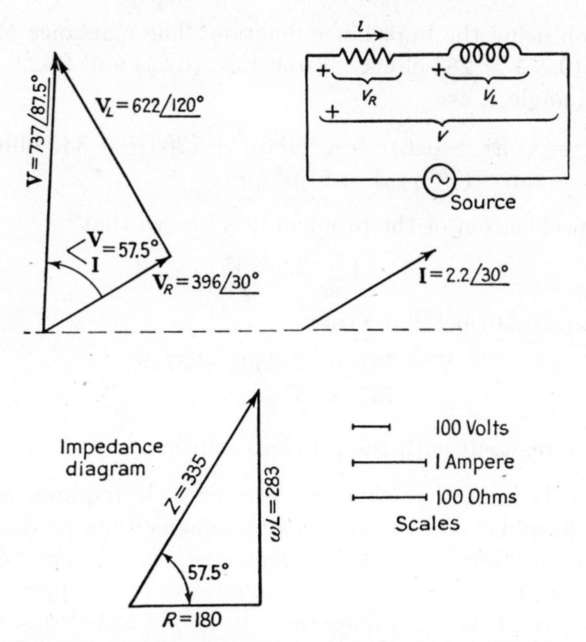


The sinor diagram is constructed as shown in the figure. First the current sinor $\mathbf{I} = 2.2\underline{/30°}$ is drawn ($2.2 = 3.11/\sqrt{2}$). Then the sinors

$$\mathbf{V}_R = (180)(2.2)\underline{/30°} = 396\underline{/30°}$$

$$\mathbf{V}_L = 377(0.75)(2.2)\underline{/30° + 90°} = 622\underline{/120°}$$

are drawn as shown. The summation of the sinors according to the equation

$$\mathbf{V} = \mathbf{V}_R + \mathbf{V}_L$$

can be carried out graphically, and the result obtained by accurately scaling the diagram, or it can be computed. For example,

$$V = \sqrt{V_R{}^2 + V_L{}^2} = \sqrt{(396)^2 + (622)^2} = 737 \text{ volts}$$

and

$$\angle_{\mathbf{I}}^{\mathbf{V}} = \tan^{-1}\frac{V_L}{V_R} = \tan^{-1}\frac{622}{396} = 57.5°*$$

Therefore, $\mathbf{V} = 737\underline{/30° + 57.5°} = 737\underline{/87.5°}$. The required result is

$$v = 1{,}040 \sin(377t + 1.53)$$

where the initial angle is in radians, and $1{,}040 = \sqrt{2}\,(737)$ volts.

* The symbol $\angle_{\mathbf{I}}^{\mathbf{V}}$ is interpreted as meaning the angle by which **V** leads **I**.

*b*. Solution using the impedance diagram: The reactance of the coil is $\omega L = (377)(0.75) = 283$ ohms. From Eqs. (6-21) and (6-22) the impedance $Z_s$ and angle $\zeta_s$ are

$$Z_s = \sqrt{R^2 + (\omega L)^2} = \sqrt{(180)^2 + (283)^2} = 335 \text{ ohms}$$
$$\zeta_s = \tan^{-1} (283/180) = 57.5°$$

From the specification of the problem it is known that

$$\mathbf{I} = 2.2\underline{/30°}$$

and from Eq. (6-20) it follows that

$$\mathbf{V} = (335)(2.2)\underline{/30° + 57.5°}$$
$$= 737\underline{/87.5°}$$

which is in agreement with the previous solution.

Solution *b* is somewhat shorter. However, it requires more use of established formulas and therefore more memory than method *a*. With method *a* the solution is obtained by geometry, once the sinor diagram has been drawn, and the application of fundamental principles is all that is needed to arrive at the sinor diagram. It is to be noted that the orientation of the sinor diagrams in *a* depends on the initial angles but that in any case the impedance diagram is drawn with $R$ horizontal and $\omega L$ vertical.

From the above comments it may be concluded that method *a* is preferable. Certainly it is important. However, there are situations in which the properties of the impedance triangle must be used. Example 6-2 illustrates such a case.

**Example 6-2.** In the series circuit specified in Example 6-1 let the potential be $v = 354 \cos (377t - \pi/4)$ volts. Find the equation for the current.

*Solution.* In order to adhere to the standard notation for initial angles, the potential can be written $v = 354 \sin (377t + \pi/4)$. Its sinor representation is

$$\mathbf{V} = 250\underline{/45°}$$

The dimensions of the impedance triangle can be borrowed from part *b* of Example 6-1.

$$Z_s = 335 \text{ ohms}$$
$$\zeta_s = 57.5°$$

The sinor $\mathbf{I}$ is obtained from Eq. (6-25).

$$\mathbf{I} = 250/335\underline{/45° - 57.5°} = 0.745\underline{/-12.5°}$$

The solution for the current is therefore

$$i = 1.06 \sin (377t - 0.218)$$

where the angle is in radians and $i$ is in amperes.

It is noted that there is no way to use the potentials $\mathbf{V}_R$ and $\mathbf{V}_L$ as aids in arriving at the solution, as was done in part *a* of Example 6-1, because

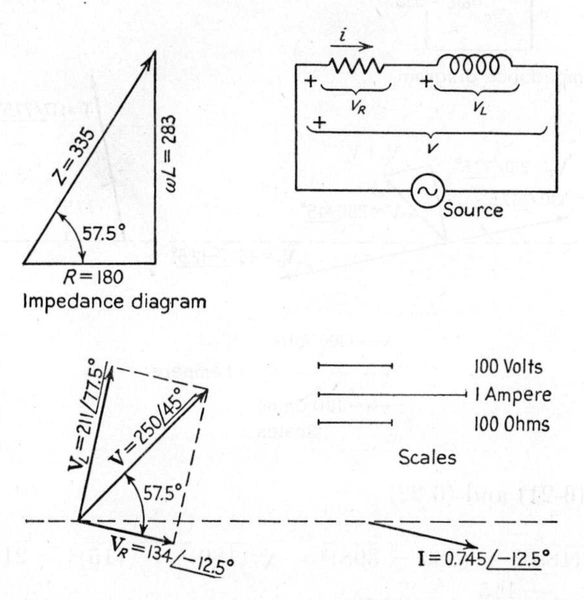


**I** is not known at the beginning. The potentials $\mathbf{V}_R$ and $\mathbf{V}_L$ can be obtained now that the current is known; thus, in volts,

$$\mathbf{V}_R = (180)(0.745)\underline{/-12.5°} = 134\underline{/-12.5°}$$
$$\mathbf{V}_L = (283)(0.745)\underline{/90° - 12.5°} = 211\underline{/77.5°}$$

The sinor diagram includes a check of the relation $\mathbf{V} = \mathbf{V}_R + \mathbf{V}_L$.

**Example 6-3.** The circuit specified in Example 6-1 is augmented by the addition of a series capacitor $C = 6.67\ \mu f$. The potential across the circuit is the same as specified in Example 6-2; $v = 354 \sin (377t + \pi/4)$ in volts. Use sinor representations to obtain equations for the current and the potentials $v_R$, $v_L$, and $v_C$ as functions of time.

*Solution.* The impedance diagram is shown. Its dimensions are

$$\omega L = (377)(0.75) = 283 \text{ ohms}$$
$$\frac{1}{\omega C} = \frac{10^6}{(377)(6.67)} = 398 \text{ ohms}$$

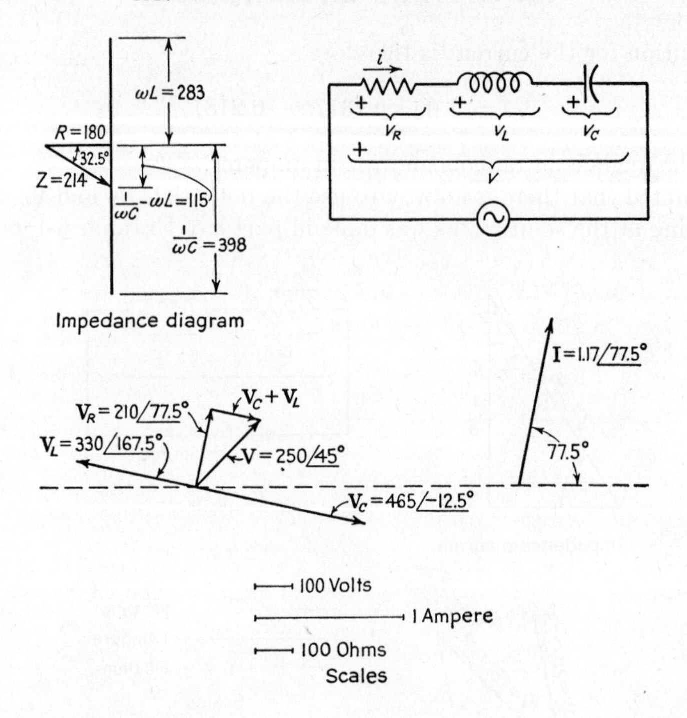


From Eqs. (6-21) and (6-22)

$$Z_s = \sqrt{(180)^2 + (283 - 398)^2} = \sqrt{(180)^2 + (115)^2} = 214 \text{ ohms}$$

$$\zeta_s = \tan^{-1} \frac{-115}{180} = -32.5°$$

This is the angle by which the potential leads the current (that is, $v$ lags $i$ by 32.5°). The sinor for the potential is $\mathbf{V} = 250\underline{/45°}$, and so from Eq. (6-25) the current sinor, in amperes, is

$$\mathbf{I} = {}^{250}\!/_{214}\underline{/45° - (-32.5°)} = 1.17\underline{/77.5°}$$

From the current sinor the following sinors are found:

$$\mathbf{V}_R = (180)(1.17)\underline{/77.5°} = 210\underline{/77.5°}$$
$$\mathbf{V}_L = (283)(1.17)\underline{/90° + 77.5°} = 330\underline{/167.5°}$$
$$\mathbf{V}_C = (398)(1.17)\underline{/-90° + 77.5°} = 465\underline{/-12.5°}$$

They are shown in the accompanying diagram. The corresponding sinusoidal functions, in amperes and volts, are

$$
\begin{aligned}
i &= 1.66 \sin (377t + 1.35) \\
v_R &= 298 \sin (377t + 1.35) \\
v_L &= 467 \sin (377t + 2.93) \\
v_C &= 658 \sin (377t - 0.22)
\end{aligned}
$$

where initial angles are in radians.

**6-5. Parallel-connected Elements.** This case is the dual of the series circuit discussed in Sec. 6-4. The development parallels the previous one. The circuit of Fig. 6-12 obeys the equation

$$i = i_G + i_C + i_L \qquad (6\text{-}27)$$

which becomes

$$i = Gv + C\frac{dv}{dt} + \frac{1}{L}\int v\,dt \qquad (6\text{-}28)$$

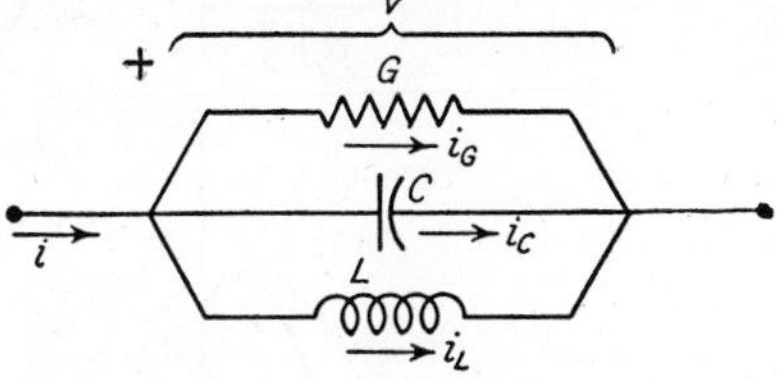


FIG. 6-12. Reference conditions for the basic parallel circuit.

The circuit is solved by assuming the potential is given by Eq. (6-1) and finding the current $i$. Equations for the various terms of Eq. (6-28) are found in Table 6-1. It follows that

$$i = \sqrt{2}\,V\left[G \sin (\omega t + \alpha) + \omega C \cos (\omega t + \alpha) - \frac{1}{\omega L} \cos (\omega t + \alpha)\right] \qquad (6\text{-}29)$$

The three terms of this equation and their sum are shown in Fig. 6-13. The dimensions of the resultant current wave are obtained from the sinor diagram of Fig. 6-14. The sinors are defined in accordance with the following list:

$\mathbf{I}$ symbolizes $i$
$\mathbf{I}_G$ symbolizes $i_G$
$\mathbf{I}_C$ symbolizes $i_C$
$\mathbf{I}_L$ symbolizes $i_L$
$\mathbf{V}$ symbolizes $v$

The sinor diagram of Fig. 6-14 shows that the current is symbolically represented by

$$\mathbf{I} = Y_p V \underline{/\alpha + \eta_p} \qquad (6\text{-}30)^*$$

where

$$Y_p = \sqrt{G^2 + \left(\omega C - \frac{1}{\omega L}\right)^2} \qquad (6\text{-}31)$$

and

$$\eta_p = \tan^{-1} \frac{\omega C - (1/\omega L)}{G} \qquad (6\text{-}32)$$

* See footnote, page 109.

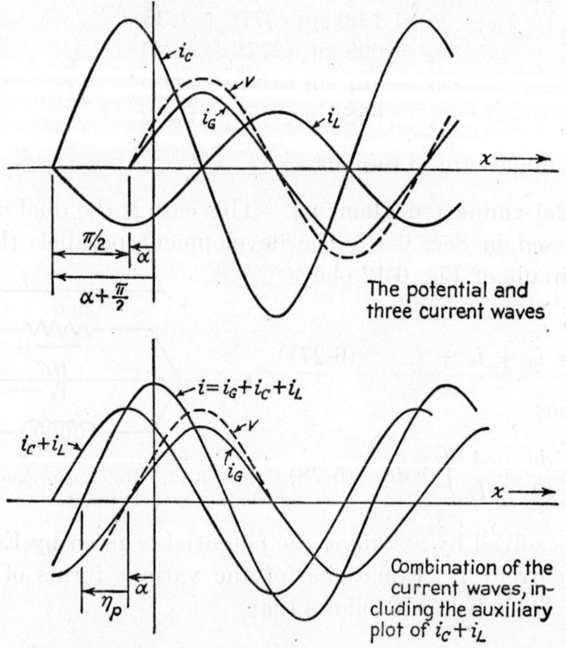


FIG. 6-13. Sinusoidal waves of potential difference and currents in the basic series circuit of Fig. 6-12.

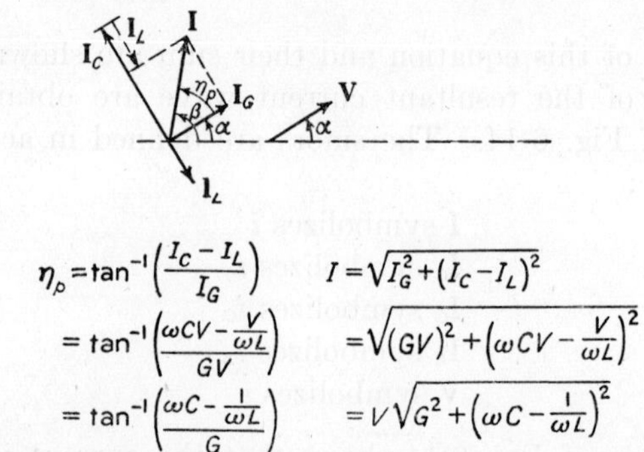


FIG. 6-14. Sinor diagram for the basic parallel circuit.

These equations provide the information needed to write the expression for $i$ as a function of time, thus:

$$i = \sqrt{2}\, Y_p V \sin\,(\omega t + \alpha + \eta_p) \tag{6-33}$$

$Y_p$ is called the *admittance* of the circuit, because it is a measure of the degree to which current is "admitted" to the circuit. In similarity with impedance, an admittance phasor

$$\mathbf{Y}_p = Y_p\underline{/\eta_p} \tag{6-34}$$

is defined. It can be represented by an admittance diagram, as in Fig. 6-15, which is similar to the sinor diagram obtained if the potential is unity but differs in the same way that the impedance diagram differs from the sinor diagram of the series circuit.

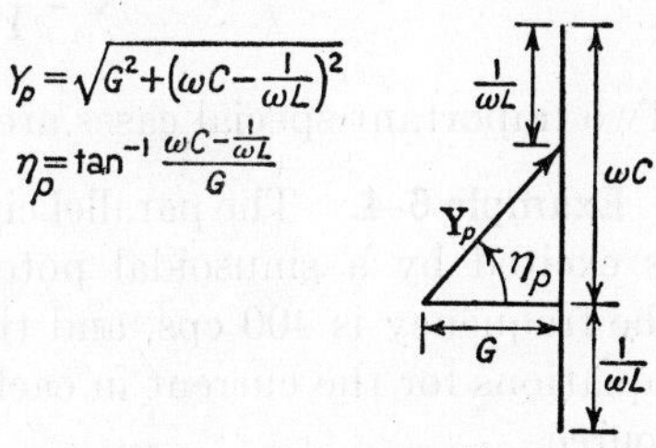

$Y_p = \sqrt{G^2 + \left(\omega C - \frac{1}{\omega L}\right)^2}$
$\eta_p = \tan^{-1} \frac{\omega C - \frac{1}{\omega L}}{G}$
$\frac{1}{\omega L}$
$\omega C$
$Y_p$
$\eta_p$
$G$
$\frac{1}{\omega L}$


Fig. 6-15. Admittance diagram for the basic parallel circuit.

So far, the development shows how the terminal current is found for a parallel circuit, if the potential across it is given. However, the results may be inverted, to give the potential if the current is known. Thus, suppose the current is given by Eq. (6-2). From Fig. 6-14 it is found that the sinor representation for the potential is

$$\mathbf{V} = \frac{I}{Y_p} \underline{/\beta - \eta_p} \tag{6-35}$$ *

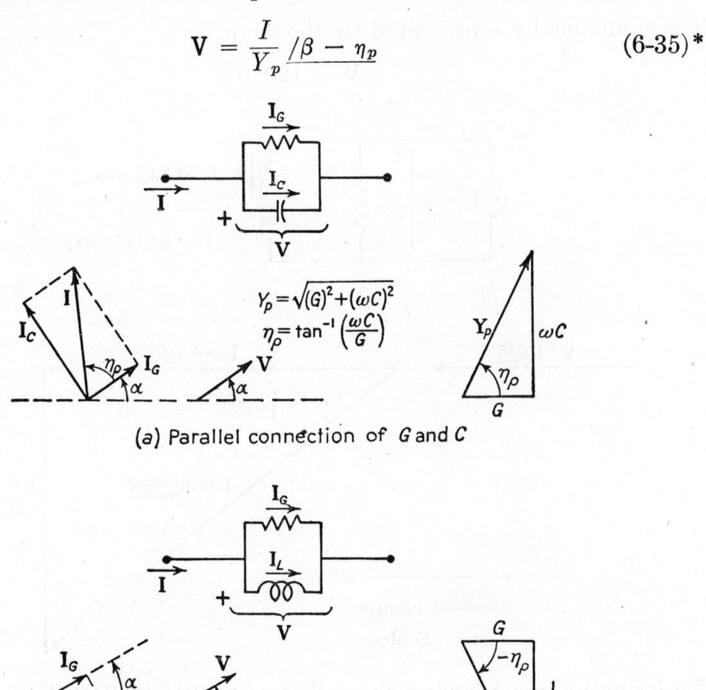


Fig. 6-16. Special cases of the basic parallel circuit.

* See footnote, p. 109.

As a time function the potential is

$$v = \sqrt{2}\,\frac{I}{Y_p}\sin(\omega t + \beta - \eta_p) \tag{6-36}$$

Two important special cases are summarized in Fig. 6-16.

**Example 6-4.** The parallel circuit shown in the accompanying diagram is excited by a sinusoidal potential source. The initial angle is zero, the frequency is 400 cps, and the effective value is 120 volts. Find the equations for the current in each branch and the current supplied by the source.

*Solution.* The equation for the potential of the source is

$$v = \sqrt{2}\,(120)\sin 2{,}150t$$

It is symbolically represented by the sinor

$$\mathbf{V} = 120\underline{/0^\circ}$$

$i$ $v$ $i_G$ $i_L$ G = 0.04 mho

L = 0.0127 henry

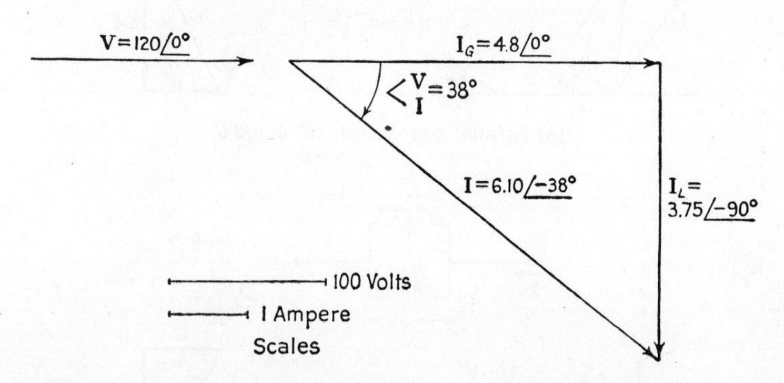


The inductive reactance of the coil is $\omega L = (2{,}510)(0.0127) = 32$ ohms. The sinors for the branch currents are

$$\mathbf{I}_G = \tfrac{120}{25}\underline{/0^\circ} = 4.8\underline{/0^\circ} \text{ amp}$$
$$\mathbf{I}_L = \tfrac{120}{32}\underline{/-90^\circ} = 3.75\underline{/-90^\circ} \text{ amp}$$

The sinor for the source current is

$$\mathbf{I} = \mathbf{I}_G + \mathbf{I}_L$$

The necessary construction is given in the accompanying diagram. The numerical specifications are

$$I = \sqrt{(4.8)^2 + (3.75)^2} = 6.10 \text{ amp}$$

$$\angle_{\mathbf{I}}^{\mathbf{V}} = \tan^{-1}\frac{3.75}{4.8} = 38°$$

It follows that

$$\mathbf{I} = 6.10\underline{/-38°} \text{ amp}$$

The time equations for the various currents, in amperes, are

$$i_G = 6.79 \sin 2{,}510t$$
$$i_L = 5.31 \sin (2{,}510t - \pi/2)$$
$$i = 8.63 \sin (2{,}510t - 0.664)$$

where initial angles are in radians.

**Example 6-5.** Let the current $i$ for the circuit of Example 6-4 be

$$i = \sqrt{2}\,(5) \sin (2{,}510t - 0.262)$$

Find the time equation for $v$.

*Solution.* To solve this, it is necessary first to find the admittance. It is diagrammatically shown in the accompanying figure, and its dimensions are computed from Eqs. (6-31) and (6-32).

$$G = 1/25 = 0.04 \text{ ohm}$$

$$\frac{1}{\omega L} = \frac{1}{(2{,}510)(0.0127)} = 0.0312 \text{ mho}$$

$$Y_p = \sqrt{(0.04)^2 + (0.0312)^2} = 0.0507 \text{ mho}$$

$$\eta_p = \tan^{-1}\frac{-0.0312}{0.04} = -38°$$

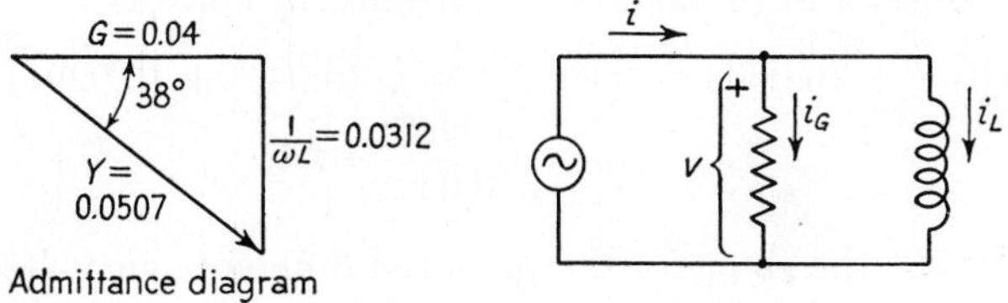


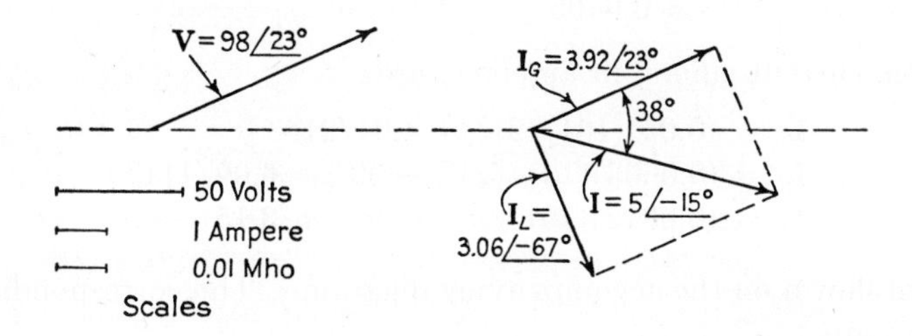

The current sinor is known from the given data

$$\mathbf{I} = 5\underline{/-15^\circ} \text{ amp}$$

and the potential sinor is obtained from Eq. (6-35),

$$\mathbf{V} = \frac{5}{0.0507}\underline{/-15^\circ - (-38^\circ)} = 98.6\underline{/23^\circ} \text{ volts}$$

The corresponding time equation is

$$v = 139.5 \sin (2{,}510t + 0.402) \qquad \text{volts}$$

where the initial angle is in radians.

The currents $\mathbf{I}_G$ and $\mathbf{I}_L$ can be obtained from $\mathbf{V}$.

$$\mathbf{I}_G = (0.04)(98.6)\underline{/23^\circ} = 3.94\underline{/23^\circ}$$
$$\mathbf{I}_L = (0.0312)(98.6)\underline{/-90^\circ + 23^\circ} = 3.08\underline{/-67^\circ}$$

The sinor diagram shown checks the relation $\mathbf{I} = \mathbf{I}_G + \mathbf{I}_L$.

**Example 6-6.** The circuit of Example 6-5 is augmented by a parallel-connected capacitor $C = 24 \times 10^{-6}$ farad, as shown in the diagram. Let the current $i$ have an effective value of 5 amp with an initial angle of 57°. Use sinor representations to obtain equations for the potential across the combination and the current in each branch.

*Solution.* The current is symbolically represented by the sinor $\mathbf{I} = 5\underline{/57^\circ}$ amp. The pertinent quantities for the admittance diagram are

$$\omega C = (2{,}510)(24 \times 10^{-6}) = 0.0603 \text{ mho}$$
$$\frac{1}{\omega L} = \frac{1}{(2{,}510)(0.0127)} = 0.0312 \text{ mho}$$

From Eqs. (6-31) and (6-32), the admittance in mhos is

$$Y_p = \sqrt{(0.04)^2 + (0.0603 - 0.0312)^2} = \sqrt{(0.04)^2 + (0.0291)^2} = 0.0495$$
$$\eta_p = \tan^{-1}\frac{0.0291}{0.04} = 36^\circ$$

From Eq. (2-35) the sinor for the potential difference in volts is

$$\mathbf{V} = \frac{5}{0.0495}\underline{/57^\circ - 36^\circ} = 101\underline{/21^\circ}$$

The three current sinors, in amperes, are

$$\mathbf{I}_G = (0.04)(101)\underline{/21^\circ} = 4.04\underline{/21^\circ}$$
$$\mathbf{I}_C = (0.0603)(101)\underline{/21^\circ + 90^\circ} = 6.09\underline{/111^\circ}$$
$$\mathbf{I}_L = (0.0312)(101)\underline{/21^\circ - 90^\circ} = 3.15\underline{/-69^\circ}$$

They are shown on the accompanying diagram. The corresponding time functions are

$$i_G = 5.72 \sin (2{,}510t + 0.367)$$
$$i_C = 8.63 \sin (2{,}510t + 1.94)$$
$$i_L = 4.46 \sin (2{,}510t - 1.20)$$

where the initial angles are in radians.

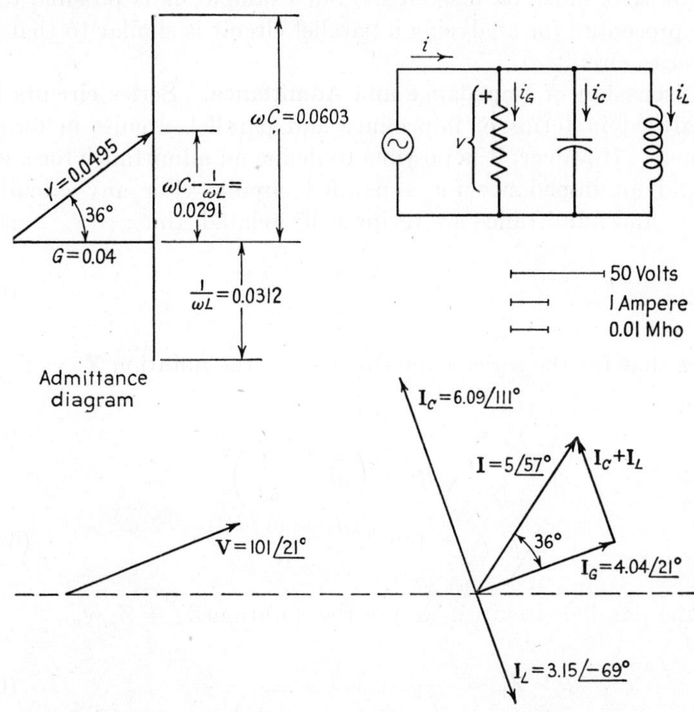


**6-6. Comments on Duality.** In the preceding discussion it is noted that the parallel circuit is analyzed along the same lines as the series circuit. An effort should be made to observe the analogies between the two developments. They are examples of the duality principles described in Chap. 5.

A full use of the principles of duality would have made it unnecessary to develop the parallel circuit independently. Its analysis could have been obtained by making systematic interchanges of symbols. These interchanges are included in the following table.

*Dual quantities*

| | |
|---|---|
| Potential | Current |
| Impedance | Admittance |
| Resistance | Conductance |
| Inductance | Capacitance |
| Angle by which potential leads current | Angle by which current leads potential |
| Reactance | Susceptance |
| Impedance | admittance |

Although memory techniques are to be minimized, a certain amount of memory is needed. The concept of duality is an aid to the memory because it reduces approximately by half the amount of material that must be remembered. In addition, it reduces the number of patterns of thought that must be mastered. For example, it is possible to say that the procedure for analyzing a parallel circuit is similar to that used for the series circuit.

**6-7. Discussion of Impedance and Admittance.** Series circuits have been analyzed in terms of impedance and parallel circuits in terms of admittance. However, it is possible to define an admittance for a series circuit and an impedance for a parallel circuit. For any circuit, its impedance and admittance are reciprocally related, thus:

$$Z = \frac{1}{Y} \tag{6-37}$$

It follows that for the series circuit, if we use the notation $\mathbf{Y}_s = Y_s/\underline{\eta_s}$,

$$Y_s = \frac{1}{\sqrt{R^2 + \left(\omega L - \dfrac{1}{\omega C}\right)^2}} \tag{6-38}$$

$$\eta_s = -\tan^{-1}\frac{\omega L - (1/\omega C)}{R} \tag{6-39}*$$

and for the parallel circuit, if we use the notation $\mathbf{Z}_p = Z_p/\underline{\zeta_p}$

$$Z_p = \frac{1}{\sqrt{G^2 + \left(\omega C - \dfrac{1}{\omega L}\right)^2}} \tag{6-40}$$

$$\zeta_p = -\tan^{-1}\frac{\omega C - (1/\omega L)}{G} \tag{6-41}*$$

In subsequent developments the concepts of impedance and admittance are carried to more general cases. It is not necessary that the circuit consist of either series or parallel connections exclusively. An impedance and admittance can be found for any passive network.

**6-8. Significance of Initial Angle.** A change in initial angle of a sinusoidal wave amounts to a change in the zero point on the time axis. This is an arbitrary matter, so it is permissible to change the angular

* The negative sign appears on Eq. (6-39) because $\tan^{-1} (\omega L - 1/\omega c)/R$ is the angle by which the potential leads the current, and $\eta_s$ is the angle by which the current leads the potential. A similar discussion shows why a negative sign is needed in Eq. (6-41).

position of a group of sinors as long as all sinors of the group are changed by like amounts.*

In the application of sinor diagrams to circuits, one sinor is usually placed in the horizontal position and used as a datum for the measurement of the angular positions of the others. For example, in the series circuit the current sinor is usually placed horizontally. Similarly, for the parallel circuit the potential sinor is usually drawn horizontally. However, this is possible only if no extraneous condition, such as a relation to another part of the circuit, dictates the position. In order to include this contingency, the general treatments of this chapter do not use the horizontal position for these sinors.

**6-9. Inductor with Winding Resistance.** In the previous treatments inductors are regarded as being ideal. That is, it is assumed that the potential across an inductor is proportional to the rate of change of current. An actual inductor can be replaced by an equivalent circuit, consisting of ideal elements.

Figure 6-17 indicates how the resistance is really distributed throughout the coil and how it is considered lumped in the equivalent circuit. The

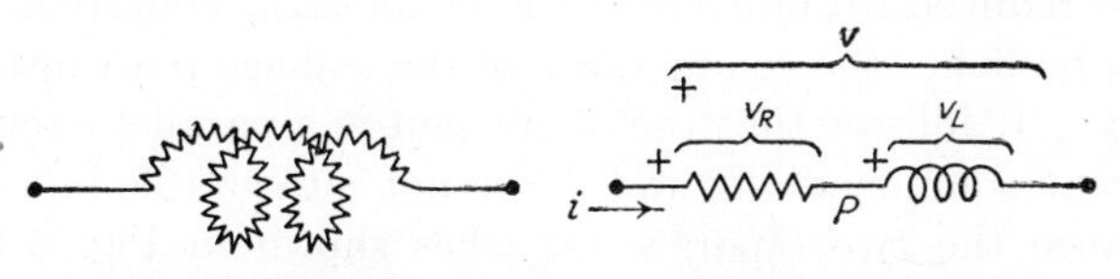


FIG. 6-17. Equivalent circuit of an actual (physical) inductor.

circuit shown at (*b*) is analyzed in accordance with the techniques of Sec. 6-4.

The question may arise as to why the equivalent is a series rather than parallel circuit. The answer is obtained by considering the behavior of the circuit as the frequency is gradually reduced. A parallel circuit would approach a short circuit. This would be contrary to fact, because on direct current the coil still has resistance.

The potentials $v_R$ and $v_L$ cannot be measured in a laboratory setup, because point $P$ is not accessible. However, there are means of obtaining these potentials, either by computation or from auxiliary measurements.

The circuit of Fig. 6-17*b* is a true equivalent only as long as the frequency does not become so high that the coil no longer behaves as an inductance, as described in Sec. 2-13. For all situations for which an inductor may be regarded as a lumped element, Fig. 6-17*b* is an equivalent circuit.

* Whenever time enters into the analysis of a physical system the zero on the time scale is arbitrary. There is no such thing as an absolute time scale.

**6-10. Capacitor with Insulation Conductance.** Practical capacitors are usually much more nearly perfect than are inductors. There are many instances, however, where leakage through the dielectric must be taken into account.

In the leaky dielectric there are many conducting paths through the dielectric. This is indicated in Fig. 6-18. The equivalent circuit is shown at (*b*).

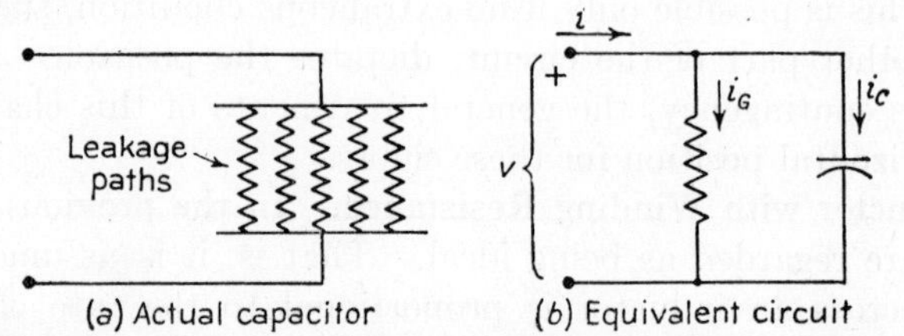


FIG. 6-18. Equivalent circuit of an actual (physical) capacitor.

The equivalent circuit must be a parallel circuit. To see this, consider that a series circuit of $R$ and $C$ would approach an open circuit as the frequency is reduced toward zero. Under the same conditions the actual capacitor approaches the conductance of the leakage path rather than an open circuit. It follows that the equivalent is a parallel circuit.

The current components $i_R$ and $i_C$ are not measurable in a laboratory setup, because the two separate branches shown in Fig. 6-18*b* do not actually exist. However, these current components can be found by computation, after suitable data are known.

**Example 6-7.** A coil with internal resistance $R_i = 4$ ohms and inductance $L = 0.15$ henry is connected in series with a resistor $R = 15$ ohms. Find the equation for the potential $v_L$ across the inductor when the potential across the combination is $v = 65 \sin \omega t$ volts. The frequency is 60 cps.

*Solution.* Use sinors and let

$$\mathbf{I} \text{ symbolize } i$$
$$\mathbf{V} \text{ symbolize } v$$
$$\mathbf{V}_L \text{ symbolize } v_L$$

Also adopt the notation

$$\mathbf{Z}_s = Z_s/\underline{\zeta_s} = \text{impedance of the combination}$$
$$\mathbf{Z}_c = Z_c/\underline{\zeta_c} = \text{impedance of the coil}$$

These impedances are shown in the accompanying diagrams. The reactance of the coil is $\omega L = (377)(0.15) = 56.6$ ohms, and the specifications

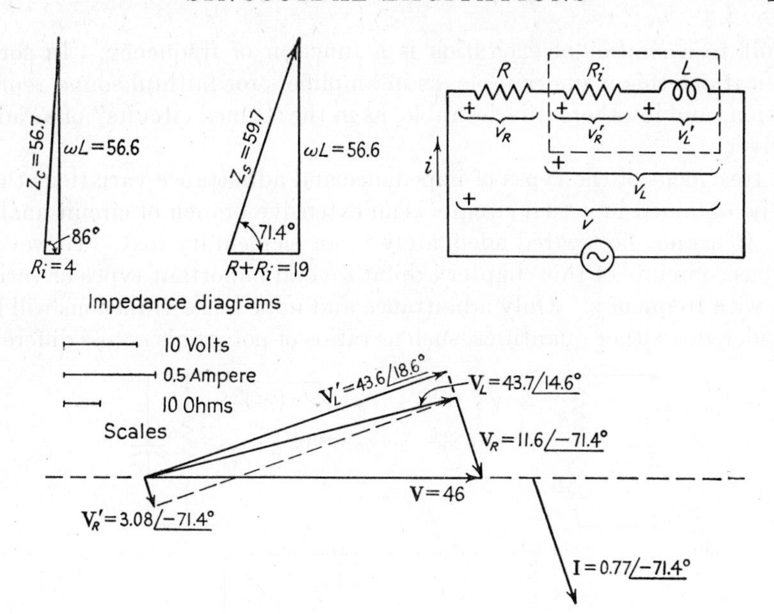


of the admittance diagrams are

$$Z_s = \sqrt{(19)^2 + (56.6)^2} = 59.7 \text{ ohms}$$

$$\zeta_s = \tan^{-1}\frac{56.6}{19} = 71.4°$$

$$Z_c = \sqrt{(4)^2 + (56.6)^2} = 56.7 \text{ ohms}$$

$$\zeta_c = \tan^{-1}\frac{56.6}{4} = 86°$$

The current sinor, in amperes, is obtained from Eq. (6-25) as

$$\mathbf{I} = \frac{45.9}{59.7}\underline{/-71.4°} = .77\underline{/-71.4°}$$

Then Eq. (6-20) can be applied to the impedance of the coil to give

$$\mathbf{V}_L = (56.7)(0.77)\underline{/86° - 71.4°} = 43.7\underline{/14.6°}$$

The corresponding equation for the potential difference in volts is

$$v_L = 61.8 \sin (377t + 0.255)$$

where the initial angle is in radians.

**6-11. Variable Frequency—Resonance.** In many of the formulas describing circuit behavior the frequency parameter appears, in the reactance and susceptance terms. In general, the response of an a-c circuit to a sinusoidal excitation is a function of frequency. In some applications this is undesirable, as in amplifiers for faithful sound reproduction, and in others it is desirable, as in the "tuned circuits" of a radio receiver.

A treatment of the types of impedance and admittance variations that can be obtained in actual circuits is an extensive branch of circuit analysis. It cannot be treated adequately in an elementary text. However, the basic circuits of this chapter exhibit several important types of variation with frequency. Only admittance and impedance variations will be considered. Other quantities, such as ratios of potentials across different

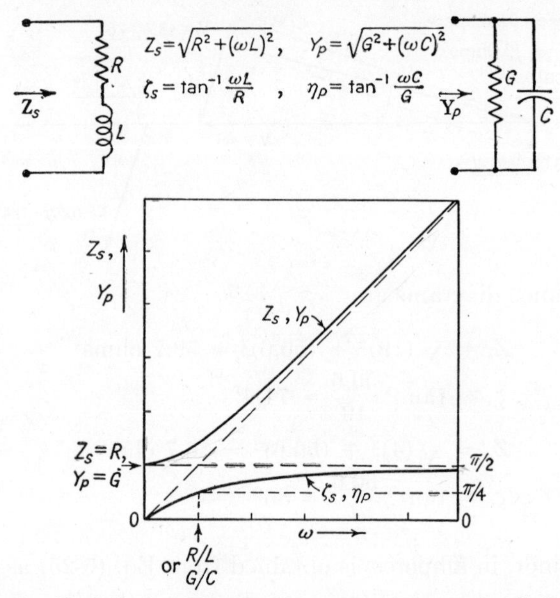


FIG. 6-19. Variable frequency for the series $R$-$L$ or parallel $G$-$C$ circuit.

parts of the circuit, can be cited as other examples. Duality is used to make the treatment as broad as possible.

Graphs are given for the two quantities needed to describe a phasor impedance or admittance, *viz.*, its magnitude and angle. When the magnitude curve represents impedance, the angle curve is the angle by which the potential leads the current. When the magnitude curve is an admittance, the angle curve is the angle by which the current leads the potential.

Figure 6-19 shows the impedance for a series connection of $R$ and $L$, or the admittance for a parallel connection of $G$ and $C$. The impedance of the series circuit, or admittance of the parallel circuit, starts at a low value, which is determined by the resistance or conductance. With increasing frequency it approaches the dotted line, the characteristic of the reactance or susceptance.

Figure 6-20 gives similar information for the series *R-C* or parallel *G-L* circuit. In this case the *R* or *G* element predominates more and more as the frequency increases.

The case shown in Fig. 6-21 is the basis for most of the tuned circuits used in radio applications. The magnitude curve is a plot of Eqs. (6-21) and (6-31), and the angle curve is a plot of Eqs. (6-22) and (6-32). Because $X_L = \omega L$ and $X_C = -1/\omega C$ vary in opposite ways with fre-

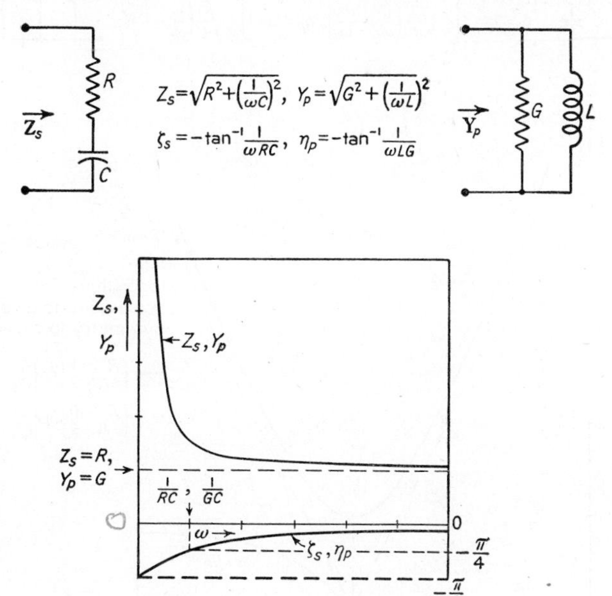


FIG. 6-20. Variable frequency for the series *R-C* or parallel *G-L* circuit.

quency, there is a frequency at which they cancel. The impedance of the series circuit, or admittance of the parallel circuit, is a minimum at this frequency. It is called the frequency of *resonance*. For either circuit it is the point at which

$$\omega L = \frac{1}{\omega C} \tag{6-42}$$

Expressing the angular frequency of resonance by $\omega_0$, it follows that

$$\omega_0 = \frac{1}{\sqrt{LC}} \tag{6-43}$$

The circuits of Fig. 6-21 are called *resonant* circuits. The special case of a resonant circuit with $R = 0$ or $G = 0$ is represented by the dotted lines in Fig. 6-21.*

A complete description of the possible responses of the series or parallel circuit includes plots of $\mathbf{Z}_p$ and $\mathbf{Y}_s$. Graphs of these are obtained by computing the reciprocals of the magnitudes and the negatives of the angles of $\mathbf{Y}_p$ and $\mathbf{Z}_s$. The results are shown in Fig. 6-22.*

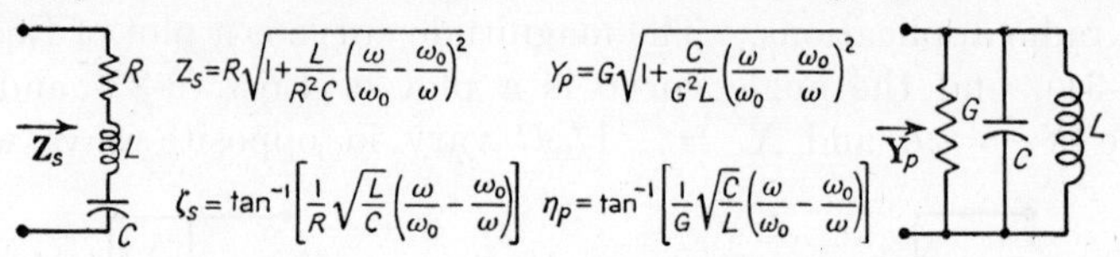


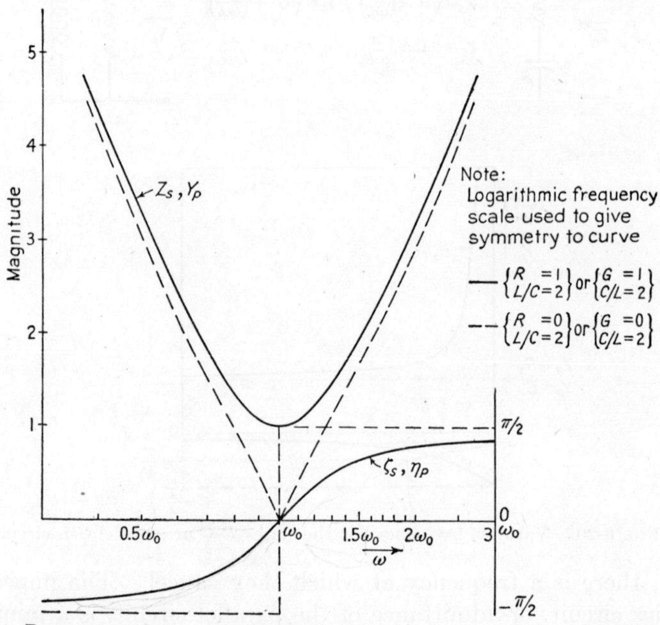


FIG. 6-21. Resonance phenomena in an electric circuit presented as impedance of the series circuit and admittance of the parallel circuit.

The similarity between $Z_s$ and $Y_p$ and between $\zeta_s$ and $\eta_p$ is emphasized by writing Eqs. (6-21) and (6-22),

$$Z_s = R\sqrt{1 + \frac{L}{R^2C}\left(\frac{\omega}{\omega_0} - \frac{\omega_0}{\omega}\right)^2} \tag{6-44}$$

$$\zeta_s = \tan^{-1}\frac{1}{R}\sqrt{\frac{L}{C}}\left(\frac{\omega}{\omega_0} - \frac{\omega_0}{\omega}\right) \tag{6-45}$$

* This analysis is approximately valid for the parallel connection of $C$ with an inductor having small series resistance. See Sec. 10-5.

and Eqs. (6-31) and (6-32),

$$Y_p = G\sqrt{1 + \frac{C}{G^2L}\left(\frac{\omega}{\omega_0} - \frac{\omega_0}{\omega}\right)^2} \tag{6-46}$$

$$\eta_p = \tan^{-1}\frac{1}{G}\sqrt{\frac{C}{L}}\left(\frac{\omega}{\omega_0} - \frac{\omega_0}{\omega}\right) \tag{6-47}$$

The factors $L/R^2C$ and $C/G^2L$ are important in their influence on the shape of the curves. The larger they are, the narrower are the curves.

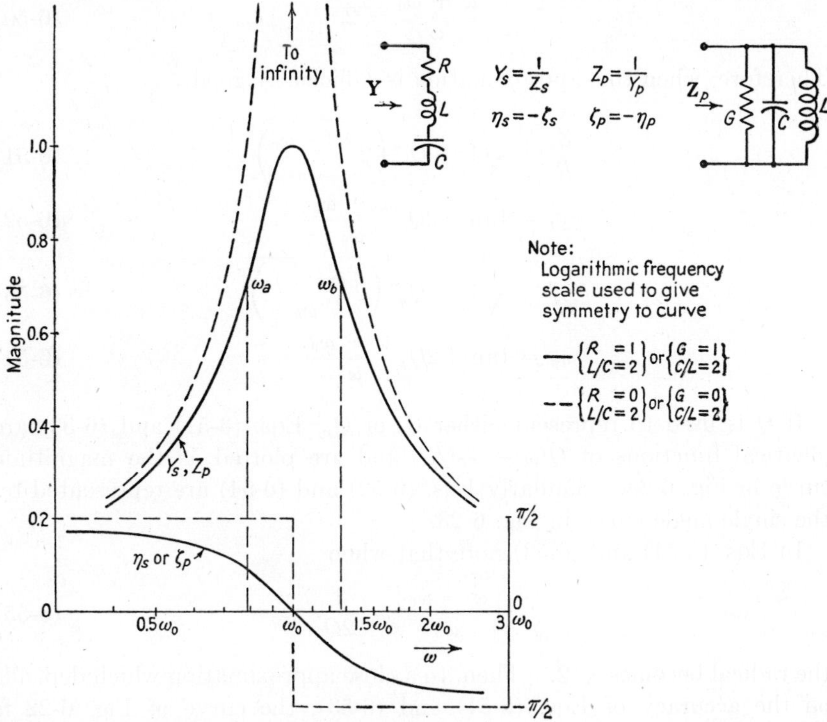


FIG. 6-22. Resonance phenomena in an electric circuit, presented as admittance of the series circuit and impedance of the parallel circuit.

Because of this relationship they are important parameters and are represented by particular symbols, as follows:

$$Q_s = \frac{1}{R}\sqrt{\frac{L}{C}} \qquad \text{series circuit}$$

$$Q_p = \frac{1}{G}\sqrt{\frac{C}{L}} \qquad \text{parallel circuit} \tag{6-48}$$

They are called the circuit $Q$'s.

The $Q$ of a circuit is an important parameter because it is a measure of the sharpness of the peak of Fig. 6-22. In fact, $Q$ can be used to give a numerical estimate of the width of the curve. To do this, note that

$$\frac{\omega}{\omega_0} - \frac{\omega_0}{\omega} = \left(\frac{\omega - \omega_0}{\omega_0}\right)\left(\frac{\omega + \omega_0}{\omega}\right) \tag{6-49}$$

and that $(\omega - \omega_0)/\omega_0$ is the fractional deviation of frequency from the point of resonance. Furthermore, note that if $|\omega - \omega_0|$ is small

$$\frac{\omega + \omega_0}{\omega} \approx 2 \tag{6-50}$$

Therefore, when this approximation is sufficiently good,

$$\frac{Z_s}{R} = \sqrt{1 + Q_s^2\left(2\frac{\omega - \omega_0}{\omega_0}\right)^2} \tag{6-51}$$

$$\zeta_s = \tan^{-1} 2Q_s \frac{\omega - \omega_0}{\omega_0} \tag{6-52}$$

$$\frac{Y_p}{G} = \sqrt{1 + Q_p^2\left(2\frac{\omega - \omega_0}{\omega_0}\right)^2} \tag{6-53}$$

$$\eta_p = \tan^{-1} 2Q_p \frac{\omega - \omega_0}{\omega_0} \tag{6-54}$$

If $Q$ is used to represent either $Q_s$ or $Q_p$, Eqs. (6-51) and (6-53) are identical functions of $Q(\omega - \omega_0)/\omega_0$ and are plotted as the magnitude curve in Fig. 6-23. Similarly Eqs. (6-52) and (6-54) are represented by the single angle curve in Fig. 6-23.

In Eqs. (6-51) and (6-53) note that when

$$\left|\frac{\omega - \omega_0}{\omega_0}\right| = \frac{1}{2Q} \tag{6-55}$$

the radical becomes $\sqrt{2}$. Then, to a close approximation which depends on the accuracy of Eqs. (6-51) and (6-53), the curve of Fig. 6-22 is 0.707 times the maximum value, or the curve of Fig. 6-21 is 1.414 times the minimum value. The two values of $\omega$ satisfying Eq. (6-55) are designated by $\omega_b$ and $\omega_a$ in Fig. 6-22. From Eq. (6-55) it follows that approximately

$$\frac{\omega_b - \omega_a}{\omega_0} = \frac{1}{Q} \tag{6-56}$$

The quantity $\omega_b - \omega_a$ is *defined* as the *bandwidth* of the circuit. Equation (6-56) shows that the bandwidth, expressed as a fraction of $\omega_0$, is the reciprocal of the $Q$ of the circuit. The larger the $Q$, the narrower the bandwidth.

It is instructive to note under what conditions approximation (6-50) is justified. The left hand side of relation (6-50) can be written

$$\frac{\omega + \omega_0}{\omega_0} = \frac{\dfrac{\omega - \omega_0}{\omega_0} + 2}{\dfrac{\omega - \omega_0}{\omega_0} + 1} \tag{6-57}$$

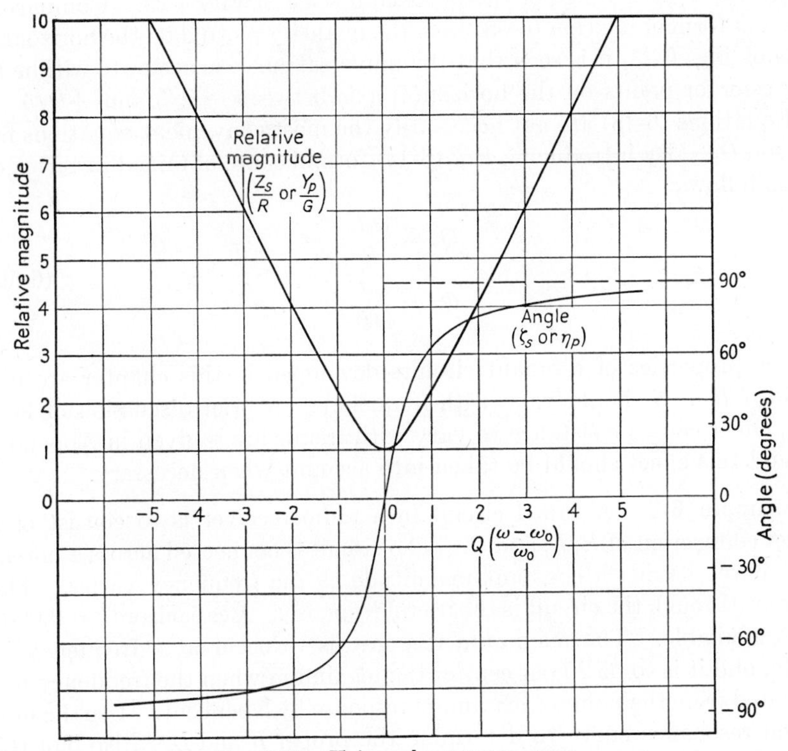


FIG. 6-23. Universal resonance curve.

In order to obtain a numerical appraisal of the errors introduced by relation (6-50), let a range of variation of $\omega$ be found such that $(\omega + \omega_0)/\omega_0$ will not differ from 2 by more than 10 per cent. Equation (6-57) shows that this requirement will be more than met if $\omega$ lies in a range which can be specified in either of the following ways:

$$\left|\frac{\omega - \omega_0}{\omega_0}\right| < \frac{1}{5} \quad \text{or} \quad \frac{4\omega_0}{5} < \omega < \frac{6\omega_0}{5} \tag{6-58}$$

From Eq. (6-49) it is seen that the per cent error of $(\omega/\omega_0) - (\omega_0/\omega)$ is the same as the per cent error of $(\omega + \omega_0)/\omega_0$, and so it follows that the error of $Z_s$ or $Y_p$ will be less than 10 per cent if $\omega$ lies within range (6-58). When using this information it is important to realize that the largest error of $Z_s$ or $Y_p$ will prevail when $\omega$ is at the edge of the range given by relation

(6-58). One useful conclusion is obtained by comparing the first form of relation (6-58) with Eq. (6-55), showing that if $\omega$ satisfies Eq. (6-55) the corresponding $Z_s$ or $Y_p$ will be within 10 per cent of $\sqrt{2}$ times the minimum value, if $Q > 2.5$. Therefore, Eq. (6-56) gives the nominal bandwidth to this degree of accuracy, if $Q > 2.5$. Another useful conclusion gives the useable range of the horizontal scale of Fig. 6-23. Comparing the first form of relation (6-58) with the quantity plotted on the horizontal axis of Fig. 6-23, it is seen that the universal curve is accurate within 10 per cent for points on the horizontal axis between $-Q/5$ and $+Q/5$.

Equations (6-48) are not necessarily the most convenient equations for $Q_s$ and $Q_p$. By introducing Eq. (6-43) formulas are obtained in terms of $\omega_0$ as follows:

$$
\begin{aligned}
Q_s &= \frac{\omega_0 L}{R} \\
Q_p &= \frac{\omega_0 C}{G}
\end{aligned}
\tag{6-59}
$$

The properties of resonant circuits developed in this chapter are not valid if $R$ or $G$ should vary with frequency. A brief discussion of how skin effect causes resistance to vary with frequency is given in Appendix A, and this effect should be taken into account when necessary.

**Example 6-8.** A tuned circuit in a radio receiver is to consist of a series connection of $R$, $L$, and $C$. The circuit is connected across a potential source having a constant magnitude as the frequency varies. The current through the circuit is the useful response. A capacitor $C = 0.0005$ μf is available. The maximum response is to occur at a frequency of 1 Mc, and it is to be 20 per cent of the maximum when the frequency has deviated from the point of maximum response by 5 per cent. Use the universal resonance curve to determine the proper $R$ and $L$. Also plot the ratio $I/V$ and the angle by which $\mathbf{I}$ leads $\mathbf{V}$, as functions of frequency, from the universal resonance curve and also as computed from the exact formula.

*Solution.* The value of $L$ is found from the equation $\omega_0 = 1/\sqrt{LC}$, giving

$$
\begin{aligned}
L &= \frac{1}{\omega_0^2 C} \\
&= \frac{10^{-6}}{4\pi^2(0.0005)} = 5.07 \times 10^{-5} \text{ henry}
\end{aligned}
$$

Next refer to the universal resonance curve of Fig. 6-23. It is found that the impedance would be five times the minimum when the abscissa variable is 2.45. When the impedance is five times the minimum, the current response is 20 per cent of the maximum. Therefore, at this point

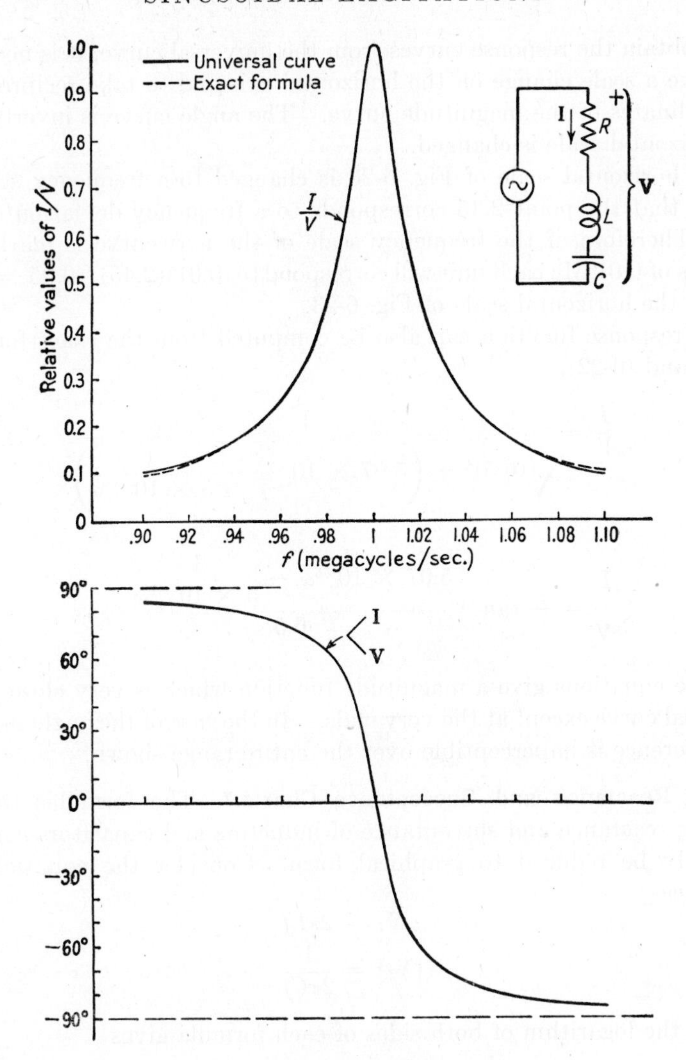


the frequency difference is specified to be 0.05 Mc, giving

$$Q \frac{\omega - \omega_0}{\omega} = Q(0.05) = 2.45$$

or

$$Q = 49$$

The value of $R$ can be found from Eqs. (6-59)

$$R = \frac{\omega_0 L}{Q} = \frac{2\pi(10^6)(5.07 \times 10^{-5})}{49} = 6.5 \text{ ohms}$$

To obtain the response curves from the universal curve, it is necessary to make a scale change on the horizontal axis and to take reciprocals of the ordinates of the magnitude curve. The angle curve is inverted and its horizontal scale is changed.

The horizontal scale of Fig. 6-23 is changed to a frequency scale by noting that the point 2.45 corresponds to a frequency deviation of 0.05 Mc. Therefore, if the frequency scale of the new curve is marked off in units of 0.01 Mc each unit will correspond to (0.01)(2.45)/(0.05 = 0.490 unit of the horizontal scale of Fig. 6-23.

The response function can also be computed from the exact formulas (6-21) and (6-22),

$$\frac{I}{V} = \frac{1}{\sqrt{(6.5)^2 + \left(5.07 \times 10^{-5}\omega - \frac{1}{5 \times 10^{-10}\omega}\right)^2}}$$

and

$$\angle\frac{\mathbf{I}}{\mathbf{V}} = -\tan^{-1}\frac{5.07 \times 10^{-5}\omega - \frac{1}{5 \times 10^{-10}\omega}}{6.5}$$

These equations give a magnitude function which is very close to the universal curve except at the very ends. In the case of the angle function the difference is imperceptible over the entire range shown.

**6-12. Reactance and Susceptance Charts.*** The formulas for calculating reactance and susceptance of inductors and capacitors can conveniently be reduced to graphical form. Consider the equations for reactance

$$X_L = 2\pi Lf$$
$$|X_C| = \frac{1}{2\pi Cf} \qquad (6\text{-}60)$$

Taking the logarithm of both sides of each formula gives

$$\log X_L = \log (2\pi L) + \log f$$
$$\log |X_C| = -\log (2\pi C) - \log f \qquad (6\text{-}61)$$

showing that the curves of reactance vs. frequency are straight lines when plotted on log-log scales. Inductive reactance has a positive slope and capacitive reactance has a negative slope.

A family of curves can be plotted for each equation with $L$ and $C$ as parameters. Furthermore, due to the cyclical properties of a loga-

* The material of Sec. 6-12 is largely of a reference nature, and it is preferable to omit it in a first reading.

rithmic graph, it is possible to present all the information in one "cycle" of logarithmic graph paper. For example, suppose

$$\begin{aligned} L &= L' \times 10^h \quad \text{henry} \\ C &= C' \times 10^c \quad \text{farad} \\ f &= f' \times 10^n \quad \text{cps} \end{aligned} \tag{6-62}$$

where $L'$, $C'$, each has a restricted range near 1. Then

$$X_L = X_L' \times 10^{n+h+1} \tag{6-63}$$

where

$$X_L' = \left(\frac{2\pi}{10} L'f'\right) \tag{6-64}$$

The graph can be labeled in $L'$, $f'$, and $X_L'$ and the decimal point, given by the factor $10^{n+h+1}$, can be calculated on the side, as with slide-rule calculations. The 10 in the denominator of Eq. (6-64) is arbitrarily introduced to give $X_L'$ a convenient range of values.

Similarly, for the capacitance let

$$|X_C| = |X_C'| \times 10^{-n-c-2} \tag{6-65}$$

where

$$|X_C'| = \frac{100}{2\omega C'f'} \tag{6-66}$$

The 100 in the numerator of Eq. (6-66) is introduced for convenience, to give a reasonable scale for $X_C'$. A graph for $X_C$ can be labeled in $X_C'$ and the decimal point obtained from the factor $10^{-n-c-2}$.

A chart showing relationships among $f'$, $X_L'$ and $|X_C'|$ is given in Fig. 6-24. In addition to being useful in finding reactances, the reactance chart can be used to find the resonant frequency for a given $L$ and $C$. At resonance $X_L = |X_C|$, and therefore

$$X_L' \times 10^{n+h+1} = |X_C'| \times 10^{-n-c-2} \tag{6-67}$$

At a point of intersection on the chart between a curve of constant $L'$ and a curve of constant $C'$, $X_L' = |X_C'|$ and therefore

$$n + h + 1 = -n - c - 2$$

or

$$n = -\frac{h + c + 3}{2} \tag{6-68}$$

Two intersections are possible for given $L$ and $C$, depending on how $h$ and $c$ are chosen. A choice should be made so that $h + c$ is odd in order to obtain an integral value of $n$.

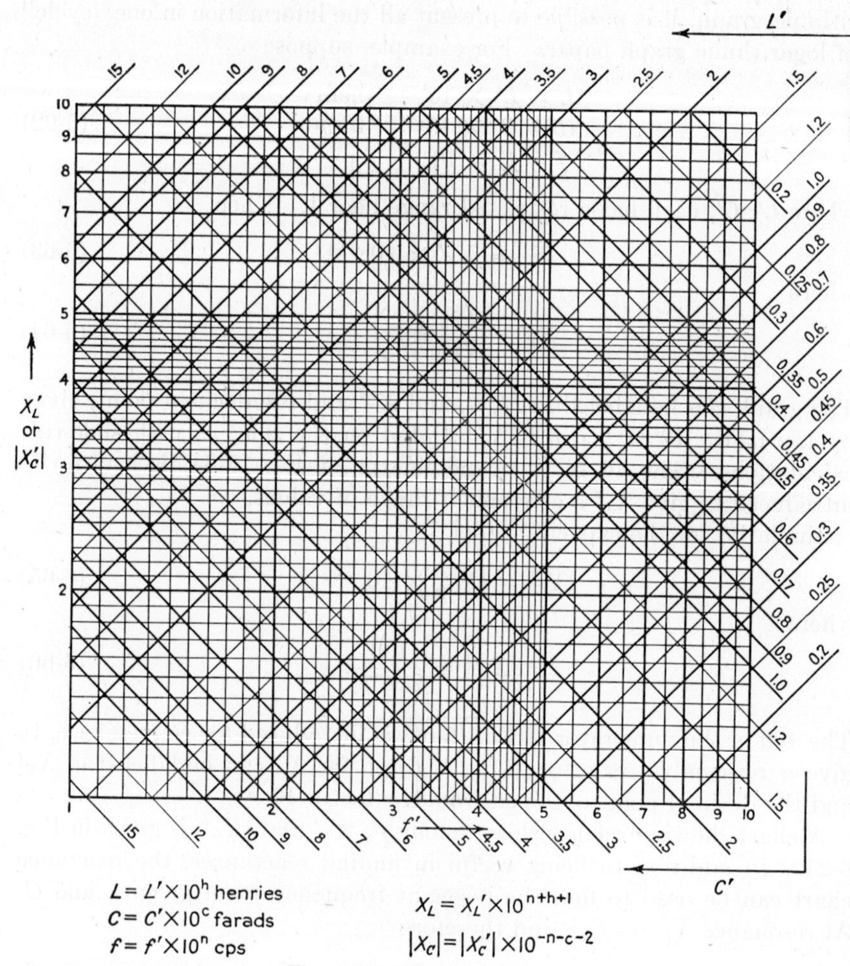


Fig. 6-24. Reactance chart.

**Example 6-9.** An inductance $L = 0.025$ henry and capacitance $C = 0.013$ $\mu$f are given. Find the reactance of each at a frequency of 3200 cps, and find their resonant frequency when combined in series.

Consider $L$ first. $L' = 2.5$ with $h = -2$, and $f' = 3.2$ with $n = 3$. These coordinates locate the point on the chart for which $X_{L'} = 5.00$. Therefore,

$$X_L = 5.0 \times 10^{3-2+1} = 500 \text{ ohms}$$

For $C$ we have $C' = 1.3$ with $c = -8$. The chart gives $|X_{C'}| = 3.80$. The reactance is then

$$|X_C| = 3.80 \times 10^{-3+8-2} = 3800 \text{ ohms}$$

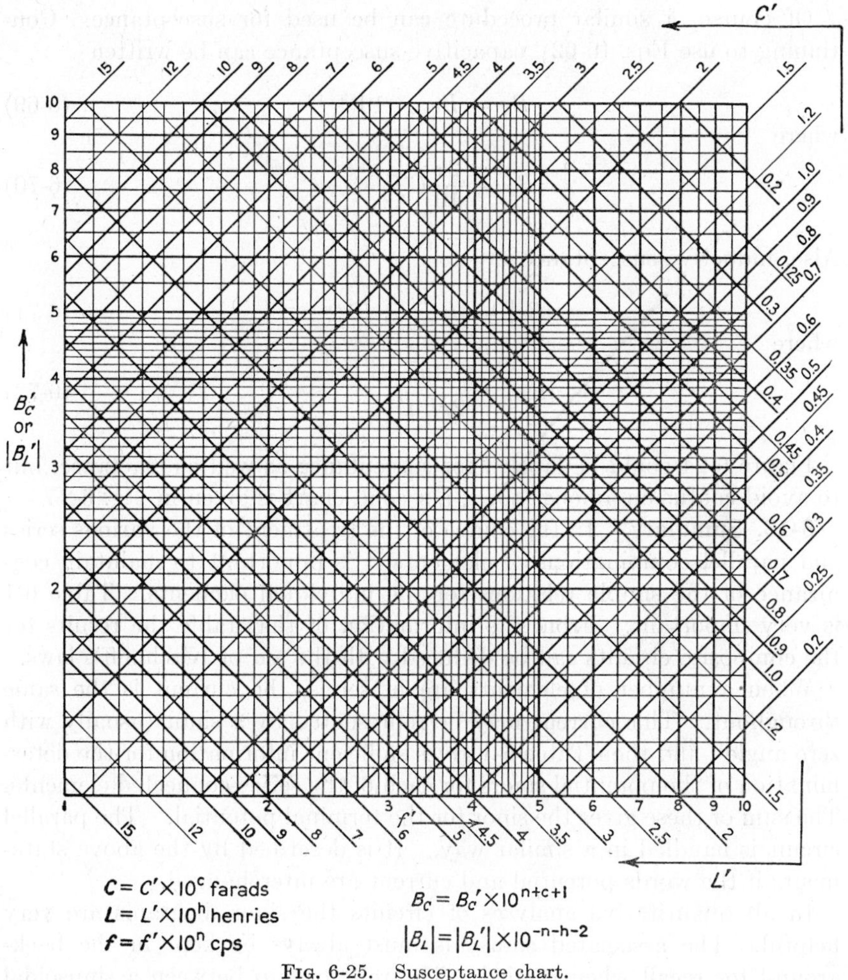


FIG. 6-25. Susceptance chart.

In finding the resonant frequency note that curves for $L' = 2.5$ and $C' = 1.3$ intersect. However, in that case $h + c = -10$, an even number, and so $n$ would be odd and the frequency scale would have to be multiplied by $\sqrt{10}$. It is more convenient to take the point for which $L' = 0.25$ and $C' = 1.3$ and $h + c = -9$. The corresponding value of $n$, given by Eq. (6-68), is $n = 3$. From the chart $f' = 8.90$, and therefore the resonant frequency is

$$f = 8.90 \times 10^3 \qquad \text{cps}$$

Of course, a similar procedure can be used for susceptance. Continuing to use Eqs. (6-62), capacitive susceptance can be written

$$B_C = B_{C'} \times 10^{n+c+1} \tag{6-69}$$

where

$$B_{C'} = \frac{2\pi}{10} C'f' \tag{6-70}$$

Also, inductive susceptance is

$$|B_L| = |B_L'| \times 10^{-n-h-2} \tag{6-71}$$

where

$$|B_{L'}| = \frac{100}{2\pi L'f'} \tag{6-72}$$

Figure 6-24 could be labeled for susceptance as well as reactance, but to avoid confusion among labels, a second chart is given in Fig. 6-25.

**6-13. Summary.** In the course of the treatment of the various series and parallel combinations of elements it is important to maintain cognizance of the simple relations for the individual elements. Table 6-1 is very important. From the information of that table the results for the composite circuits can be deduced with the aid of Kirchhoff's laws.

When a number of elements are in series, the current is the same throughout. This current may be represented by a sinor (usually with zero angle), and then Table 6-1 gives sufficient information for the determination of the potential sinors for each of the series-connected elements. The sum of these gives the sinor for the terminal potential. The parallel circuit is handled in a similar way. It is described by the above statements if the words potential and current are interchanged.

In all quantitative analyses of circuits the sinor diagrams are very helpful. The associated sinusoids must always be kept in the background for recall when needed. The relationship between a sinusoidal wave and its sinor representation should never be forgotten.

The basic integrodifferential equations for series and parallel circuits are such that when a potential difference is sinusoidal the current is also sinusoidal, except for possible d-c components, which are considered separately. The circuit, however, has the effect of determining the *relative magnitudes* of the terminal potential and terminal current and the *phase-angle difference* between potential and current. These two basic circuits are dually related. The usual interchange of current and potential takes place in going from one type of circuit to the other. Also, the impedance of the series circuit is the dual of the admittance of the parallel circuit. In the series circuit the situation of a potential leading a current is replaced, in the dual parallel case, by a current leading the potential.

From the results of Chap. 6 it is possible to solve only simple types of circuits. Nothing more is given than the properties of the pure series or pure parallel circuits. The treatments of more complex circuits are based very heavily on these results, but before they can be attempted, it is necessary to evolve the necessary mathematical technique for the facile handling of sinor diagrams of greater complexity.

## PROBLEMS

**6-1.** An inductor of 0.2 henry is connected to a sinusoidal potential source having a peak value of 150 volts. Assume the potential is expressed as a sine function, with zero initial angle.

*a.* Write the time function for the current in the inductor for frequencies of 60 and 250 cps. Sketch curves of the potential and current for each case, showing their relative dimensions. Clearly label the graphs to correspond with a diagram of the inductor, on which is shown the reference conditions.

*b.* Draw to scale the sinor diagram for each of the above cases. Label these diagrams to correspond to the reference conditions indicated on the diagram of the inductor.

*c.* Plot curves showing the variation of the reactance $X_L$ and the susceptance $B_L$ as they vary with frequency in the range from 30 to 300 cps.

**6-2.** A capacitor of $2.5 \times 10^{-6}$ farad is connected to the potential source specified in Prob. 6-1.

*a.* Write the time function for the current in the capacitor, for frequencies of 60 and 250 cps. Sketch curves of the potential and current for each case, showing their relative dimensions. Clearly label the graphs to correspond with a diagram of the capacitor on which the reference conditions are included.

*b.* Draw to scale the sinor diagram for each of the above cases. Label these diagrams to correspond with the reference conditions indicated on the diagram of the capacitor.

*c.* Plot curves showing the variation of the susceptance $B_C$ and the reactance $X_C$ as functions of frequency in the range from 30 to 300 cps.

**6-3.** A resistor of 15 ohms and an inductor of 0.03 henry are connected in series, as in Fig. 6-11*a*. Use the potential and current reference conditions shown in the figure. The potential across the combination is $v = 160 \sin (\omega t + \pi/6)$ volts. At frequencies of 60 and 120 cps, do the following:

*a.* Find the impedance of the circuit.

*b.* Find the angle by which the potential across the combination leads the current.

*c.* Draw the sinor diagram, showing the current, the potential across the combination, and the potential across each element.

*d.* Draw the impedance triangle.

*e.* Write the equation for the current as a function of time.

*f.* Write the equations for the potentials $v_R$ and $v_L$ as functions of time.

**6-4.** A resistor of 120 ohms and a capacitor of $8 \times 10^{-6}$ farad are connected in series, as in Fig. 6-11*b*. Use the potential and current reference conditions shown. Assume the circuit is excited by a potential $v = 450 \sin (\omega t + 140°)$ volts. At frequencies of 60 and 120 cps, do the following:

*a.* Find the impedance of the circuit.

*b.* Find the angle by which the potential across the combination lags the current.

*c.* Draw the sinor diagram, showing the current, the potential across the combination, and the potential across each element.

*d.* Draw the impedance triangle.

*e.* Write the equation for the current as a function of time.

*f.* Write the equations for the potentials $v_R$ and $v_C$ as functions of time.

**6-5.** The resistor and capacitor specified in Prob. 6-4 are connected in parallel. Use the reference conditions shown in Fig. 6-16*a*, and let the current in the external leads be $i = 2.5 \sin (\omega t - 4\pi/3)$ amp. For the frequencies 60 and 120 cps, do the following:

*a.* Find the admittance of the circuit.

*b.* Find the angle by which the current to the parallel combination leads the potential.

*c.* Draw the sinor diagram, showing the potential, the current into the combination, and the current in each element.

*d.* Draw the admittance triangle.

*e.* Write the equation for the potential across the combination, as a time function.

*f.* Write the equations for the currents $i_G$ and $i_C$ as functions of time.

**6-6.** The resistor and inductor specified in Prob. 6-3 are connected in parallel, as in Fig. 6-16*b*. Let the current in the leads be $i = 18 \sin (\omega t - \pi/4)$ amp. Use the reference conditions shown in the figure. For frequencies of 60 and 120 cps, do the following:

*a.* Find the admittance of the circuit.

*b.* Find the angle by which the current to the combination lags the potential.

*c.* Draw the sinor diagram, showing the potential, the current into the combination, and the current in each element.

*d.* Draw the admittance triangle.

*e.* Write the equation for the potential across the combination, as a time function.

*f.* Write the equations for the currents $i_G$ and $i_L$ as time functions.

**6-7.** In the series circuit shown in Fig. 6-7, let $R = 150$ ohms, $L = 0.01$ henry, and $C = 0.64 \times 10^{-6}$ farad. Use the reference conditions shown. The potential across the circuit is known to be $v = 65 \sin (\omega t - 60°)$ volts. For frequencies of 1,000 and 3,000 cps, do the following:

*a.* Find the impedance of the circuit.

*b.* Find the angle by which the potential across the combination leads the current.

*c.* Draw the sinor diagram, showing the current, the potential across each element, and the potential across the combination.

*d.* Draw the impedance diagram.

*e.* Write the equation for the current as a function of time.

*f.* Write equations for $v_R$, $v_L$, and $v_C$ as functions of time.

*g.* Compute the frequency at which the impedance is like a pure resistance.

**6-8.** The parallel circuit shown in Fig. 6-12 has the values $G = 1/R = 0.005$ mho, $L = 0.015$ henry, and $C = 0.425 \times 10^{-6}$ farad. Use the reference conditions shown. The current to the combination is $i = 8 \sin (\omega t + 110°)$ amp. For frequencies of 800 and 2,000 cps, do the following.

*a.* Find the admittance of the circuit.

*b.* Find the angle by which $i$ leads $v$.

*c.* Draw the sinor diagram showing the potential, the current in each element, and the total current to the combination.

*d.* Draw the admittance diagram.

*e.* Write the equation for the potential as a function of time.

*f.* Write equations for $i_G$, $i_L$, and $i_C$, as functions of time.

*g.* Compute the frequency at which the admittance is like a pure conductance.

**6-9.** Consider the circuit shown in Fig. P6-9. Each of the generators is driven from the same shaft, with positive connection between them, so that each has the same frequency, and the potential sources retain fixed relative phase differences. These potentials are given, in volts, by the functions

$$v_1 = 170 \cos \omega t$$
$$v_2 = 170 \cos (\omega t + 120°)$$
$$v_3 = 170 \cos (\omega t - 120°)$$

The frequency is 50 cps.

*a.* Draw the necessary sinor diagrams to find the equations for $i_1$, $i_2$, and $i_3$ as functions of time.

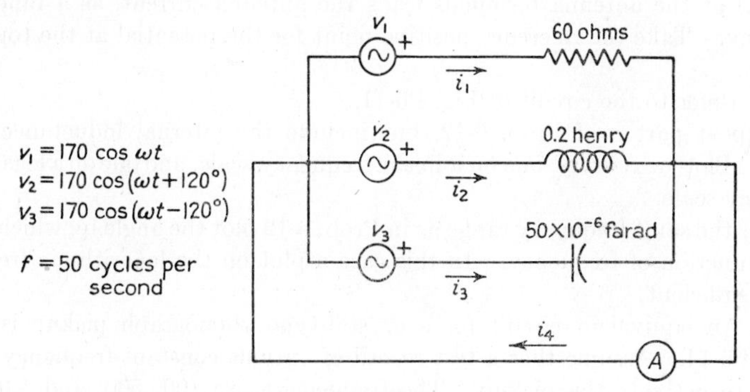


FIG. P6-9.

*b.* Write the expression for the sinor representation $\mathbf{I}_4$ of the current $i_4$. Graphically combine the sinors in the way necessary to determine the current $\mathbf{I}_4$, and specify the indication of ammeter $A$ connected in the common lead. Also, write the time function for $i_4$.

**6-10.** Repeat Prob. 6-9, with the inductor interchanged with the capacitor.

**6-11.** The circuit in the rectangle labeled "Antenna" in Fig. P6-11 is an equivalent circuit for a radio transmitting antenna of length small compared with a wavelength. The transmitter is represented by the potential source and the inductor in the rectangle on the left. The resistor accounts for power radiation and power loss in the antenna wire, and the capacitance represents the capacitance from the elevated wire to ground. For this example the frequency is $40 \times 10^6$ cps.

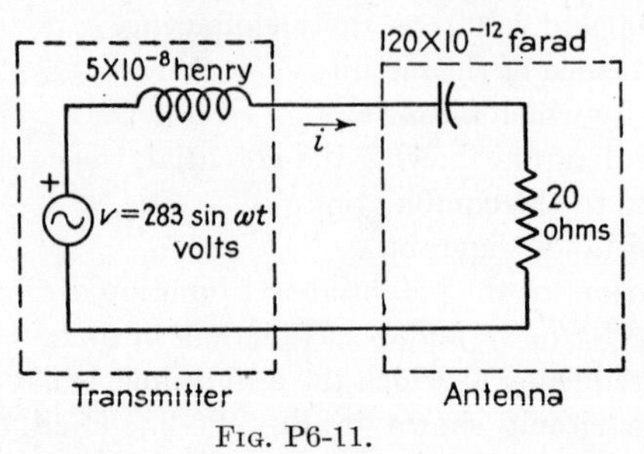


FIG. P6-11.

*a.* Assuming the values specified on the diagram, compute the effective value of the current flowing from the transmitter.

*b.* Which type of ammeter could be used at this frequency?

*c.* To what value should the inductance of the source be changed, to give the maximum antenna current?

**6-12.** Refer to the equivalent circuit for radio antenna, as given in Fig. P6-11.

*a.* Plot a curve showing the variation of the impedance of the antenna as a function of frequency, over the range from 30 to 80 Mc.

*b.* For this same frequency range plot the variation of the angle by which the potential at the antenna terminals leads the antenna current, as a function of frequency. Take the reference-positive point for the potential at the top of the diagram.

**6-13.** Refer to the circuit of Fig. P6-11.

*a.* Repeat part *a* of Prob. 6-12, but include the internal inductance of the source. Plot two curves, one on a linear frequency scale, and one on a logarithmic frequency scale.

*b.* For the same frequency range as in Prob. 6-12 plot the angle by which $v$ leads $i$, as a function of frequency. In this case a plot on the logarithmic frequency scale is sufficient.

**6-14.** An equivalent circuit for a crystal-type phonograph pickup is shown in Fig. P6-14. Assume that a test record of various constant-frequency signals is used to activate the pickup. The frequencies are 100, 500, and 5,000 cps. Assume the record is made so that the potential source has an amplitude which is independent of frequency. (In the case of actual records there is a deviation from this.) The capacitor is due to the inevitable capacitance between the electrodes attached to the crystal. The resistor across which the potential appears is part of the external circuit. (The equivalence of the given circuit to the actual device can be proved by methods described in Chap. 9.)

*a.* Construct a sinor diagram for a frequency of 500 cps. Take the sinor for the potential source as horizontal, and show the current and the output potential $\mathbf{V}_2$.

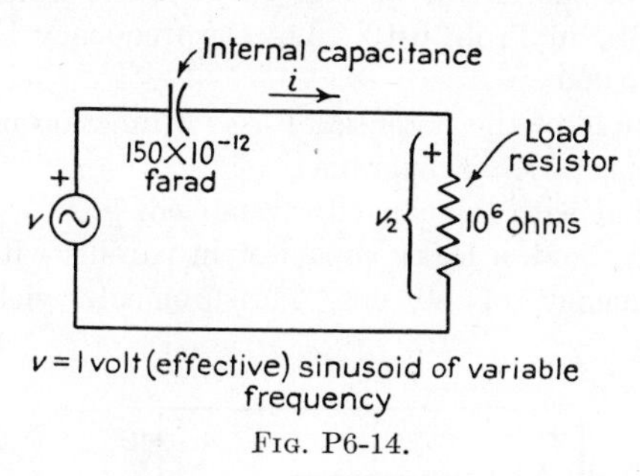


FIG. P6-14.

*b.* Draw a composite sinor diagram, showing the locus of the sinor $\mathbf{V}_2$ as frequency varies over the range specified. The diagram should be so arranged that all the sinors for $\mathbf{V}_2$ have their tail ends at the same point.

**6-15.** Assume that laboratory measurements on the circuit shown in Fig. P6-15 give the following information: $V_1 = 50$ volts, $V_2 = 60$ volts, and $V = 85$

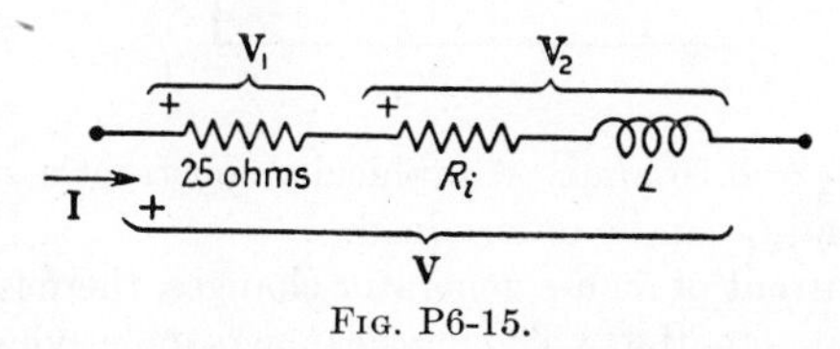


FIG. P6-15.

volts. $R_i$ is the internal resistance of the inductor. Graphically construct the sinor diagram for the circuit and from it determine the values of $R_i$ and $L$. The frequency is 60 cps.

**6-16.** A magnetic-type phonograph pickup can be represented by the circuit of Fig. P6-16. When operated on a record of the type described in Prob. 6-14,

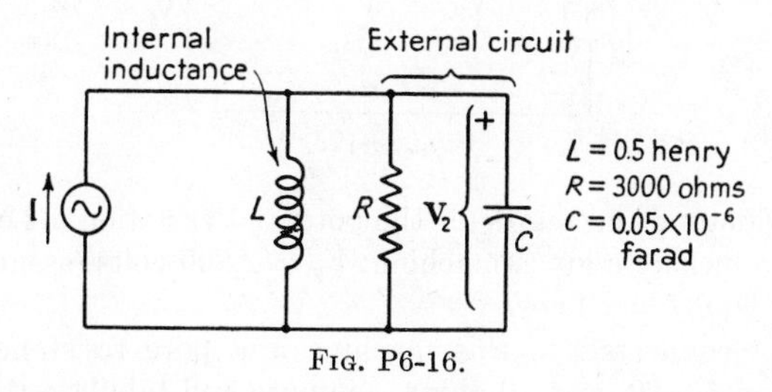


FIG. P6-16.

it is possible to show that the magnitude of the equivalent current source is constant, as frequency varies. (The equivalent circuit is derived with the aid of information contained in Chap. 9.) The resistor and capacitor are an external network connected to the device. Draw sinor diagrams for the circuit, taking the current source as $0.3 \times 10^{-3}$ amp. Take the current sinor in a horizontal position. Two sinor diagrams are to be drawn, at frequencies of 500 and 5,000 cps.

**6-17.** The output of the circuit of Fig. P6-16 is the potential $\mathbf{V}_2$. Use the current source specified in Prob. 6-16. Let the frequency have the successive values 100, 500, and 5,000 cps.

*a.* Plot the magnitude of the potential $V_2$, as a function of frequency, determining it from appropriate sinor diagrams.

*b.* Repeat part *a*, but with the capacitor removed.

**6-18.** Figure P6-18 shows a leaky capacitor in parallel with a resistor of 300 ohms. At the frequency of 60 cps, measurements yield $I = 0.57$ amp,

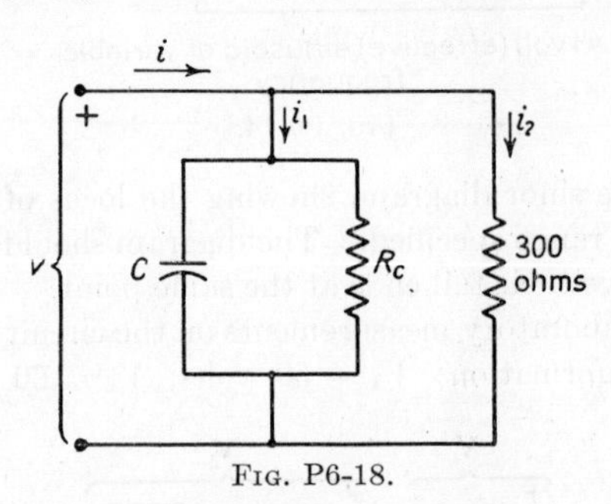


Fig. P6-18.

$I_1 = 0.5$ amp, and $I_2 = 0.16$ amp. Graphically construct a sinor diagram from which values of $R_c$ and $C$ can be determined.

**6-19.** When the current of an a-c generator changes, there is an accompanying change in its terminal potential. The physical facts underlying this phenomenon are approximately represented by the "equivalent circuit" shown in Fig. P6-19.

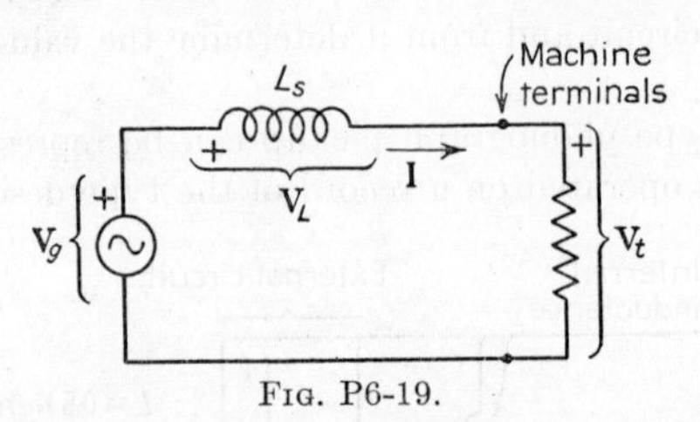


Fig. P6-19.

The fictitious inductor $L_s$ accounts for the potential variation. Let the following be the specified values for a given machine: $V_g = 2{,}200$ volts (assumed constant), $L_s = 0.06$ henry, and $f = 60$ cps.

*a.* The "load" connected to this machine is a pure resistance of value $R$. For values of $R = 50$, 20, and 10 ohms, compute and tabulate the load current and the potential across the load. Also tabulate the value of the angle between $\mathbf{V}_g$ and $\mathbf{V}_t$. Use sinor diagrams where required, to aid in the computation.

*b.* For each of the conditions in part *a* plot a sinor diagram showing the sinors $\mathbf{I}$, $\mathbf{V}_L$, and $\mathbf{V}_t$ on $\mathbf{V}_g$ as a common base. The sinors $\mathbf{I}$ and $\mathbf{V}_t$ are to have a common origin. Plot the locus of the current sinor $\mathbf{I}$ and of the potential sinor $\mathbf{V}_t$.

**6-20.** The same generator specified in Prob. 6-19 is connected to a load consisting of the series connection of the variable resistor of the previous problem and an 80-$\mu$f capacitor, as shown in Fig. P6-20.

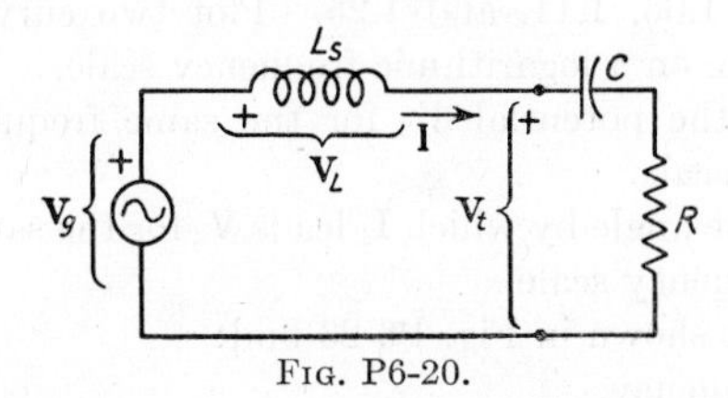


FIG. P6-20.

*a.* Compute and tabulate the current, terminal potential, and angle between $\mathbf{V}_t$ and $\mathbf{V}_g$ for each value of resistance specified in Prob. 6-19.

*b.* Use the results of part *a* to construct a sinor diagram on a common $V_g$ base, showing all cases on the same diagram. Draw this diagram with a common origin for the **I** and $\mathbf{V}_t$ sinors. Draw the locus of **I** and of $\mathbf{V}_t$.

**6-21.** Figure P6-21 shows a circuit which can be used to boost the "low" frequencies of an audio-frequency system. Take $\mathbf{V}_1 = 1\underline{/0°}$ volt.

*a.* Draw a sinor diagram showing $\mathbf{V}_2$, and any other quantities needed to find it, at frequencies of 50, 100, 400, 1,000, and 5,000 cps.

*b.* Plot a graph of the ratio $V_2/V_1$ as a function of frequency, obtaining the necessary information graphically from part *a*.

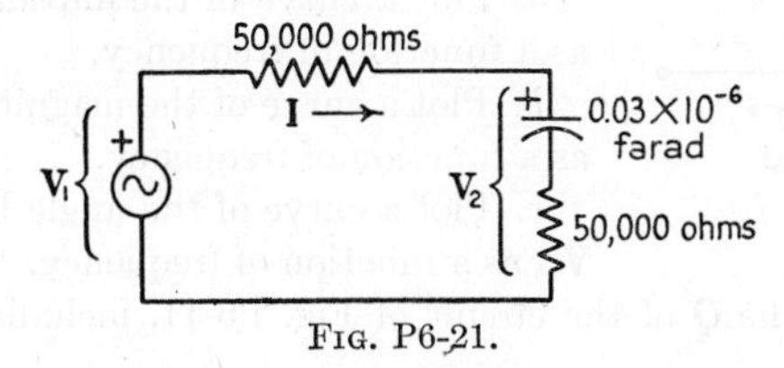


FIG. P6-21.

*c.* Plot a graph of the angle by which $\mathbf{V}_2$ lags $\mathbf{V}_1$, as a function of frequency, obtaining the necessary information graphically from part *a*.

**6-22.** A tuned vacuum-tube amplifier of a radio can be represented approximately by the circuit shown in Fig. P6-22. In many cases the vacuum tube can

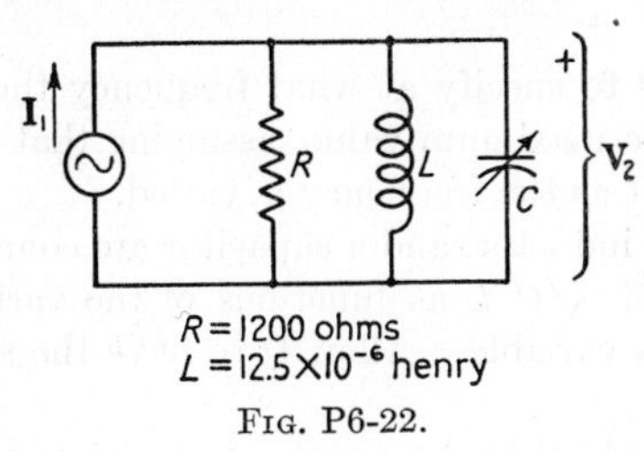


FIG. P6-22.

be represented by a current source as is done here. $\mathbf{I}_1$ represents the incoming signal, and $\mathbf{V}_2$ represents the output potential. $\mathbf{I}_1$ may be assumed constant, at the value $0.01\underline{/0°}$ amp.

*a.* What value must $C$ have to make $V_2$ a maximum when $f = 10^6$ cps?

*b.* Plot a graph of the admittance of this circuit as a function of frequency, using the value of $C$ obtained in (*a*). Compute data points at $f/f_0 = 0.8$, 0.9, 0.93, 0.97, 1.00, 1.03, 1.06, 1.11, and 1.25. Plot two curves, one on a linear frequency scale and one on a logarithmic frequency scale.

*c.* Plot a graph of the potential $V_2$ for the same frequency range. Use a logarithmic frequency scale.

*d.* Plot a graph of the angle by which $\mathbf{I}_1$ leads $\mathbf{V}_2$ for the same frequency range. Use a logarithmic frequency scale.

**6-23.** For the circuit shown in Fig. P6-23 find:

*a.* The resonant frequency.

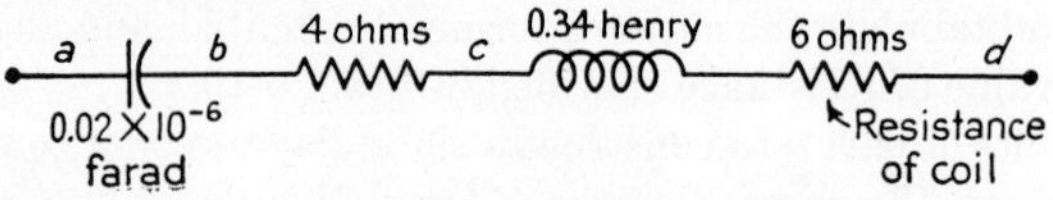

a b 4 ohms c 0.34 henry 6 ohms d

0.02×10⁻⁶ farad

Resistance of coil

Fig. P6-23.

*b.* The impedance of the circuit at resonance.

*c.* With a potential $\mathbf{V}_{ad} = 10\underline{/0°}$ volts what are the quantities $\mathbf{I}_{ad}$, $\mathbf{V}_{ab}$, $\mathbf{V}_{bc}$, and $\mathbf{V}_{cd}$ at resonance?

*d.* What is the $Q$ of the circuit?

**6-24.** Consider the circuit shown in Fig. P6-24. The frequency is variable, between 200 and 5,000 cps, and at all times the potential $\mathbf{V}_{ac}$ is $100\underline{/0°}$ volts.

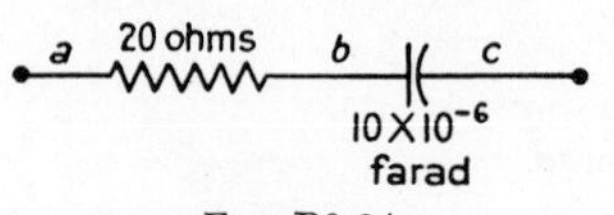


Fig. P6-24.

*a.* Plot a curve of the impedance of the circuit as a function of frequency.

*b.* Plot a curve of the magnitude of the current as a function of frequency.

*c.* Plot a curve of the angle by which $\mathbf{I}_{ab}$ leads $\mathbf{V}_{ab}$ as a function of frequency.

**6-25.** *a.* What is the $Q$ of the circuit of Fig. P6-11, including the inductance of the source?

*b.* Use this value of $Q$ to specify the frequency at which the current delivered to the antenna is $1/\sqrt{2}$ times the maximum current, assuming a constant magnitude of potential as the frequency is varied.

*c.* What is the $Q$ of the circuit of Fig. P6-22 when $C$ is adjusted for resonance at $f = 1$Mc.

*d.* Use this value of $Q$ to specify at what frequency the potential across the circuit is $1/\sqrt{2}$ times the maximum value, assuming that the magnitude of the current source is constant as the frequency is varied.

**6-26.** *a.* A resistor, an inductor, and a capacitor are connected in series. Plot curves of the quantity $Z_s\sqrt{C/L}$ as functions of the variable $\omega\sqrt{LC}$. Use a logarithmic scale for this variable. Allow $Q$ to have the successive values 1, 5, and 10.

*b.* For what circuit would these be curves of admittance?

*c.* Label the scales obtained in (*a*) so that one of the curves (designate which one) will represent the impedance of the circuit where $R = 2{,}000$ ohms, $L = 2.0$ henry, and $C = 0.02 \times 10^{-6}$ farad. In this case the vertical scale will be impedance, and the horizontal scale will be frequency.

*d.* One of the curves obtained in (*a*) can be used to represent the case $R = 316$ ohms, $L = 0.2$ henry, and $C = 0.02 \times 10^{-6}$ farad. Designate which curve can be used. Also, label the $Z_s \sqrt{C/L}$ scale so that it will become actual impedance, and label the $\omega \sqrt{LC}$ scale so that it will become actual frequency.

*e.* Repeat (*d*) for the case $R = 100$ ohms, $L = 3.0$ henrys, and

$$C = 0.12 \times 10^{-4} \text{ farad.}$$

**6-27.** Figure P6-27 shows the equivalent circuit of an amplifier in a "radio-frequency" stage of a radio receiver. The $Q$ of the circuit is 45. Assume the strength of the current source is constant at 0.002 amp effective value. Plot a

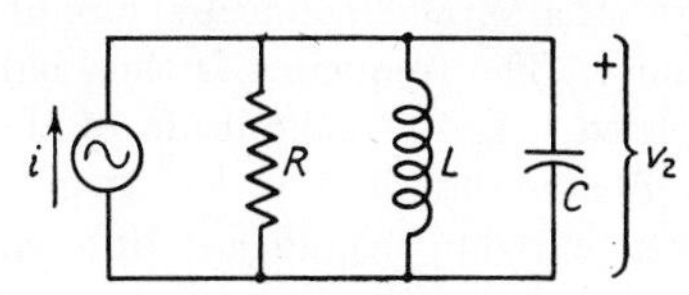


With variable frequency maximum impedance of circuit is 21,000 ohms.

FIG. P6-27.

graph of the effective value of the potential $v_2$ and the angle by which $v_2$ leads $i$. Plot over the range of frequencies in both directions from $\omega_0$, to where the response is one-tenth of the maximum. Label the frequency axis in $\omega/\omega_0$.

## QUESTIONS

**6-1.** In the development of the relation between potential and current, for the sinusoidal case, in an inductor and a capacitor, the integration constant was made zero. Decide whether this is always the case, and justify its being taken as zero in this case.

**6-2.** How are reactance and susceptance defined?

**6-3.** As defined in the text, are the reactance and susceptance of an inductor both positive quantities? How does each vary with frequency?

**6-4.** What is the dual of the reactance of an inductor? What is the dual of the susceptance of an inductor?

**6-5.** How is impedance defined? Consider the formula for the impedance of the series circuit of $R$, $L$, and $C$. Investigate whether this reduces to the formulas for the resistance or reactance of single elements if any two elements are shorted out.

**6-6.** What range of values can $\zeta_s$ have for a circuit consisting of $R$ and $C$ in series?

**6-7.** Suppose an impedance of $5\underline{/60^\circ}$ ohms is connected across a potential of 10 sin $\omega t$ volts. Using the usual reference conditions, what is the equation for the current in the circuit? If the circuit has only two elements; what types are they?

**6-8.** A series-connected combination of $R$ and $C$ takes a certain current at a given frequency. The frequency is then doubled, but the potential across the combination remains the same. Will the current be double the previous value, more than double, or less than double?

**6-9.** How is admittance defined? Consider the formula for the admittance of the parallel connection of $G$, $C$, and $L$. Investigate whether this reduces to the formulas for the conductance or susceptance of single elements if any two are removed.

**6-10.** What range of values can $\eta_p$ have for a circuit consisting of $G$ and $L$ in parallel?

**6-11.** The current through a parallel combination of elements is 2 cos $\omega t$ amp. The admittance of the combination is $0.1\underline{/30°}$. Using the usual reference conditions, what is the equation for the potential across the combination? If the circuit has only two elements, what types are they?

**6-12.** The potential across a parallel-connected circuit of $G$ and $C$ has a certain value at a given frequency. The frequency is then halved, but the magnitude of the total current is fixed. Is the magnitude of the new potential exactly half the previous value, greater than half, or less than half?

**6-13.** Do you think there is any significant difference between the impedance diagram of a series circuit and the sinor diagram of its various potentials? Answer the same question for the admittance diagram as compared with the sinor diagram of the currents of a parallel circuit.

**6-14.** When a sinor diagram is drawn for a circuit, can the initial angle of each sinusoid be chosen independently?

**6-15.** What happens to the admittance of a series $R$-$L$-$C$ circuit as the frequency approaches (*a*) zero, (*b*) infinity?

**6-16.** What happens to the impedance of a parallel $G$-$C$-$L$ circuit as the frequency approaches (*a*) zero, (*b*) infinity?

**6-17.** How is it known that the equivalent circuit of an inductor having winding resistance is the series combination of $R$ and $L$, rather than a parallel combination, if the equivalent circuit is to be valid for varying frequency?

**6-18.** Explain how it is known that the equivalent circuit of a capacitor with leaky dielectric, which will be valid for variable frequency, is $G$ in parallel with $C$, rather than a series circuit?

**6-19.** What is the formula for the angle of the impedance diagram of a parallel combination of a resistor and a capacitor?

**6-20.** What is the formula for the angle of the admittance diagram of a series combination of a resistor and a capacitor?

**6-21.** If the variation of impedance of a series circuit of $R$, $L$, and $C$ is known, how can the concept of duality be used to predict the variation of the admittance of a parallel circuit of $G$, $C$, and $L$, with variable frequency?

**6-22.** How is the width of the response curve of a resonant circuit related to the $Q$ of the circuit?

**6-23.** The universal resonance curve involves two different approximations. What are they?

**6-24.** Explain why the exact resonance curve is symmetrical with respect to $\omega_0$, when plotted on a logarithmic scale of $\omega_0$, while the universal curves has symmetry on a linear scale of $\omega$.

**6-25.** What is the impedance of a series circuit at $\omega = \omega_0$? What is the admittance of a parallel circuit at $\omega = \omega_0$? Are these answers linked by duality?

# CHAPTER 7

# POWER

**7-1. Introduction.** The transmission of power is an important consideration in most applications of electricity. This is true in communication as well as power applications. In the case of alternating currents power takes on a more general significance than with direct currents. The direction of power flow may reverse during a cycle, and it is therefore necessary to include power as an entity to be represented by an algebraic quantity.

**7-2. Instantaneous Power.** Consider the circuit of Fig. 7-1. Each rectangle represents a general circuit branch, the details of which are of no concern. Each may include a source. A solution of the network will provide knowledge of the potential difference $v$ and the current $i$.

Let the typical curves labeled $v$ and $i$ in Fig. 7-2 be the potential and current, as determined from a solution of the network. Consider the product

$$p = vi \tag{7-1}$$

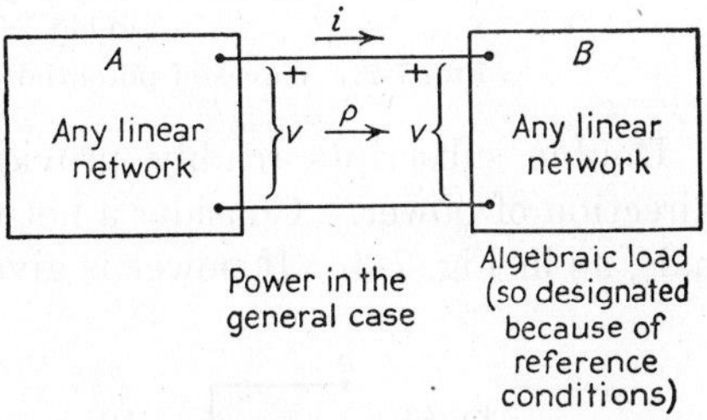

A
Any linear network
B
Any linear network
Power in the general case
Algebraic load (so designated because of reference conditions)

FIG. 7-1. Reference direction for power.

which represents the power transfer in watts. The plot of $p$ is included in Fig. 7-2. When either $v$ or $i$ is negative (but not both), the product is negative. It follows that $p$ is an algebraic quantity.

The reference direction for power is established as follows: When $v$ and $i$ are each positive, power will flow into rectangle $B$. Therefore the reference direction for $p$ is as shown in Fig. 7-1.

In Fig. 7-2, when the power curve is above the axis, the power is toward the right, as indicated. When the curve is negative, power flows to the left.

This is a distinctive feature of power in a-c circuits. During part of the cycle a network may absorb energy and then return all or part of it later in the cycle. Perfect inductors and capacitors return all the energy they absorb.

In circuit terminology the part of the network toward which the reference direction of power points is called the *algebraic load.* The power reference direction points away from the part of the network which may be called the *algebraic source.** These definitions apply only if the two networks are connected by no more than two wires. In Fig. 7-1 rectangle $A$ is an algebraic source and rectangle $B$ is an algebraic load.

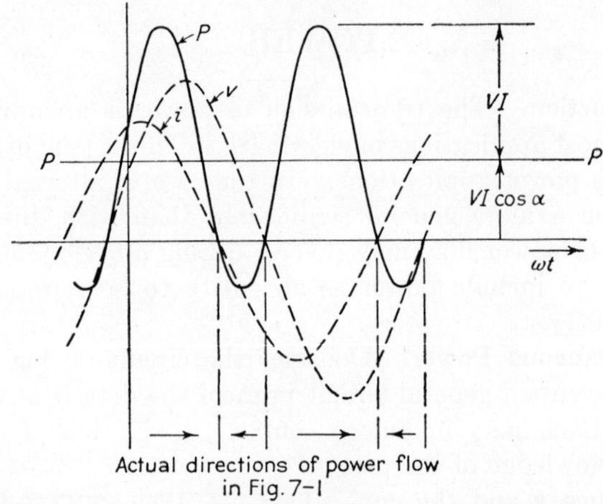


FIG. 7-2. Waves of potential difference, current, and power.

Double subscripts readily provide information about the reference direction of power. Consider a network branch between a pair of terminals, as in Fig. 7-3. If power is given by the product

$$p = v_{ab}i_{ab} \tag{7-2}$$

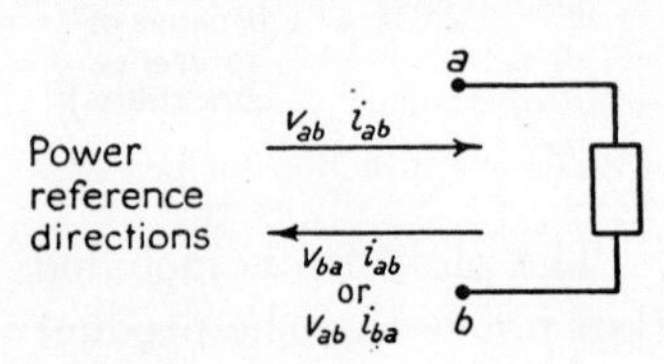


FIG. 7-3. Reference directions for power as related to double subscript notation.

its reference direction is toward the branch between ($a$) and ($b$). If power is given by the product

$$p = v_{ba}i_{ab} = v_{ab}i_{ba} \tag{7-3}$$

its reference direction is away from the branch between ($a$) and ($b$).

**7-3. The Sinusoidal Case.** Let the potential and current of Fig. 7-2 be

$$\begin{aligned} v &= \sqrt{2}\, V \sin (\omega t + \alpha) \\ i &= \sqrt{2}\, I \sin (\omega t + \beta) \end{aligned} \tag{7-4}$$

The equation for the power is

$$p = 2VI \sin (\omega t + \alpha) \sin (\omega t + \beta) \tag{7-5}$$

* An algebraic load is an abstract thing. It depends on the choice of potential and current reference conditions. It is a load (actual load) when the average power to it is positive.

The product of sines can be reduced by using the trigonometric identity $(\sin A)(\sin B) = [\cos (A - B) - \cos (A + B)]/2$. Equation (7-5) becomes

$$p = VI \cos (\alpha - \beta) - VI \cos (2\omega t + \alpha + \beta) \tag{7-6}$$

This shows that the power curve consists of two parts: a constant component, represented by the line $PP$ of Fig. 7-2, and a sinusoidal component of double frequency. The line $PP$ serves as the axis of the double-frequency sinusoid.

**7-4. Average Power.** The sinusoidal term in Eq. (7-6) cannot represent a net transfer of energy, because its average value is zero. The constant term provides the net transfer of energy. The correct name for the constant term is *average power* but sometimes it is referred to as *power* in the sinusoidal case.

Average power is represented by the symbol $P$. Thus

$$P = VI \cos \theta \tag{7-7}$$

where $\theta$ is either $\alpha - \beta$ or $\beta - \alpha$. Average power is the product of potential and current (effective values) and the cosine of the phase difference between them. It is measured in watts.

Average power is an algebraic quantity. It becomes negative if the absolute value of $|\theta|$ is between $\pi/2$ and $\pi$ rad. The reference direction of $P$ is the same as for instantaneous power.

**7-5. Volt-amperes and Power Factor.** The formula for average power includes the product $VI$. It is the expression that would give the power if alternating currents and potentials could be treated as if they were constant. For this reason this product is sometimes called the *apparent power*. There may actually be no power involved in this product, as when $|\theta| = 90°$. Apparent power is represented by the symbol

$$S = VI \tag{7-8}$$

Its unit is the volt-ampere (abbreviation va).

The average power is sometimes written in the form

$$P = F_p S \tag{7-9}$$

in which $F_p$ is a factor by which the volt-ampere product is multiplied to give the average power. $F_p$ is called the *power factor* of the circuit. It is explicitly defined by

$$F_p = \frac{P}{S} \tag{7-10}$$

By comparison with Eq. (7-7) it is seen that, for the sinusoidal case,

$$F_p = \frac{VI \cos \theta}{VI} = \cos \theta \tag{7-11}$$

It would appear that $F_p$ is an algebraic quantity, since $\theta$ can become negative. However, it is customary to use $F_p$ only after the direction of power flow has been established. In that case, its magnitude is all that is required. Thus, for practical purposes, with sinusoidal waves of $v$ and $i$,

$$F_p = |\cos \theta| \tag{7-12}$$

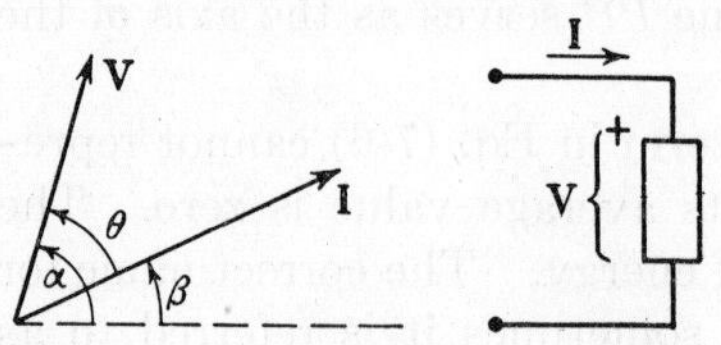


FIG. 7-4. Typical sinors for an algebraic load when it is an actual load also. (If it is an actual energy source, $\theta$ is greater than 90°.)

**7-6. Average Power and Sinor Diagrams.** Average power is readily interpreted by the sinor diagrams of potential and current. Reference is made to the general diagrams of Fig. 7-4. The reference direction for power is toward the rectangle, thus making the rectangle the algebraic load, as defined in Sec. 7-2.

Two interpretations for power are illustrated in Fig. 7-5. The equation for average power may be written in either of the forms

$$\begin{aligned} P &= I(V \cos \theta) = IV_1 \\ P &= V(I \cos \theta) = I_1 V \end{aligned} \tag{7-13}$$

For the first equation the potential is resolved into two components, one in phase with the current, and one in quadrature with it. For the second equation the current is resolved into two components, one in phase with the potential, and the other in quadrature with it.

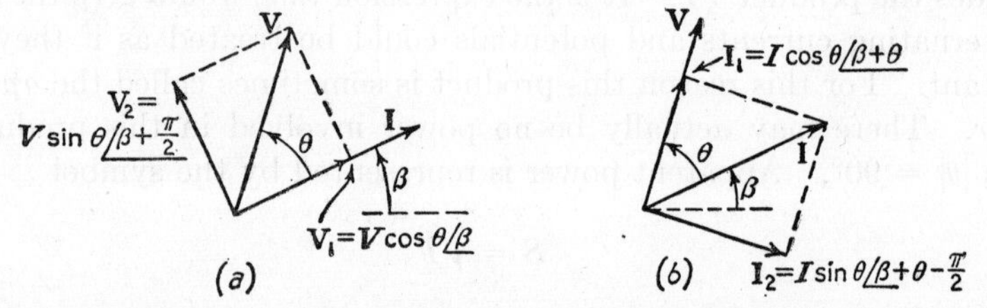


FIG. 7-5. Resolution of sinors into power-producing components, (a) for the potential, and (b) for the current.

In words, the essence of the information of Fig. 7-5 is that if sinors are known for the potential and current for some two-terminal section of a circuit, average power is obtained by projecting the potential sinor on the current sinor (or vice versa) and multiplying the collinear components.

This is generalized by saying that power is produced only by inphase components of potential and current.

**7-7. Reactive Volt-amperes.** The interpretation of power from the sinor diagram leads to the definition of an auxiliary quantity known as *reactive volt-amperes* (sometimes called reactive "power"). The quantity of reactive volt-amperes is given by the formula

$$N = VI \sin \theta \tag{7-14}$$

It is possible to give this a physical interpretation which is useful in the analysis of power transmission systems. However, for the considerations of basic circuit analysis, it may be left as a purely algebraic quantity. It is arbitrarily defined to be positive for an algebraic load when the potential leads the current (by an angle less than $\pi$ rad).

The diagrams of Fig. 7-5 serve as an aid in interpreting the reactive volt-amperes. Equation (7-14) may be written in either of the forms

$$\begin{aligned} N &= I(V \sin \theta) = IV_2 \\ N &= V(I \sin \theta) = VI_2 \end{aligned} \tag{7-15}$$

where $V_2$ and $I_2$ are interpreted in the diagrams.

A useful formula relating volt-amperes, reactive volt-amperes, and power is obtained by squaring Eqs. (7-7) and (7-14) and adding, thus:

$$S^2 = P^2 + N^2 \tag{7-16}$$

As previously indicated, from the viewpoint of pure circuit analysis, reactive volt-amperes is not an important quantity. It does, however, have considerable importance in applications to power transmission, and deserves some consideration, as a fundamental concept. It also has significance in a more generalized interpretation of power, to be found in a later chapter. The abbreviation *var*, meaning volt-amperes reactive, is used as a unit of measurement for $N$.

**7-8. Power in Series and Parallel Circuits.** The circuits of Chap. 6 are of sufficient basic interest to warrant the detailed consideration of power relations in them. The principles of duality are used to provide simultaneous information for the series and parallel circuits. For each type of circuit, two approaches are used to yield the same results. This is done with the aim of providing as much insight as possible. From the magnitudes of the appropriate sinors in Fig. 7-6 it is evident that

$$\begin{aligned} F_p &= \cos \theta = \cos \zeta = \frac{IR}{IZ} = \frac{R}{Z} \qquad \text{series} \\ F_p &= \cos \theta = \cos \eta = \frac{VG}{VY} = \frac{G}{Y} \qquad \text{parallel} \end{aligned} \tag{7-17}$$

The power factors for the two circuits are dually related. They are determined completely by the impedance (or admittance) and series resistance (or shunt conductance) of the circuits. These results apply only to the simple circuits considered.

A second method of arriving at these results has the advantage of going back to the first principles. It is based on the idea that power can

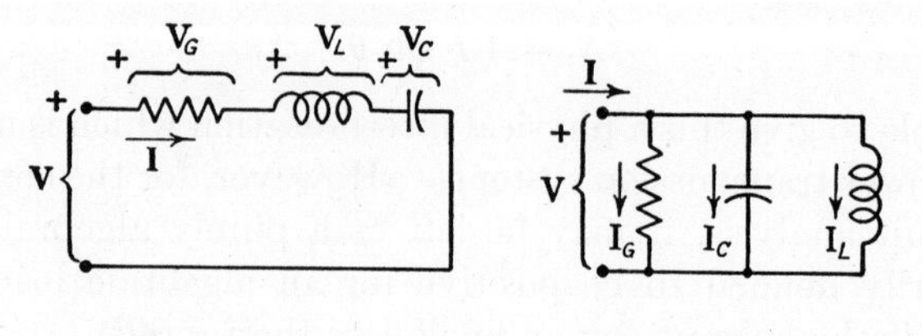


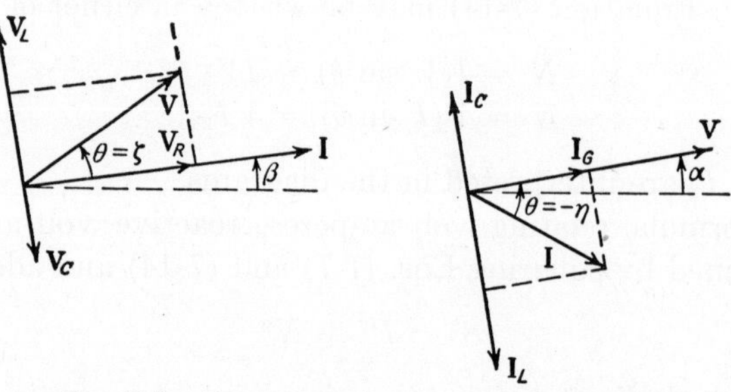


FIG. 7-6. Power in series and parallel circuits.

be dissipated only in a resistor (barring active circuit elements such as motors). Thus,

$$\begin{aligned} P_s &= V_R I = (IR)I = I^2R \qquad \text{series} \\ P_p &= I_G V = (VG)V = V^2G \qquad \text{parallel} \end{aligned} \tag{7-18}$$

Introducing the concepts of impedance and admittance, the apparent powers are

$$\begin{aligned} S &= VI = (IZ)I = I^2Z \qquad \text{series} \\ S &= VI = V(VY) = V^2Y \qquad \text{parallel} \end{aligned} \tag{7-19}$$

In each of these cases the formulas for $P$ and $S$ from Eqs. (7-18) and (7-19) may be substituted into the defining equation for power factor to give

$$\begin{aligned} F_p &= \frac{P_s}{S} = \frac{I^2R}{I^2Z} = \frac{R}{Z} \qquad \text{series} \\ F_p &= \frac{P_p}{S} = \frac{V^2G}{V^2Y} = \frac{G}{Y} \qquad \text{parallel} \end{aligned} \tag{7-20}$$

which are in agreement with Eqs. (7-17).

**Example 7-1.** The potential across a series combination of $R$ and $C$ is 150 volts, effective value. If $R = 25$ ohms and $1/\omega C = 15$ ohms, find the power dissipated in the resistor.

*Solution.* The solution is given in three forms.

*a.* The impedance of the circuit is

$$Z = \sqrt{(25)^2 + (15)^2} = 29.2 \text{ ohms}$$

The current is

$$I = \frac{150}{29.2} = 5.13$$

Since the initial angles are not specified, the current sinor can be made horizontal and the sinor diagram of potentials constructed as shown.

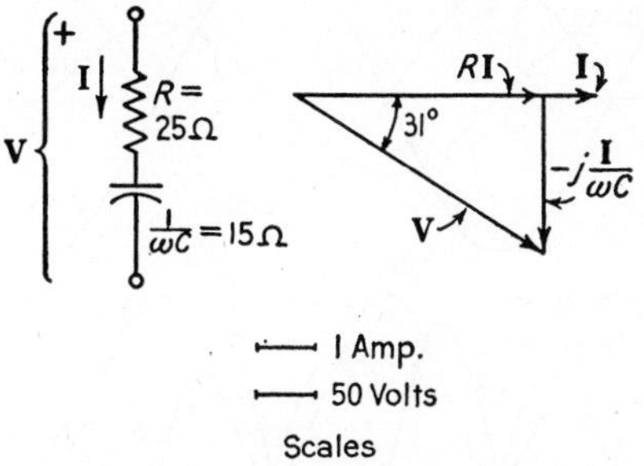

I Amp.
50 Volts
Scales

The potential **V** is

$$\mathbf{V} = \mathbf{V}_R + \mathbf{V}_C = 150\underline{/-31^\circ}$$

The power is

$$\begin{aligned} P = VI \cos \theta &= (150)(5.13) \cos (-31^\circ) \\ &= (150)(5.13)(0.856) = 658 \text{ watts} \end{aligned}$$

*b.* This method is nearly the same as method *a* except that it progresses without use of a sinor diagram. The impedance $Z = 29.2$ ohms and current $I = 5.13$ amp are computed as in (*a*). The power factor is

$$F_p = \frac{R}{Z} = \frac{25}{29.2} = 0.856$$

The power is

$$P = (150)(5.13)(0.856) = 658 \text{ watts}$$

*c.* In this case the power factor is not found explicitly. The current is found as in the above cases, and then Eqs. (7-18) are applied to give

$$P = I^2R = (5.13)^2(25) = 658 \text{ watts}$$

**7-9. Power Relations in Resonant Circuits, Interpretation of Circuit Q.** Consider the series circuit shown in Fig. 7-7*a*, and assume that the current is

$$i = \sqrt{2}\, I \sin \omega t \tag{7-21}$$

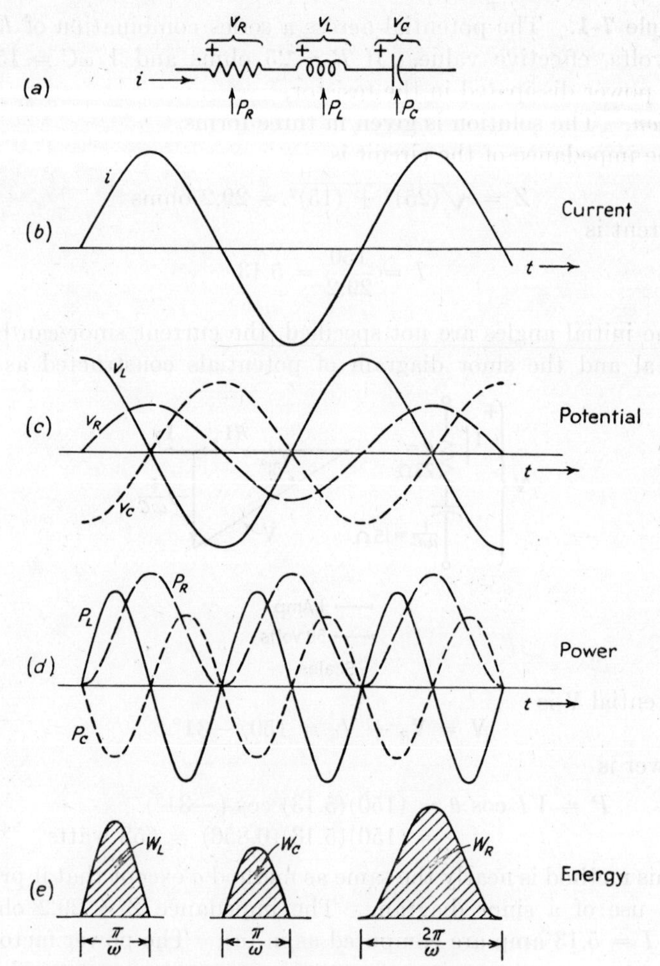


FIG. 7-7. Power and energy relations in a series circuit of $R$, $L$, and $C$.

In the light of the developments in Chap. 6 it is known that the potentials across the individual elements are

$$
\begin{aligned}
v_R &= \sqrt{2}\, RI \sin \omega t \\
v_L &= \sqrt{2}\, \omega LI \sin\left(\omega t + \frac{\pi}{2}\right) = \sqrt{2}\, \omega LI \cos \omega t \\
v_C &= \sqrt{2}\, \frac{I}{\omega C} \sin\left(\omega t - \frac{\pi}{2}\right) = -\sqrt{2}\, \frac{I}{\omega C} \cos \omega t
\end{aligned}
\tag{7-22}
$$

Graphs of these waves are shown in Fig. 7-7c.

Now consider each element successively as an algebraic load. In each case the power is the product of $i$ by the corresponding $v$. The three expressions

$$\begin{aligned} p_R &= 2I^2R \sin^2 \omega t = I^2R(1 - \cos 2\omega t) \\ p_L &= 2\omega LI^2 \sin \omega t \cos \omega t = \omega LI^2 \sin 2\omega t \\ p_C &= -\frac{2I^2}{\omega C} \sin \omega t \cos \omega t = -\frac{I^2}{\omega C} \sin 2\omega t \end{aligned} \tag{7-23}$$

are obtained. Graphs of them are shown in Fig. 7-7*d*. As would be expected, the power into the resistor is always positive. However, the power curves for $L$ and $C$ are as much above the axis as below it. When the curve is above the axis, power is flowing into the element, and when it is below, power is leaving the element. Power alternately flows in and out of the $L$ and $C$ elements. Each of them stores energy during half of a cycle and then returns the stored energy to the circuit during the following half cycle. When $L$ is absorbing energy the capacitor is discharging it, and vice versa.

Energy transfer is the time integral of power. Thus the maximum energy stored in $L$ is the area under a positive half-cycle pulse of $p_L$. A similar statement holds for the energy stored in $C$. Areas corresponding to these integrals are shown in Fig. 7-7*e*. These latter diagrams are to be regarded as pictorial representations of areas, rather than as time graphs, so their horizontal positions are not significant. A third area is shown. It represents the energy dissipated in $R$ during a cycle.

The three energy quantities indicated in the diagram can be found by computing the areas of the figures. The cases of $L$ and $C$ are similar, because their power curves have the same shape, so they can be considered together. In these cases the area is a positive pulse of a sinusoid. This area may be taken as the average value multiplied by the base. From Chap. 3 it is known that the pulse average of a sinusoid is $1/\pi$ times the peak value. The peak values are obtainable from Eqs. (7-23). It follows that

$$\begin{aligned} W_L &= \frac{1}{\pi}\omega LI^2\frac{\pi}{\omega} = LI^2 \\ W_C &= \frac{1}{\pi}\frac{I^2}{\omega C}\frac{\pi}{\omega} = \frac{I^2}{\omega^2 C} \end{aligned} \tag{7-24}$$

Note that these are the *maximum* energy storages during the cycle.

Now consider the energy dissipated in $R$ during a cycle. For this shape of wave the average power is half the peak value, or $I^2R$ in this case, and so the time for a cycle is $2\pi/\omega$ sec. Therefore,

$$W_R = I^2R\frac{2\pi}{\omega} \tag{7-25}$$

Now consider the special case when $\omega = \omega_0$, where $\omega_0$ is given by Eq. (6-43). This is the frequency of resonance. When Eq. (6-43) is substituted for $\omega_0$, the last three equations become:

$$\begin{aligned} W_L &= LI^2 \\ W_C &= LI^2 \\ W_R &= 2\pi(I^2R\sqrt{LC}) \end{aligned} \tag{7-26}$$

In this case $W_L = W_C$, indicating that the amount of energy storage is the same in both nondissipative elements.

A significant result is obtained by taking the ratio of the energy storage in either reactive element to the quantity $W_R/2\pi$. It is

$$\frac{W_L}{(W_R/2\pi)} = 2\pi\frac{W_L}{W_R} = \frac{1}{R}\sqrt{\frac{L}{C}} \tag{7-27}$$

Comparing this with Eqs. (6-48) shows it to be the $Q$ of the series circuit. Thus, the $Q$ of a resonant circuit of $R$, $L$, and $C$ is $2\pi$ times the ratio of maximum energy storage to the energy dissipated per cycle, when the frequency is at resonance.

The concept of duality may be invoked to include the parallel circuit. In that case the right-hand side of Eq. (7-27) takes on the form of the second equation of (6-48). $W_L$ is replaced by the energy stored in the capacitor of the parallel circuit, and $W_R$ is replaced by the energy dissipated in the shunt conductance, during a cycle. The two cases are generalized by the single formula

$$Q_s,\ Q_p = 2\pi\frac{\text{maximum energy storage during a cycle}}{\text{energy dissipated per cycle}} \tag{7-28}$$

It is to be emphasized that this applies only when $\omega = \omega_0$.

**7-10. Measurement of A-C Power.** In d-c circuits power can always be measured by taking the product of current and potential difference. It has been shown that this is not the case with alternating currents. A special type of meter, called a *wattmeter*, must be used.

An electrodynamometer movement similar to Fig. 3-17 can be used to measure average power. The moving and stationary coils are provided with separate leads, and the meter is connected in a circuit in the manner shown in Fig. 7-8. The instantaneous deflecting force on the movable coil is proportional to the product $(i)(i_m)$. However, $R$ is large enough to make the reactance of the moving coil negligible, so $i_m$ is proportional to $v$. Therefore, the force on the coil is proportional to $(v)(i)$, the instantaneous power. Instantaneous power fluctuates at such a rapid rate that the pointer settles at the average value. It is noted that symbols for instantaneous quantities are used in this proof. It is therefore a general proof, including sinusoidal variations as a special case.

The product $(v)(i)$ is not exactly the power delivered to the load, because $i$ includes the current $i_m$. It is possible to compensate for this by allowing $i_m$ to flow through auxiliary stationary coils in such a direction as to cancel the effect of that part of $i$ which is due to $i_m$. Such an instrument is said to be *compensated.* For a compensated meter to indicate

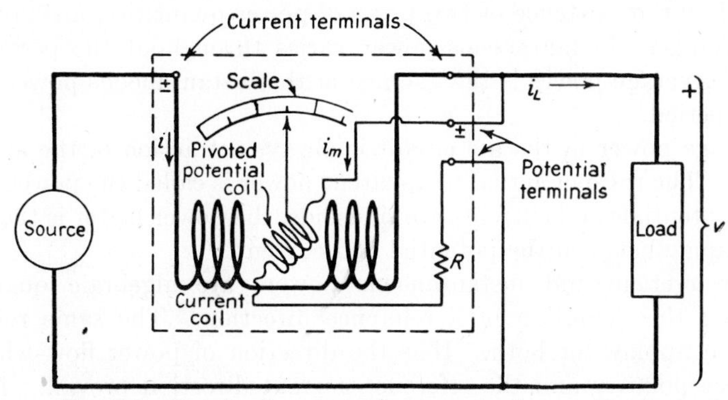


FIG. 7-8. Details of an electrodynamometer type wattmeter.

correctly, the potential-coil connections must be made on the side of the meter toward the load.

Two of the terminals are labeled $\pm$ as an aid in connecting the meter properly in the circuit. They may be thought of as corresponding to the $+$ terminals of the ammeter and voltmeter that would be used in the d-c case. The positions of the two $\pm$ signs in Fig. 7-8 are correct to make the meter indicate upscale when average power actually flows toward the load.

In some applications the direction of power flow is not known. The meter can be used to find that direction. The proper connections to make the meter indicate upscale are found by trial, and then the current-coil $\pm$ terminal will be on the source side of the meter. The potential-coil connections must always be related to the current-coil connections as shown in Fig. 7-8. This is illustrated by the diagrams of Fig. 7-9.

*The direction of pointer deflection should not be reversed by interchanging potential-coil leads.* To do so places nearly the full line potential between the two coils. Electrostatic forces can then cause an error, and the potential may break down the insulation between the coils. When properly connected nearly the full potential appears across $R$.

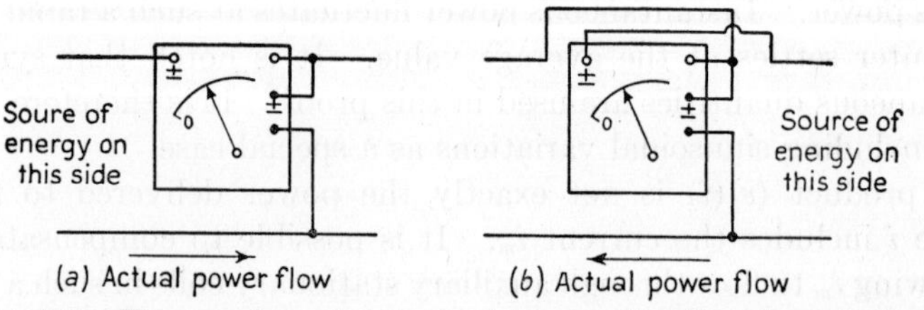


Fig. 7-9. The use of a wattmeter to determine direction of power flow.

**7-11. Summary.** In the consideration of a-c circuits it is necessary to appreciate the existence of two types of power quantities, instantaneous and average. Instantaneous power varies throughout the period of a cycle. Average power is the average of the instantaneous power, taken over a period.

Average power in the a-c circuit is always a fraction of the apparent power. The ratio of actual to apparent power is called the power factor. When potentials and currents are sinusoids, the power factor is the cosine of the angle between the potential and current.

Both average and instantaneous powers are algebraic quantities, requiring the definition of a reference direction. The same reference direction applies for both. It is the direction of power flow when the reference polarity and the reference current direction prevail. In considering power it is always necessary to keep attention fixed on a single two-terminal portion of the circuit.

In considering the power flow toward or away from any branch of a network, it is necessary to be sure that the branch has only two external connections. That is, it must be joined to the remainder of the circuit by only two connections. Internally, it may be as complex as desired.

For simple series and parallel circuits the power factor is easily determined from the circuit parameters themselves. This is a principle which will receive further expansion after the necessary mathematical techniques have been developed for more complicated circuits.

## PROBLEMS

**7-1.** In Fig. P7-1 a constant potential d-c source is connected to two resistors. A short circuit is periodically connected across one of the resistors by the rotating switch shown. The switch places a short circuit across the resistor once each 0.2 sec, and the short circuit endures for 0.05 sec.

*a.* Compute the power delivered by the battery and the power delivered to each resistor when the switch is open and when the switch is closed.

*b.* Compute the average power delivered by the battery and the average power delivered to $R_1$ and to $R_2$. The average is to be obtained for a complete cycle of operation.

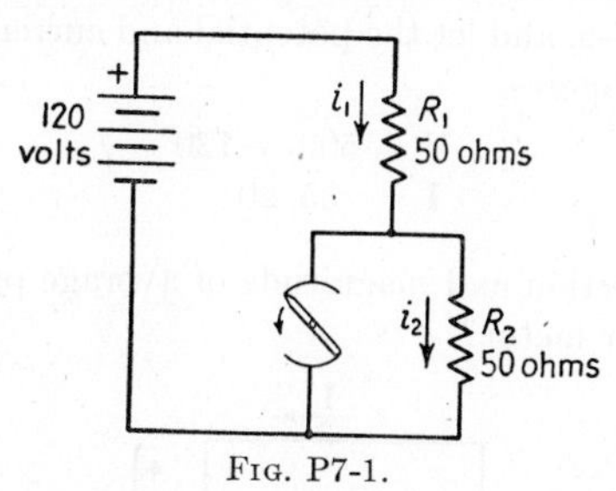


FIG. P7-1.

**7-2.** The rotating switch in Fig. P7-2 provides alternate open- and short-circuit conditions. The circuit is closed for a duration of 0.15 sec, and closing occurs at a rate of 2.5 per second.

*a.* Compute the values (as algebraic quantities) of $p_1$, $p_2$, $p_3$, and $p_4$ for the time when the switch is open and when it is closed.

*b.* Compute the average values of $p_1$, $p_2$, $p_3$, and $p_4$, taken over a complete cycle of operation.

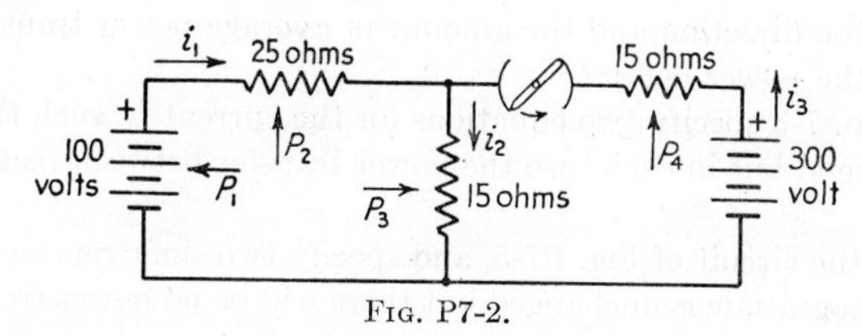


FIG. P7-2.

**7-3.** For the circuit shown in Fig. P7-3 oscillographic measurements show that

$$v_{ab} = 2{,}828 \sin (\omega t + 20°) \quad \text{volt}$$
$$i_{ab} = 70.7 \cos (\omega t - 20°) \quad \text{amp}$$

*a.* Plot a curve of instantaneous power delivered to the rectangle on the right.

*b.* Specify the magnitude and direction of average power transfer.

*c.* What is the power factor?

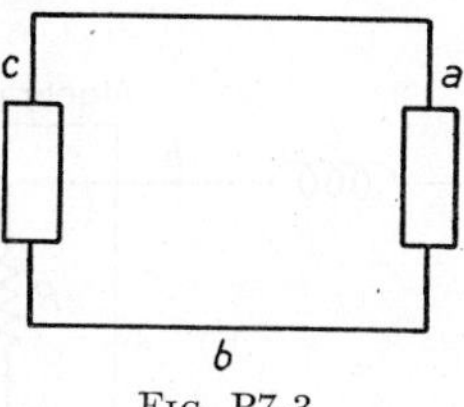


FIG. P7-3.

**7-4.** Refer to Fig. P7-3, and let the potential be the same as specified in Prob. 7-3. The current is $i_{ab} = 70.7 \sin (\omega t - 110°)$.

*a.* Plot a curve of instantaneous power delivered to the rectangle on the right.

*b*. Specify the magnitude and direction of average power transfer.

*c*. What is the power factor?

**7-5.** Refer to Fig. P7-5, and let the potential and current be represented by the sinors, in volts and amperes,

$$\mathbf{V} = 500\underline{/-120°}$$
$$\mathbf{I} = 35\underline{/20°}$$

*a*. What are the direction and magnitude of average power transfer?

*b*. What is the power factor?

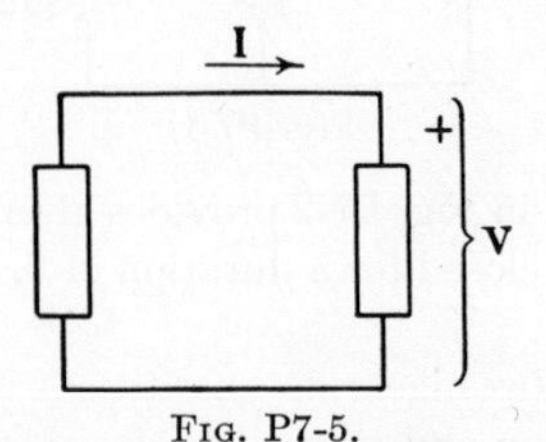


Fig. P7-5.

**7-6.** Refer to Fig. P7-5, and let the current be given by the same sinor as in Prob. 7-5. Let the potential be $\mathbf{V} = 500\underline{/60°}$ volts.

*a*. What is the direction and the amount of average power transfer?

*b*. What is the power factor?

**7-7.** In Prob. 7-3 specify two equations for the current $i_{ab}$ such that its magnitude is unchanged but in each case the power transfer between rectangles will be zero.

*b*. Refer to the circuit of Fig. P7-5, and specify two sinor representations for **V** such that its magnitude is unchanged but there will be no power transfer between rectangles.

**7-8.** The elements within the dotted rectangle of Fig. P7-8 are to be viewed as an algebraic load. The two potential sources are, in volts,

$$v_1 = 1414 \cos \omega t$$
$$v_2 = 1414 \sin \omega t$$

For each of the three cases $X_L$ = O, R, and 4R, do the following:

*a*. Draw a diagram showing sinors symbolizing $i_{bc}$ and $i_{bc}R$. Include the sinors which symbolize $v_1$ and $v_2$.

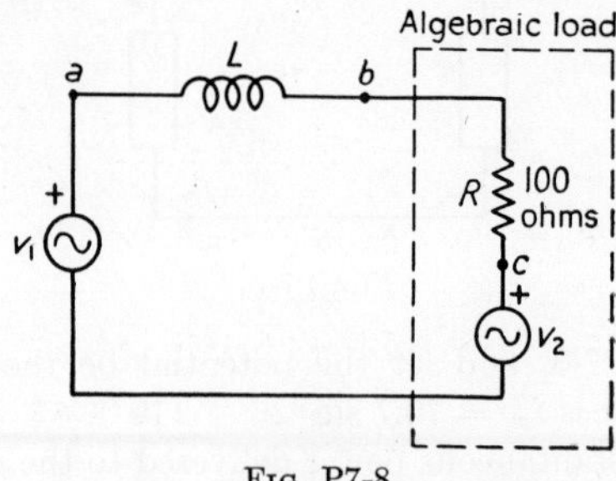


Fig. P7-8.

*b.* Draw the pertinent sinors for finding the average power delivered to the rectangle, labeling them clearly.

*c.* From the graphically constructed sinor diagrams, determine the average power flow between the rectangle and the rest of the circuit, in magnitude and direction for each case.

*d.* Determine the power factor of the rectangle in each case.

**7-9.** For the circuit shown in Fig. P7-9 determine the average power dissipated in the resistor by the following methods:

*a.* Compute the current and potential sinors $\mathbf{V}_{ab}$ and $\mathbf{I}_{ba}$, and determine the power from them. $v_{ab}$ is in volts.

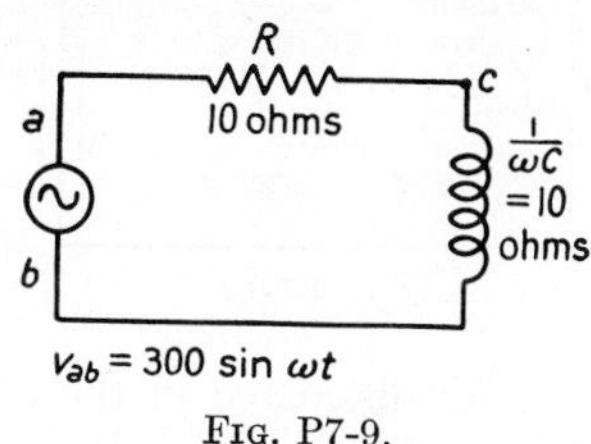


FIG. P7-9.

*b.* Determine the power from the $I^2R$ product.

*c.* Determine the power factor from the circuit parameters, in accordance with Eqs. (7-17).

*d.* Determine the power from the product $F_P(VI)$, using the power factor obtained in part *c.*

**7-10.** Refer to Prob. 6-11. At frequencies of 30, 65, and 100 Mc compute the following:

*a.* The power factor of the antenna circuit (represented by the *R-C* combination).

*b.* The power factor of the circuit seen by the potential source.

*c.* The power delivered to the resistor (the power radiated plus the power dissipated in the conductors).

**7-11.** Consider the circuit of Fig. P7-11. The reactances specified are at a frequency of 100 cps. At frequencies of 50, 100, and 200 cps find:

*a.* The power factor of the circuit.

*b.* The average power taken by the circuit from the current source.

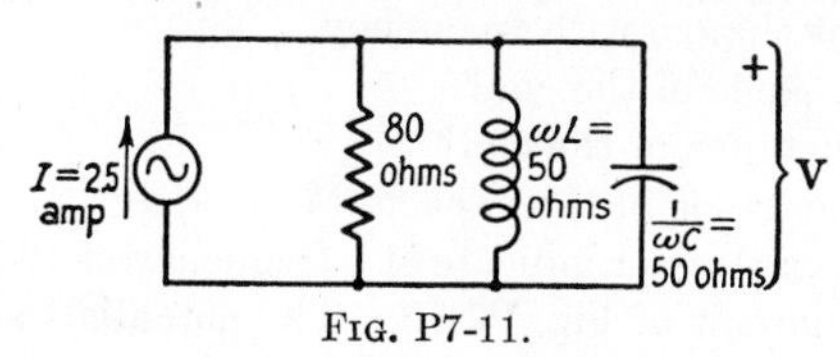


FIG. P7-11.

**7-12.** Figure P7-12 portrays an a-c source, represented by the circle on the left, transmitting power to a distant load, represented by the rectangle. The transmission line introduces resistance $R$ and inductance $L$ into the circuit. The load takes a power of 500 kw at a power factor of 0.75. The potential at the load is $\mathbf{V}_2 = 20{,}000\underline{/0°}$ volts.

*a.* Determine the magnitude of the circuit $I_1$.

*b.* For two cases, $\mathbf{I}_1$ leading and also lagging $\mathbf{V}_2$, determine the potential $\mathbf{V}_1$, using a graphical construction of sinors.

*c.* Determine the power factor of the load presented to the generator for each of the two cases specified in (*b*).

*d.* Determine the average power delivered by the generator by computing the product $F_P(VI)$. Do this for each case specified in (*c*).

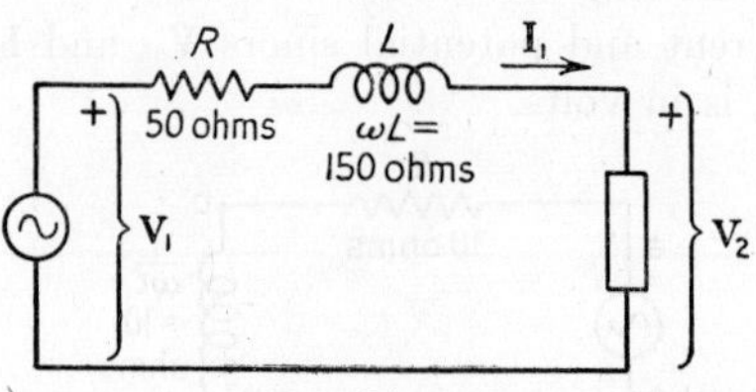


FIG. P7-12.

*e.* Compute the average power dissipated in the resistor, and add it to the average power taken by the load. Do this for each of the two cases, and compare the result with the answers obtained in (*d*).

**7-13.** Consider the circuit of Fig. P6-27. Use the energy concept of $Q$ of a resonant circuit to find the current through the inductance and capacitance branches, at resonance. Use may be made of the fact that at resonance the admittance is equal to the conductance of the resistive branch.

**7-14.** A coil having a resistance of 10 ohms is connected to a 110-volt 60-cps source. An ammeter placed in the circuit reads 5 amp.

*a.* What is the inductance of the coil?

*b.* What is the power factor of the coil?

*c.* What is the average power taken from the source?

**7-15.** A coil of unknown inductance and resistance and an unknown "perfect" capacitor are connected in series. They are connected across a potential of 120 volts, which operates at variable frequency. The magnitude of the potential remains constant. A wattmeter and an ammeter are connected in the circuit. At a frequency of 120 cps the current is 1.8 amp, and the average power is 64.8 watts. When the frequency is 140 cps, the current is 6 amp. It is assumed that the resistance does not change with frequency.

*a.* What is the resistance of the coil?

*b.* What is the inductance of the coil?

*c.* What is the capacitance of the capacitor?

*d.* What would the wattmeter indicate at a frequency of 163 cps?

**7-16.** Consider the circuit of Fig. P7-16. The potentials are, in volts,

$$v_1 = 7{,}070 \sin 377t$$
$$v_2 = 3{,}535 \sin (377t + \alpha)$$

where $\alpha$ is variable between the limits of 0 and $\pi$.

*a.* Draw sinor diagrams for values of $\alpha = 0, \pi/4, \pi/2, 3\pi/4$, and $\pi$.

*b.* Consider an upscale indication on the wattmeter as positive. For each of the values of $\alpha$ specified in (*a*) determine the indication on the wattmeter.

*c.* Analytically calculate the value of $\alpha$ for which the wattmeter indication would be zero.

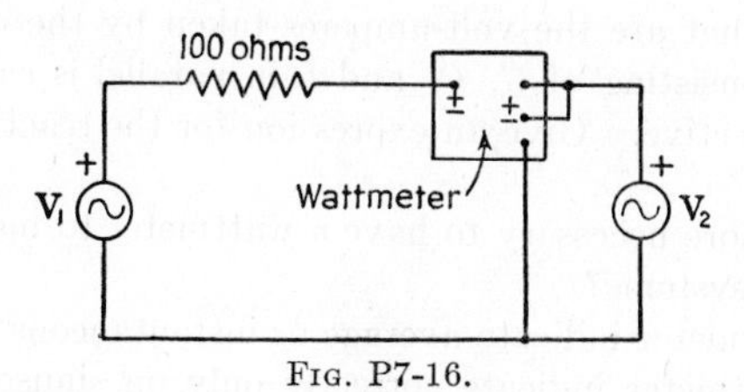


Fig. P7-16.

## QUESTIONS

**7-1.** What is the reference direction for power, as given by the product $v_{ab}i_{ab}$?

**7-2.** How is the reference direction of power flow related to the reference conditions for potential and current?

**7-3.** If current and potential are sinusoidal, under what condition does the power not reverse direction of flow during a cycle?

**7-4.** What is the meaning of the term "algebraic load"? Is it an absolute characteristic of a part of a circuit, or does it depend on the definition of potential and current reference conditions?

**7-5.** Is it necessary to know which part of a network actually absorbs power in order to define part of a network as an "algebraic load"?

**7-6.** How do you know that the trigonometric term of Eq. (7-6) makes no contribution to the average power?

**7-7.** Is the reference direction for average power the same as for instantaneous power?

**7-8.** Does the definition of power factor have any meaning if currents and potentials are not sinusoidal?

**7-9.** Why is the absolute-value symbol used in Eq. (7-12)?

**7-10.** If a load is connected to a generator through a long transmission line, which would be more indicative of the power loss in the transmission line, the apparent power or the real power at the load?

**7-11.** What is the power factor of an algebraic load consisting of a resistor, a capacitor, and inductor?

**7-12.** What is the power factor of a series circuit of $R$ and $L$, in terms of the circuit parameters?

**7-13.** What is the power factor of a series circuit of $R$ and $C$, in terms of the circuit parameters?

**7-14.** What is the power factor of a parallel circuit of $G$ and $L$, in terms of the circuit parameters?

**7-15.** What is the power factor of a parallel circuit of $G$ and $C$, in terms of the circuit parameters?

**7-16.** Can duality principles be used to relate the power factors of series and parallel circuits?

**7-17.** A circuit consisting of $R$ and $L$ in series is connected to a potential source of effective value $V$. What is the expression for the volt-amperes taken by the combination?

**7-18.** A circuit consisting of $R$ and $C$ in series is carrying a sinusoidal current of $I$ amp effective. What are the volt-amperes taken by the combination?

**7-19.** A circuit consisting of $G$, $C$, and $L$ in parallel is carrying a sinusoidal current of $I$ amp effective. Give an expression for the reactive volt-amperes to the circuit.

**7-20.** Why is it more necessary to have a wattmeter to measure power in a-c systems than in d-c systems?

**7-21.** Does a wattmeter indicate average or instantaneous power?

**7-22.** Does a wattmeter indicate correctly only on sinusoidal waves, or can the shape deviate from the sinusoidal form?

**7-23.** A wattmeter is indicating power correctly in a certain circuit. What would be the effect on the indication of (*a*) reversing the connections to the current coil, (*b*) reversing connections to the potential coil, (*c*) reversing connections to both coils?

**7-24.** How can a wattmeter be used to indicate the direction of power flow in a circuit?

**7-25.** A series circuit consisting of $R$, $L$, and $C$ in series is taking $W$ watts from the source to which it is connected. In terms of the $Q$ of the circuit what is the maximum energy stored in the inductor?

**7-26.** What is the power factor of a series resonant circuit at the resonant frequency? What is the power factor when the frequency has the value for which the magnitude of the impedance is $\sqrt{2}$ times the value of the impedance at resonance?

**7-27.** In a certain series circuit of $R$, $L$, and $C$ which is sinusoidally excited at a particular frequency, the maximum energy storage in the inductor is greater than the maximum energy storage in the capacitor. Is the operating frequency above or below resonance?

**7-28.** In a parallel circuit of $G$, $C$, and $L$ which is sinusoidally excited at a particular frequency, the maximum energy storage is greater in the inductor than in the capacitor. Is the frequency of operation above or below resonance?

**7-29.** At a certain instant of time, in a sinusoidally excited $R$-$L$-$C$ circuit, the energy storage in the inductor is a maximum. What fraction of a cycle later is the energy storage a maximum in the capacitor? What fraction of a cycle after maximum storage in the inductor is the rate of dissipation greatest in the resistor? Do the answers to these questions depend upon the frequency?

**7-30.** A series $R$-$L$-$C$ circuit is carrying a current having a triangular wave shape with zero full-cycle average value. Its frequency is the resonant frequency of the circuit (resonance, of course, being defined for the sinusoidal case). How would you expect the maximum stored energies in $L$ and $C$ to compare with each other if there is no d-c charge on the capacitor?

# CHAPTER 8

# APPLICATIONS OF COMPLEX QUANTITIES

**8-1. Introduction.** There is a limit to the complexity of circuit that can be solved by the methods so far presented. In some cases the geometry of phasor quantities becomes extremely complex. In others a solution is impossible by these methods.

For such cases the techniques to be introduced in this chapter are required. They represent the application of that branch of mathematics known as complex-function theory. Fortunately, the portion of the theory required is quite simple, so that no appreciable digression into mathematics is required. It is necessary only to define a new type of quantity and a few simple manipulations with it.

Care should be exercised to make sure there is no confusion between definition and proof. Certain relations are true merely by definition. That is, if a quantity $A$ has not previously been defined and $B$ is some known quantity, to write $A = B$ is to define $A$. No proof of the relation is required.

As a word of precaution it should be mentioned that in the application of the mathematics of complex quantities there is some obscuring of the physical facts. This price must be paid for great simplification in the techniques of solution.

**8-2. Complex Numbers.** The number system ordinarily used to represent physical situations consists of *real* numbers. Real numbers correspond to points on a straight line, as indicated in Fig. 8-1. Positive numbers are one side of zero, and negative numbers on the other.

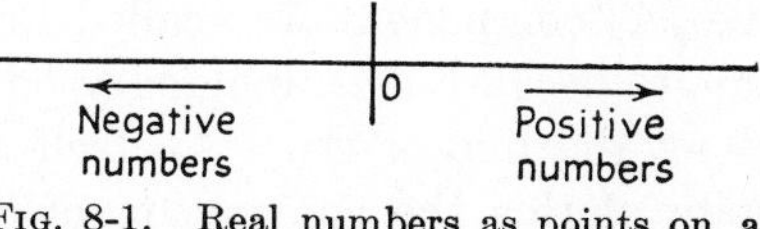

FIG. 8-1. Real numbers as points on a line.

A *complex number* can be represented by a point in a plane. Such a point can also determine a directed line from the origin to the point, and so a complex number has the same geometrical interpretations as a phasor quantity (sinor, impedance, admittance, or other quantities to be introduced). It can therefore be used to represent a phasor, so the same symbol designation is used (*i.e.*, bold-face type or a distinguishing mark).†

† The reader may wonder why two names are used for one type of quantity. The reason is that certain simple problems, like those of Chap. 6, can be solved without the mathematics of complex quantities. For the benefit of workers who meet only

Let the symbol **A** represent either of the directed lines shown at (*a*) or (*b*) of Fig. 8-2. Several methods are used to write **A** in a form suitable for use in mathematical manipulations. One method is to refer to Fig. 8-2*a* and *define* the rectangular form

$$\mathbf{A} = A_1 + jA_2 \qquad \text{rectangular form} \tag{8-1}$$

The components $A_1$ and $A_2$ cannot be added together. The symbol $j$ is introduced before $A_2$ to indicate this, and as a reminder that $A_2$ is at right angles to $A_1$. Further developments yield more information about $j$.

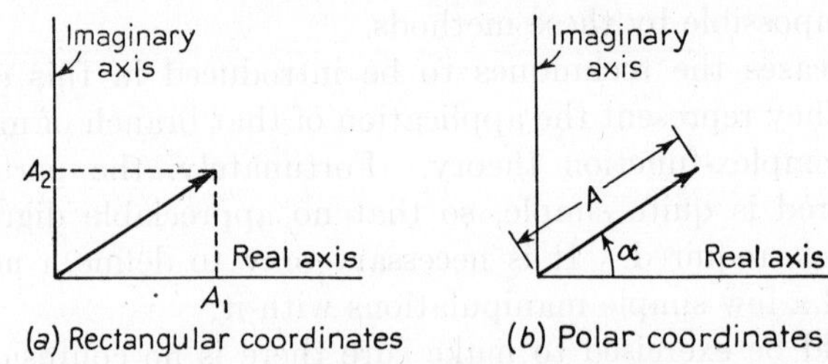

(*a*) Rectangular coordinates (*b*) Polar coordinates

FIG. 8-2. A complex number **A** shown as a point (or directed line) in a plane. Interpretation of the rectangular form $\mathbf{A} = A_1 + jA_2$ is shown at (*a*), and of the polar form $\mathbf{A} = A\underline{/\alpha}$ is shown at (*b*).

$A_1$ is said to be the *real part* and $A_2$ the *imaginary part* of the complex number **A**. These names can be misleading, so a brief explanation is given. If all points should fall on the horizontal line, the graphical representation would be the same as Fig. 8-1. Hence, the horizontal line is called the real axis and $A_1$ the real part. When the theory of complex numbers was being developed, it was thought that a number which could not be represented on a line could not "exist." Accordingly, the $jA_2$ component was called imaginary. The name is slightly unfortunate because it is imaginary only in the sense that it cannot be added along the line of $A_1$. $A_2$ itself (without the $j$) is a real number. In spite of this the convention of calling it the imaginary part of **A** has persisted.† Thus, the word "imaginary" is to be interpreted as an adjective meaning "perpendicular to the real axis." To cite a numerical example, the number $\mathbf{A} = 3 + j4$ is complex. Its real part is 3, and 4

such simple problems, it is convenient to have a name which does not bring in a concept which they do not use. However, when the mathematics of complex quantities is used, it is convenient to call a phasor quantity a complex quantity.

† In order to emphasize that there is no real difference in the nature of "real" and "imaginary" parts of a complex number, the names "consentor part" and "sentor part" have been suggested. See E. R. Mata, Los Vectores de la electrodinàmica y los "Vectores" de la electrotecnia, *Revista Mexicana de Electricidad*, March, 1950.

is its imaginary part, although 4 is a real number. Thus, it is seen that a complex number is really a pair of real numbers.

This viewpoint is furthered by *defining* the polar form

$$\mathbf{A} = A\underline{/\alpha} \qquad \text{polar form} \tag{8-2}$$

This makes no reference to real and imaginary parts, although two real quantities again appear, namely, $A$ and $\alpha$. They are shown in Fig. 8-2*b*. $A$ is called the *magnitude* or *modulus* and $\alpha$ the *angle* or *argument*. By allowing $A_1$ and $A_2$ to be positive or negative or by making $A$ positive and allowing $\alpha$ to have values between $-\pi$ and $\pi$, **A** can represent a point anywhere in the plane. The plane on which complex numbers are plotted is called the complex plane.

It is necessary to have a means of transferring from one system of writing a complex number to the other. The formulas for conversion are obtained from Fig. 8-2. They are as follows:

$$\begin{aligned} A_1 &= A \cos \alpha \\ A_2 &= A \sin \alpha \end{aligned} \tag{8-3}$$

and

$$\begin{aligned} A &= \sqrt{A_1^2 + A_2^2} \\ \alpha &= \tan^{-1} \frac{A_2}{A_1} \end{aligned} \tag{8-4}$$

Equations (8-3) suggest a third form for **A**, which is really the rectangular form, in terms of the quantities $A$ and $\alpha$, thus:

$$\mathbf{A} = A(\cos \alpha + j \sin \alpha) \qquad \text{trigonometric form} \tag{8-5}$$

It is called the trigonometric form because of the appearance of trigonometric functions.

**8-3. Manipulations with Complex Quantities.** Complex quantities are valuable in circuit analysis because of the manipulations that can be carried out with them. The manipulations needed are those common to ordinary algebra and calculus. They are defined in such a way as to become identical with the familiar ones for real quantities in the event the imaginary parts of the quantities are zero.

Most of these manipulations, such as addition, involve two complex quantities. Accordingly, let the notation

$$\begin{aligned} \mathbf{A} &= A_1 + jA_2 = A\underline{/\alpha} \\ \mathbf{B} &= B_1 + jB_2 = B\underline{/\beta} \end{aligned} \tag{8-6}$$

represent any pair of complex quantities, either variables or constants.

*Equality.* Two complex numbers are defined as being equal when their portrayal on the complex plane indicates that they are identical points.

Mathematically this means that either of the following *pairs* of equations are necessary to specify the equality **A** = **B**:

$$\begin{aligned} A_1 &= B_1 \\ A_2 &= B_2 \end{aligned} \tag{8-7}$$

or

$$\begin{aligned} A &= B \\ \alpha &= \beta \end{aligned} \tag{8-8}$$

Since two quantities are needed to specify a complex number, two equations are required to express the equality of two complex numbers. Either of these sets may be used. The choice depends on the form in which the numbers happen to be expressed.

*Addition and Subtraction.* Addition of two complex numbers is *defined* by the equation

$$\mathbf{A} + \mathbf{B} = (A_1 + B_1) + j(A_2 + B_2) \tag{8-9}$$

Subtraction is of course a special case of addition, so it follows that **A** − **B** is given in rectangular form by

$$\mathbf{A} - \mathbf{B} = (A_1 - B_1) + j(A_2 - B_2) \tag{8-10}$$

Addition and subtraction are always done in the rectangular form. If two numbers are in the polar form, they must be converted to the rectangular form before being added or subtracted. Addition and subtraction are illustrated in Fig. 8-3.

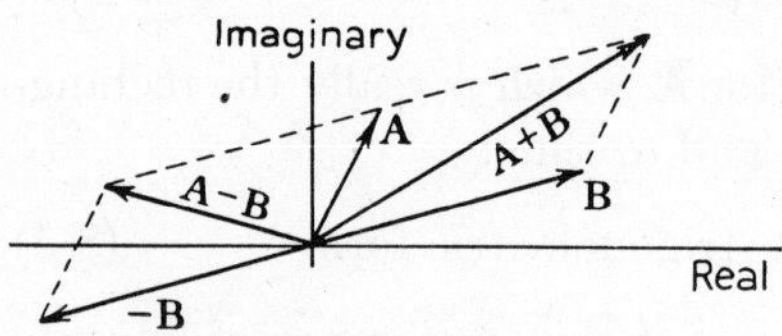

FIG. 8-3. Addition and subtraction of complex numbers.

*Multiplication and Division.* Multiplication and division are *defined* in polar notation. In multiplying two complex numbers their magnitudes are multiplied, and their angles are added. Thus

$$\mathbf{AB} = AB\underline{/\alpha + \beta} \tag{8-11}$$

Similarly, for division, the magnitudes are divided, and the angle of the denominator is subtracted from the angle of the numerator. As an illustration of this,

$$\frac{\mathbf{A}}{\mathbf{B}} = \frac{A}{B}\underline{/\alpha - \beta} \tag{8-12}$$

The rectangular forms may be used also. To demonstrate this, it is first necessary to consider the special case where **A** = **B** = $j$. In polar form these are **A** = **B** = $(1)\underline{/\pi/2}$, so their product is

$$(j)(j) = (1)\underline{/\pi/2}\,(1)\underline{/\pi/2} = (1)\underline{/\pi} = -1 \tag{8-13}$$

This process may be repeated any number of times, thus:

$$\begin{aligned} j^2 &= -1 \\ j^3 &= -j \\ j^4 &= 1 \\ j^5 &= j \\ &\text{etc.} \end{aligned} \tag{8-14}$$

Since $j^2 = -1$, it follows that $j$ may be interpreted as

$$j = \sqrt{-1} \tag{8-15}$$

It also follows that

$$\frac{1}{j} = -j \tag{8-16}$$

In rectangular form, two complex quantities are multiplied as binomials, using $-1$ in place of the $j^2$ which appears. Thus,

$$\mathbf{AB} = (A_1 + jA_2)(B_1 + jB_2) = (A_1B_1 - A_2B_2) + j(A_2B_1 + A_1B_2) \tag{8-17}$$

Division of **A** by **B** is accomplished by multiplying numerator and denominator by $B_1 - jB_2$. This eliminates all $j$ terms from the denominator. Thus,

$$\frac{\mathbf{A}}{\mathbf{B}} = \frac{(A_1 + jA_2)(B_1 - jB_2)}{(B_1 + jB_2)(B_1 - jB_2)} = \left(\frac{A_1B_1 + A_2B_2}{B_1^2 + B_2^2}\right) + j\left(\frac{A_2B_1 - A_1B_2}{B_1^2 + B_2^2}\right) \tag{8-18}$$

It is not self-evident that Eqs. (8-17) and (8-18) are, respectively, equivalent to Eqs. (8-11) and (8-12). A routine application of trigonometry is sufficient to establish their equivalence.

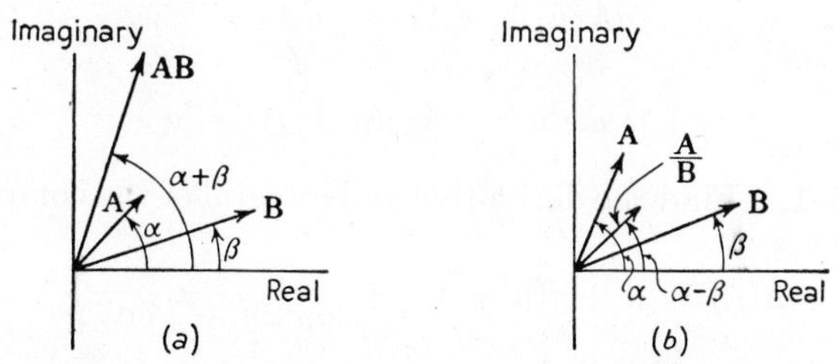


FIG. 8-4. Multiplication and division of complex numbers.

Multiplication and division of complex numbers are geometrically illustrated in Fig. 8-4.

The *reciprocal* of a complex number is a special case of division. The formula for a reciprocal may be written in either of the forms

$$\frac{1}{\mathbf{A}} = \frac{1}{A}\underline{/-\alpha}$$

$$\frac{1}{\mathbf{A}} = \frac{1}{A_1 + jA_2} = \frac{A_1}{A_1^2 + A_2^2} - j\frac{A_2}{A_1^2 + A_2^2} \tag{8-19}$$

*Conjugate.* With complex numbers there is occasionally need for a quantity termed the "conjugate" or "complex conjugate." The conjugate of **A** is given the symbol **A***. It may be defined in either the rectangular or the polar form. For example, consider the **A** of Eqs. (8-6). Its complex conjugate is *defined* by

$$\mathbf{A}^* = A_1 - jA_2$$

whence (8-20)

$$\mathbf{A}^* = A\underline{/-\alpha}$$

The geometric interpretation is shown in Fig. 8-5. Note that the conjugate is used in the process of division.

*Differentiation and Integration.* It frequently happens that complex quantities are functions of some independent variable. This applies to both the magnitude and the angle, or to the real and imaginary parts. In electrical-engineering practice, this independent variable is usually the angular frequency $\omega$ or the time $t$. In order not to favor one of these over the other, a general symbol $u$ is used in the definitions.

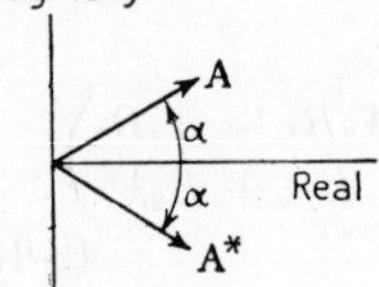

FIG. 8-5. The complex conjugate.

The definition has the simplest interpretation if it is applied to the rectangular form. Let $\mathbf{A}(u) = A_1(u) + jA_2(u)$ be used to represent a complex quantity which is a function of $u$. Its derivative and integral with respect to $u$ are *defined* by the following:

$$\frac{d\mathbf{A}(u)}{du} = \frac{dA_1}{du} + j\frac{dA_2}{du}$$
$$\int A(u)\,du = \int A_1\,du + j\int A_2\,du \tag{8-21}$$

**Example 8-1.** Find the derivative and integral of the complex function

$$\mathbf{A}(u) = u + j(u+1)^2 + \frac{1}{\sin 2u + j\cos 2u}$$

*Solution.* The definitions of the derivative and integral are given for the rectangular form. Therefore the second part is converted to the rectangular form as follows:

$$\frac{1}{\sin 2u + j\cos 2u} = \frac{\sin 2u - j\cos 2u}{\sin^2 2u + \cos^2 2u} = \sin 2u - j\cos 2u$$

Therefore

$$\mathbf{A}(u) = u + \sin 2u + j[(u + 1)^2 - \cos 2u]$$

This can be differentiated and integrated, giving

$$\frac{d\mathbf{A}(u)}{du} = 1 + 2 \cos 2u + j[2(u + 1) + 2 \sin 2u]$$

$$\int \mathbf{A}(u)\, du = \frac{u^2}{2} - \frac{\cos 2u}{2} + j\left[\frac{(u + 1)^3}{3} - \frac{\sin 2u}{2}\right]$$

**8-4. Exponential Form.** Differentiation and integration of complex quantities are defined for the rectangular form. They may not be used on the polar form. However, a form closely related to the polar can be defined, which can be differentiated and integrated.

Consider the complex quantity $\epsilon^{j\alpha}$, where $\epsilon = 2.718$, the base of natural logarithms. This is an unusual arrangement of symbols when viewed in the light of the usual definitions of exponentials. For example, $a^2$ means the product of $a$ by itself, $a^{3/2}$ the square root of $a$ cubed, etc. That is, the meaning of real exponents is defined in terms of powers and roots. No such interpretation of $\epsilon^{j\alpha}$ is possible, because the exponent is imaginary. It is *defined* by its power-series expansion, obtained from the Maclaurin expansion.

The coefficients of Maclaurin's series stem from the derivatives of the function. The derivative and integral of $\epsilon^{j\alpha}$ are *defined* to have the same forms as with a real exponent. Thus,

$$\frac{d\epsilon^{j\alpha}}{d\alpha} = j\epsilon^{j\alpha}$$

$$\int \epsilon^{j\alpha}\, d\alpha = \frac{1}{j}\epsilon^{j\alpha} \qquad (8\text{-}22)\dagger$$

It is found that the Maclaurin series, and therefore the *defining* formula, for $\epsilon^{j\alpha}$ is

$$\epsilon^{j\alpha} = 1 + j\alpha - \frac{\alpha^2}{2} - j\frac{\alpha^3}{3!} + \frac{\alpha^4}{4!} + j\frac{\alpha^5}{5!} - \cdots$$

$$= \left(1 - \frac{\alpha^2}{2} + \frac{\alpha^4}{4!} - \cdots\right) + j\left(\alpha - \frac{\alpha^3}{3!} + \frac{\alpha^5}{5!} - \cdots\right) \qquad (8\text{-}23)$$

† Equations (8-22) define the derivative and integral of $\epsilon^{j\alpha}$. At this stage $\epsilon^{j\alpha}$ is a form without meaning. Therefore Eqs. (8-22) are not in conflict with Eqs. (8-21) which applies to the meaningful rectangular form. Equation (8-23) defines $\epsilon^{j\alpha}$ in such a way that Eqs. (8-21) and (8-22) become equivalent for the function $\epsilon^{j\alpha}$, as may be checked on Eq. (8-25).

The Maclaurin series for sin $\alpha$ and cos $\alpha$ are

$$\cos \alpha = 1 - \frac{\alpha^2}{2} + \frac{\alpha^4}{4!} - \cdots$$
$$\sin \alpha = \alpha - \frac{\alpha^3}{3!} + \frac{\alpha^5}{5!} - \cdots \quad (8\text{-}24)$$

Therefore, it is proved that

$$\epsilon^{j\alpha} = \cos \alpha + j \sin \alpha \quad (8\text{-}25)$$

In this identity $\alpha$ is any real quantity. It may be the angle of the complex number **A**. If Eq. (8-25) is multiplied throughout by $A$, to give

$$A\epsilon^{j\alpha} = A(\cos \alpha + j \sin \alpha) \quad (8\text{-}26)$$

it follows from Eq. (8-5) that

$$\mathbf{A} = A\epsilon^{j\alpha} \qquad \text{exponential form} \quad (8\text{-}27)$$

The utility of the exponential form lies in the compactness of mathematical manipulations in which it is used.

The polar form is used most frequently in specifying a numerical value, as in the complex number $5\underline{/48°}$. In this form the angle is most often in degrees, although radians may be used. In the exponential form radians are always used. The exponential form of the above number would be $5\epsilon^{j0.84}$. However, the exponential form finds greatest application when the complex quantity is a variable, as in $A\epsilon^{j\alpha}$, where $\alpha$ is a variable quantity.

Examples of the use of the exponential form are as follows: Let **A** and **B** be the complex quantities given in Eqs. (8-6). The product and quotient are

$$\mathbf{AB} = AB\epsilon^{j(\alpha+\beta)}$$
$$\frac{\mathbf{A}}{\mathbf{B}} = \frac{A}{B}\epsilon^{j(\alpha-\beta)} \quad (8\text{-}28)$$

**8-5. Complex Quantities and Sinusoids.** It is demonstrated in Chap. 2 that the vertical or horizontal projection of a line rotating at constant angular velocity generates a sinusoid. Complex notation offers a convenient method of describing this motion. Consider a rotating line of unit length in the complex plane, making zero angle with the real axis when $t = 0$, as shown in Fig. 8-6. The position of its extremity is given by the complex quantity

$$\epsilon^{j\omega t} = \cos \omega t + j \sin \omega t \quad (8\text{-}29)$$

since its variable angular position is $\omega t$.

Equation (8-29) implies a relationship between complex quantities and sinusoidal functions. It is convenient to introduce a notation which makes this explicit. If the symbol for a complex quantity is prefixed by the letters Re, this means that only the real part should be considered. Similarly, the prefix Im implies the imaginary part. In this notation, Eq. (8-29) yields the following formulas:

$$\sin \omega t = \text{Im}\ (\epsilon^{j\omega t}) \tag{8-30}$$

and

$$\cos \omega t = \text{Re}\ (\epsilon^{j\omega t}) \tag{8-31}$$

The symbols Im and Re are to be thought of as representations of functions, just as sin, cos, log, etc.

Now consider a sinusoidal function, such as $\sqrt{2}\ V \sin\ (\omega t + \alpha)$. This has been symbolically represented by the sinor

$$\mathbf{V} = V\underline{/\alpha} \tag{8-32}$$

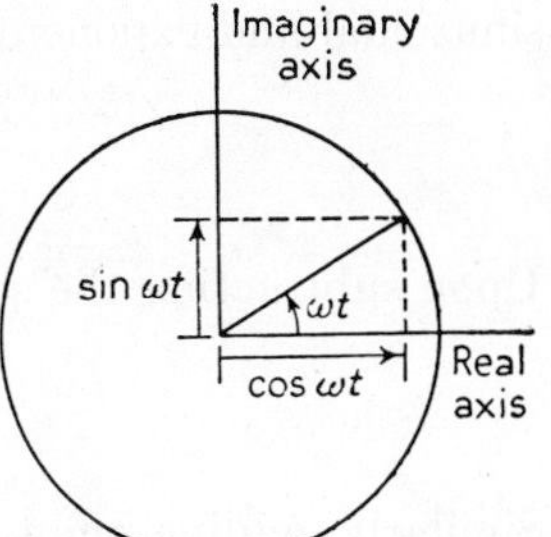


FIG. 8-6. The geometric generator of a sinusoid in the complex plane. Radius of circle = 1.

as illustrated in Fig. 8-7$a$. This figure differs from previous sinor diagrams only in the labeling of the axes.

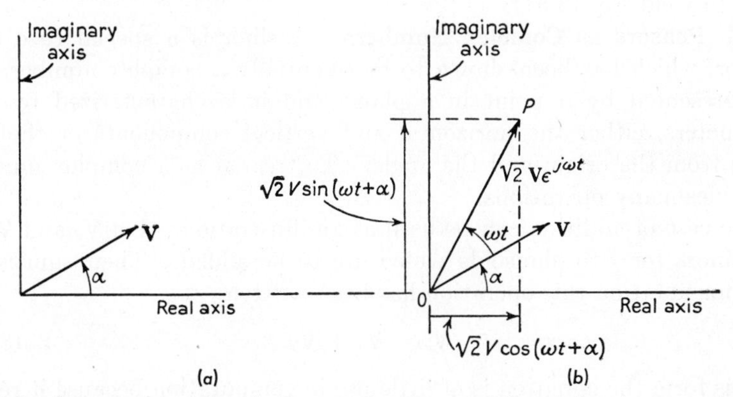


FIG. 8-7. Sinor representation in the complex plane and its relation to sine and cosine functions of time.

Now take an alternate viewpoint, starting with **V** in the complex form

$$\mathbf{V} = V\epsilon^{j\alpha} \tag{8-33}$$

Multiplying both sides of this by $\epsilon^{j\omega t}$ gives

$$\mathbf{V}\epsilon^{j\omega t} = V\epsilon^{j(\omega t+\alpha)} \tag{8-34}$$

Therefore, from Eq. (8-26), as illustrated in Fig. 8-7*b*,

$$\sqrt{2}\, V \sin (\omega t + \alpha) = \text{Im} (\sqrt{2}\, \mathbf{V} \epsilon^{j\omega t}) \tag{8-35}$$
$$\sqrt{2}\, V \cos (\omega t + \alpha) = \text{Re} (\sqrt{2}\, \mathbf{V} \epsilon^{j\omega t}) \tag{8-36}$$

Further interpretation of the above relation is given in Sec. 8-6.

Equation (8-29) leads to two other important formulas relating the sinusoidal and exponential functions. Consider the pair of equations

$$\begin{aligned} \epsilon^{j\omega t} &= \cos \omega t + j \sin \omega t \\ \epsilon^{-j\omega t} &= \cos \omega t - j \sin \omega t \end{aligned} \tag{8-37}$$

Upon subtracting the second from the first,

$$\sin \omega t = \frac{\epsilon^{j\omega t} - \epsilon^{-j\omega t}}{2j} \tag{8-38}$$

Similarly, adding one to the other gives

$$\cos \omega t = \frac{\epsilon^{j\omega t} + \epsilon^{-j\omega t}}{2} \tag{8-39}$$

Equation (8-38) is related to Eq. (8-30) in the following way: By taking the difference of $\epsilon^{j\omega t}$ and $\epsilon^{-j\omega t}$, the real parts cancel, leaving the imaginary part. Equation (8-39) is a similar device for discarding the imaginary part, to yield Eq. (8-31).

**8-6. Phasors as Complex Numbers.** A sinor is a special case of a phasor, which has been shown to be essentially a complex number. It is represented by a point in a plane, and it is characterized by two parameters, either the horizontal and vertical components or the distance from the origin and the angle. To treat it as a complex number simplifies many operations.

The case of addition can be used as an illustration. Let $\mathbf{V}_a$ and $\mathbf{V}_b$ be the sinors for two sinusoids which are to be added. Their sum is $\mathbf{V}_c$. In sinor notation this operation has been written

$$\mathbf{V}_c = \mathbf{V}_a + \mathbf{V}_b \tag{8-40}$$

In this form the equation is of little use in computation because it represents a geometric operation. If the original sinors are written as complex numbers, Eq. (8-40) can be used in numerical calculation. For example, suppose

$$\begin{aligned} \mathbf{V}_a &= 100 + j80 \\ \mathbf{V}_b &= 60 - j150 \end{aligned} \tag{8-41}$$

The rectangular complex form for $\mathbf{V}_c$ is

$$\mathbf{V}_c = (100 + 60) + j(80 - 150) = 160 - j70 \tag{8-42}$$

In other words, complex notation makes it possible to include the addition of horizontal and vertical components in *one* symbolic equation.

Now consider Eq. (8-35) which is repeated

$$\text{Im}\,(\sqrt{2}\,\mathbf{V}\epsilon^{j\omega t}) = \sqrt{2}\,V \sin(\omega t + \alpha) \tag{8-43}$$

where $\mathbf{V} = V\epsilon^{j\alpha}$. This is a precise relationship between a complex constant (sinor **V**) and a sinusoid. The comparable notation used in earlier chapters is

$$\mathbf{V} \text{ symbolizes } \sqrt{2}\,V \sin(\omega t + \alpha) \tag{8-44}$$

This comparison emphasizes that the precise formulation of Eq. (8-43) can replace the symbolism of Eq. (8-44) for showing the relationship between a sinusoid and its sinor. To be able to do this is a convenience in circuit analysis, because Eq. (8-43) can be differentiated and integrated. Differentiation and integration are not possible with Eq. (8-44).

**8-7. Applications to Circuit Analysis.** The advantage of complex algebra for addition of sinors has been shown. However, its usefulness

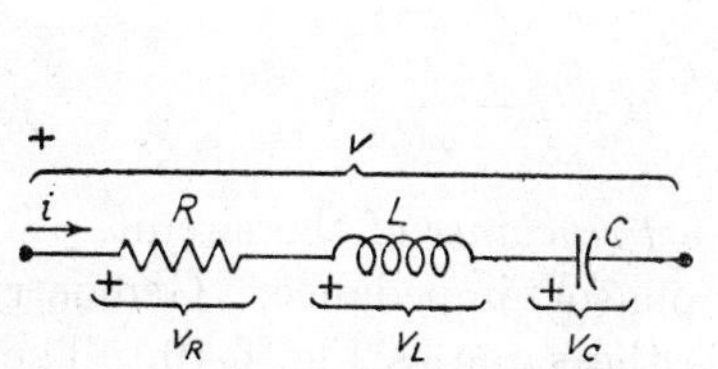


FIG. 8-8. The basic series circuit.

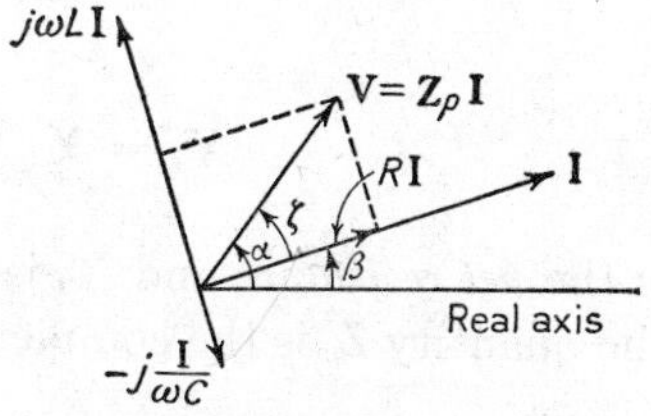


FIG. 8-9. Sinor diagram for the basic series circuit.

goes far beyond this, as is partly demonstrated by the following development. In one sense this section is a repetition of Secs. 6-4 and 6-5 and so may seem to be superfluous, but this is not true. The development given here is intended to show how the same results are obtained by the use of complex algebra and thereby to lay the groundwork for the more complicated situations in which complex algebra is necessary.

Consider the circuit of Fig. 8-8 and its sinor diagram as given in Fig. 8-9. In sinor form the potential equation for the circuit is

$$\mathbf{V} = \mathbf{V}_R + \mathbf{V}_L + \mathbf{V}_C \tag{8-45}$$

Let **I** be the sinor for the current. It is now regarded as a complex number. The potential $\mathbf{V}_R$ is in phase with the current, and its magnitude is $IR$. Therefore $\mathbf{V}_R = R\mathbf{I}$. The potential $\mathbf{V}_L$ leads the current by 90°, and its magnitude is $\omega LI$; and the potential $\mathbf{V}_C$ lags the current by 90°, and its magnitude is $(I/\omega C)$. A multiplication by $j$ rotates a phasor quantity counterclockwise (lead direction) 90°, and a multiplication by $-j$ rotates a phasor clockwise (lag direction) 90°. Therefore

$$\begin{aligned} \mathbf{V}_R &= R\mathbf{I} \\ \mathbf{V}_L &= j\omega L\mathbf{I} \\ \mathbf{V}_C &= -j\frac{1}{\omega C}\mathbf{I} \end{aligned} \tag{8-46}$$

Substituting these in Eq. (8-45) gives

$$\mathbf{V} = \left[R + j\left(\omega L - \frac{1}{\omega C}\right)\right]\mathbf{I} \tag{8-47}$$

This relation can be abbreviated to

$$\mathbf{V} = \mathbf{Z}_s\mathbf{I} \tag{8-48}$$

or it can be inverted to give

$$\mathbf{I} = \frac{\mathbf{V}}{\mathbf{Z}_s} \tag{8-49}$$

where

$$\mathbf{Z}_s = R_s + jX_s \tag{8-50}$$

and

$$X_s = X_L + X_C = \omega L - \frac{1}{\omega C} \tag{8-51}$$

$R_s$ is the *net resistance* and $X_s$ is the *net reactance* of the circuit.

The quantity $\mathbf{Z}_s$ is the complex (or phasor) impedance. Geometrically it is the same as Fig. 6-10. The only difference is in the labeling of the real and imaginary axes, as shown in Fig. 8-10. It is recalled that in Chap. 6, for no apparent reason, the convention was introduced of always drawing the resistance component of an impedance triangle in the horizontal direction. The reason for this can now be seen; it was done in order to have the $\mathbf{Z}$ of Chap. 6 become identical with the complex impedance.

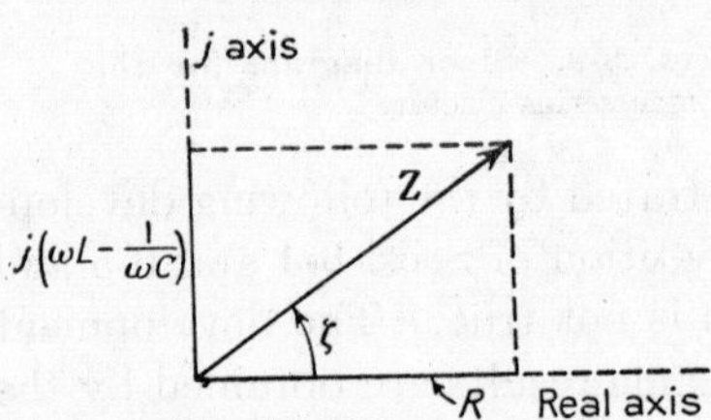


FIG. 8-10. Diagram of the complex impedance of the basic series circuit.

If the complex numbers are put in polar form, it is found that Eqs. (8-48) and (8-49) are, respectively, identical with Eqs. (6-20) and (6-25). However, the important difference is that in Chap. 6 the concept of multiplying or dividing phasors (now complex quantities) was not available. This is the important contribution of this chapter to circuit analysis. Complex notation is brought to its full meaning in Chaps. 10 and 11.

The following example is given as an aid in relating this chapter with Chap. 6. It is numerically identical with Example 6-3.

**Example 8-2.** In Fig. 8-8 let $R = 180$ ohms, $L = 0.75$ henry, and $C = 6.67$ μf. The potential is symbolically represented by the sinor $\mathbf{V} = 250\underline{/45°}$ volts, and the frequency is 60 cps. Find the sinor **I** in amperes.

*Solution.* *a.* Using the rectangular form, the complex impedance is

$$\mathbf{Z}_s = 180 + j(283 - 398) = 180 - j115$$

where $283 = (377)(0.75)$ and $398 = 10^6/(377)(6.67)$ are the reactance components. In rectangular form the potential is

$$\begin{aligned}\mathbf{V} &= 250(\cos 45° + j \sin 45°)\\ &= 176.8 + j176.8\end{aligned}$$

By Eq. (8-49) the current is

$$\begin{aligned}\mathbf{I} &= \frac{176.8 + j176.8}{180 - j115}\\ &= \frac{(176.8 + j176.8)(180 + j115)}{(180 - j115)(180 + j115)}\\ &= \frac{31{,}820 - 20{,}330 + j(31{,}820 + 20{,}330)}{32{,}400 + 13{,}225}\\ &= \frac{11{,}490 + j52{,}150}{45{,}625} = 0.251 + j1.143 = 1.17\underline{/77.5°}\end{aligned}$$

*b.* Using the polar form, the impedance is

$$\begin{aligned}\mathbf{Z}_s &= \sqrt{(180)^2 + (115)^2}\ \underline{/\tan^{-1}(-115/180)}\\ &= 214\underline{/-32.5°} \text{ ohms}\end{aligned}$$

The equation for the current, in amperes, is then

$$\mathbf{I} = \frac{250\underline{/45°}}{214\underline{/-32.5°}} = 1.17\underline{/77.5°}$$

A similar analysis can be given for the parallel circuit of Fig. 8-11. The properties of the sinor diagram of Fig. 8-12 are expressed by

$$\mathbf{I} = \mathbf{Y}_p\mathbf{V} \tag{8-52}$$

or

$$\mathbf{V} = \frac{\mathbf{I}}{\mathbf{Y}_p} \tag{8-53}$$

Equations (8-52) and (8-53) are duals of Eqs. (8-48) and (8-49) and they are the counterparts of Eqs. (6-30) and (6-35), in complex notation. The *complex admittance* is shown in Fig. 8-13, and is given by

$$\mathbf{Y}_p = G_p + jB_p \tag{8-54}$$

The admittance diagram is the same as Fig. 6-15, except for the labeling of the real and imaginary axes.

$G_p$ and $B_p$ are, respectively, the *net conductance* and *net susceptance* of the circuit. For the parallel circuit, $G$ is the conductance of the resistor, and

$$B_p = B_C + B_L = \omega C - \frac{1}{\omega L} \tag{8-55}$$

Equation (8-50) applies specifically to the series circuit, and Eq. (8-54) applies to the parallel circuit. However, as described in Sec. 6-7, it is

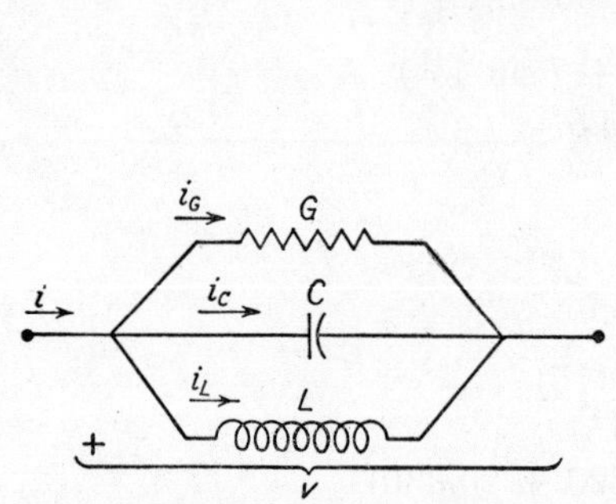


FIG. 8-11. The basic parallel circuit.

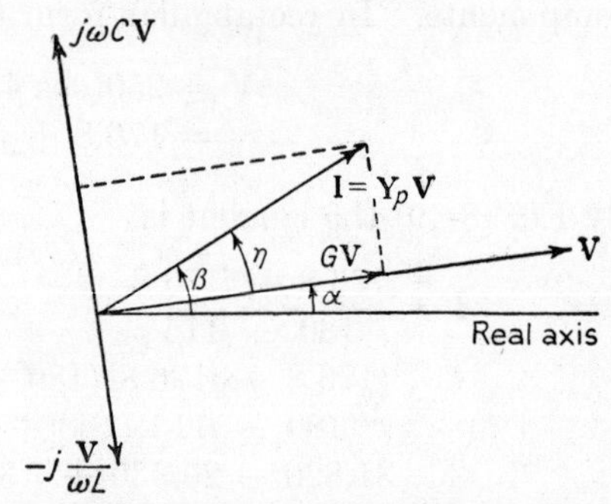


FIG. 8-12. Sinor diagram for the basic parallel circuit.

possible to specify an admittance for a series circuit and an impedance for a parallel circuit.

For the series case

$$\mathbf{Y}_s = \frac{1}{R_s + jX_s} = \frac{R_s}{R_s^2 + X_s^2} - j\frac{X_s}{R_s^2 + X_s^2} \tag{8-56}$$

and for the parallel case

$$\mathbf{Z}_p = \frac{1}{G_p + jB_p} = \frac{G_p}{G_p^2 + B_p^2} - j\frac{B_p}{G_p^2 + B_p^2} \tag{8-57}$$

Consider the formula for the admittance of the series circuit. The real and imaginary parts are, respectively, a conductance and a susceptance, but not of the elements of the series circuit. That is, the real part of the admittance is not $1/R_s$, and the imaginary part is not $1/X_s$. The real and imaginary parts may be looked upon as the conductance and susceptance of an imagined equivalent parallel circuit.

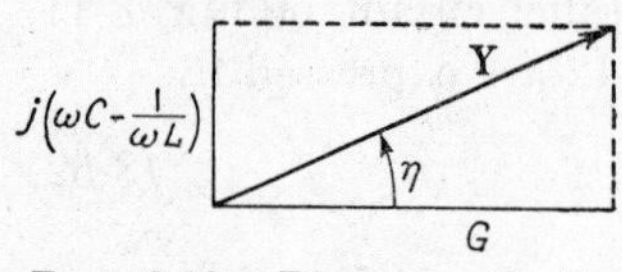


FIG. 8-13. Diagram of the complex admittance of the basic parallel circuit.

A similar statement applies to the impedance of the parallel circuit. Its real and imaginary parts are not the resistance and reactance of the elements of the parallel circuit. They are, rather, the resistance and reactance of an imagined equivalent series circuit.

The subject of equivalence of series and parallel circuits is given a more detailed treatment in Sec. 10-5. Meanwhile, as a numerical illustration, consider the following example.

**Example 8-3.** Find the admittance of the series circuit specified in Example 8-2.

*Solution.* From the computations in Example 8-2 it is known that the impedance is

$$\mathbf{Z}_s = 180 - j115 \text{ ohms}$$

Following the procedure outlined above, the admittance is

$$\begin{aligned}\mathbf{Y}_s = \frac{1}{\mathbf{Z}_s} &= \frac{180}{(180)^2 + (115)^2} + j\frac{115}{(180)^2 + (115)^2}\\ &= \frac{180}{45{,}625} + j\frac{115}{45{,}625}\\ &= 0.00394 + j0.00252 \text{ mho}\end{aligned}$$

When viewed from its terminals, the given series circuit is the same as a parallel combination of a resistor having a conductance of 0.00394 mho, and a capacitor having a susceptance of 0.00252 mho. It is important to note that this equivalence holds *only at the given frequency.* If the frequency is changed the parameters of the equivalent circuit change.

**8-8. Excitations in Exponential Form.** The work of this section is supplementary. It parallels the previous developments and gives insight into the meaning of complex notation when used in circuit analysis. Consider the problem of finding the potential-current relationship in the general series circuit of Fig. 8-8. The controlling equation is

$$v = Ri + L\frac{di}{dt} + \frac{1}{C}\int i\,dt \tag{8-58}$$

The same equation is treated in Chap. 6 by assuming $i$ to be a sinusoidal function. This continues to be the case, but complex notation is used, writing

$$i = \text{Im}\,(\sqrt{2}\,I\epsilon^{j(\omega t+\beta)}) \tag{8-59}$$

The derivative of the imaginary part of a complex function is identical with the imaginary part of the derivative. A similar statement is true for the integral. Therefore,

$$\begin{aligned}\frac{d}{dt}\text{Im}\,(\sqrt{2}\,I\epsilon^{j(\omega t+\beta)}) &= \text{Im}\,(\sqrt{2}\,j\omega I\epsilon^{j(\omega t+\beta)})\\ \int \text{Im}\,(\sqrt{2}\,I\epsilon^{j(\omega t+\beta)}) &= \text{Im}\left(\frac{\sqrt{2}\,I}{j\omega}\,\epsilon^{j(\omega t+\beta)}\right)\end{aligned} \tag{8-60}$$ †

† The integration constant is set equal to zero because d-c components are not to be included.

Substituting these into Eq. (8-58) gives

$$v = \text{Im}\,(\sqrt{2}\,RI\epsilon^{j(\omega t+\beta)}) + \text{Im}\,(\sqrt{2}\,j\omega LI\epsilon^{j(\omega t+\beta)}) + \text{Im}\left(\frac{\sqrt{2}\,I}{j\omega C}\,\epsilon^{j(\omega t+\beta)}\right) \tag{8-61}$$

$$v = \text{Im}\left\{\sqrt{2}\,I\left[R + j\left(\omega L - \frac{1}{\omega C}\right)\right]\epsilon^{j(\omega t+\beta)}\right\} \tag{8-62}$$

This explicit formula for the potential is obtained in one line, rather than the several steps required in Chap. 6.

Of course, Eq. (8-62) is in need of interpretation. The quantity within the brackets in Eq. (8-62) is the complex impedance given by Eq. (8-50). Also, $I\epsilon^{j\beta}$ **I** can be written so Eq. (8-62) can be written

$$v = \text{Im}\,[\sqrt{2}\,(\mathbf{ZI})\epsilon^{j\omega t}] \tag{8-63}$$

The product within the parentheses is the complex form for the sinor **V**. Hence, Eq. (8-48) has been derived without recourse to the earlier treatment.

If needed, the sinusoidal time function is obtained by writing **I** and **V** in exponential form and taking the imaginary part, thus:

$$v = \text{Im}\,(\sqrt{2}\,ZI\epsilon^{j(\omega t+\beta+\zeta)}) = \sqrt{2}\,ZI\sin\,(\omega t + \beta + \zeta) \tag{8-64}$$

The last form is identical with Eq. (6-23).

It is significant that the symbol Im plays no part in the process of determining amplitude and phase relationships. It enters only when a specific time function is required. As far as amplitude and phase relationships are concerned, the symbol Re (meaning real part) could just as well have been used. It would also be possible to eliminate either of the symbols Im or Re. In more advanced work this is sometimes done.

The physical significance of the unimportance of the symbol Im or Re is very simple. It means that *amplitude* and *phase-difference* relations do not depend on the position of the waves on the time axis.

The integrodifferential equation of the parallel circuit can be analyzed in exactly the same manner. In view of their dual relationship this would contribute nothing new in the way of understanding.

**8-9. Power in Complex Notation.** Consider the algebraic load of Fig. 8-14, and let the potential and current sinors ($\mathbf{V} = V\epsilon^{j\alpha}$, $\mathbf{I} = I\epsilon^{j\beta}$) of Fig. 8-15 be a typical condition. The power and reactive volt-amperes have been defined by

$$\begin{aligned} P &= VI\cos\,(\alpha - \beta) \\ N &= VI\sin\,(\alpha - \beta) \end{aligned} \tag{8-65}$$

respectively.

With this in mind, consider the product of the complex quantities **V** and **I***. Let this product be the complex quantity **S**. Reference to the definition of the complex conjugate shows that

$$\mathbf{S} = \mathbf{VI}^* = Ve^{j\alpha}Ie^{-j\beta} = VIe^{j(\alpha-\beta)} \qquad (8\text{-}66)$$

Another way to write this is

$$\mathbf{S} = VI \cos(\alpha - \beta) + jVI \sin(\alpha - \beta) \qquad (8\text{-}67)$$

Comparison with Eq. (8-65) yields

$$\mathbf{S} = P + jN \qquad (8\text{-}68)$$

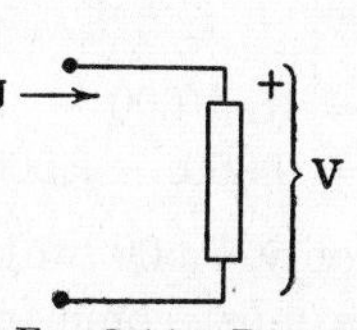


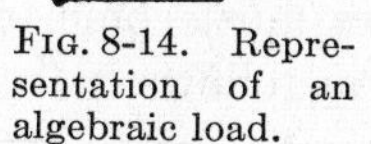
FIG. 8-14. Representation of an algebraic load.

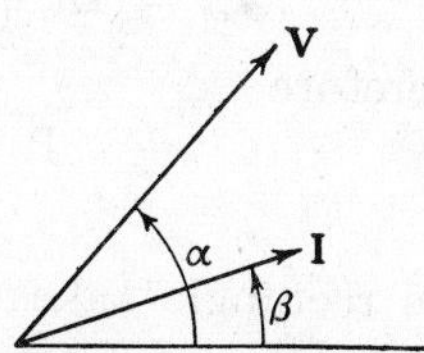


FIG. 8-15. General potential and current sinors for Fig. 8-14.

Thus, the complex quantity **S** has a real part which is algebraically the power going into the algebraic load. The imaginary part is the reactive volt-amperes. **S** can be plotted graphically, as in Fig. 8-16.

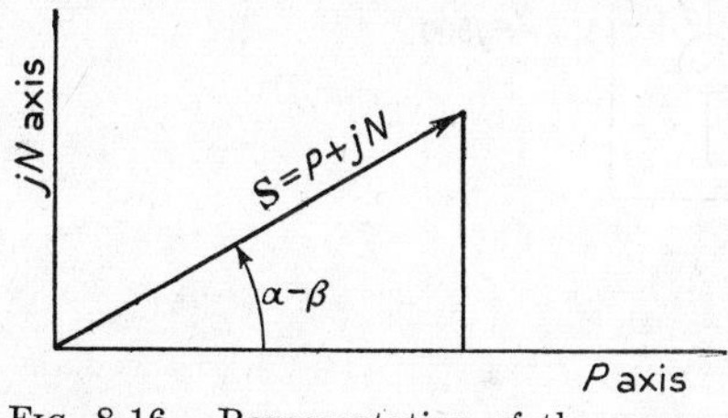


FIG. 8-16. Representation of the power triangle in the complex plane.

This is a very convenient device for finding power and reactive volt-amperes. Although the proof was given using the exponential form, the technique can be used in all forms. The concept of power is thus extended to make it a phasor quantity.

**Example 8-4.** For the circuit shown on page 184, determine the power delivered to the resistor $R$, the power delivered to the dotted rectangle, and the power delivered to or by the source on the right.

*Solution.* The impedance of the resistor and inductor connected in series is, in ohms,

$$\mathbf{Z} = 40 + j20$$

The potential across this impedance is

$$\mathbf{V}_{ad} = \mathbf{V}_{ab} + \mathbf{V}_{bd} = 500 + j500 \text{ volts}$$

Therefore the current is

$$\mathbf{I} = \frac{500 + j500}{40 + j20} = \frac{(500 + j500)(40 - j20)}{1{,}600 + 400}$$
$$= 15 + j5 \text{ amp}$$

*a.* Let $P_1$ be the power delivered to the resistor.

$$P_1 = \text{Re}\,(\mathbf{V}_{cd}\mathbf{I}^*) = \text{Re}\,[(R\mathbf{I})\mathbf{I}^*]$$
$$= \text{Re}\,[40(15 + j5)(15 - j5)]$$
$$= 40(225 + 25) = 10{,}000 \text{ watts}$$

*b.* Let $P_2$ be the power delivered to the reactangle.

$$P_2 = Re\,(\mathbf{V}_{cb}\mathbf{I}^*)$$

But

$$\mathbf{V}_{cb} = \mathbf{I}R + \mathbf{V}_{db} = 600 + j200 - j500 = 600 - j300$$

Therefore

$$\begin{aligned} P_2 &= \text{Re}\,[(600 - j300)(15 - j5)] \\ &= 9{,}000 - 1{,}500 = 7{,}500 \text{ watts} \end{aligned}$$

The rectangle takes only 7,500 watts, while the resistor takes 10,000 watts. The difference must come from the source within the rectangle. This may be checked as follows.

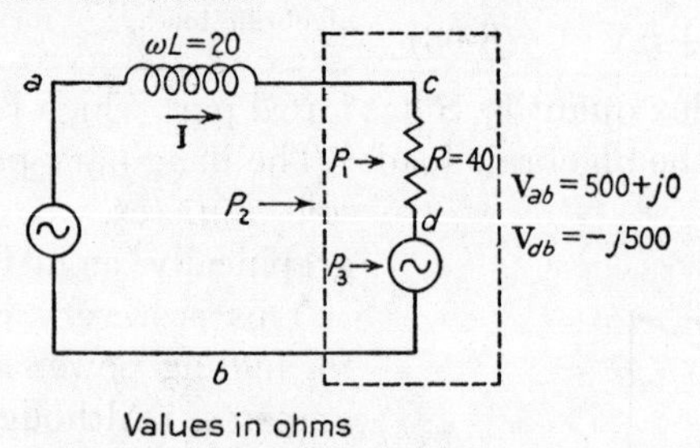

Values in ohms

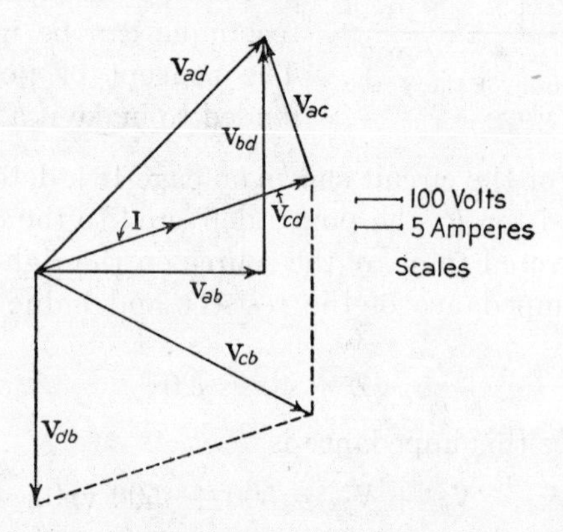


*c.* Let $P_3$ be the power delivered to the source within the rectangle (considering it as an algebraic load).

$$\begin{aligned} P_3 &= \text{Re}\,(\mathbf{V}_{db}\mathbf{I}^*) \\ &= \text{Re}\,[(-j500)(15 - j5)] = -2{,}500 \text{ watts} \end{aligned}$$

The negative sign shows that this is really an energy source, as expected from the results of (*a*) and (*b*).

**8-10. Summary.** It is shown that phasor quantities can be treated as complex quantities; simplifying the analysis of series and parallel circuits and providing an interpretation of complex impedance and admittance for each. This is the really significant result, because it leads to the ability to solve a-c circuits by techniques very similar to the ones learned for d-c circuits.

A second contribution of the complex-quantity approach is in the calculation of power and reactive volt-amperes. By multiplying the potential sinor by the conjugate of the current sinor, the power and reactive volt-amperes are obtained as, respectively, the real and imaginary parts of the product.

## PROBLEMS

**8-1.** Write

| | |
|---|---|
| $3 + j6$ | in polar form |
| $-4 + j8$ | in polar form |
| $-5 - j6$ | in polar form |
| $7 - j$ | in polar form |
| $11\underline{/35^\circ}$ | in rectangular form |
| $7.5\underline{/135^\circ}$ | in rectangular form |
| $8.2\underline{/-90^\circ}$ | in rectangular form |
| $6.7\underline{/-20^\circ}$ | in rectangular form |

**8-2.** The results of Prob. 8-1 may be used in this problem. Obtain the results for the following combinations of complex numbers:

| | |
|---|---|
| $(3 + j6) + (-4 + j8)$ | in rectangular and polar form |
| $11\underline{/35^\circ} + 7.5\underline{/135^\circ}$ | in rectangular and polar form |

**8-3.** The results of Prob. 8-1 may be used in this problem. Obtain the results for the following combinations of complex numbers:

| | |
|---|---|
| $(-5 - j6)(7 - j)$ | in rectangular and polar form |
| $(8.3\underline{/-90^\circ})(6.7\underline{/-20^\circ})$ | in rectangular and polar form |
| $\dfrac{3 + j6}{-5 - j6}$ | in rectangular and polar form |
| $\dfrac{7.5\underline{/531^\circ}}{6.7\underline{/-20^\circ}}$ | in rectangular and polar form |

**8-4.** Specify the complex conjugate of each of the complex numbers given in Prob. 8-1. Give the result in polar and rectangular form in each case. The results obtained in Prob. 8-1 may be used where applicable.

**8-5.** Use Eqs. (8-38) and (8-39) to prove the identities

*a.* $\sin(x + y) = \sin x \cos y + \cos x \sin y$

*b.* $\cos(x + y) = \cos x \cos y - \sin x \sin y$

*c.* $\sin^2 x + \cos^2 x = 1$

**8-6.** Use Eqs. (8-38) and (8-39) to prove the identities

*a.* $\sin \dfrac{x}{2} = \sqrt{\dfrac{1 - \cos x}{2}}$

*b.* $\cos \frac{x}{2} = \sqrt{\frac{1 + \cos x}{2}}$

*c.* $\sin x + \sin y = 2 \sin \frac{x + y}{2} \cos \frac{x - y}{x}$

**8-7.** Obtain the derivative, with respect to $x$, of each of the complex quantities which follow. Give the results in rectangular form.

*a.* $A(x) = 3x^2 + j \cos 2x$

*b.* $A(x) = \sqrt{x + x^2}\, \epsilon^{j3x}$

**8-8.** Express each of the complex numbers of Prob. 8-1 in exponential form. The results obtained in Prob. 8-1 may be used where applicable.

**8-9.** Use complex notation to obtain the sinor representation of the function

$$v = \sqrt{2}\,[25 \sin (\omega t + 30°) - 10 \sin \omega t + 15 \cos \omega t]$$

Express the result as a time function also.

**8-10.** The potential across the series connection of a 15-ohm resistance and a 20-ohm inductive reactance is

$$v = 14.14 \sin \omega t$$

Use the methods of complex algebra to obtain the equation for the current in the circuit as a function of time. Use the usual reference conditions.

**8-11.** The current in the leads to a parallel circuit consisting of 0.2 mho conductance and 0.3 mho capacitive susceptance is

$$i = 7.07 \cos \omega t$$

Use the methods of complex algebra to obtain the equation for the potential across the combination. Use the usual reference conditions.

**8-12.** Consider the circuit of Fig. P8-12. In complex notation, the potential $\mathbf{V}_2$ is $150 + j0$ volts. Determine the complex expressions for the current and

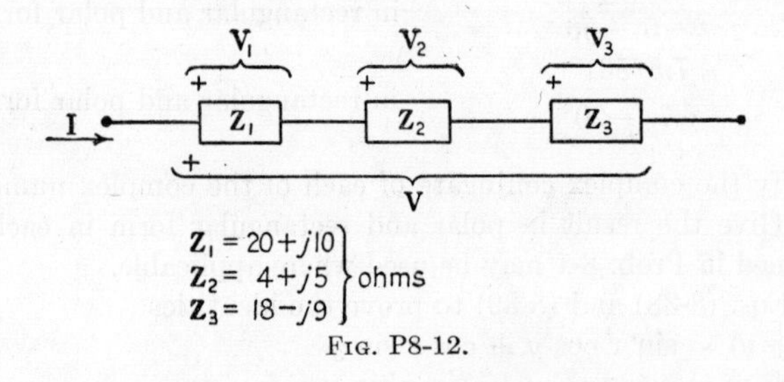


FIG. P8-12.

the three potentials indicated, and give the time-function equivalents of **V** and **I**. Also, find the complex admittance of the combination.

**8-13.** Consider the circuit of Fig. P8-13. In complex notation the current $\mathbf{I}_2$ is $0 + j5$ amp. Determine the complex expressions for the potential and the three currents indicated, and give the time-function equivalents of **V** and **I**. Also, find the complex impedance of the combination.

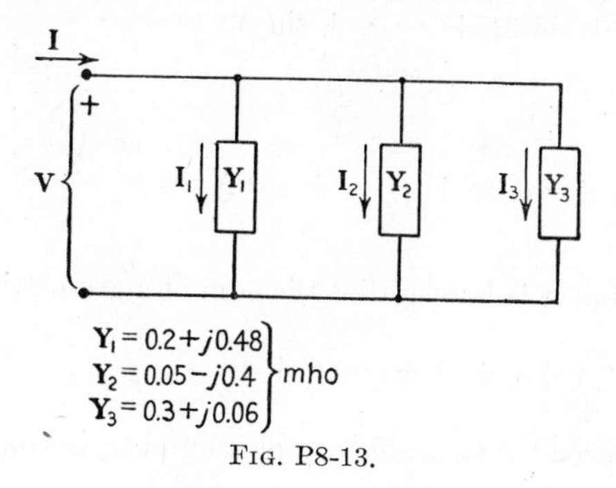


FIG. P8-13.

**8-14.** Use the results obtained in Prob. 8-12 and 8-13 to find the average power delivered to each rectangle in each circuit. Also, find the average power delivered to each combination of three rectangles.

**8-15.** Use complex algebra to find the quantities asked for in Probs. 6-9 and 6-10.

**8-16.** Use complex algebra to find $R_i$ and $L$ in Prob. 6-15.

**8-17.** Use complex algebra to solve Prob. 6-17.

**8-18.** Use complex algebra to find $R_c$ and $C$ in Prob. 6-18.

**8-19.** Use complex algebra to solve part *a* of Prob. 6-19.

**8-20.** Use complex algebra, instead of graphical construction, to do parts *b* and *c* of Prob. 6-21.

**8-21.** Use complex algebra, instead of graphical construction, to obtain the results asked for in parts *c* and *d* of Prob. 7-8.

**8-22.** Use complex algebra to do Prob. 7-11.

**8-23.** Use complex algebra to do Prob. 7-12.

**8-24.** Use complex algebra to do Prob. 7-15.

**8-25.** Use complex algebra to do parts *b* and *c* of Prob. 7-16.

**8-26.** A resistor of 25 ohms is in series with an inductor of 0.01 henry. The potential across the combination is $v = 185 \sin (\omega t + 20°)$, and the frequency is 300 cps. Express this potential in the exponential form, similar to Eq. (8-35), and solve the differential equation of the circuit for the current in the circuit. Finally, write it as a real function of time, after first obtaining it as an exponential form similar to Eq. (8-35).

**8-27.** Do Prob. 8-26 using Eq. (8-38) for the sine function.

**8-28.** A resistor of 25 ohms, an inductor of 0.01 henry, and a capacitor of $50 \times 10^{-6}$ farad are connected in parallel. The total current to the combination is $i = 6.4 \cos (\omega t - 40°)$, and the frequency is 300 cps. Express the current in the exponential form, similar to Eq. (8-36), and solve the integrodifferential equation of the circuit for the potential across the combination, as a function of time. First solve for the potential in an exponential form similar to Eq. (8-36).

**8-29.** Do Prob. 8-28 using Eq. (8-39) for the cosine function.

**8-30.** Prove the identities

*a.* $$\sin x + \sin 2x + \sin 3x + \cdots + \sin Nx = \frac{\sin\left(\frac{N+1}{2}x\right)\sin\left(\frac{Nx}{2}\right)}{\sin\left(\frac{x}{2}\right)}$$

*b.* $$\cos x + \cos 2x + \cos 3x + \cdots + \cos Nx = \frac{\cos\left(\frac{N+1}{2}x\right)\sin\left(\frac{Nx}{2}\right)}{\sin\left(\frac{x}{2}\right)}$$

HINT: From algebra it is known that the sum of a geometric series is

$$1 + r + r^2 + \cdots + r^M = \frac{r^{M+1} - 1}{r - 1}$$

Use this with $r$ replaced by a suitable complex number, in conjunction with Eqs. (8-38) and (8-39).

## QUESTIONS

**8-1.** Is it possible to consider real numbers as special cases of complex numbers?

**8-2.** Is the "imaginary part" of a complex number really "imaginary"?

**8-3.** Is the magnitude of a complex number usually considered as an algebraic or an arithmetic quantity?

**8-4.** Is the angle of a complex number usually considered as an algebraic or an arithmetic quantity?

**8-5.** To what system of coordinates used in analytic geometry do the rectangular and polar forms of expressing complex numbers correspond?

**8-6.** Can the definition of equality of two complex numbers be given equally well in terms of either the rectangular or the polar form?

**8-7.** Would it be possible to define addition of complex numbers in terms of the polar form?

**8-8.** Would it be possible to define multiplication of complex numbers in terms of the rectangular form?

**8-9.** Could division of complex numbers be defined in the rectangular form?

**8-10.** How are the real and imaginary parts of a complex number related to the real and imaginary parts of its conjugate?

**8-11.** Could the conjugate of a complex number be defined equally well in either the rectangular or the polar form?

**8-12.** What difference is there between the polar and exponential forms of a complex number?

**8-13.** What would you say to the question: How do we know that the series expansion for $\epsilon^{j\alpha}$ is a valid representation for this function?

**8-14.** Could the exponential form of a complex quantity be used to define its derivative with respect to its argument (angle)? with respect to its real part?

**8-15.** Use the exponential expressions for sine and cosine functions to obtain the usual identities for sin $(A + B)$ and cos $(A + B)$.

**8-16.** Use the exponential form of complex quantities to show that sinors can be used to obtain the sum of two sinusoidal time functions.

**8-17.** How is it possible to express circuit relations (such as $\mathbf{V} = \mathbf{ZI}$) with one equation, when complex quantities are used, whereas in Chap. 6 two equations were needed?

**8-18.** So far as the simple series and parallel circuits considered in Chap. 6 are concerned, what would you say is the main contribution of complex quantities to the solution and understanding of a-c circuits?

**8-19.** Would complex quantities be useful in the analysis of a d-c circuit?

**8-20.** Is the fact that $j = \sqrt{-1}$ of any particular significance in the application of complex quantities to circuit analysis?

**8-21.** Suppose a circuit is excited by a potential of any one of the following forms: $\sin \omega t$, $\cos \omega t$, $\sin (\omega t + \alpha)$, $\cos (\omega t + \alpha)$, $\epsilon^{j\omega t}$, $\epsilon^{j(\omega t+\alpha)}$. Explain why the same complex algebra applies in all cases, for finding the sinor representation of the response current. That is, explain why an expression such as $\mathbf{V} = \mathbf{IZ}$ applies to all of them without change.

**8-22.** Suppose there is a circuit of $R$ and $L$ in series in which the current is $i = \sqrt{2}\, I \sin \omega t$. Is it proper to write the equation for the potential difference as $v = \sqrt{2}\,(R + j\omega L)\, I \sin \omega t$?

**8-23.** Power can be represented by a complex quantity. Does this complex quantity represent a sinusoid?

**8-24.** Would it make any difference if power is taken as Re $(\mathbf{VI}^*)$ or Re $(\mathbf{IV}^*)$? Would there be any difference in reactive power if it is taken as Im $(\mathbf{VI}^*)$ or Im $(\mathbf{IV}^*)$?

**8-25.** Is the complex power changed if the initial angles of the potential and current wave are both changed by the same amount?

**8-26.** Could the identities specified in Prob. 8-5, be proved by using Eqs. (8-30) and (8-31)?

# CHAPTER 9

# NETWORK TERMINOLOGY AND NOTATION

**9-1. Introduction.** The analysis of electric networks is largely dependent on systems of simplification. A network is broken down into basic components, to which the two Kirchhoff laws can be applied. In order to make the simplification as complete as possible, it is necessary to agree on the terminology to be used. The definition, explanation, and illustration of terminology is the objective of this chapter.

It should be understood that if any of the elements of a physical network deviate from the ideal, by being distributed or nonlinear, an equivalent network of ideal elements must be substituted for it, usually on paper, before it can be analyzed. An equivalent network is also needed if Kirchhoff's laws are not valid in the given network because of excessively large loops or junctions. When formulating an equivalent network to replace a given physical network, certain approximations are usually necessary. A consideration of what these approximations are, and what errors can be tolerated, is not within the scope of an elementary course in circuit analysis, and so all networks treated in this text are assumed to be ideal.

**9-2. Network Terminology.** Figure 9-1*a* is a convenient starting point. It embodies all the essential features of the more complex networks, to be encountered later. In general, a network consists of a number of *nodes* (*junctions*) which are connected together by *branches*. This results in the formation of one or more network *loops* (*meshes*). These three types of circuit features are labeled in Fig. 9-1*a*, showing two nodes, two branches, and one loop.* There is no limit on the number of branches coming together at a node, or in the number of branches forming a loop, as suggested by Fig. 9-1*b*.

There is a certain amount of ambiguity in the application of these terms. First it is to be noted that connecting wires are considered as perfect conductors. Therefore, all points connected by a continuous

* There is lack of uniformity in the literature in the use of the terms *loop* and *mesh*, and *node* and *junction*. Some authors give slightly different meanings to the words *mesh* and *loop*. However, recent IRE standards (see *Proc. IRE*, p. 27, January, 1951) give *mesh* and *node* as preferred terms, with *loop* and *junction* as alternates. In this text loop and node are given preference because they seem to predominate in recent literature.

line form a single node. This is illustrated in Fig. 9-2. Furthermore, there is a considerable variation possible in the choice of branches if the circuit is at all extensive.

In the choice of a branch it is always necessary to bear in mind that the relationship between its terminal potential and terminal current must be known. There are two categories of branches for which this is true,

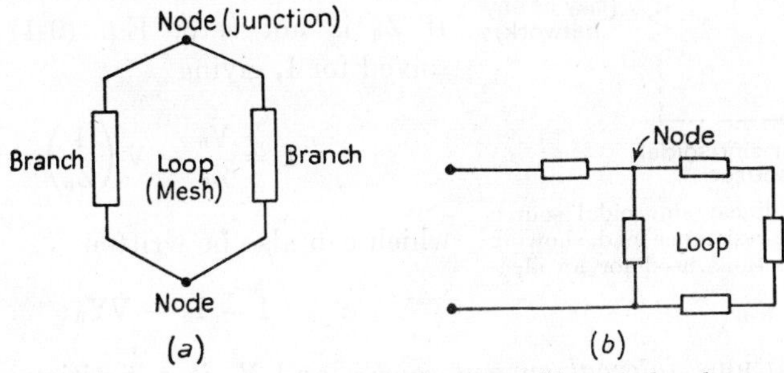


FIG. 9-1. Illustration of the concepts of loop and node.

*passive branches*, consisting of resistors, inductors, and capacitors alone or in various combinations; and *active branches*, which include sources and possibly passive elements also.

As the theory of network analysis unfolds, it will be found that more and more complicated circuits can be treated collectively as single branches. In the beginning they will be confined to the rather simple combinations described in the next two sections.

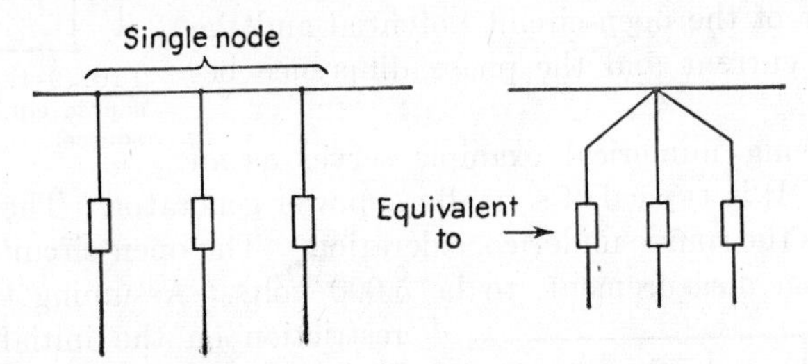


FIG. 9-2. Various appearances of a node on a circuit diagram.

**9-3. Linear Sources.** The rectangle of Fig. 9-3 represents a *linear sinusoidal source*, *defined* as a source for which the potential-current relationship can be written as a *linear* equation in complex quantities. This means that by suitable choice of constants the equation

$$\mathbf{V} = \mathbf{V}_0 - \mathbf{I}\mathbf{Z}_0 \tag{9-1}$$

can be made to apply. At a fixed frequency $\mathbf{V}_0$ and $\mathbf{Z}_0$ are constants. $\mathbf{V}_0$ is a fictitious *internal potential source*, and $\mathbf{Z}_0$ is a fictitious *internal impedance*. $\mathbf{V}_0$ and $\mathbf{Z}_0$ may vary with frequency, but they are independent of current. Equation (9-1) shows that a linear source can be represented on a diagram by the circuit of Fig. 9-4. This equivalent is called a *potential-source equivalent* for the given source.

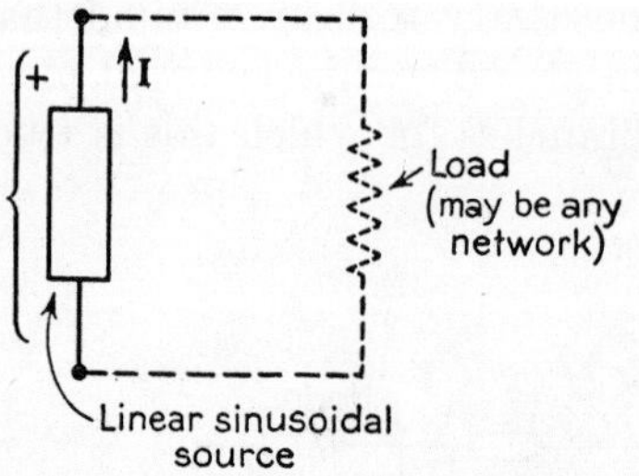

FIG. 9-3. A linear sinusoidal source connected to a resistance load, showing reference directions used for an algebraic source.

The condition for a sinusoidal source to be linear can be given in another way. If $\mathbf{Z}_0$ is not zero, Eq. (9-1) can be solved for **I**, giving

$$\mathbf{I} = \frac{\mathbf{V}_0}{\mathbf{Z}_0} - \mathbf{V}\left(\frac{1}{\mathbf{Z}_0}\right) \tag{9-2}$$

which can also be written

$$\mathbf{I} = \mathbf{I}_0 - \mathbf{V}\mathbf{Y}_0 \tag{9-3}$$

$\mathbf{I}_0$ is a fictitious *internal current source*, and $\mathbf{Y}_0$ is a fictitious *internal admittance*. Equation (9-3) is the equation for the equivalent circuit of Fig. 9-5 which is called the *current-source equivalent* for the given source.

The details of how the internal properties of a source are determined are treated in studies of electric machinery and electronics. In many cases an approximate circuit is all that can be obtained because the actual device is not linear. In most cases $\mathbf{V}_0$ and $\mathbf{Z}_0$ (or $\mathbf{I}_0$ and $\mathbf{Y}_0$) can be found from a measurement of the open-circuit potential and the short-circuit current and the phase difference between them.

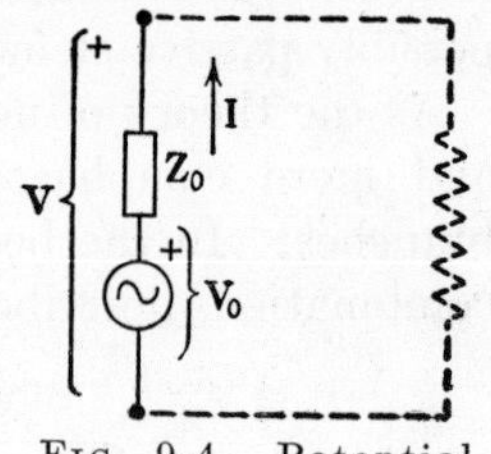


FIG. 9-4. Potential source equivalent of a source.

The following numerical example serves as an illustration. It is typical of a small a-c power generator. The rectangle of Fig. 9-6*a* is the source under consideration. The open-circuit potential is found, from measurement, to be 5,000 volts. Assuming there is no restriction on the initial angle of $\mathbf{V}_0$, it may be taken as zero. The complex (sinor) representation is therefore

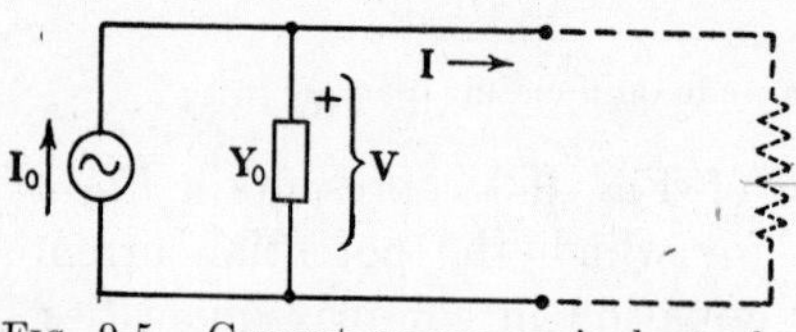


FIG. 9-5. Current source equivalent of a source.

$$\mathbf{V}_0 = 5{,}000 + j0 \tag{9-4}$$

Measurement shows that on short circuit the current $\mathbf{I}_{sc}$ is 120 amp, and measurement on d-c shows that the resistance component of the internal impedance is 3.6 ohms. Using the notation $\mathbf{Z}_0 = R_0 + jX_0$ the above data yields

$$\sqrt{R_0^2 + X_0^2} = \frac{5000}{120} = 41.6$$

from which $X_0 = \sqrt{(41.6)^2 - (3.6)^2} = 41.4$ ohms. The internal impedance of the generator is therefore

$$\mathbf{Z}_0 = 3.6 + j41.4 = 41.6\underline{/85°} \text{ ohms} \tag{9-5}$$

The equivalent circuit is the one shown in Fig. 9-6*b*. When a source operates at variable frequency, like a microphone or phonograph pickup, the test must be carried out at several frequencies, to ensure an equivalent circuit that is valid throughout the range of operating frequencies.

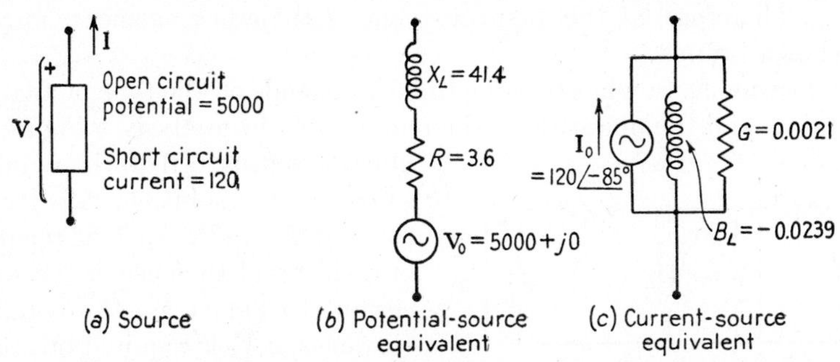


FIG. 9-6. Numerical example showing two equivalent circuits for a source.

Reference to Eqs. (9-2) and (9-3) shows that the current-source equivalent can be obtained from the same data. For example, the short-circuit current is

$$\mathbf{I}_0 = 120\underline{/-85°} \text{ amp} \tag{9-6}$$

and

$$\mathbf{Y}_0 = \frac{1}{\mathbf{Z}_0} = 0.024\underline{/-85°} = 0.0021 - j0.0239 \text{ mhos} \tag{9-7}$$

The circuit is shown in Fig. 9-6*c*.

It is to be emphasized that any source can be replaced by either a potential-source equivalent or a current-source equivalent only *as far as the current and potentials at its terminals are concerned.* The internal power loss in the machine can be represented approximately by only one equivalent, and possibly by neither of them. To understand this, note that Fig. 9-4 can have no internal power loss on open circuit, because there is no current in $\mathbf{Z}_0$, but that Fig. 9-5 has possible power loss in $\mathbf{Y}_0$ on open circuit.

Many of the historically older sources, such as the electrolytic cell and electromagnetic generators, are closely approximated internally by the potential-source equivalent. Various devices employing electron tubes are internally more closely approximated by the current-source equivalent. In some cases neither equivalent serves very well to represent the internal losses. This is true for any device for which losses are related partly to current and partly to potential difference. There are many such devices. A further discussion of these matters would lead to a digression into the study of electric machinery and electronics. In circuit analysis we are satisfied to know how to determine the parameters of a circuit which is *equivalent at the terminals.*

**9-4. Passive Branches.** Section 6-2 gives the potential-current relationships for resistors, inductors, and capacitors, and Secs. 6-4 and 6-5 give similar relationships for series and parallel combinations of $R$, $L$, and $C$. Therefore, at this point any one of these arrangements may be treated as a branch.

The decision as to what to call a branch depends on the type of analysis undertaken and the quantities to be found from the analysis. Figure 9-7 illustrates this. If $\mathbf{I}_L$ is required as part of the solution, it is logical to treat $R_1$ and $L$ each as separate branches and to consider the series circuit of $R_2$ and $C$ as a third branch. However, if $\mathbf{V}_C$ is required but there is no need for $\mathbf{I}_L$, $R_2$ and $C$ could each be considered a branch and $R_1$ and $L$ could be combined to form a single branch. The details of how these ideas are incorporated in the actual solution are found in Chaps. 10 and 11. Subsequent developments show how series-parallel combinations can be treated as branches. For example, in Chap. 10 it is shown that everything to the right of the dotted line in Fig. 9-7 can be treated as a branch. It is important to note that *in no case does a branch have more than two terminals.* It may have any number of junctions and loops in its internal structure, but it may have only two external leads.

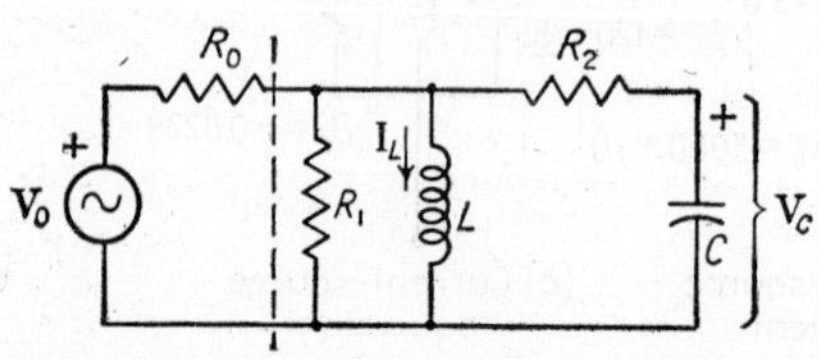

FIG. 9-7. Factors affecting choice of branches.

It is usually convenient to consider the internal impedance or admittance of a source as a branch, although it cannot be perceived physically. For example, $R_0$ of Fig. 9-7 would be considered a circuit branch in formulating the solution of the network.

**9-5. Choice of Reference Conditions.** Current reference directions and potential reference polarities must be set up throughout a network before it can be solved by any of the methods to be taken up. When a loop or node is completely isolated, reference conditions can be chosen arbitrarily. However, this is not always the case.

Figure 9-8 shows this for nodes. All current reference directions can be arbitrary at node ($a$). However, at node ($b$) the reference direction of $i_4$ has already been established, and it cannot be changed.

The dual of this is shown in Fig. 9-9. The reference polarities shown can be chosen arbitrarily for loop (*a*). When reference polarities are then chosen for loop (*b*), potential $v_4$ has been established.

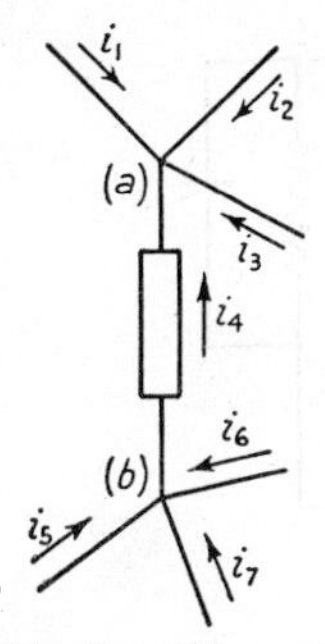


Fig. 9-8. Illustration of how choice of a current reference direction at one junction can establish a reference direction at a related junction.

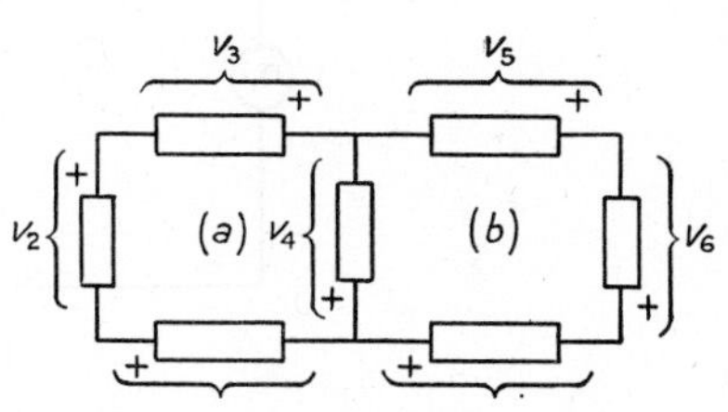


Fig. 9-9. Illustration of how choice of a reference polarity in one loop can establish a reference polarity in a related loop.

**9-6. Precaution in Use of Double Subscripts.** When there are parallel branches, double-subscript notation can lead to ambiguities in the case of currents. Figure 9-10*a* is a case in point. The only meaning that could be attached to $i_{12}$ would be the combined current of the two branches. In order to distinguish one branch from the other, it is necessary to include an extra symbol, as shown in Fig. 9-10*b*. The extra symbol would not be needed for the potential, because $v_{12} = v_{13}$.

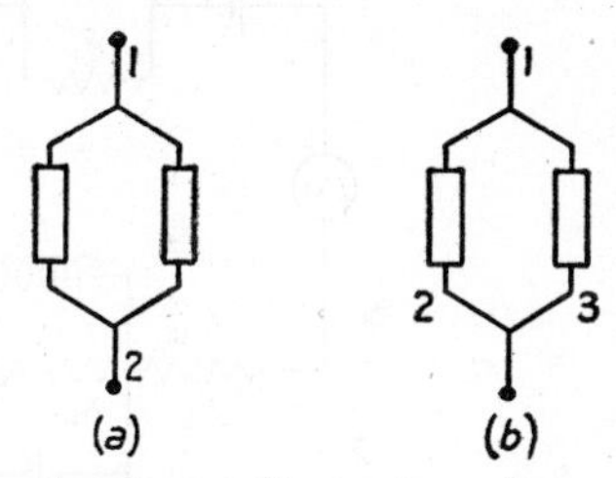


Fig. 9-10. Illustration of possible ambiguities when using double subscripts with parallel branches.

**9-7. Summary.** When an extensive circuit is analyzed, it is broken down into a number of branches connected together at nodes, so that the combination forms one or more loops. Branches are either passive or active. At least one active branch is needed to activate a network.

A branch can sometimes be a combination of smaller branches. When that is the case, there will be nodes and loops within the branch, but they receive no consideration. They become internal details as far as the branch is concerned when viewed from its terminals. It is to be emphasized that a branch can have only two terminals.

Active branches can be represented either by potential-source or current-source equivalents. Either of these introduces fictitious branches which have meaning for the analysis of the circuit but which do not usually exist in the actual source.

## PROBLEMS

**9-1.** Consider the circuit shown in Fig. P9-1.

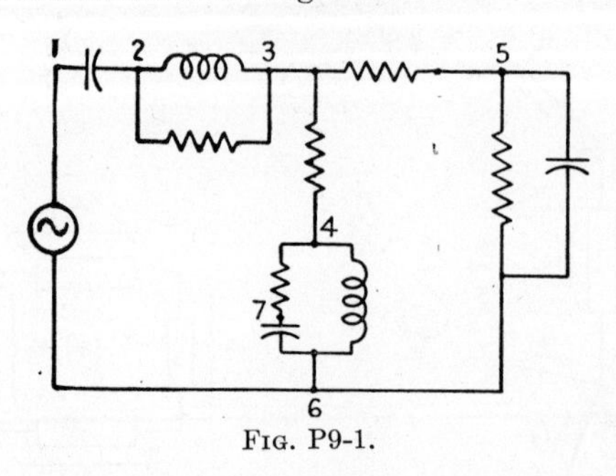


Fig. P9-1.

*a.* Identify the maximum number of branches that are discernible, and determine the number of nodes the circuit would have for this viewpoint.

*b.* Except for the source, let each branch be a special case of the general branch shown in Fig. 6-7. For this viewpoint identify the branches, and determine the number of nodes.

**9-2.** Refer to the circuit of Fig. P9-2.

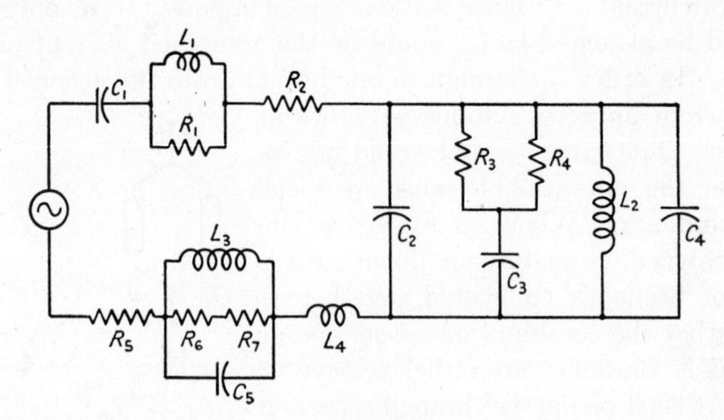


Fig. P9-2.

*a.* Assume that each branch is to be a special case of either Fig. 6-7 or Fig. 6-12. Redraw the circuit in its simplest form within the limitations of this stipulation. Identify each branch, and determine the number of nodes for this viewpoint.

*b.* Assume each branch is to be a special case of Fig. 6-7 only. Identify each branch, and determine the number of branches and nodes for this viewpoint.

*c.* Let each branch be a special case of Fig. 6-12 only. Identify each branch, and determine the number of branches and nodes.

**9-3.** The potential-source equivalent circuit is to be found for a magnetic phonograph pickup operated from a 400-cps constant-frequency test record. A vacuum-tube voltmeter is available for measuring potentials without appreciably disturbing the circuit while so doing. The open-circuit potential is measured and found to be 0.2 volt. Then a resistor of 2000 ohms and an adjustable capacitor are connected in series across the terminals of the pickup. The potential across the resistor is measured while the capacitor is varied. It is found that when $C = 0.81 \times 10^{-6}$ farad, the potential across the resistor is a maximum and equal to 0.113 volt. Specify the potential-source equivalent circuit completely for the frequency at which measurements were made.

**9-4.** A radio antenna situated in the radiation field from a transmitter is a source. An experimental procedure is carried out using the circuit of Fig. P9-4. For simplicity it is assumed that negligible error is introduced by neglecting the resistance of the coil. The angular frequency of the radiation is $\omega$. First the circuit is adjusted so that the resonant frequency of the parallel circuit is equal to $\omega$, and the potential across the circuit measured with a vacuum-tube voltmeter. Then either $L$ or $C$ is adjusted until the current attains a maximum value. This

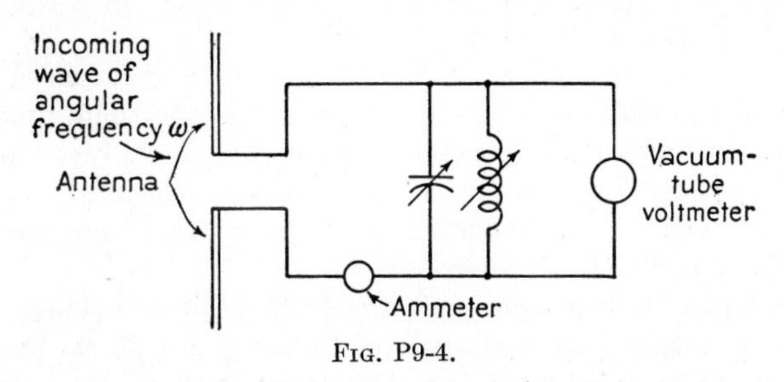


FIG. P9-4.

value is read, and the corresponding values of $L$ and $C$ are determined. The following data are obtained at a frequency of 1 Mc: When $L$ and $C$ are at resonance for the operating frequency the potential is 0.12 volt. The current is a maximum and equal to 0.009 amp when $L = 5 \times 10^{-6}$ henry and $C = 0.185 \times 10^{-8}$ farad. Specify the potential-source equivalent circuit.

**9-5.** An experimental procedure is to be used to find the equivalent circuit of an a-c generator. (Because of magnetic saturation such a generator is not a true linear source, but these effects are to be neglected.) The open circuit potential is 5,000 volts. Measurement of the resistance of the windings on direct-current gives 0.85 ohm. With reasonable accuracy the same resistance may be assumed to prevail at the machine's frequency (60 cps). That is, skin effect (the increase of resistance as frequency increases owing to crowding of the current to the surface of the conductor) is neglected. The terminals of the machine are then short-circuited and the current measured. It is found to be 300 amp. What is the potential-source equivalent circuit for this machine?

**9-6.** Obtain the current-source equivalent circuit for the device described in Prob. 9-3.

**9-7.** Obtain the current-source equivalent circuit for the antenna described in Prob. 9-4.

**9-8.** Obtain the current-source equivalent circuit of the a-c generator specified in Prob. 9-5.

## QUESTIONS

**9-1.** Does the term "branch" include both active and passive elements?

**9-2.** Is there any restriction on the number of leads coming together at a node?

**9-3.** Is it necessary for three or more leads to come together at a single point for it to be considered a node?

**9-4.** Is there any difference in meaning of the words "mesh" and "loop," and "node" and "junction," as they are used in this text?

**9-5.** Why do you think the technique of breaking a network down into loops and nodes is important?

**9-6.** Is there any restriction on the number of branches on the side of a loop?

**9-7.** So far as the *internal* operation of a source is concerned, is there any difference between the potential-source equivalent and the current-source equivalent of a source?

**9-8.** Would you expect the impedance of a potential-source equivalent of a source to be independent of frequency, in general?

**9-9.** Suppose you are interested in obtaining a circuit which accurately accounts for the internal power loss in a source. Do you think that one or the other of the source equivalents (potential or current) would serve to do this, or might it possibly take a more complicated circuit in some cases?

**9-10.** Why do you suppose potential-source equivalents were historically the first to be introduced in circuit analysis?

**9-11.** To completely determine the equivalent circuit of a source, it is necessary to know the magnitude and angle of the short-circuit current. In some cases it may be difficult to make the angle measurement. Can you devise an experimental procedure for finding the short-circuit current in magnitude and angle?

**9-12.** Is a branch always a single element?

**9-13.** Do you think it would be possible to define a linear source without the aid of complex algebra?

**9-14.** What is the difference between a passive and an active branch?

**9-15.** Is it possible to have a loop within a branch?

# CHAPTER 10

# ANALYSIS OF NETWORKS

**10-1. Introduction.** The techniques so far developed have been applicable only to simple series and parallel circuits. However, practical problems often involve circuits of greater complexity. A general method of analysis which will be applicable in all cases is needed.

It is possible to reduce all cases to two general methods of attack, either of which is applicable in all cases. However, certain cases deserve special consideration because they are solvable by the direct application of the methods of Chap. 8. These cases provide the subject matter of Chap. 10.

While studying Chaps. 10 and 11 the reader will do well to heed the parallels that exist between the general methods of analyzing a-c and d-c networks. As far as the formal procedures are concerned, the only difference is that complex quantities are used in an a-c network analysis.

**10-2. Step-by-step Method.** In many cases it is possible to build up a solution by the repeated application of Kirchhoff's laws in a number of

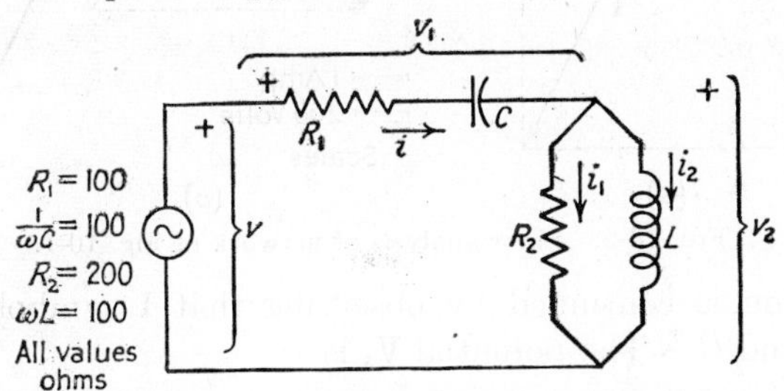


FIG. 10-1. Example of a circuit solvable by step-by-step application of Kirchhoff's laws.

steps. Whether or not such a procedure is possible depends on the given information.

It is impossible to generalize problems of this sort, so two typical examples are given. They deal with circuits having passive elements in series-parallel connection. Consider Fig. 10-1 as the first example. Let $i_1$ be given, in amperes, as

$$i_1 = 7.07 \sin \omega t \tag{10-1}$$

The problem is to find the potential $v$. In complex notation, the sinor $\mathbf{I}_1$ is

$$\mathbf{I}_1 = 5 + j0 \tag{10-2}$$

The sinor $\mathbf{V}_2$, in volts, can be found from the relation

$$\mathbf{V}_2 = \mathbf{I}_1 R_2 = (5 + j0)(200) = 1{,}000 + j0 \qquad (10\text{-}3)$$

From a knowledge of $\mathbf{V}_2$, it follows that $\mathbf{I}_2$ is

$$\mathbf{I}_2 = \frac{\mathbf{E}_2}{j\omega L} = \frac{1{,}000}{j100} = -j10 \qquad (10\text{-}4)$$

Kirchhoff's current law at either of the nodes gives

$$\mathbf{I} = \mathbf{I}_1 + \mathbf{I}_2 = 5 - j10 \qquad (10\text{-}5)$$

The sinor diagram representing this is shown at (*a*) in Fig. 10-2.

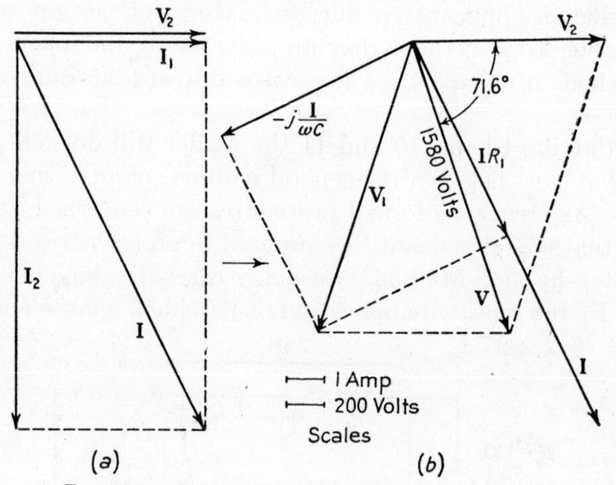


FIG. 10-2. Sinor analysis of network of Fig. 10-1.

The solution is continued by observing that $\mathbf{I}$ symbolizes a current through $R_1$ and $C$. The potential $\mathbf{V}_1$ is

$$\mathbf{V}_1 = \mathbf{I}\left(R_1 - j\frac{1}{\omega C}\right) = (5 - j10)(100 - j100)$$
$$= 500 - 1{,}000 - j(500 + 1{,}000) = -500 - j1{,}500 \qquad (10\text{-}6)$$

The reference conditions are so arranged that Kirchhoff's potential law for the left-hand loop is

$$\mathbf{V} = \mathbf{V}_1 + \mathbf{V}_2 = -5{,}000 - j1{,}500 + 1{,}000 + j0$$
$$= 500 - j1{,}500 = 1{,}580\underline{/-71.6^\circ} \qquad (10\text{-}7)$$

The remaining portion of the sinor diagram is shown in Fig. 10-2*b*. The time function corresponding to $\mathbf{V}$ is

$$v = 2{,}240 \sin(\omega t - 71.6^\circ) \qquad (10\text{-}8)$$

The previous example has a single source $v$. Under special conditions, it is possible to use a similar step-by-step analysis when there is more than one source. The second illustration is an example of this.

Consider the circuit of Fig. 10-3, a typical power-transmission problem. The circle on the right is a 500-volt potential source which is to absorb 6 kw of power at a power factor of 0.8 with the current lagging. The

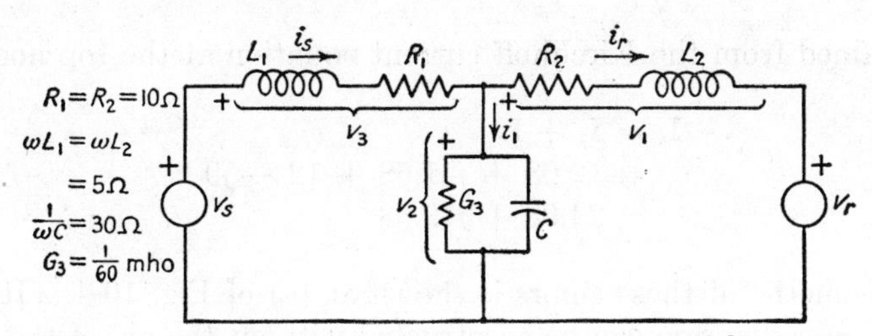


FIG. 10-3. Illustration of a network with two potential sources.

potential difference $v_s$ is to be found. To start the problem, let the potential $v_r$ be

$$v_r = 707 \sin \omega t \tag{10-9}$$

or

$$\mathbf{V}_r = 500 + j0 \tag{10-10}$$

The receiver current is such that the power, in watts, is

$$6{,}000 = V_r I_r(0.8) = 500(0.8)I_r \tag{10-11}$$

Hence

$$I_r = \frac{6{,}000}{400} = 15 \text{ amp} \tag{10-12}$$

and it lags $\mathbf{V}_r$ by $\cos^{-1} 0.8 = 37°$, giving

$$\begin{aligned} \mathbf{I}_r &= 15(\cos 37° - j \sin 37°) \\ &= 12 - j9 \end{aligned} \tag{10-13}$$

The potential sinor $\mathbf{V}_1$ is

$$\begin{aligned} \mathbf{V}_1 &= (12 - j9)(R_2 + j\omega L_2) = (12 - j9)(10 + j5) \\ &= 165 - j30 \end{aligned} \tag{10-14}$$

Hence,

$$\begin{aligned} \mathbf{V}_2 &= \mathbf{V}_1 + \mathbf{V}_r = 165 - j30 + 500 \\ &= 665 - j30 \end{aligned} \tag{10-15}$$

by Kirchhoff's law for potentials for the right-hand loop.

The current $\mathbf{I}_1$ is

$$\begin{aligned}\mathbf{I}_1 &= \mathbf{V}_2\left(\frac{1}{R_3} + j\omega C\right) = (665 - j30)(0.0167 + j0.033) \\ &= (11.08 + 1) + j(22.18 - 0.5) \\ &= 12.08 + j21.68 \qquad (10\text{-}16)\end{aligned}$$

$\mathbf{I}_s$ is obtained from the Kirchhoff current equation at the top node; thus

$$\begin{aligned}\mathbf{I}_s &= \mathbf{I}_1 + \mathbf{I}_r \\ &= 12.08 + j21.68 + 12 - j9 \\ &= 24.08 + j12.68 \qquad (10\text{-}17)\end{aligned}$$

The geometry of these sinors is shown at (*a*) of Fig. 10-4. It is seen that the sinor diagram can be constructed without the aid of the algebra

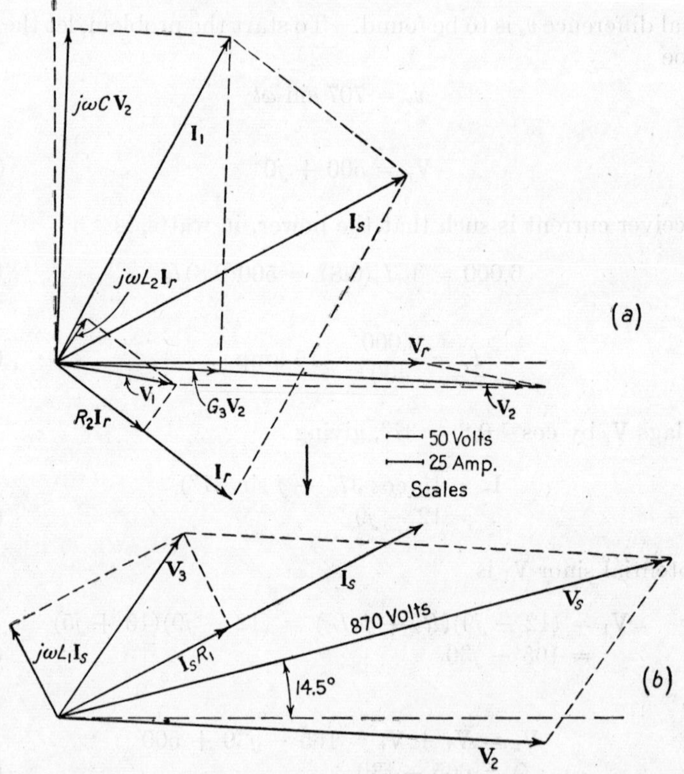


Fig. 10-4. Sinor diagram for the network of Fig. 10-2.

of complex quantities, although the algebra is convenient for getting accurate numerical results.

From $\mathbf{I}_s$ it follows that

$$\begin{aligned}\mathbf{V}_3 &= \mathbf{I}_s(R_1 + j\omega L_1)\\ &= (24.08 + j12.68)(10 + j5)\\ &= 177.4 + j247.2 \end{aligned} \tag{10-18}$$

Finally, an application of the Kirchhoff potential law to the left-hand loop yields

$$\begin{aligned}\mathbf{V}_s = \mathbf{V}_3 + \mathbf{V}_2 &= 177.4 + j247.2 + 665 - j30\\ &= 842 + j217 = 870\underline{/14.5^\circ} \text{ volts}\end{aligned} \tag{10-19}$$

The construction for this result is shown in Fig. 10-4*b*. The sinors $\mathbf{I}_s$ and $\mathbf{V}_2$ are obtained from Fig. 10-4*a*. The time variable potential $v_s$ is

$$v_s = 1{,}230 \sin(\omega t + 14.5^\circ) \tag{10-20}$$

This method applies if only one unknown quantity appears at a time. However, in the case of networks having only one source it is not necessary to know the numerical value of the sinor from which the step-by-step analysis begins. For example, Fig. 10-1 can be solved for $i_1$ if $v$ is given. Using sinor notation, the solution is obtained by assigning to $\mathbf{I}_1$ an *arbitrary numerical* value (call it $\mathbf{I}_1'$) and then finding the corresponding numerical value of $\mathbf{V}$ (call it $\mathbf{V}'$). Since the network elements are linear, $\mathbf{I}_1$ is proportional to $\mathbf{V}$, and so the solution is $\mathbf{I}_1 = \mathbf{I}_1'(\mathbf{V}/\mathbf{V}')$.

**10-3. Combination of Impedances and Admittances.** The real utility of complex algebra in circuit analysis is yet to be demonstrated. As an introduction it is helpful to summarize the results of Chap. 8. If the rectangle of Fig. 10-5 represents either a pure series circuit of $R$, $L$, and $C$ or a pure parallel circuit of $G$, $L$, and $C$, it may be treated in terms of either of the formulas

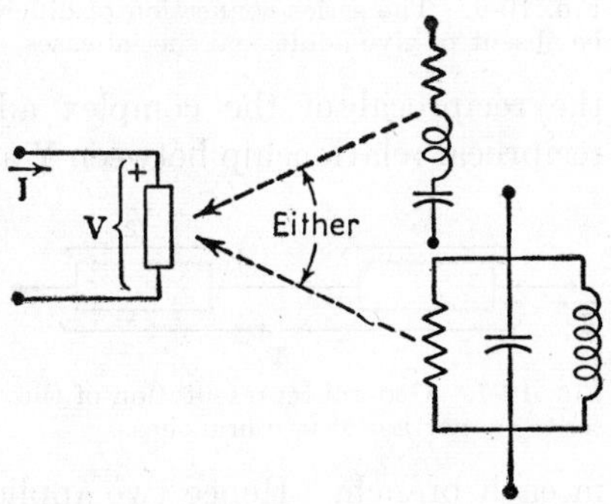


FIG. 10-5. The two basic, dually related branches, for which impedance and admittance formulas are given in Eqs. (10-22) and (10-23).

$$\mathbf{V} = \mathbf{Z}\mathbf{I}$$

or

$$\mathbf{I} = \mathbf{Y}\mathbf{V} \tag{10-21}$$

In these

$$\mathbf{Z} = \begin{cases} R + j\left(\omega L - \dfrac{1}{\omega C}\right) & \text{series circuit} \\[2ex] \dfrac{1}{G + j\left(\omega C - \dfrac{1}{\omega L}\right)} & \text{parallel circuit} \end{cases} \tag{10-22}$$

$$\mathbf{Y} = \begin{cases} G + j\left(\omega C - \dfrac{1}{\omega L}\right) & \text{parallel circuit} \\ \dfrac{1}{R + j\left(\omega L - \dfrac{1}{\omega C}\right)} & \text{series circuit} \end{cases} \tag{10-23}$$

There is some danger of confusion in this compact notation. It is not intended to say that the complex impedance of a series circuit is always

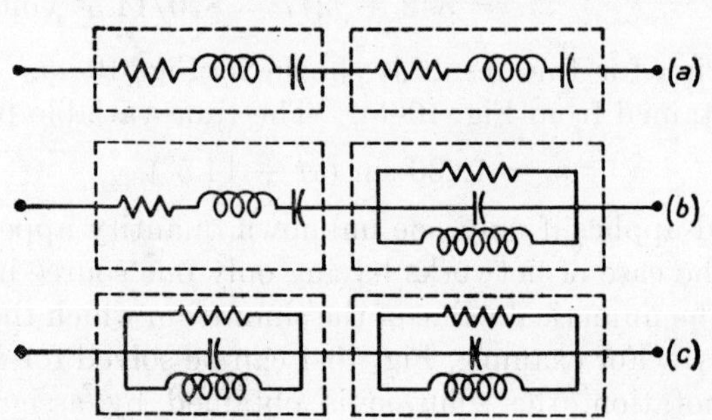


Fig. 10-6. The series connection of different types of branches. Various elements may be absent to give additional special cases.

the reciprocal of the complex admittance of a parallel circuit. The reciprocal relationship between **Y** and **Z** holds only when they both apply to the *identical* circuit.

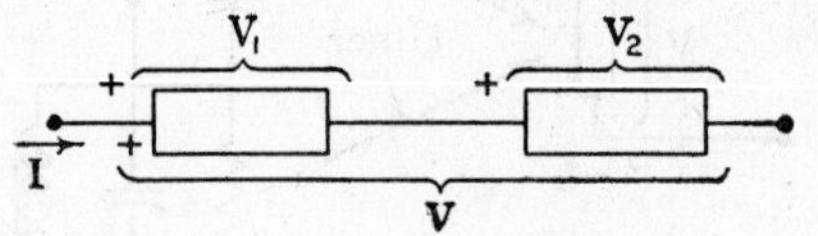


Fig. 10-7. General representation of the series connection of two branches.

Consider the examples of Fig. 10-6, which are all represented by Fig. 10-7. Networks within dotted rectangles of Fig. 10-6 are treated as branches. The current is the same in each branch. Hence two applications of the first equation of (10-21) give

$$\begin{aligned} \mathbf{V}_1 &= \mathbf{Z}_1\mathbf{I} \\ \mathbf{V}_2 &= \mathbf{Z}_2\mathbf{I} \end{aligned} \tag{10-24}$$

From Kirchhoff's potential law

$$\mathbf{V} = \mathbf{V}_1 + \mathbf{V}_2 = (\mathbf{Z}_1 + \mathbf{Z}_2)\mathbf{I} \tag{10-25}$$

This may be rewritten

$$\mathbf{V} = \mathbf{Z}_{eq}\mathbf{I} \tag{10-26}$$

where we have introduced an equivalent impedance

$$\mathbf{Z}_{eq} = \mathbf{Z}_1 + \mathbf{Z}_2 \tag{10-27}$$

Equation (10-25) may also be written

$$\mathbf{I} = \mathbf{Y}_{eq}\mathbf{V} \tag{10-28}$$

where we have introduced an equivalent admittance

$$\mathbf{Y}_{eq} = \frac{1}{\mathbf{Z}_1 + \mathbf{Z}_2} \tag{10-29}$$

Equations (10-26) and (10-28) are generalizations of Eqs. (10-21). They represent extensions of the concepts of impedance and admittance.

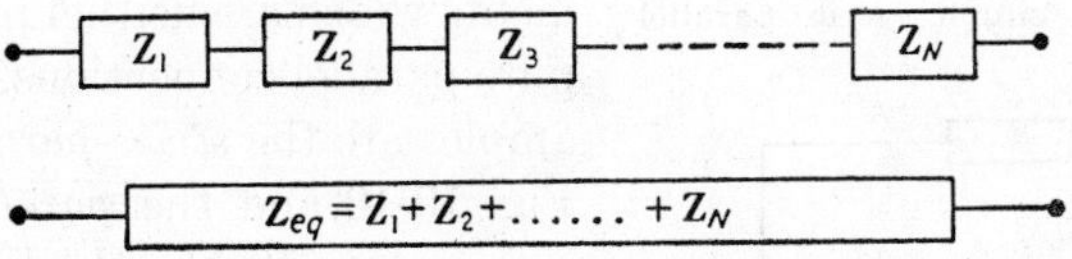

FIG. 10-8. The equivalent impedance of a series-connected combination of $N$ impedance branches.

The same procedure could be carried out again, with a third branch connected in the series arrangement. It is not necessary to continue the proof for this. It would follow exactly the same pattern as the two-branch case. In fact, there is no limit on the number of branches that can be treated. The result for the general case can be stated for a series connection of $N$ branches, as in Fig. 10-8. The equivalent impedance is

$$\mathbf{Z}_{eq} = \mathbf{Z}_1 + \mathbf{Z}_2 + \mathbf{Z}_3 + \cdots + \mathbf{Z}_N \tag{10-30}$$

and the corresponding admittance is

$$\mathbf{Y}_{eq} = \frac{1}{\mathbf{Z}_1 + \mathbf{Z}_2 + \mathbf{Z}_3 + \cdots + \mathbf{Z}_N} \tag{10-31}$$

It is possible to project these results, by means of duality, to a parallel connection of any number of branches. The paralell connection of a number of branches, as in Fig. 10-9, gives an admittance formula which is the dual of Eq. (10-30), thus:

$$\mathbf{Y}_{eq} = \mathbf{Y}_1 + \mathbf{Y}_2 + \mathbf{Y}_3 + \cdots + \mathbf{Y}_N \tag{10-32}$$

The formula for the impedance is

$$\mathbf{Z}_{eq} = \frac{1}{\mathbf{Y}_1 + \mathbf{Y}_2 + \mathbf{Y}_3 + \cdots + \mathbf{Y}_N} \tag{10-33}$$

which is the dual of Eq. (10-31).

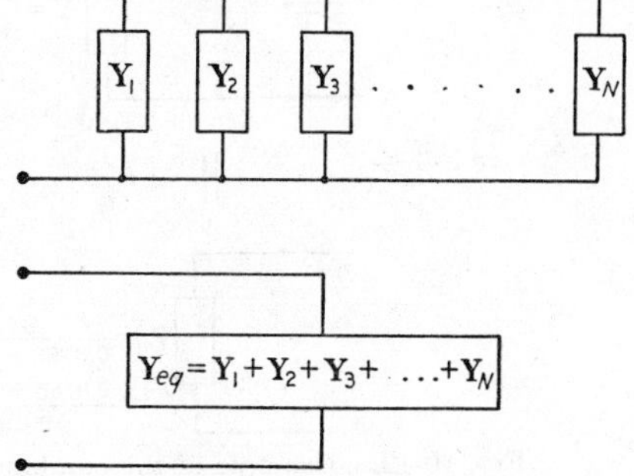


FIG. 10-9. The equivalent admittance of a parallel-connected combination of $N$ admittance branches.

It has been stated that the branch of a circuit is any combination of elements for which an impedance or admittance formula is known. The techniques of this section make it possible to consider the combination (series or parallel) of a number of branches to be a branch itself. With the concept of equivalent impedances and admittances it is possible to obtain formulas for the impedances and admittances of arrangements of elements which are neither pure series nor pure parallel connections. Simple examples are the *series-parallel* circuit of Fig. 10-10 and the *parallel-series* circuit of Fig. 10-11. In Fig. 10-10, for example, Eq. (10-33) can be used to find the impedance of the two parallel-connected elements, and then Eq. (10-30) can be used to find the impedance of the complete circuit. A similar (dual) procedure applies to Fig. 10-11. Procedures like this can often be a useful adjunct to the step-by-step method. However, a circuit can be reduced in this way only when successive series and parallel combinations can be found within the circuit structure (see Fig. 11-15*a* for an example of a network in which the procedure is not possible.)

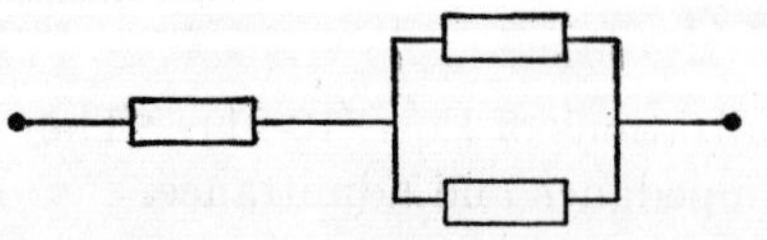

FIG. 10-10. A simple series-parallel network.

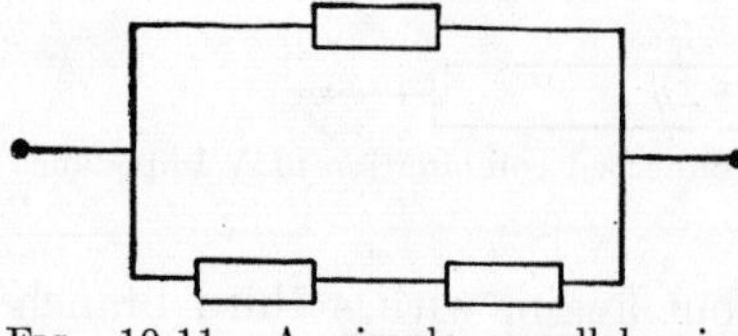

FIG. 10-11. A simple parallel-series network.

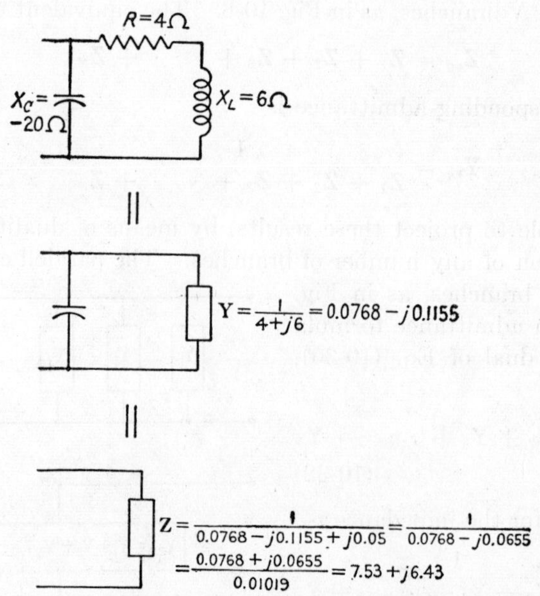


FIG. 10-12. Example of the combination of impedances and admittances.

Figures 10-12 and 10-13 give pictorial presentations of this process of reducing a network. It is often helpful to use diagrams of this type.

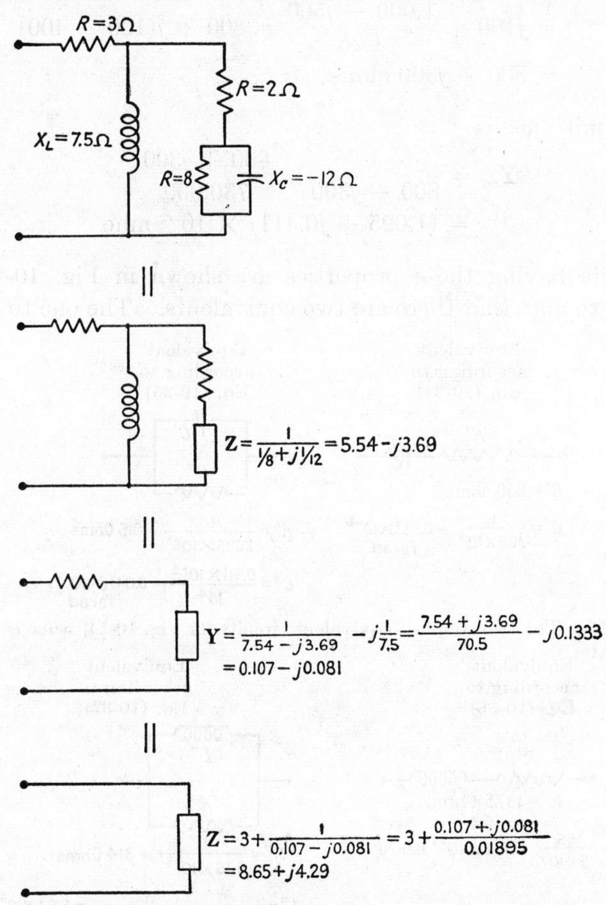


FIG. 10-13. Example of the combination of impedances and admittances.

**10-4. Equivalent Impedance and Admittance, at Fixed Frequency.** The ideas of equivalence used in Sec. 10-3 pertain to *formulas* for impedances and admittances. They do not in general imply that an equivalent circuit can be found which will be valid at all frequencies. However, at a fixed frequency it is possible to develop an equivalent circuit, as illustrated by Fig. 10-14. As a specific example, let $\omega = 10^4$ rad/per sec. The impedance is

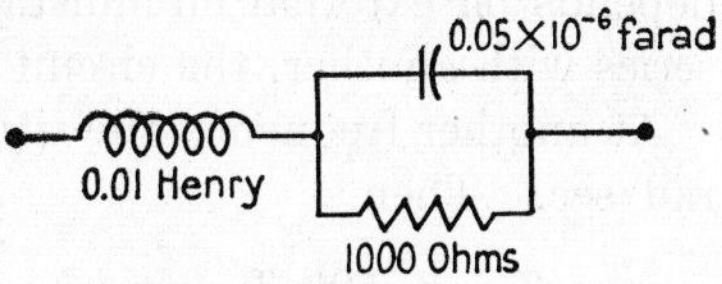

FIG. 10-14. Specific example of a series-parallel circuit.

$$\begin{aligned}\mathbf{Z}_{eq} &= j100 + \frac{1}{10^{-3} + j0.5 \times 10^{-3}} \\ &= j100 + \frac{1{,}000 - j500}{1.25} = 800 + j(100 - 400) \\ &= 800 - j300 \text{ ohms} \end{aligned} \tag{10-34}$$

and the admittance is

$$\begin{aligned}\mathbf{Y}_{eq} &= \frac{1}{800 - j300} = \frac{800 + j300}{730{,}000} \\ &= (1.095 + j0.411) \times 10^{-3} \text{ mho}\end{aligned} \tag{10-35}$$

Two circuits having these properties are shown in Fig. 10-15. It is instructive to note that there are two equivalents. The one to be chosen

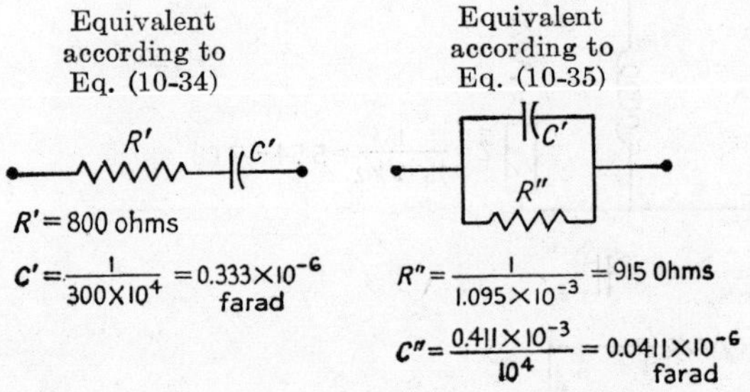

Equivalent according to Eq. (10-34)
Equivalent according to Eq. (10-35)
R'
C'
R''
R' = 800 ohms
C' = 1/(300X10⁴) = 0.333X10⁻⁶ farad
R'' = 1/(1.095X10⁻³) = 915 Ohms
C'' = 0.411X10⁻³/10⁴ = 0.0411X10⁻⁶ farad

FIG. 10-15. The two simplest equivalent circuits for Fig. 10-14, when $\omega = 10^4$.

Equivalent according to Eq. (10-36)
Equivalent according to Eq. (10-37)
R'
L'
L''
R''
R' = 137.5 Ohms
L' = 156/(5X10⁴) = 3.12X10⁻³ Henry
R'' = 1/(3.18X10⁻³) = 314 Ohms
L'' = 1/(3.61X10⁻³X5X10⁴) = 5.54X10⁻³ Henry

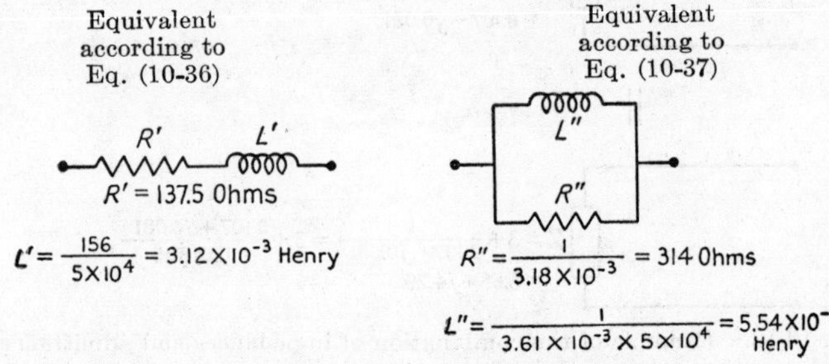

FIG. 10-16. The two simplest equivalent circuits for Fig. 10-14, when $\omega = 5 \times 10^4$.

depends on external circumstances. For example, if the network is in series with another, the circuit at (a) would be the natural one to use.

At another frequency the situation is different. Suppose $\omega = 5 \times 10^4$ rad/sec. Then

$$\mathbf{Z}_{eq} = j500 + \frac{1}{10^{-3} + j2.5 \times 10^{-3}} = 137.5 + j156 \text{ ohms} \tag{10-36}$$

and

$$\mathbf{Y}_{eq} = \frac{1}{137.5 + j156} = (3.18 - j3.61) \times 10^{-3} \text{ mho} \tag{10-37}$$

The corresponding circuits are shown in Fig. 10-16. At $\omega = 10^4$ the equivalent circuits are capacitive, but at $\omega = 5 \times 10^4$ they are inductive. It is also seen that the resistive components of the equivalent circuits vary with frequency, indicating that they do not represent actual resistors.

In power-circuit analysis equivalent circuits of this type are useful, because the frequency is constant. In communication work they are also useful, when the range of frequency variation is small enough to be considered sensibly constant as far as the equivalent circuit is concerned.

**10-5. Series and Parallel Equivalent Circuits.** This section is a generalization of the treatment of the impedance of a parallel circuit and the admittance of a series circuit in Sec. 8-7. Consider the two general circuits of Fig. 10-17. The one shown at (*a*) is the general series equivalent circuit. The rectangle represents a reactance, either capacitive or inductive. Similarly, the rectangle in the general parallel equivalent circuit represents a susceptance.

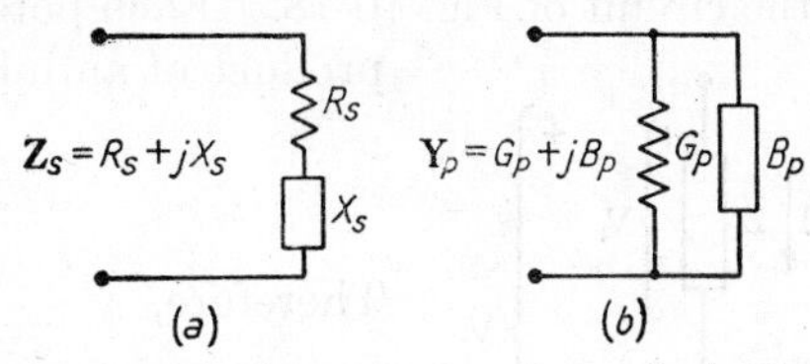


FIG. 10-17. Equivalent series and parallel circuits.

Since the two circuits are to be equivalent,

$$G_p + jB_p = \mathbf{Y}_p = \frac{1}{\mathbf{Z}_s} = \frac{1}{R_s + jX_s} \tag{10-38}$$

The term on the right can be reduced by performing the indicated division, giving

$$G_p + jB_p = \mathbf{Y}_p = \frac{R_s}{R_s^2 + X_s^2} - j\frac{X_s}{R_s^2 + X_s^2} \tag{10-39}$$

For Eq. (10-39) to be true it is necessary that the real and imaginary parts be equal individually. Also,

$$R_s^2 + X_s^2 = Z^2 = \frac{1}{Y^2} \tag{10-40}$$

where subscripts have been dropped from $Z$ and $Y$, because both circuits have the same impedance or admittance. Therefore

$$\begin{aligned} G_p &= \frac{R_s}{Z^2} \\ B_p &= -\frac{X_s}{Z^2} \end{aligned} \tag{10-41}$$

Convenient forms for these are

$$\frac{R_s}{G_p} = Z^2$$
$$\frac{X_s}{B_p} = -Z^2 \qquad (10\text{-}42)$$

These forms may be solved for the components of either **Z** or **Y**, depending on which are given.

**10-6. Distribution of Potential Differences and Currents.** Consider the circuit of Fig. 10-18. Each potential difference is proportional to the product of an impedance and the current, thus:

$$\mathbf{V}_1 = \mathbf{Z}_1\mathbf{I}$$
$$\mathbf{V}_2 = \mathbf{Z}_2\mathbf{I} \qquad (10\text{-}43)$$

Therefore,

$$\frac{\mathbf{V}_1}{\mathbf{V}_2} = \frac{\mathbf{Z}_1}{\mathbf{Z}_2}$$
$$\frac{\mathbf{V}_1}{\mathbf{V}} = \frac{\mathbf{Z}_1}{\mathbf{Z}_1 + \mathbf{Z}_2} \qquad (10\text{-}44)$$
$$\frac{\mathbf{V}_2}{\mathbf{V}} = \frac{\mathbf{Z}_2}{\mathbf{Z}_1 + \mathbf{Z}_2}$$

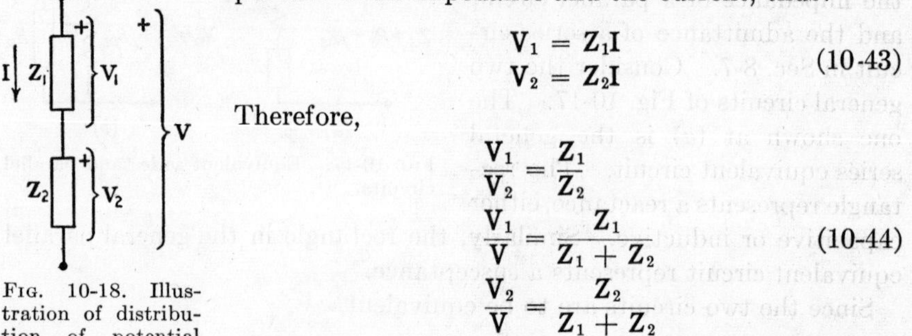


Fig. 10-18. Illustration of distribution of potential differences.

In words these results may be stated by saying that in a series connection of branches the potential differences distribute in the same ratio as the impedances of the branches. Although the example is given for only two branches in series, it can be proved for any number.

Figure 10-19 is the dual of the above. The current in a branch is the product of the potential difference by the admittance of the branch, thus:

$$\mathbf{I}_1 = \mathbf{Y}_1\mathbf{V}$$
$$\mathbf{I}_2 = \mathbf{Y}_2\mathbf{V} \qquad (10\text{-}45)$$
$$\mathbf{I} = (\mathbf{Y}_1 + \mathbf{Y}_2)\mathbf{V}$$

Taking ratios of these gives

$$\frac{\mathbf{I}_1}{\mathbf{I}_2} = \frac{\mathbf{Y}_1}{\mathbf{Y}_2}$$
$$\frac{\mathbf{I}_1}{\mathbf{I}} = \frac{\mathbf{Y}_1}{\mathbf{Y}_1 + \mathbf{Y}_2} \qquad (10\text{-}46)$$
$$\frac{\mathbf{I}_2}{\mathbf{I}} = \frac{\mathbf{Y}_2}{\mathbf{Y}_1 + \mathbf{Y}_2}$$

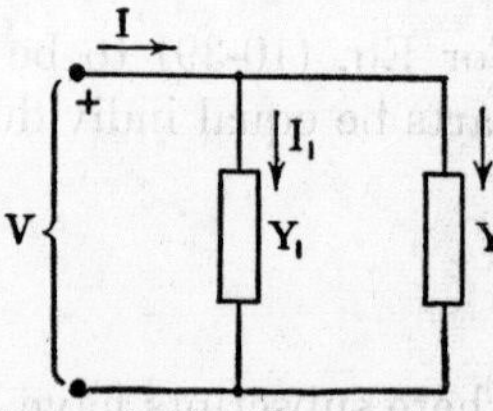

Fig. 10-19. Illustration of distribution of currents.

This proves that when branches are connected in parallel the currents in individual branches are distributed in the ratio of the admittances of the branches. The statement may be extended to any number of branches.

**10-7. Summary.** The general solution of networks is based on the breaking up of the network into a system of branches. For each branch the relationship between potential and current follows a known law.

The isolated relationships between potential and current, for the various branches, are tied together by Kirchhoff laws. In some cases enough information is known to make it possible to apply one Kirchhoff law to find a new quantity. If this can be done repeatedly, the circuit can be solved by the step-by-step method.

The rules for finding equivalent impedance and admittance are important results of the step-by-step process. Impedances in series add, and admittances in parallel add, if expressions for them are written in the complex form.

Only networks having no sources can be reduced to an equivalent impedance or admittance. Networks which include sources can be converted to equivalent circuits by theorems developed in Chap. 11.

## PROBLEMS

**10-1.** For the circuit shown in Fig. P10-1 determine:

*a.* The complex impedance of the circuit.

*b.* The current **I**, if $\mathbf{V} = 150 + j0$ volts.

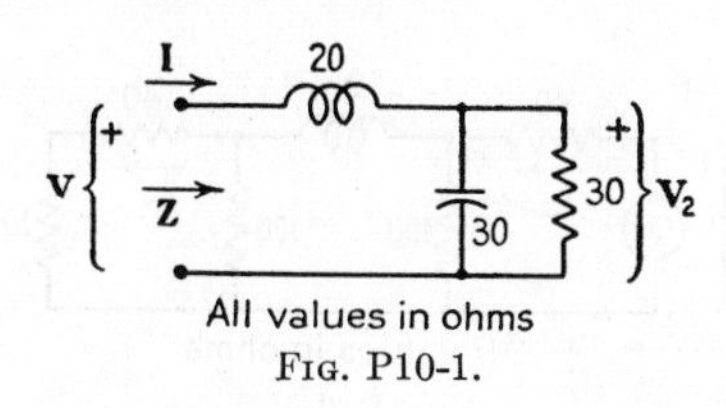


FIG. P10-1.

*c.* The power taken by the circuit.

*d.* The potential $\mathbf{V}_2$.

**10-2.** The circuit of Fig. P10-2 is an equivalent for a vacuum-tube amplifier. The potential $v_2$ is measured and found to have an effective value of 0.5 volts.

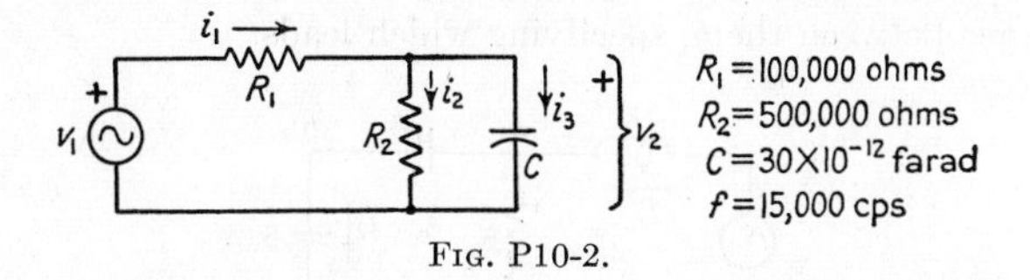


FIG. P10-2.

For purposes of discussion asume $v_2$ is given, in volts, by the formula

$$v_2 = 0.707 \cos \omega t$$

Use complex notation wherever possible to:

*a.* Find the equation for the potential $v_1$.

*b.* Find the complex impedance seen by the potential source.
*c.* Find the power dissipated in each resistor.
*d.* Draw a sinor diagram for the circuit.
*e.* Specify the phase difference between the potentials $v_1$ and $v_2$.

**10-3.** The current source for the circuit of Fig. P10-3, in amperes, is

$$i = 5 \sin \left( \omega t - \frac{\pi}{2} \right)$$

Use complex notation wherever possible to:
*a.* Find the equation for the potential $v$.
*b.* Find the power absorbed by the circuit.
*c.* Find the power dissipated in each resistor.

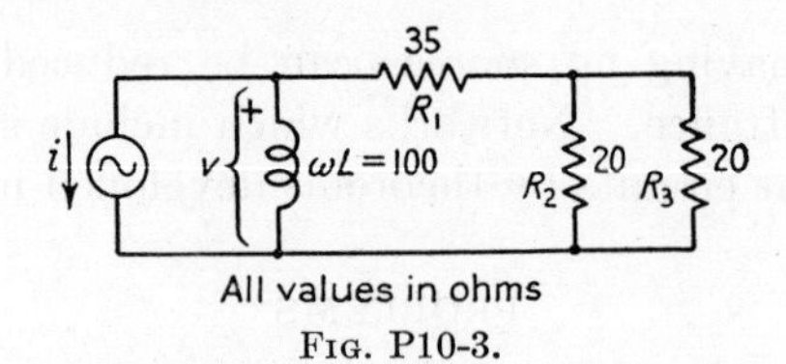


FIG. P10-3.

**10-4.** For the circuit of Fig. P10-4 $\mathbf{I}_a = 10 + j0$ amp. Determine:
*a.* The potential $\mathbf{V}_1$.
*b.* The current $\mathbf{I}_b$.

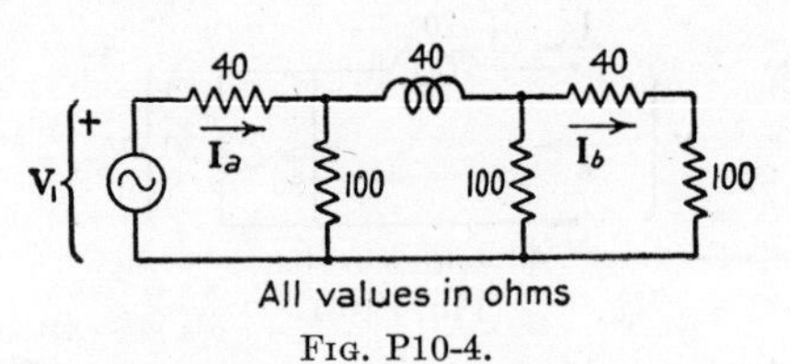


FIG. P10-4.

*c.* The power taken by the device.
*d.* The power absorbed by each resistor.

**10-5.** For the circuit of Fig. P10-5 use complex algebra to:
*a.* Determine the ratio of the magnitudes of the currents $i_1$ and $i_2$ and the phase difference between them, specifying which leads.

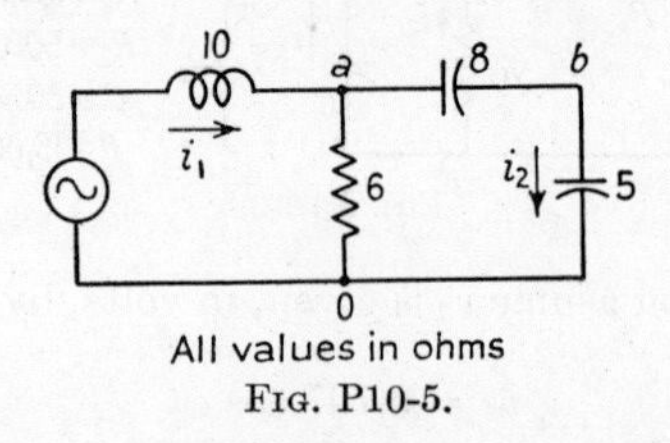


FIG. P10-5.

*b.* Determine the ratio of the magnitudes of the potentials $v_{a0}$ and $v_{b0}$ and the phase difference between them, specifying which leads.

**10-6.** For the circuit shown in Fig. P10-6 the current is $\mathbf{I}_1 = 0 + j10$ amp.

*a.* Find the current $\mathbf{I}_{cb}$.

*b.* What is the complex admittance of the section between points (*a*) and (*b*)?

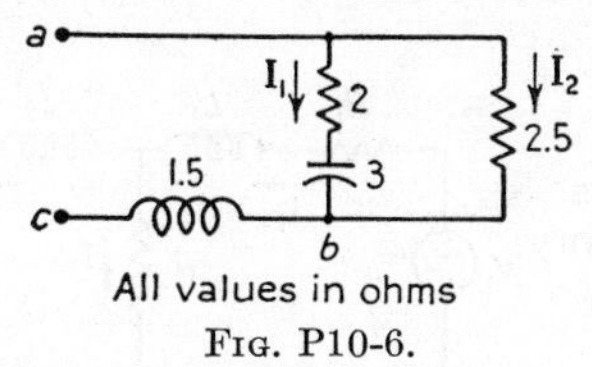


FIG. P10-6.

*c.* What is the impedance of the entire circuit?

*d.* Find the potential $\mathbf{V}_{ac}$.

**10-7.** The circuit shown in Fig. P10-7 is an equivalent circuit for an amplifying circuit such as is sometimes used in television receivers.

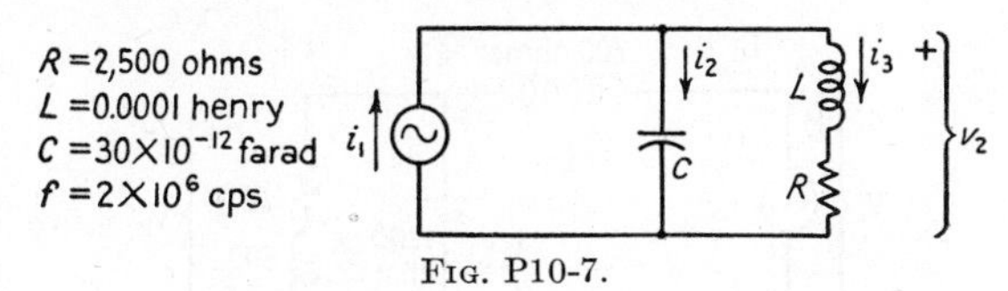


FIG. P10-7.

*a.* Find the complex expression for the current source if $\mathbf{V}_2 = 0.5 + j0$ volts.

*b.* What is the admittance of that portion of the circuit seen by the current source?

*c.* Find the power dissipated by the resistor.

*d.* Draw a sinor diagram for the conditions specified.

**10-8.** The circuit of Fig. 10-8 represents a power-transmission system. Capacitor $C'$ is to be omitted for parts (*a*), (*b*), and (*c*). The resistors $R$, the inductors

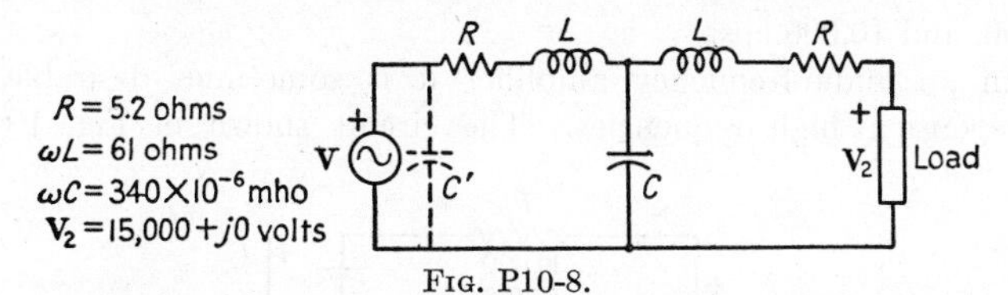


FIG. P10-8.

$L$, and the capacitor $C$ approximately represent a transmission line. The load takes 500 kw at a power factor 0.9, with the current lagging.

*a.* Find the potential across the generator terminals.

*b.* At what power factor does the generator operate?

*c.* How much power is delivered by the generator, and what is the power loss in the transmission system?

*d.* What would be the size of the added capacitor $C'$ to make the generator operate at unity power factor? The frequency is 60 cps.

**10-9.** A resistor $R_3$ is supplied 25,000 watts from two generators as shown in Fig. P10-9. The potential sources are adjusted to make the effective value of $\mathbf{I}_1$ equal twice the effective value of $\mathbf{I}_2$, and so that $\mathbf{I}_1$ leads $\mathbf{I}_2$ by 90°. $\mathbf{I}_3$ is assumed to be real.

*a.* Find the complex expressions for the currents $\mathbf{I}_1$ and $\mathbf{I}_2$.

*b.* Find the complex expressions for the potentials $\mathbf{V}_1$ and $\mathbf{V}_2$.

*c.* Find the power delivered by each potential source and the power factor at which it operates.

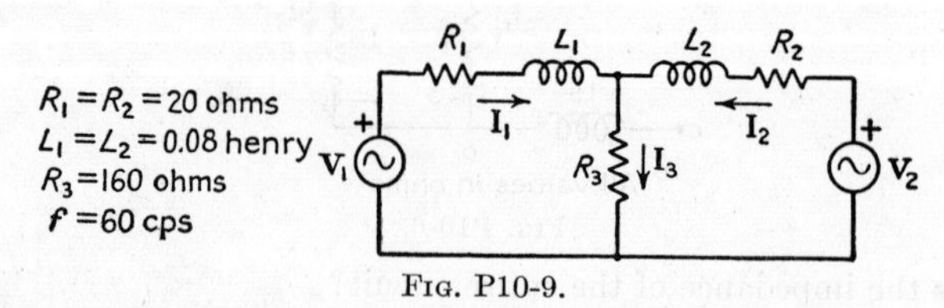


FIG. P10-9.

**10-10.** Figure P10-10 shows a circuit which may be used as a low-pass filter. Its properties are characterized by the transmission function $\mathbf{V}_2/\mathbf{V}_1$, which

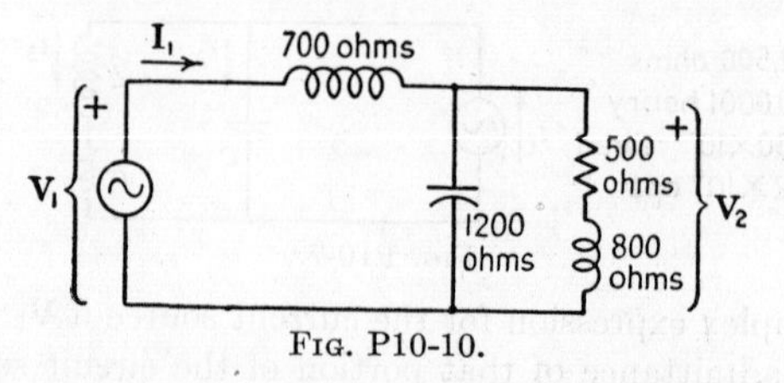


FIG. P10-10.

approaches unity at low frequencies and zero at high frequencies. The reactances indicated on the diagram are for a frequency of 2,700 cps.

*a.* Find the complex expression for $\mathbf{V}_2/\mathbf{V}_1$, as a function of frequency, in polar form.

*b.* Evaluate the expression obtained in part (*a*) at frequencies 1,000, 2,700, 4,000, 7,000, and 10,000 cps.

**10-11.** In an audio-frequency amplifier it is sometimes desirable to have reduced response at high frequencies. The circuit shown in Fig. P10-11 will

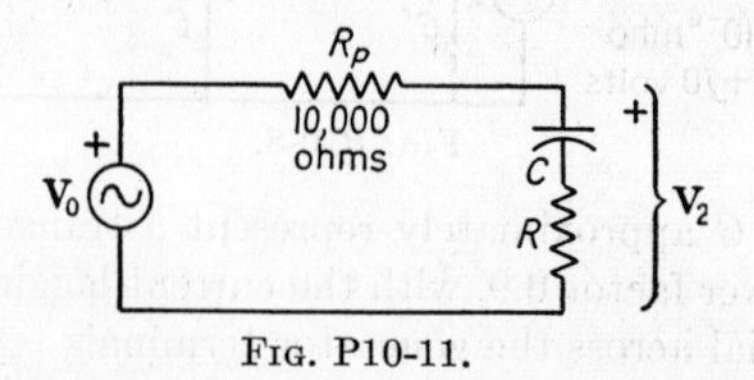


FIG. P10-11.

accomplish this to some extent. The resistor $R_p$ and the potential $\mathbf{V}_0$ represent the equivalent circuit of the vacuum tube. They may be considered to be independent of frequency for the range of frequencies to be encountered in this problem. $R$ and $C$ are to be chosen so that $|\mathbf{V}_2/\mathbf{V}_0|$ will have the values 0.93, and 0.6, for the respective frequencies of 800 and 3,000 cps.

*a.* Determine the required values of $R$ and $C$.

*b.* At each of the specified frequencies determine the phase difference between $\mathbf{V}_0$ and $\mathbf{V}_2$, always specifying which leads.

**10-12.** In the circuit shown in Fig. P10-12 the parallel branch of $R$ and $C$ will accentuate the high frequencies of an audio amplifier. As in Prob. 10-11, $\mathbf{V}_0$ and

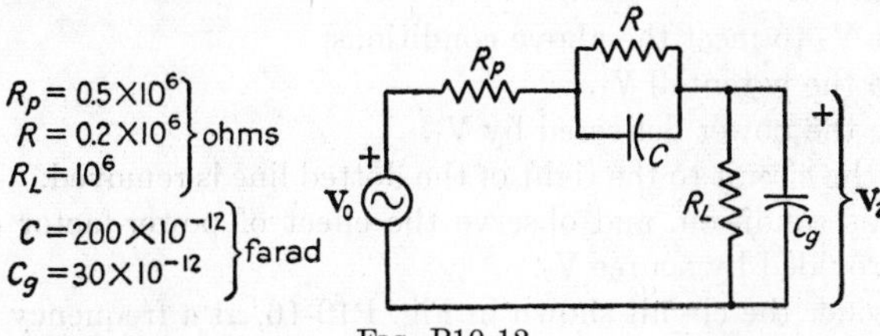


FIG. P10-12.

$R_p$ are the elements of the potential-source equivalent of the vacuum tube which drives the circuit. Let $\mathbf{V}_2'$ and $\mathbf{V}_2$ be values of output potential when $f = 15{,}000$ and 2,000 cps, respectively.

*a.* Compute the ratio $V_2'/V_2$ when the $R$-$C$ circuit is in place.

*b.* Compute the ratio $V_2'/V_2$ when the $R$-$C$ circuit is removed and replaced by a direct connection.

**10-13.** The low-frequency response of an amplifier can be accentuated by the circuit of Fig. P10-13. The vacuum tube has been replaced by a current-source

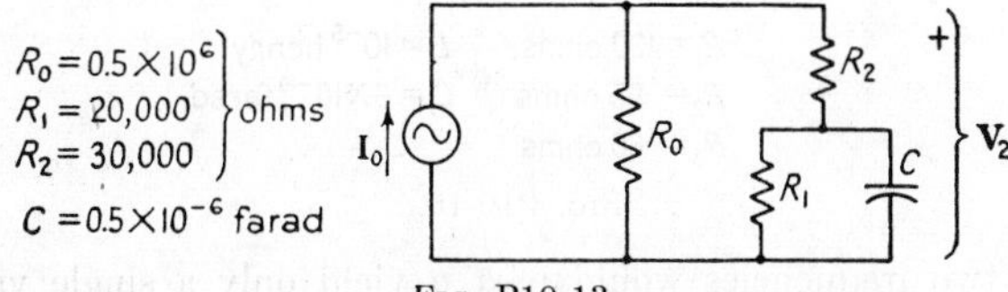


FIG. P10-13.

equivalent. Let $\mathbf{I}_0 = 0.001 + j0$ amp. Derive a formula for $\mathbf{V}_2$ as a function of frequency and evaluate it at frequencies of 10, 25, 50, and 100 cps?

**10-14.** Refer to the data and circuit of Prob. 7-16. The resistor is replaced by the series connection of $R$ and $L$, where $R = 150$ ohms and $\omega L = 75$ ohms.

*a.* Compute the indication of the wattmeter for values of $\alpha = 0, \pi/4, \pi/2$, and $3\pi/4$.

*b.* Calculate the two values of $\alpha$ at which the wattmeter indication is zero.

**10-15.** Figure P10-15 shows a generator supplying power to a load through a transmission line. A second source is connected to the load, through a short

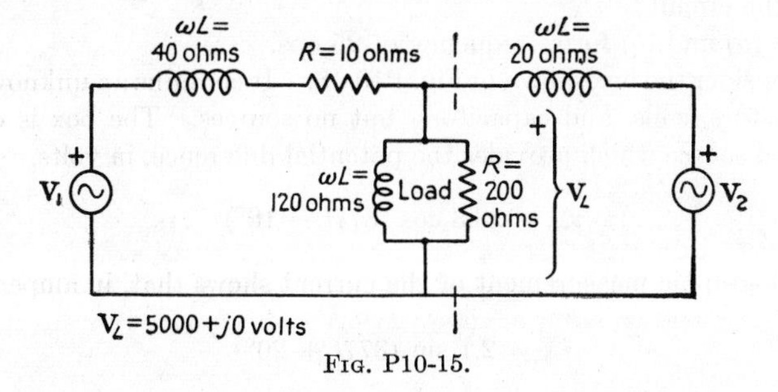


FIG. P10-15.

transmission line. The potential of source $\mathbf{V}_2$ is to be adjusted so that it takes or delivers no power but so that the load plus the network to its right will have unity power factor.

*a.* Compute $\mathbf{V}_2$ to meet the above conditions.

*b.* Compute the potential $\mathbf{V}_1$.

*c.* Compute the power delivered by $\mathbf{V}_1$.

*d.* Suppose the circuit to the right of the dotted line is removed. Repeat parts *b* and *c* for this condition, and observe the effect of power-factor correction at the load, as provided by source $\mathbf{V}_2$.

**10-16.** Consider the circuit shown in Fig. P10-16, at a frequency of $3.6 \times 10^6$ cps.

*a.* Determine two values of $C_2$ that will make the portion to the right of the dotted line appear as a pure resistance.

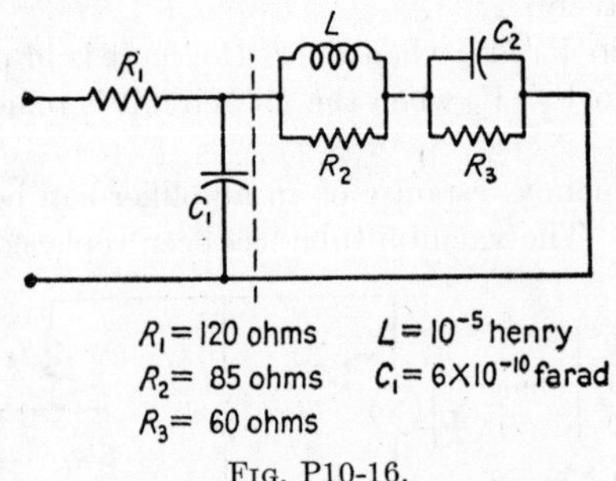


Fig. P10-16.

*b.* At what two frequencies would part *a* yield only a single value for $C_2$? The series-circuit equivalent is to have only two elements.

*c.* Determine the series-circuit equivalent of the entire circuit when $C_2$ has the smaller of the two values determined in part *a*.

*d.* Determine the parallel-circuit equivalent for the entire circuit, for the condition specified in part *c*.

**10-17.** Consider the circuit shown in Fig. P10-15. Let the part to the right of the dotted line be removed. The frequency is 60 cps.

*a.* What two elements connected in series would serve as an equivalent circuit for the remaining part of the circuit?

*b.* What two elements connected in parallel would be equivalent to the remaining part of the circuit?

*c.* Repeat (*a*) and (*b*) for a frequency of 25 cps.

**10-18.** Consider the box shown in Fig. P10-18. It contains an unknown assortment of resistors, coils, and capacitors, but no sources. The box is connected to an external source which provides the potential difference, in volts,

$$v_{ab} = 28.3 \cos (377t - 10°)$$

and an oscillographic measurement of the current shows that, in amperes, it is

$$i_{ab} = 2.1 \sin (377t + 20°)$$

*a.* Draw the parallel circuit which is equivalent, at this frequency, to the contents of the box. Evaluate the constants of the circuit.

*b.* Draw the series circuit which is equivalent, at this frequency, to the contents of the box. Evaluate the constants of the circuit.

*c.* What is the impedance of the resulting circuit if the box is connected in series with a resistance of 5 ohms and a capacitance of 300 $\mu$f?

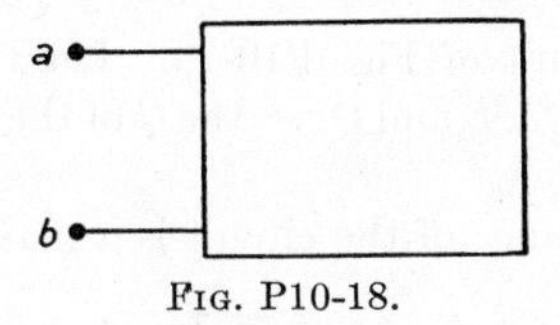


FIG. P10-18.

*d.* What is the admittance of the resulting circuit if the box is connected in parallel with the circuit consisting of the parallel connection of a conductance of 0.25 mho and a capacitance of 400 $\mu$f?

**10-19.** Consider the circuit of Fig. P10-19. Frequency is variable. Let $Q_s$

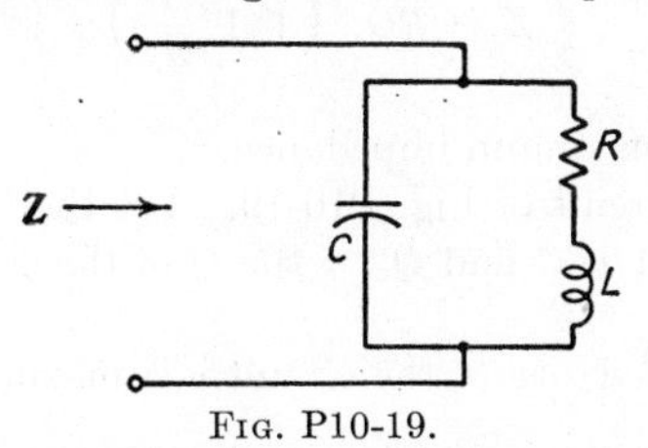


FIG. P10-19.

be the $Q$ of the circuit if all elements are in a series connection and let

$$\omega_0 = \frac{1}{\sqrt{LC}}.$$

*a.* Prove that the impedance is a real quantity when

$$\omega = \omega_0 \sqrt{1 - \frac{1}{Q_s^2}}$$

*b.* Prove that at the frequency specified in (*a*)

$$Z = RQ_s^2$$

**10-20.** Refer to the circuit of Fig. P10-19 and the definitions of $Q_s$ and $\omega_0$ given in Prob. 10-19.

*a.* Prove that the impedance is a maximum when

$$\omega = \omega_0 \sqrt{\sqrt{1 + \frac{2}{Q_s^2}} - \frac{1}{Q_s^2}}$$

*b.* Prove that at the frequency specified in (*a*) the impedance has the value $\mathbf{Z} = Z\epsilon^{j\zeta}$, where

$$Z = RQ^2 \frac{1}{\sqrt{2Q_s^2\left(\sqrt{1+\frac{2}{Q_s^2}}-1\right)-1}}$$

$$\zeta = -\tan^{-1}\sqrt{\sqrt{1+\frac{2}{Q_s^2}}-\frac{1}{Q_s^2}}\,Q\left(\sqrt{1+\frac{2}{Q_s^2}}-1\right)$$

**10-21.** Refer to the circuit of Fig. P10-19. Let the frequency be fixed and $C$ be variable. Let $C_0 = 1/\omega^2 L$ and $Q_s =$ the $Q$ of the circuit in series connection when $C = C_0$.

*a.* Prove that the impedance of the circuit is a maximum when

$$C = C_0 \frac{1}{1 + (1/Q_s^2)}$$

*b.* Prove that the impedance is real and has the value

$$Z = RQ_s^2\left(1 + \frac{1}{Q_s^2}\right)$$

when $C$ is adjusted for maximum impedance.

**10-22.** Refer to the circuit of Fig. P10-19. Let the frequency be fixed and $L$ be variable. Let $L_0 = 1/\omega^2 C$ and $Q_s =$ the $Q$ of the circuit in series connection when $L = L_0$.

*a.* Prove that the impedance of the circuit is a maximum when

$$L = L_0 \frac{1 + \sqrt{1 + (4/Q_s^2)}}{2}$$

*b.* Prove that the impedance is real and has the value

$$Z = RQ^2\sqrt{\frac{1 + (4/Q_s^2) + \sqrt{1 + (4/Q_s^2)}}{4 + Q_s^2[1 - \sqrt{1 + (4/Q_s^2)}]}}$$

when $L$ is adjusted to give maximum impedance.

## QUESTIONS

**10-1.** What criterion must always be satisfied if the step-by-step method is to be applicable to a network?

**10-2.** Whenever the step-by-step method is applicable, is it possible to do without complex numbers and use a graphical solution, provided that the graphical solution is sufficiently accurate?

**10-3.** Will the presence of more than one source in a network always prevent the use of the step-by-step method in its solution?

**10-4.** How can a resistor and a capacitor be combined in a circuit to provide a potential that leads a given potential by 45°?

**10-5.** How can a resistor and a capacitor be combined in a circuit to provide a potential that lags a given potential by 45°?

**10-6.** Which one of the Kirchhoff laws is required in order to prove that when branches are connected in series their impedances are added?

**10-7.** Which one of the Kirchhoff laws is required in order to prove that when branches are connected in parallel their admittances are added?

**10-8.** Must a series circuit always be treated in terms of its impedance, and a parallel circuit in terms of its admittance; or is it proper to speak of the admittance of a series circuit and the impedance of a parallel circuit?

**10-9.** If you are given a series circuit which includes some coils or capacitors, is it always possible to construct a parallel circuit that is equivalent to it (*a*) if the frequency is fixed, (*b*) if the frequency is allowed to vary?

**10-10.** A coil in series with a resistor $R$ is to be replaced by an equivalent consisting of the parallel connection of a coil and a resistor. At fixed frequency, how does the value of the parallel resistor vary as $R$ varies?

**10-11.** Given a passive network with two terminals; is it always possible to obtain a series circuit of a variety of elements which will be equivalent to the original network as frequency varies?

**10-12.** Are the laws for the distribution of potentials with series branches and the distribution of currents for parallel branches dually related?

**10-13.** Make up some problems which cannot be solved by the step-by-step methods.

# CHAPTER 11

# ANALYSIS OF NETWORKS (CONTINUED)

**11-1. Introduction.** In many networks, sources are distributed throughout a network in such a way that the step-by-step process cannot be used. More powerful methods are needed. These break down into two categories, the simultaneous application of Kirchhoff's laws, and various circuit theorems by which circuits can be simplified. These methods are essentially the same as their d-c counterparts, the only difference being that complex notation is used.

As a general rule it may be said that the powerful general methods introduced in Chap. 11 should be used only when warranted by the needs of the problem. To use them on a problem that can be solved by the more direct methods of Chap. 10 usually leads to unnecessary complications. Therefore, Chap. 11 should be regarded as supplementing, but not superseding, Chap. 10.

**11-2. General Network Solution Using Branch Currents.** Figure 11-1 can be used to illustrate this method. In order to be as general as possible, the illustration is set up with one potential source and one current

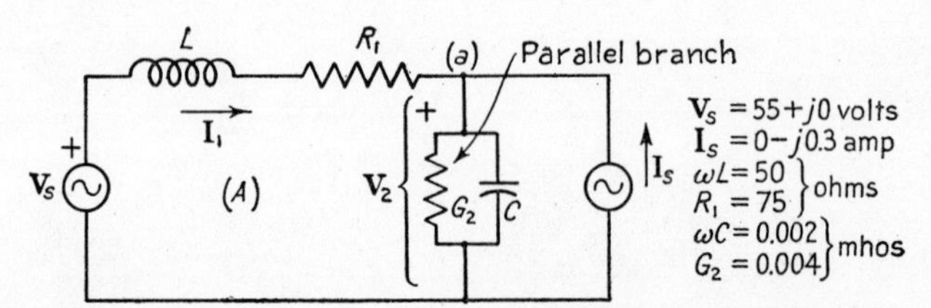


FIG. 11-1. Typical network with potential and current sources.

source. The sources are known quantities. One current $\mathbf{I}_1$ and one potential $\mathbf{V}_2$ are to be found.

An equation expressing the Kirchhoff current law is written for each node, except one, at which *three* or more leads come together. Kirchhoff potential equations are written for successive loops until enough equations are obtained to solve for all the unknowns.

At node (*a*) the Kirchhoff current law is

$$\mathbf{I}_1 + \mathbf{I}_s = (G_2 + j\omega C)\mathbf{V}_2 \qquad (11\text{-}1)$$

and the Kirchhoff potential equation for loop $(A)$ is

$$\mathbf{V}_s = (R_1 + j\omega L)\mathbf{I}_1 + \mathbf{V}_2 \tag{11-2}$$

No equation is needed for the loop on the right, because it adds only a current source which is already known.

The insertion of numerical values gives

$$\begin{aligned} \mathbf{I}_1 - (0.004 + j0.002)\mathbf{V}_2 &= j0.3 \\ (75 + j50)\mathbf{I}_1 + \mathbf{V}_2 &= 55 \end{aligned} \tag{11-3}$$

The rules for manipulating complex quantities are similar to those for real quantities. It is therefore permissible to solve these equations by the techniques applicable to simultaneous equations in real variables. Although there are only two equations in this case, determinants are used to illustrate the method.

The solution for $\mathbf{I}_1$, in amperes, is

$$\mathbf{I}_1 = \frac{\begin{vmatrix} j0.3 & -(0.004 + j0.002) \\ 55 & 1 \end{vmatrix}}{\begin{vmatrix} 1 & -(0.004 + j0.002) \\ 75 + j50 & 1 \end{vmatrix}} = \frac{j0.3 + 0.22 + j0.11}{1 + 0.3 - 0.1 + j(0.2 + 0.15)}$$

$$= \frac{0.22 + j0.41}{1.2 + j0.35} = \frac{0.465\angle 61.7^\circ}{1.25\angle 16.2^\circ}$$

$$= 0.372\angle 45.5^\circ = 0.262 + j0.266 \tag{11-4}$$

Similarly, the potential difference $\mathbf{V}_2$, in volts, is given by

$$\mathbf{V}_2 = \frac{\begin{vmatrix} 1 & j0.03 \\ 75 + j50 & 55 \end{vmatrix}}{1.2 + j0.35} = \frac{55 - j22.5 + 15}{1.2 + j0.35} = \frac{70 - j22.5}{1.2 + j0.35}$$

$$= \frac{73.5\angle -17.8^\circ}{1.25\angle 16.2}$$

$$= 58.7\angle -34^\circ = 48.8 - j33 \tag{11-5}$$

It is interesting to compare the roles played by complex quantities in this technique and in the step-by-step method. In the step-by-step method complex quantities are an aid in carrying out the geometrical processes indicated by the sinor diagrams. Otherwise, complex notation is not essential. In the simultaneous solution of equations, however, complex notation is essential. Except in the simplest of cases, there is no way to carry out the simultaneous solution of several equations by graphical construction alone.

The techniques described up to this point are adequate for the solution of any linear-circuit problem. They do not, however, always yield the most direct solution. The remaining sections of this chapter present various theorems which are useful for the simplification of network solutions. They are particularly useful when a complete solution is not required.

**11-3. Superposition Theorem.** Consider the solution for $\mathbf{I}_1$ in Sec. 11-2. The determinantal form of Eq. (11-4) can be expanded as

$$\mathbf{I}_1 = j0.3 \frac{1}{1.2 + j0.35} + 55 \frac{0.004 + j0.002}{1.2 + j0.35} \tag{11-6}$$

The factor $j0.3$ is the current source, and the factor 55 is the potential source. Suppose the potential source were zero. Then the current due to the current source alone would be

$$\mathbf{I}_{1i} = j0.3 \frac{1}{1.2 + j0.35} \tag{11-7}$$

If the current source were zero, the current due to the potential source acting alone would be

$$\mathbf{I}_{1v} = 55 \frac{0.004 + j0.002}{1.2 + j0.35} \tag{11-8}$$

From Eq. (11-6) it is seen that the current due to both sources is

$$\mathbf{I}_1 = \mathbf{I}_{1i} + \mathbf{I}_{1v} \tag{11-9}$$

This example illustrates the superposition theorem. The example could be extended to a circuit with any number of sources. As long as a network is *linear*, its response will be a summation of terms, one due to each source. Each of these terms is independent of the others.

It is not necessary to set up the simultaneous equations to obtain the partial solutions due to the individual sources. One source can be placed in the circuit at a time, and direct methods can be used to find the response due to it. *Potential sources are removed and replaced by short circuits, while current sources are removed and the positions left open.*

The direct application of the superposition theorem can be illustrated by the same example. If the potential source is removed from Fig. 11-1, the circuit of Fig. 11-2 is obtained. The current $\mathbf{I}_s$ divides in the ratio of the admittances, giving

$$\mathbf{I}_{1i} = -\frac{1/(75 + j50)}{0.004 + j0.002 + [1\ (75 + j50)]}(-j0.3)$$

$$= \frac{j0.3}{0.3 - 0.1 + j(0.15 + 0.2) + 1} = \frac{j0.3}{1.2 + j0.35} \tag{11-10}$$

The current due to the potential source acting alone is found from Fig. 11-3. It is

$$\mathbf{I}_{1v} = \frac{55 + j0}{75 + j50 + [1/(0.004 + j0.002)]}$$
$$= \frac{55(0.004 + j0.002)}{1.2 + j0.35} = \frac{0.22 + j0.11}{1.2 + j0.35} \tag{11-11}$$

The total current, in amperes, is

$$\mathbf{I}_1 = \mathbf{I}_{1i} + \mathbf{I}_{1v}$$
$$= \frac{+j0.3 + 0.22 + j0.11}{1.2 + j0.35} = 0.262 + j0.266 \tag{11-12}$$

which agrees with Eq. (11-4).

The superposition theorem is applicable to either a potential or a current response. For example, a similar result could have been obtained for $\mathbf{V}_2$.

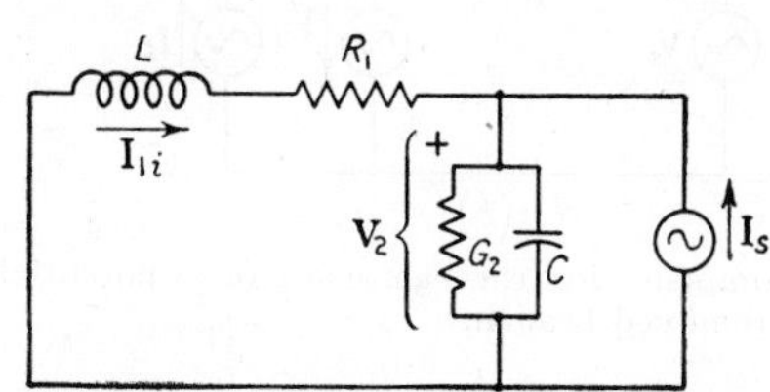


FIG. 11-2. Network of Fig. 11-1, with potential source removed. $\mathbf{I}_s = -j0.3$.

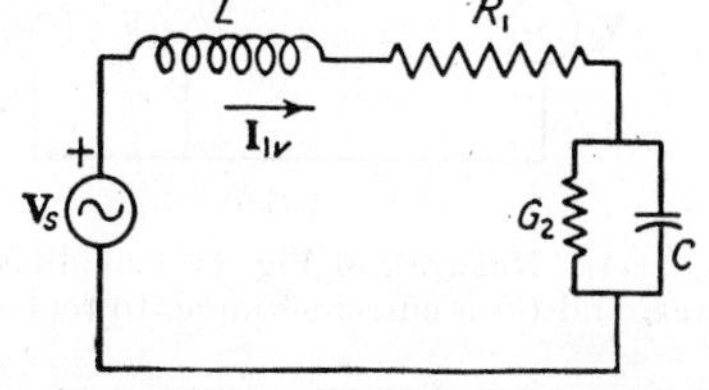


FIG. 11-3. Network of Fig. 11-1, with current source removed. $\mathbf{V}_s = 55 + j0$.

In general form the superposition theorem for the above example can be written

$$\mathbf{I}_1 = \mathbf{K}_i\mathbf{I}_s + \mathbf{K}_v\mathbf{V}_s \tag{11-13}$$

In the above case the parameters are

$$\begin{aligned} \mathbf{K}_i &= -\frac{1}{1.2 + j0.35} \\ \mathbf{K}_v &= \frac{0.004 + j0.002}{1.2 + j0.35} \\ \mathbf{I}_s &= -j0.3 \\ \mathbf{V}_s &= 55 + j0 \end{aligned} \tag{11-14}$$

The fact that the solution can appear in the form of Eq. (11-13) is important. Superposition is seldom the shortest method of obtaining a solution. However, in the literal form it is useful in proving other theorems, as in Sec. 11-5.

The superposition theorem also applies when networks have sources of different frequencies. The response due to each source acting alone is found, using sinors and complex notation. Then the time functions, which are symbolized by these sinors, are written, and finally these *time functions* are added together. It is important to understand that sinors symbolizing sinusoids of different frequencies *cannot* be added to give a meaningful result. Further information on the superposition of responses of different frequencies is given in Chap. 15.

**11-4. Compensation Theorem.** Any branch of a network can be replaced by a different branch as long as its potential and current remain unchanged. When the original branch is passive, either a potential source or a current source is usually used for the substituted branch. This principle is sometimes useful in analyzing network behavior, but it is useless in finding numerical solutions because *the solution must be known before the substitution can be made.* An application is found in Sec. 11-6.

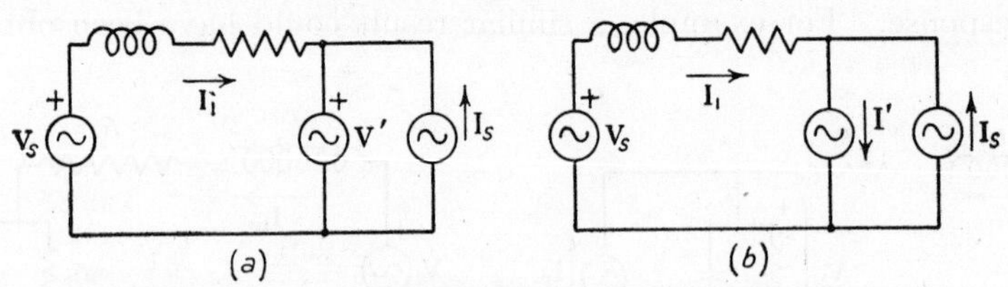


FIG. 11-4. Network of Fig. 11-1 modified by compensation theorem using (*a*) a potential source, and (*b*) a current source, to replace the removed branch.

The circuit of Fig. 11-1 can be used as an example of this theorem. The parallel branch can be replaced by a potential source

$$\mathbf{V}' = \mathbf{V}_2 = 48.8 - j33 \qquad (11\text{-}15)$$

which is obtained from the previous solution. Since $\mathbf{V}_2$ is the same as before, all other currents and potentials must be the same. The equivalent circuit is shown in Fig. 11-4*a*.

Another equivalent circuit is obtained by replacing the parallel branch by a current source $\mathbf{I}'$. Its specification can be obtained from the previous solution of the original network, from which $\mathbf{I}_1$ is known to be $0.262 + j0.266$. A current equation gives

$$\mathbf{I}' = 0.262 + j0.266 - j0.3 = 0.262 - j0.034 \qquad (11\text{-}16)$$

The equivalent network is shown in Fig. 11-4*b*. In some cases it is helpful to invert the substitution; *i.e.*, to replace a source by a passive branch. Probs. 11-2 and 11-3 at the end of this chapter can be simplified by using this principle. For the most general viewpoint the substituted branch can be considered a special case of a general source, for which the circuits of Figs. 9-4 and 9-5 are general representations. It is only necessary that $\mathbf{V}_0$ and $\mathbf{Z}_0$ (or $\mathbf{I}_0$ and $\mathbf{Y}_0$) be chosen so that $\mathbf{V}$ and $\mathbf{I}$ can have the values prevailing for the original branch.

**11-5. Helmholtz Equivalent-source Theorems (Thévenin and Norton Theorems).** Section 10-3 deals with the relationship between potential difference and current of a two-terminal network having no internal sources. An extension of this to networks which do include internal sources is now to be considered. A general portrayal of the situation to be treated is shown in Fig. 11-5*a*. The rectangle represents any combination of sources of any types, and other elements. One specific example is shown in Fig. 11-5*b*. The network must be linear.

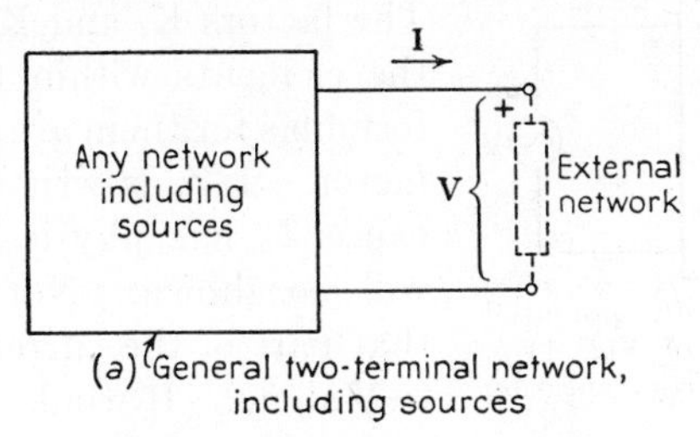


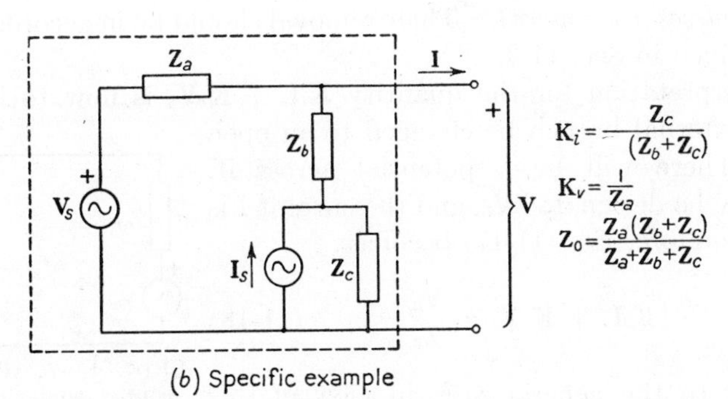


FIG. 11-5. Network to which the Helmholtz equivalent-source theorems apply.

At the outset it is important to realize that attention is directed at the *relationship* between the potential difference and current, but not at their actual values. The *relationship*, in the form of an equation, depends only on the elements within the network, while *actual values* depend on the external network as well. To keep the notation as simple as possible, let there be a single potential source $\mathbf{V}_s$ and a single current source $\mathbf{I}_s$ within the rectangle of Fig. 11-5*a*, both of the same frequency.

Let some sort of external branch be connected, so that there can be both a potential difference **V** and a current **I** as shown in Fig. 11-5*a*. Also assume that **V** and **I** are known from a solution of the network, which may have been carried out by one of the known methods. No matter what the form of the original external branch, it can be replaced by a potential source as shown in Fig. 11-6. This change is justified by the compensation theorem. Any method of solution will lead to a formula for **I** which can be written

$$\mathbf{I} = \mathbf{K}_i\mathbf{I}_s + \mathbf{K}_v\mathbf{V}_s - \frac{1}{\mathbf{Z}_0}\mathbf{V} \tag{11-17}†$$

Equation (11-17) is really an expression of the superposition theorem. The form of this equation is important. The factors $\mathbf{K}_i$ and $\mathbf{K}_v$ are functions of the elements within the network, but formulas for them are not needed. The factor $-1/\mathbf{Z}_0$ is written differently because $\mathbf{Z}_0$ has physical significance, as will be shown. Note that $-\mathbf{V}/\mathbf{Z}_0$ is that part of the current **I** which is due to **V** alone. It would be the total current if $\mathbf{V}_s$ and $\mathbf{I}_s$ were each zero. This is equivalent to saying that $\mathbf{Z}_0$ is the impedance of the network *when all internal sources are removed.* Their removal should be in accordance with the rule given in Sec. 11-3.

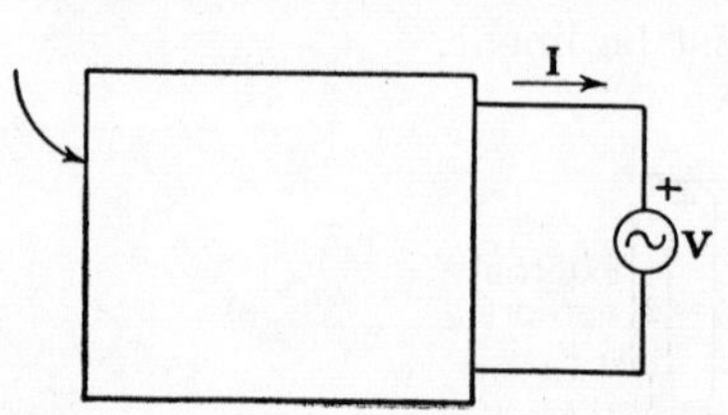

Fig. 11-6. Connection of a potential source to the terminals of Fig. 11-5, in accordance with the compensation theorem.

An interpretation for the quantity $\mathbf{K}_i\mathbf{I}_s + \mathbf{K}_v\mathbf{V}_s$ is now to be found. Let the external branch be changed to an open circuit. There will be a potential across it, which may be designated $\mathbf{V}_0$, and the current **I** is zero. Therefore, Eq. (11-17) becomes

$$\mathbf{K}_i\mathbf{I}_s + \mathbf{K}_v\mathbf{V}_s = \frac{\mathbf{V}_0}{\mathbf{Z}_0} \tag{11-18}$$

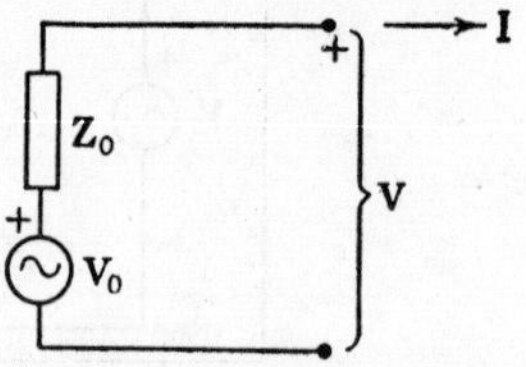

Returning to the general case, in view of this result Eq. (11-17) can be written

$$\mathbf{I} = \frac{\mathbf{V}_0 - \mathbf{V}}{\mathbf{Z}_0}$$

or

$$\mathbf{V} = \mathbf{V}_0 - \mathbf{Z}_0\mathbf{I} \tag{11-19}$$

Fig. 11-7. Potential-source equivalent of the network within the rectangle of Fig. 11-5*a*, as obtained by the Helmholtz-Thévenin theorem. Note that the potential-source equivalent includes a potential source *and* a series passive branch.

Equations (11-19) are similar to Eq. (9-1). The only difference is that Eqs. (11-9) come from a network, and Eq. (9-1) comes from a device—a source. They both lead to the same type of equivalent circuit, consisting of a potential source in series with an impedance. The equivalent circuit is shown in Fig. 11-7. A similar proof, leading to the same conclusions,

† $\mathbf{K}_i$ and $\mathbf{K}_v$ are merely unknown parameters, as in Eq. (11-13). They are not necessarily the same in Eqs. (11-13) and (11-17).

would be possible if the rectangle should be allowed more than two sources.

When Fig. 11-7 is used to represent a network, it may be called the *Helmholtz potential-source equivalent* or the *Helmholtz-Thévenin equivalent;* and the fact of the equivalence is called the *Helmholtz-Thévenin theorem.*

It is emphasized that $\mathbf{V}_0$ is the potential across the terminals, on open circuit, and that $\mathbf{Z}_0$ is the impedance of the network, with all internal sources removed in accordance with the rule stated in Sec. 11-3. Both quantities can be found by calculation, or by experiment, in specific cases.

Another useful equivalent is obtained by writing Eqs. (11-19) as

$$\mathbf{I} = \mathbf{I}_0 - \mathbf{Y}_0\mathbf{V}$$

where

$$\mathbf{I}_0 = \frac{\mathbf{V}_0}{\mathbf{Z}_0} \qquad \mathbf{Y}_0 = \frac{1}{\mathbf{Z}_0} \tag{11-20}$$

The first equation of (11-20) applies to the circuit of Fig. 11-8. $\mathbf{Y}_0$ is the admittance of the circuit, when all internal sources are removed. If $\mathbf{I} = \mathbf{I}_0$, the first equation of (11-20) shows that $\mathbf{V}$ must be 0. This is true on short circuit, so $\mathbf{I}_0$ is the current in the terminals when they are connected together by a short circuit. The parameters $\mathbf{Y}_0$ and $\mathbf{I}_0$ can be found analytically or experimentally.

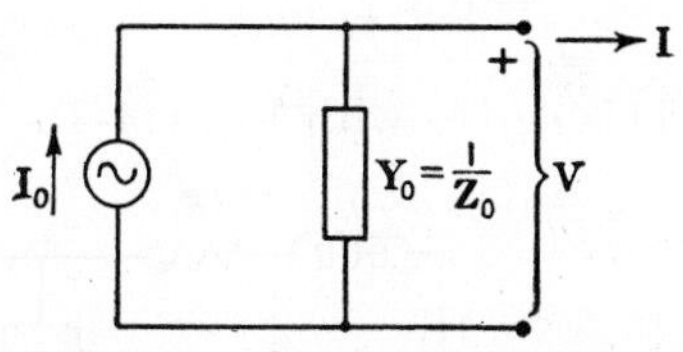


FIG. 11-8. Current-source equivalent of the network within the rectangle of Fig. 11-5*a*, as obtained by the Helmholtz-Norton theorem. Note that the current-source equivalent includes a current source *and* a parallel passive branch.

It is recalled that Fig. 11-8 is also used to represent a source, as in Fig. 9-5. When it represents a network, it may be called the *Helmholtz current-source equivalent* or the *Helmholtz-Norton equivalent;* and the fact of the equivalence is called the *Helmholtz-Norton theorem.*

These two theorems are useful when a given network is to be solved with a variety of different external branches. They are also useful when only one current or potential is required. The theorems show that any active two-terminal network can be considered as a source so far as behavior at its terminals is concerned.

**Example 11-1.** Consider Fig. 11-1, and use the Helmholtz theorems to find $\mathbf{I}_1$ and $\mathbf{V}_2$.

*Solution.* The circuit is redrawn in Fig. 11-9*b*, where it is shown that the portion to the right of the dotted line can be replaced by a Helmholtz-Thévenin equivalent. For the values specified in Fig. 11-1 the numerical

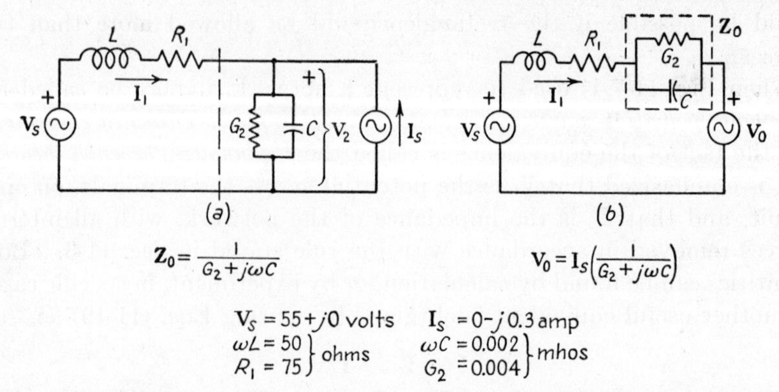


FIG. 11-9. Treatment of Fig. 11-1 by the use of the Helmholtz-Thévenin theorem.

solution, in amperes, is

$$\begin{aligned}
\mathbf{I}_1 &= \frac{55 + [j0.3/(0.004 + j0.002)]}{75 + j50 + [1/(0.004 + j0.002)]} = \frac{55 + 30 + j60}{75 + j50 + 200 - j100} \\
&= \frac{85 + j60}{275 - j50} = \frac{104/35.2°}{280/-10.3°} \\
&= 0.372/45.5° \qquad (11\text{-}21)
\end{aligned}$$

This agrees with Eq. (11-4).

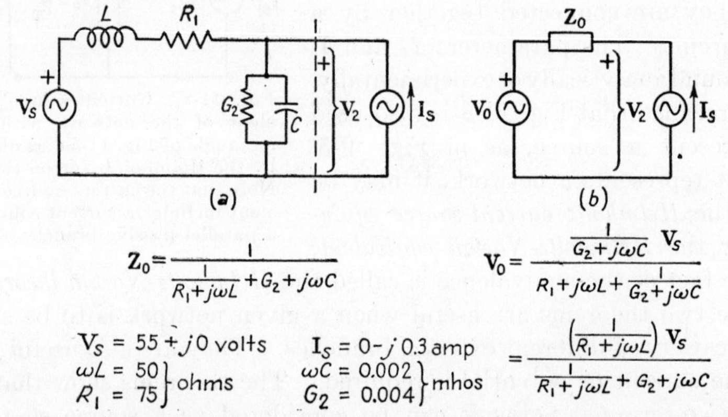


FIG. 11-10. Treatment of Fig. 11-1 by the use of the Helmholtz-Thévenin theorem.

The same circuit can be used as an illustration in a second way. All of the circuit to the left of the dotted line of Fig. 11-10*a* can be replaced by a potential-source equivalent, as shown in Fig. 11-10*b*. This equivalent is useful in finding $\mathbf{V}_2$.

The steps of the solution follow logically from Fig. 11-10*b*, as follows:

$$\mathbf{V}_2 = \frac{55\dfrac{1}{75 + j50} - j0.3}{\dfrac{1}{75 + j50} + 0.004 + j0.002} = \frac{\dfrac{55(75 - j50)}{8{,}125} - j0.13}{\dfrac{75 - j50}{8{,}125} + 0.004 + j0.002}$$

$$= \frac{0.508 - j0.338 - j0.3}{0.00925 - j0.00616 + 0.004 + j0.002} = \frac{0.508 - j0.638}{0.01325 - j0.00416}$$

$$= \frac{0.815/\underline{-51.5^\circ}}{0.0139/\underline{-17.4^\circ}} = 58.6/\underline{-34.1} = 48.6 - j32.8 \text{ volts} \tag{11-22}$$

The potential $\mathbf{V}_2$ can also be found by the use of the current-source equivalent, as illustrated in Fig. 11-11. The section to the left of the dotted line is replaced by a current-source equivalent, as in Fig. 11-11*b*.

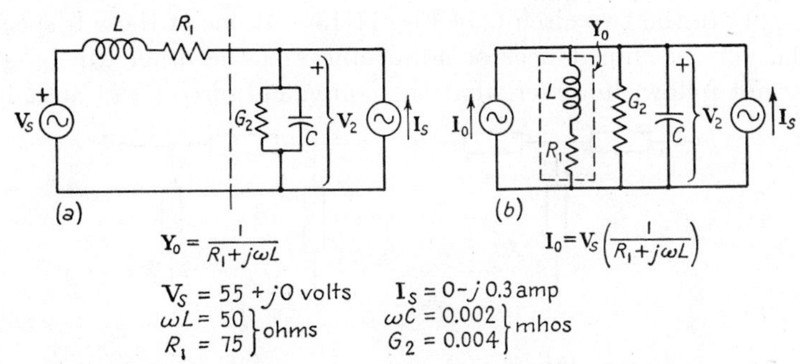


FIG. 11-11. Treatment of Fig. 11-1 by the use of the Helmholtz-Norton theorem.

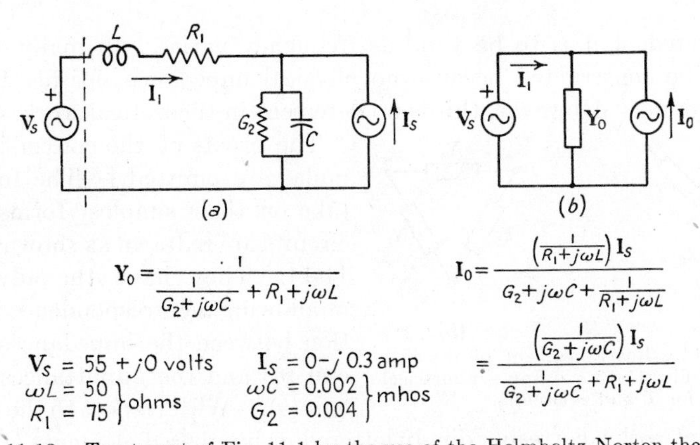


FIG. 11-12. Treatment of Fig. 11-1 by the use of the Helmholtz-Norton theorem.

The specification of the equivalent source is given in the figure. From this it follows that

$$\mathbf{V}_2 = \frac{55[1/(75 + j50)] - j0.3}{[1/(75 + j50)] + 0.004 + j0.002} \tag{11-23}$$

which is identical with the first expression in Eq. (11-22).

As a final example, consider the same circuit, with the portion to the right of the dotted line of Fig. 11-12*a* replaced by a current-source equivalent. This provides a natural setup for finding $\mathbf{I}_1$.

The derivation of the parameters of the equivalent circuit is given in the figure. The formula for $\mathbf{I}_1$ is $\mathbf{I}_1 = \mathbf{V}_s\mathbf{Y}_0 - \mathbf{I}_0$ giving

$$\mathbf{I}_1 = \frac{55[-j0.3/(0.004 + j0.002)]}{[1/(0.004 + j0.002)] + 75 + j50} \tag{11-24}$$

**11-6. T-Π and Π-T Transformations.** Many circuits can be simplified by using the so-called T-Π (also called Y-Δ) and Π-T transformations. They apply to the two circuits of Fig. 11-13. If one of these is specified, formulas for the impedances or admittances of the other can be given. It does not follow, however, that the equivalent circuit can actually be

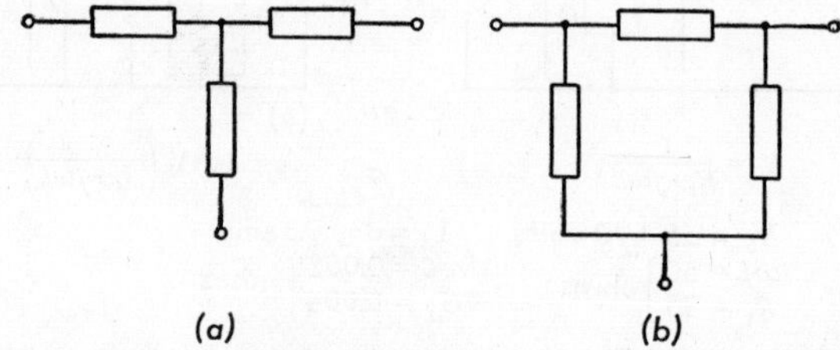


FIG. 11-13. Three-terminal networks which can be made equivalent by proper choice of parameters.

constructed, if it is to be valid as frequency varies. In many cases it cannot be constructed because no physical impedance satisfies the formulas found. However, this is no deterrent in theoretical work.

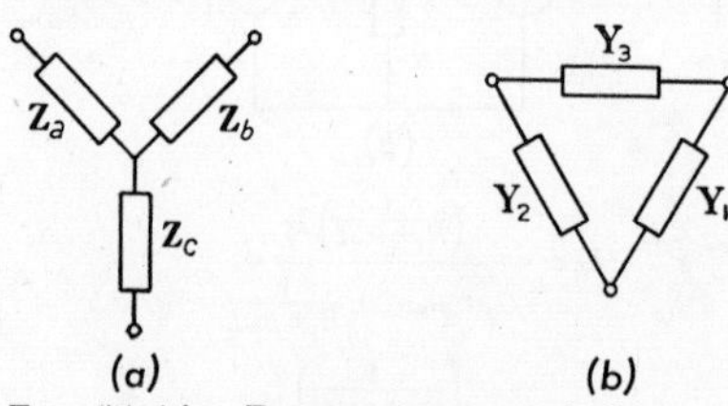


FIG. 11-14. Rearrangement of the networks of Fig. 11-13 showing symmetrical notation for T and π circuits.

The proofs of the conversion formulas are omitted.† The formulas take on their simplest forms if the circuits are redrawn as shown in Fig. 11-14. They have the advantage of allowing a correspondence in position between the impedances of circuit (*a*) and the admittances of circuit (*b*). With respect to the centers of the networks, correspondingly lettered or numbered elements (1,2,3 vs. *a*,*b*,*c*) are placed in *opposite* positions. The two sets of formulas take on

† See W. R. LePage and S. Seely, "General Network Analysis," p. 155 and also Prob. 5-35, p. 172, McGraw-Hill Book Company, Inc., New York, 1952.

similar appearances if the elements of circuit (*a*) are labeled as impedances and those of circuit (*b*) are labeled as admittances.

The conversion formulas are the following: If the T network is given, the elements of the equivalent Π network are

$$\begin{aligned}
\mathbf{Y}_1 &= \frac{\mathbf{Z}_a}{\mathbf{Z}_a\mathbf{Z}_b + \mathbf{Z}_b\mathbf{Z}_c + \mathbf{Z}_c\mathbf{Z}_a} = \frac{\mathbf{Y}_b\mathbf{Y}_c}{\mathbf{Y}_a + \mathbf{Y}_b + \mathbf{Y}_c} \\
\mathbf{Y}_2 &= \frac{\mathbf{Z}_b}{\mathbf{Z}_a\mathbf{Z}_b + \mathbf{Z}_b\mathbf{Z}_c + \mathbf{Z}_c\mathbf{Z}_a} = \frac{\mathbf{Y}_c\mathbf{Y}_a}{\mathbf{Y}_a + \mathbf{Y}_b + \mathbf{Y}_c} \\
\mathbf{Y}_3 &= \frac{\mathbf{Z}_c}{\mathbf{Z}_a\mathbf{Z}_b + \mathbf{Z}_b\mathbf{Z}_c + \mathbf{Z}_c\mathbf{Z}_a} = \frac{\mathbf{Y}_a\mathbf{Y}_b}{\mathbf{Y}_a + \mathbf{Y}_b + \mathbf{Y}_c}
\end{aligned} \qquad (11\text{-}25)\dagger$$

Similarly, the impedances of the T circuit can be obtained from the elements of the Π circuit, from the equations

$$\begin{aligned}
\mathbf{Z}_a &= \frac{\mathbf{Y}_1}{\mathbf{Y}_1\mathbf{Y}_2 + \mathbf{Y}_2\mathbf{Y}_3 + \mathbf{Y}_3\mathbf{Y}_1} = \frac{\mathbf{Z}_2\mathbf{Z}_3}{\mathbf{Z}_1 + \mathbf{Z}_2 + \mathbf{Z}_3} \\
\mathbf{Z}_b &= \frac{\mathbf{Y}_2}{\mathbf{Y}_1\mathbf{Y}_2 + \mathbf{Y}_2\mathbf{Y}_3 + \mathbf{Y}_3\mathbf{Y}_1} = \frac{\mathbf{Z}_3\mathbf{Z}_1}{\mathbf{Z}_1 + \mathbf{Z}_2 + \mathbf{Z}_3} \\
\mathbf{Z}_c &= \frac{\mathbf{Y}_3}{\mathbf{Y}_1\mathbf{Y}_2 + \mathbf{Y}_2\mathbf{Y}_3 + \mathbf{Y}_3\mathbf{Y}_1} = \frac{\mathbf{Z}_2\mathbf{Z}_3}{\mathbf{Z}_1 + \mathbf{Z}_2 + \mathbf{Z}_3}
\end{aligned} \qquad (11\text{-}26)\dagger$$

They have the same symmetrical properties as Eqs. (11-25), but with impedance and admittance elements interchanged.

One example of the usefulness of these transformations is given in Fig. 11-15. The impedance between the terminals of the circuit shown at (*a*) is required. It cannot be found by the techniques of series and parallel combinations. However, part of the circuit can be replaced by the T equivalent as shown at (*b*), after which the circuit can be treated as an ordinary series-parallel form.

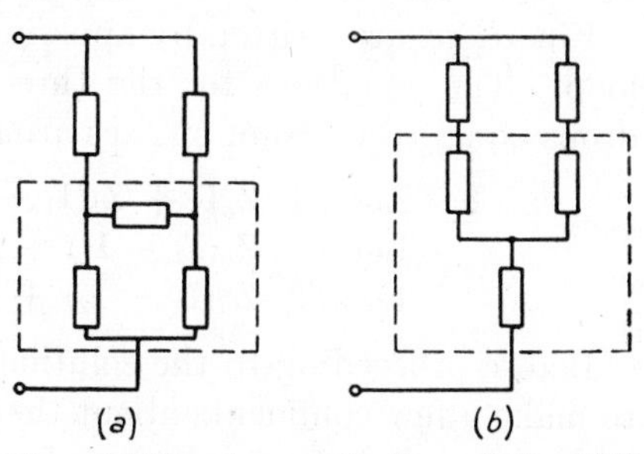

FIG. 11-15. An application of the Π-T transformation.

**11-7. General Network Solution Using Loop (Mesh) Currents.** Two systematic processes for analyzing extensive networks are in common use. The one presented here is based on the Kirchhoff potential law, and so it is convenient to have each source appearing as a potential source before the analysis is begun. The techniques of Secs. 9-3 and 11-5 are available

† These formulas show that the conversion is not possible if the denominator of the conversion formula is zero. This is a possibility for networks having *L*'s and *C*'s only.

to accomplish this.† Therefore, there is no loss in generality in assuming that the network has only potential sources.

Suppose the currents are to be found in all the impedances of the network shown in Fig. 11-16. Of course, the use of sinor notation implies that all sources are of the same frequency. Fictitious loop currents are assumed to flow on the contours of the various loops, and reference directions for them are indicated on the circuit diagram. A clockwise reference direction is usually chosen for the loop currents, but either direction may be used.

After the set of loop currents has been established, it is convenient to define two types of circuit branches. A branch that is shared by two or more loop currents is called a *common branch*, and a branch that carries

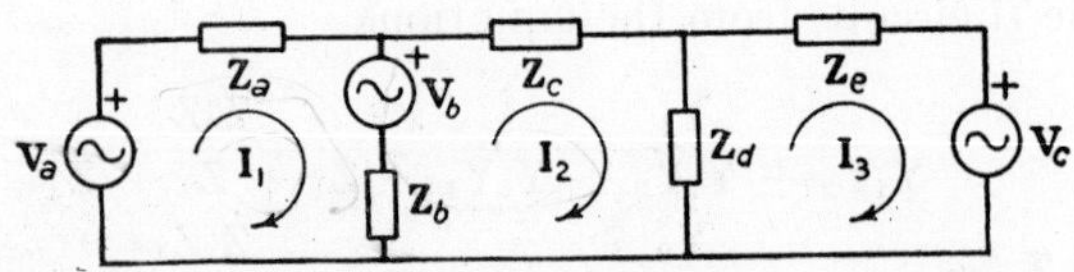


FIG. 11-16. A typical example of the loop current method of analysis.

only one loop current is called an *external branch* (or a *noncommon branch*). In Fig. 11-16 $\mathbf{Z}_c$ is an external branch and $\mathbf{Z}_d$ is a common branch. The current in a common branch is the algebraic sum of the loop currents to which it is common. Thus, in Fig. 11-16 the current downward through $\mathbf{Z}_d$ is $\mathbf{I}_2 - \mathbf{I}_3$.

Equations are written by applying the Kirchhoff potential law to each loop. The equations for the three loops, when written as the sum of drops equal to the sum of rises around each loop, are

$$\begin{aligned}
&\text{Loop 1: } \mathbf{Z}_a\mathbf{I}_1 + \mathbf{Z}_b(\mathbf{I}_1 - \mathbf{I}_2) + \mathbf{V}_b = \mathbf{V}_a \\
&\text{Loop 2: } \mathbf{Z}_b(\mathbf{I}_2 - \mathbf{I}_1) + \mathbf{Z}_c\mathbf{I}_2 + \mathbf{Z}_d(\mathbf{I}_2 - \mathbf{I}_3) = \mathbf{V}_b \\
&\text{Loop 3: } \mathbf{Z}_d(\mathbf{I}_3 - \mathbf{I}_2) + \mathbf{Z}_e\mathbf{I}_3 + \mathbf{V}_c = 0
\end{aligned} \tag{11-27}$$

Before proceeding to the solution of these equations, it is appropriate to make a few comments about them. The **ZI** terms can be rearranged, with the various **I**'s as common factors, to give

$$\begin{aligned}
(\mathbf{Z}_a + \mathbf{Z}_b)\mathbf{I}_1 - \mathbf{Z}_b\mathbf{I}_2 &= \mathbf{V}_a - \mathbf{V}_b \\
-\mathbf{Z}_b\mathbf{I}_1 + (\mathbf{Z}_b + \mathbf{Z}_c + \mathbf{Z}_d)\mathbf{I}_2 - \mathbf{Z}_d\mathbf{I}_3 &= \mathbf{V}_b \\
-\mathbf{Z}_d\mathbf{I}_2 + (\mathbf{Z}_d + \mathbf{Z}_e)\mathbf{I}_3 &= -\mathbf{V}_c
\end{aligned} \tag{11-28}$$

This set of equations can be condensed to a standard form as follows:

$$\begin{aligned}
\boldsymbol{\varrho}_{11}\mathbf{I}_1 + \boldsymbol{\varrho}_{12}\mathbf{I}_2 + \boldsymbol{\varrho}_{13}\mathbf{I}_3 &= \mathbf{E}_1 \\
\boldsymbol{\varrho}_{21}\mathbf{I}_1 + \boldsymbol{\varrho}_{22}\mathbf{I}_2 + \boldsymbol{\varrho}_{23}\mathbf{I}_3 &= \mathbf{E}_2 \\
\boldsymbol{\varrho}_{31}\mathbf{I}_1 + \boldsymbol{\varrho}_{32}\mathbf{I}_2 + \boldsymbol{\varrho}_{33}\mathbf{I}_3 &= \mathbf{E}_3
\end{aligned} \tag{11-29}$$

† For special cases see Sec. 11-10.

The quantities on the right are the *loop potential sources.* Each is the algebraic sum of the actual sources, *with those which are rises in the loop current direction taken as positive.* The terms multiplying the currents are coefficients of impedance. The coined term *copedance* is a descriptive name for them.† The symbol $\boldsymbol{\varrho}$ is a bold face rho.

A copedance such as $\boldsymbol{\varrho}_{kk}$, where $k$ represents any loop, is the sum of all impedances on the contour of the loop $k$. The copedance $\boldsymbol{\varrho}_{jk}$ represents the impedance which is common to loops $j$ and $k$. It is the *negative* of the impedance common to loops $j$ and $k$ if currents $\mathbf{I}_j$ and $\mathbf{I}_k$ have reference directions which are opposing in the common impedance. Otherwise a positive sign is used in $\boldsymbol{\varrho}_{jk}$.

For the example of Fig. 11-16, from a comparison of Eqs. (11-28) and (11-29), it follows that

$$\begin{aligned} \mathbf{E}_1 &= \mathbf{V}_a - \mathbf{V}_b \\ \mathbf{E}_2 &= \mathbf{V}_b \\ \mathbf{E}_3 &= -\mathbf{V}_c \end{aligned} \tag{11-30}$$

and

$$\begin{aligned} \boldsymbol{\varrho}_{11} &= \mathbf{Z}_a + \mathbf{Z}_b & \boldsymbol{\varrho}_{12} &= \boldsymbol{\varrho}_{21} = -\mathbf{Z}_b \\ \boldsymbol{\varrho}_{22} &= \mathbf{Z}_b + \mathbf{Z}_c + \mathbf{Z}_d & \boldsymbol{\varrho}_{13} &= \boldsymbol{\varrho}_{31} = 0 \\ \boldsymbol{\varrho}_{33} &= \mathbf{Z}_d + \mathbf{Z}_e & \boldsymbol{\varrho}_{23} &= \boldsymbol{\varrho}_{32} = -\mathbf{Z}_d \end{aligned} \tag{11-31}$$

Except for the loop potential sources, the network is completely characterized by the determinant

$$\boldsymbol{\Delta}_z = \begin{vmatrix} \boldsymbol{\varrho}_{11} & \boldsymbol{\varrho}_{12} & \boldsymbol{\varrho}_{13} \\ \boldsymbol{\varrho}_{21} & \boldsymbol{\varrho}_{22} & \boldsymbol{\varrho}_{23} \\ \boldsymbol{\varrho}_{31} & \boldsymbol{\varrho}_{32} & \boldsymbol{\varrho}_{33} \end{vmatrix} \tag{11-32}$$

By Cramer's rule for solving simultaneous equations

$$\begin{aligned} \mathbf{I}_1 &= \frac{1}{\boldsymbol{\Delta}_z} \begin{vmatrix} \mathbf{E}_1 & \boldsymbol{\varrho}_{12} & \boldsymbol{\varrho}_{13} \\ \mathbf{E}_2 & \boldsymbol{\varrho}_{22} & \boldsymbol{\varrho}_{23} \\ \mathbf{E}_3 & \boldsymbol{\varrho}_{32} & \boldsymbol{\varrho}_{33} \end{vmatrix} \\ \mathbf{I}_2 &= \frac{1}{\boldsymbol{\Delta}_z} \begin{vmatrix} \boldsymbol{\varrho}_{11} & \mathbf{E}_1 & \boldsymbol{\varrho}_{13} \\ \boldsymbol{\varrho}_{21} & \mathbf{E}_2 & \boldsymbol{\varrho}_{23} \\ \boldsymbol{\varrho}_{31} & \mathbf{E}_3 & \boldsymbol{\varrho}_{33} \end{vmatrix} \\ \mathbf{I}_3 &= \frac{1}{\boldsymbol{\Delta}_z} \begin{vmatrix} \boldsymbol{\varrho}_{11} & \boldsymbol{\varrho}_{12} & \mathbf{E}_1 \\ \boldsymbol{\varrho}_{21} & \boldsymbol{\varrho}_{22} & \mathbf{E}_2 \\ \boldsymbol{\varrho}_{31} & \boldsymbol{\varrho}_{32} & \mathbf{E}_3 \end{vmatrix} \end{aligned} \tag{11-33}$$

Equations similar to the above provide solutions for networks of any size, as long as the copedances and loop potential sources are properly

† The reader may wonder why $\mathbf{Z}_{jk}$ is not used instead of $\boldsymbol{\varrho}_{jk}$. There are two reasons: it avoids sign troubles, and it allows $\mathbf{Z}_{jk}$ to be retained for the ratio of the potential source in mesh $j$ to the current in loop $k$ (the so-called transfer impedance).

specified. It is this general applicability that makes this form of the solution so useful. In certain rare cases the determinant $\mathbf{\Delta}_z$ is zero. The method is then not applicable.

The determinant of Eq. (11-32) can be written from an inspection of the network if the following summary is kept in mind:

| | Copedances | | | Loop potential sources |
|---|---|---|---|---|
| | Loop current 1 | Loop current 2 | Loop current 3 | |
| Equation for loop 1 | Sum all impedances on loop 1 | −(Sum all impedances common to loops 1 and 2) | −(Sum all impedances common to loops 1 and 3) | Sum all potential sources on loop 1 with rises in direction of $\mathbf{I}_1$ taken positive |
| Equation for loop 2 | −(Sum all impedances common to loops 2 and 1) | Sum all impedances on loop 2 | −(Sum all impedances common to loops 2 and 3) | Sum all potential sources on loop 2 with rises in direction of $\mathbf{I}_2$ taken positive |
| Equation for loop 3 | −(Sum all impedances common to loops 3 and 1) | −(Sum all impedances common to loops 3 and 2) | Sum all impedances on loop 3 | Sum all potential sources on loop 3 with rises in direction of $\mathbf{I}_3$ taken positive |

It is emphasized that the negative signs apply only when loop current reference directions are opposite in the branch in question.

The determinant is symmetrical about a main diagonal. That is,

$$\varrho_{jk} = \varrho_{kj} \tag{11-34}$$

where $j$ and $k$ refer to any two loops. In writing such a determinant it is therefore necessary to obtain only the main diagonal and the terms on one side of it. However, all terms are preferably written in.

The concepts of loop potential sources ($\mathbf{E}_1$, $\mathbf{E}_2$, etc.) and copedances are useful in discussing and writing out generalized literal solutions. They are not needed, however, in specific numerical solutions if the above outline is followed. This is emphasized in the following numerical example.

**Example 11-2.** In the circuit of Fig. 11-16, using volts, amps, and ohms, let

$$\mathbf{V}_a = \mathbf{V}_b = 0 \qquad -\mathbf{V}_c = 50\underline{/36.8°}$$
$$\mathbf{Z}_a = j10 \qquad \mathbf{Z}_d = j6$$
$$\mathbf{Z}_b = -j5 \qquad \mathbf{Z}_e = 4$$
$$\mathbf{Z}_c = -j5$$

giving the circuit of Fig. 11-17. Find the current $\mathbf{I}_2$.

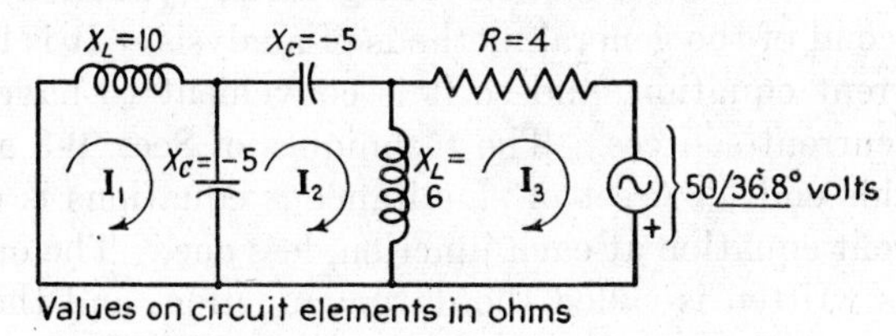


FIG. 11-17. Special case of Fig. 11-16.

*Solution*

$$\Delta_z = \begin{vmatrix} j(10-5) & -(-j5) & 0 \\ -(-j5) & j(-5-5+6) & -(j6) \\ 0 & -(j6) & (4+j6) \end{vmatrix} = \begin{vmatrix} j5 & j5 & 0 \\ j5 & -j4 & -j6 \\ 0 & -j6 & 4+j6 \end{vmatrix} \tag{11-35}$$

$$\Delta_z = -j^2(5)(4)(4+j6) + 0 + 0 + 0 - j^3(6)(6)(5) - j^2(5)(5)(4+j6)$$
$$= 80 + j120 + j180 + 100 + j150 = 180 + j450 = 485\underline{/68.2°} \tag{11-36}$$

$$\mathbf{I}_2 = \frac{1}{\Delta_z}\begin{vmatrix} j5 & 0 & 0 \\ j5 & 0 & -j6 \\ 0 & 50\underline{/36.8°} & 4+j6 \end{vmatrix} = \frac{j^2(5)(6)(50\underline{/36.8°})}{485\underline{/68.2°}}$$
$$= \frac{-1{,}500\underline{/36.8°}}{485\underline{/68.2°}}$$
$$= -3.09\underline{/-31.4°} = 3.09\underline{/148.6°}$$
$$= -2.65 - j1.60 \tag{11-37}$$

Figure 11-16 is an example of a *flat network*—a network that can be drawn on a flat surface without any crossing branches. When a network is flat, enough loop equations to solve the network will be obtained by choosing loop currents in a manner similar to that in Fig. 11-16. An example of a nonflat network is given in Fig. B-22 (Appendix B). If a network is not flat, a scheme for establishing a set of loop currents capable of providing a solution is not always apparent. A method of determining how many loop currents are needed is given in Sec. 11-9, and a rule for making sure that the loops chosen lead to an independent set of equations is given in Sec. B-10.

As a final word about the generalized loop analysis, it may be noted that loop currents in a flat network need not occupy adjacent loops, as in Fig. 11-16. In some cases it may be convenient for the loop currents to overlap, as they do in Fig. B-23; but in such cases the rule mentioned above (as given in Sec. B-10) should be applied to ensure a set of independent equations.

**11-8. General Network Solution Using Node (Junction) Potentials.** This is the second of the general methods of analysis. It is based on the Kirchhoff current equation, and so it is convenient to have all sources appearing as current sources. The techniques of Secs. 9-3 and 11-6 are available to this end.† A set of simultaneous equations is obtained by writing a current equation at each junction, less one. The one for which no equation is written is called the datum junction, and the unknowns

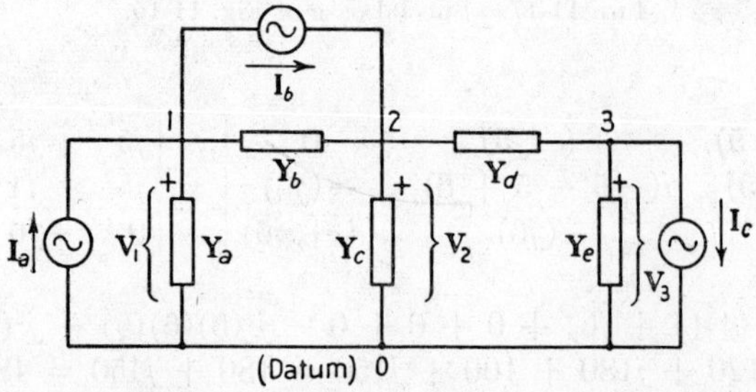


FIG. 11-18. A typical example of the node potential method of analysis.

in the equations are the potentials at the various junctions, taken with respect to the datum junction. All sources are of the same frequency.

Figure 11-18 is given as an illustration. By equating the sum of currents away from a node to the sum of the currents toward the node, three equations are obtained, as follows:

$$\begin{aligned}
&\text{Node 1: } \mathbf{Y}_a\mathbf{V}_1 + \mathbf{Y}_b(\mathbf{V}_1 - \mathbf{V}_2) + \mathbf{I}_b = \mathbf{I}_a \\
&\text{Node 2: } \mathbf{Y}_b(\mathbf{V}_2 - \mathbf{V}_1) + \mathbf{Y}_c\mathbf{V}_2 + \mathbf{Y}_d(\mathbf{V}_2 - \mathbf{V}_3) = \mathbf{I}_b \\
&\text{Node 3: } \mathbf{Y}_d(\mathbf{V}_3 - \mathbf{V}_2) + \mathbf{Y}_e\mathbf{V}_3 + \mathbf{I}_c = 0
\end{aligned} \tag{11-38}$$

A rearrangement of these yields

$$\begin{aligned}
(\mathbf{Y}_a + \mathbf{Y}_b)\mathbf{V}_1 - \mathbf{Y}_b\mathbf{V}_2 &= \mathbf{I}_a - \mathbf{I}_b \\
-\mathbf{Y}_b\mathbf{V}_1 + (\mathbf{Y}_b + \mathbf{Y}_c + \mathbf{Y}_d)\mathbf{V}_2 - \mathbf{Y}_d\mathbf{V}_3 &= \mathbf{I}_b \\
-\mathbf{Y}_d\mathbf{V}_2 + (\mathbf{Y}_d + \mathbf{Y}_e)\mathbf{V}_3 &= -\mathbf{I}_c
\end{aligned} \tag{11-39}$$

This set of equations may be considered a special case of the general set

$$\begin{aligned}
\mathfrak{d}_{11}\mathbf{V}_1 + \mathfrak{d}_{12}\mathbf{V}_2 + \mathfrak{d}_{13}\mathbf{V}_3 &= \mathbf{A}_1 \\
\mathfrak{d}_{21}\mathbf{V}_1 + \mathfrak{d}_{22}\mathbf{V}_2 + \mathfrak{d}_{23}\mathbf{V}_3 &= \mathbf{A}_2 \\
\mathfrak{d}_{31}\mathbf{V}_1 + \mathfrak{d}_{32}\mathbf{V}_2 + \mathfrak{d}_{33}\mathbf{V}_3 &= \mathbf{A}_3
\end{aligned} \tag{11-40}$$

† For special cases see Sec. 11-10.

The quantities on the right are called *node current sources*. Each is the algebraic sum of the actual current sources connected to each node, with those having reference directions toward the node taken as positive. The terms multiplying the potentials are coefficients of admittance. The name *comittance* is used for them.† The symbol $\boldsymbol{\sigma}$ is a bold face sigma.

A comittance such as $\boldsymbol{\sigma}_{kk}$, where $k$ represents any node, is the sum of all admittances connecting to node $k$, no matter where the other ends are connected. If the potential reference polarities are chosen as specified in Fig. 11-18, the comittance $\boldsymbol{\sigma}_{jk}$ is always the negative of the admittance connecting nodes $j$ and $k$. This differs from the loop case, for which there are two sign possibilities on the copedances.‡

When a network is set up for a node analysis, it is convenient to define two types of branches, as was done for the loop analysis. In a node analysis a branch connecting two nondatum nodes is called a *common branch*, and a branch connected to the datum junction is called an *external branch*, or *noncommon branch*. It should be noted that the adjectives "common" and "external" have different meanings in node and loop analyses. In Fig. 11-18, as it is set up for a node analysis, $\mathbf{Y}_b$ is a common branch and $\mathbf{Y}_c$ is an external branch.

For the example of Fig. 11-18, a comparison of Eqs. 11-39 and 11-40 shows that

$$\begin{aligned} \mathbf{A}_1 &= \mathbf{I}_a - \mathbf{I}_b \\ \mathbf{A}_2 &= \mathbf{I}_b \\ \mathbf{A}_3 &= -\mathbf{I}_c \end{aligned} \tag{11-41}$$

and

$$\begin{aligned} \boldsymbol{\sigma}_{11} &= \mathbf{Y}_a + \mathbf{Y}_b & \boldsymbol{\sigma}_{12} &= \boldsymbol{\sigma}_{21} = -\mathbf{Y}_b \\ \boldsymbol{\sigma}_{22} &= \mathbf{Y}_b + \mathbf{Y}_c + \mathbf{Y}_d & \boldsymbol{\sigma}_{13} &= \boldsymbol{\sigma}_{31} = 0 \\ \boldsymbol{\sigma}_{33} &= \mathbf{Y}_d + \mathbf{Y}_e & \boldsymbol{\sigma}_{23} &= \boldsymbol{\sigma}_{32} = -\mathbf{Y}_d \end{aligned} \tag{11-42}$$

Except for the node current sources, the network is completely characterized by the determinant

$$\boldsymbol{\Delta}_y = \begin{vmatrix} \boldsymbol{\sigma}_{11} & \boldsymbol{\sigma}_{12} & \boldsymbol{\sigma}_{13} \\ \boldsymbol{\sigma}_{21} & \boldsymbol{\sigma}_{22} & \boldsymbol{\sigma}_{23} \\ \boldsymbol{\sigma}_{31} & \boldsymbol{\sigma}_{32} & \boldsymbol{\sigma}_{33} \end{vmatrix} \tag{11-43}$$

† The dual statement of the footnote on page 233 applies here.

‡ A positive sign can appear in the equation for $\boldsymbol{\sigma}_{jk}$ if $j$ or $k$ is a reference-negative node. However, this is usually not the case.

By Cramer's rule for solving simultaneous equations

$$\mathbf{V}_1 = \frac{1}{\mathbf{\Delta}_y}\begin{vmatrix} \mathbf{A}_1 & \mathfrak{d}_{12} & \mathfrak{d}_{13} \\ \mathbf{A}_2 & \mathfrak{d}_{22} & \mathfrak{d}_{23} \\ \mathbf{A}_3 & \mathfrak{d}_{32} & \mathfrak{d}_{33} \end{vmatrix}$$

$$\mathbf{V}_2 = \frac{1}{\mathbf{\Delta}_y}\begin{vmatrix} \mathfrak{d}_{11} & \mathbf{A}_1 & \mathfrak{d}_{13} \\ \mathfrak{d}_{21} & \mathbf{A}_2 & \mathfrak{d}_{23} \\ \mathfrak{d}_{31} & \mathbf{A}_3 & \mathfrak{d}_{33} \end{vmatrix} \tag{11-44}$$

$$\mathbf{V}_3 = \frac{1}{\mathbf{\Delta}_y}\begin{vmatrix} \mathfrak{d}_{11} & \mathfrak{d}_{12} & \mathbf{A}_1 \\ \mathfrak{d}_{21} & \mathfrak{d}_{22} & \mathbf{A}_2 \\ \mathfrak{d}_{31} & \mathfrak{d}_{32} & \mathbf{A}_3 \end{vmatrix}$$

The above equations are general expressions which may be extended to a network of any size. This set of equations is the node counterpart of the general loop solution. It is to be noted, however, that they do not give the same solution. One system gives currents and the other potentials as the solution. Furthermore, the circuits used for the two illustrations are not identical.

The form of the solution can be related to the network by remembering the following summary:

| | Comittances | | | Node current source |
|---|---|---|---|---|
| | Node potential 1 | Node potential 2 | Node potential 3 | |
| Equation for node 1 | Sum all admittances connected to node 1 | −(Sum all admittances connecting nodes 1 and 2) | −(Sum all admittances connecting nodes 1 and 3) | Sum all current sources with currents toward node 1 taken positive |
| Equation for node 2 | −(Sum all admittances connecting nodes 2 and 1) | Sum all admittances connected to node 2 | −(Sum all admittances connecting nodes 2 and 3) | Sum all current sources with currents toward node 2 taken positive |
| Equation for node 3 | −(Sum all admittances connecting nodes 3 and 1) | −(Sum all admittances connecting nodes 3 and 2) | Sum all admittances connected to node 3 | Sum all current sources with currents toward node 3 taken positive |

The terms "node current sources" and "comittance" are conveniences for dealing with general solutions in literal form. However, they are not needed in specific numerical examples if the above outline is followed.

The determinant is symmetrical about its main diagonal, which means that

$$\delta_{jk} = \delta_{kj} \tag{11-45}$$

where $j$ and $k$ refer to any two nodes. It is therefore necessary to know only the terms on the main diagonal and on one side of it.

**Example 11-3.** Obtain the solution for Example 11-2, using the node-potential method.

*Solution.* The network takes on the aspect shown in Fig. 11-19 after the equivalent-current-source theorem is applied to the potential source and the impedance in series with it.

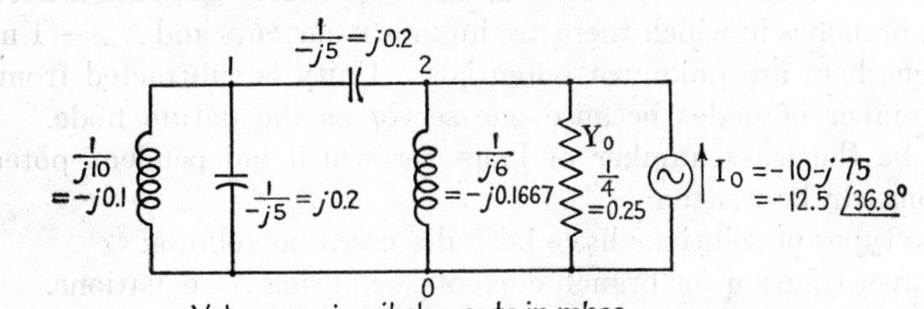


FIG. 11-19. Arrangement of the network of Fig. 11-17 for an analysis by the method of node potentials.

The current-source-equivalent theorem leads to the current source and associated admittance specified by the following:

$$\mathbf{I}_0 = \frac{\mathbf{V}_c}{\mathbf{Z}_e} = \frac{-50/36.8^\circ}{4} = -12.5/36.8^\circ = -10 - j7.5$$
$$\mathbf{Y}_0 = \frac{1}{\mathbf{Z}_e} = \frac{1}{4} = 0.25 \tag{11-46}$$

The subscripts refer to the notation of the original figure. The rule for forming the determinant gives

$$\mathbf{\Delta}_y = \begin{vmatrix} j(0.2 - 0.1 + 0.2) & -j0.2 \\ -j0.2 & 0.25 + j0.2 - j0.1667 \end{vmatrix} = \begin{vmatrix} j0.3 & -j0.2 \\ -j0.2 & 0.25 + j0.0333 \end{vmatrix}$$

$$= j0.075 - 0.01 + 0.04 = 0.03 + j0.075 \tag{11-47}$$

$$\mathbf{V}_1 = \frac{1}{\mathbf{\Delta}_y}\begin{vmatrix} 0 & -j0.2 \\ -10 - j7.5 & 0.25 + j0.033 \end{vmatrix} = \frac{1}{\mathbf{\Delta}_y} j0.2(10 + j7.5)$$

$$= \frac{1.5 - j0.2}{0.03 + j0.075} = \frac{(1.5 - j0.2)(0.03 - j0.075)}{0.00651} = \frac{0.105 + j0.1725}{0.00651}$$

$$= -16.12 - j26.5 \tag{11-48}$$

$$\mathbf{V}_2 = \frac{1}{\Delta_y}\begin{vmatrix} j0.3 & 0 \\ -j0.2 & -10 - j7.5 \end{vmatrix} = \frac{-j(0.3)(10 + j7.5)}{0.03 + j0.075}$$

$$= -24.2 - j39.8$$

The previous result may be checked by computing $\mathbf{I}_{12}$ (which is the $\mathbf{I}_2$ of Sec. 11-9). From Fig. 11-19, it is seen that

$$\mathbf{I}_{12} = (\mathbf{V}_1 - \mathbf{V}_2)j0.2 = j0.2(-16.12 - j26.5 + 24.2 + j39.8)$$
$$= j0.2(8.1 + j13.3) = -2.66 + j1.62$$

which is in agreement with Eq. (11-37).

**11-9. Numbers of Loops, Nodes, and Branches.** Suppose a network has $N_B$ branches in which there are unknown currents and $N_N - 1$ nodes at which there are unknown potentials. Unity is subtracted from the total number of nodes because one serves as the datum node. Also, let $N_L$ be the least number of loops for which independent potential equations can be written.

Three types of solutions have been discussed, as follows:

1. Direct solution for branch currents, requiring $N_B$ equations.
2. Loop analysis, requiring $N_L$ equations.
3. Node analysis, requiring $N_N - 1$ equations.

The various methods require different numbers of equations. This does not necessarily imply that more information is obtained with fewer equations in some methods. The difference lies in the difference in the information provided by the various methods. For example, loop currents do not give potentials directly. However, with the aid of auxiliary calculations one type of solution can be converted to the other.

The numbers of equations for the three methods are related in a simple way. In solving by the branch-current method, it is shown that $N_L$ potential equations and $N_N - 1$ current equations are required. Therefore

$$N_L = N_B - (N_N - 1) \qquad (11\text{-}49)$$

is a relationship for the least number of loops needed for a complete solution. This is a useful equation for complicated networks because it is always easy to pick nodes and branches, but the least number of independent loops may not be evident from an inspection of the network.

**11-10. Notes on Special Cases.** The general loop solution assumes all sources are converted to potential source equivalents before an analysis is attempted. This does not admit the case shown in Fig. 11-20*a*, because there is no branch in parallel with the current source.†

† We speak somewhat loosely of converting a current source to a potential source equivalent, or vice versa. A current source *combined with a parallel branch* can be

The impedance **Z** has no effect on the current source, so the circuit can be redrawn as shown in Fig. 11-20*b* and then solved by methods previously described.

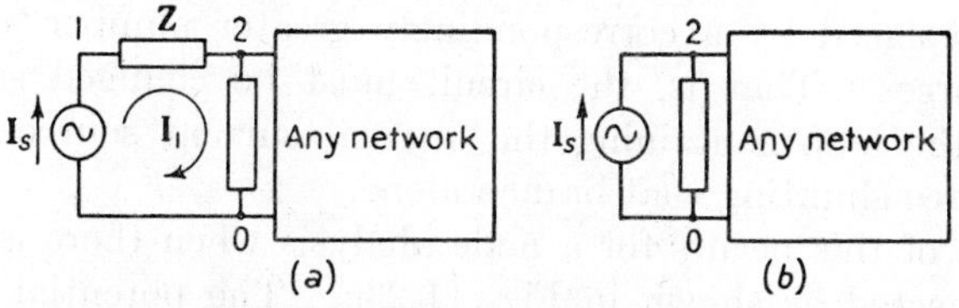


FIG. 11-20. Modification making it possible to apply the general loop analysis when a current source has a series impedance.

The dual situation is illustrated in Fig. 11-21*a*. If this is to be analyzed on a node basis, the potential source cannot be converted to a current-source equivalent because it has no series branch.

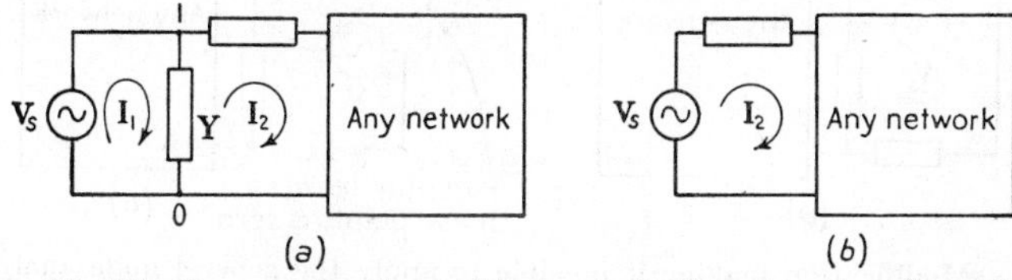


FIG. 11-21. Modification making it possible to apply the general node analysis when a potential source has a parallel admittance.

The admittance **Y** has no effect on the potential source, so it may be omitted, as in Fig. 11-21*b*. The circuit can then be treated by the standard technique.

Two other special situations can arise. A typical example is shown in Fig. 11-22*a*. The network is to be analyzed on a loop basis, and there is a current source connected as shown.

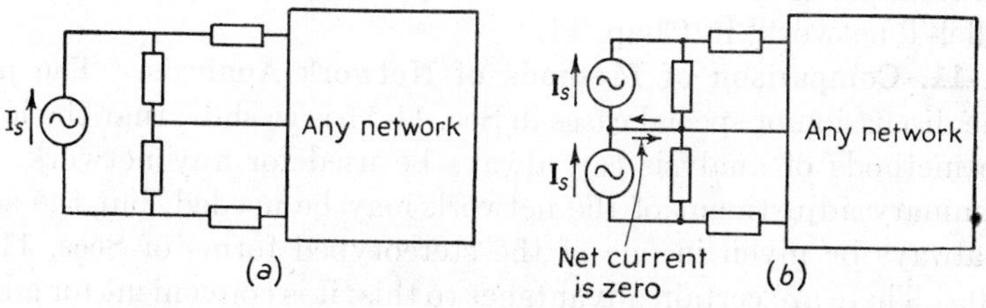


FIG. 11-22. Modification making it possible to apply the general mesh analysis when a current source is not paralleled by an admittance and is shared by two nodes.

As it stands, the current source cannot be replaced by a potential-source equivalent because there is no single branch shunting the current

---

converted to a potential-source equivalent. Similarly, a potential source must have *a series branch* if it is to be converted to a current-source equivalent. *A conversion from a potential source alone to a current source alone, or vice versa, is impossible.*

source. The required change can be made by replacing the one current source by two, as shown in Fig. 11-22*b*.

If more than two branches had appeared across the current source, it would be replaced by a correspondingly greater number of individual current sources. That is, the circuit must be changed so that each branch of the loop containing the original current source will have a current source shunting that branch alone.

The dual of this occurs for a node analysis when there is a potential source connected as shown in Fig. 11-23*a*. The potential source does not have the single series branch needed to form the current-source equivalent.

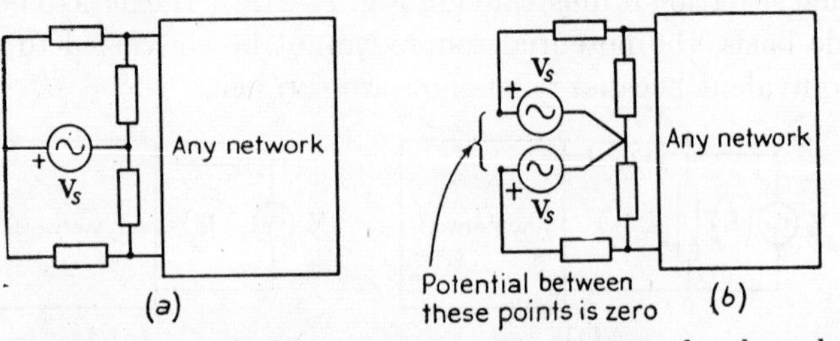


FIG. 11-23. Modification making it possible to apply the general node analysis when a potential source has no series impedance and is shared by two loops.

The circuit shown in Fig. 11-23*b* can be converted to a system of current sources in the usual way. It is equivalent to the original circuit. If more than two branches had led from the potential source, a correspondingly greater number of individual potential sources would be used. One potential source is needed, in the equivalent circuit, for each branch connected to the original potential source.

An example of the use of this technique is found in the analysis of the parallel-T network, in Chap. 14.

**11-11. Comparison of Methods of Network Analysis.** The purpose of the discussion of special cases in Sec. 11-11 is to show that the loop and node methods of analysis can always be used for any network. Some preliminary adjustment of the network may be needed, but the solution can always be given in one of the stereotyped forms of Secs. 11-9 and 11-10. There are certain advantages to this: it is convenient for advanced analysis because it yields general formulas that are valid for all networks, and it is convenient because it reduces the solution of the most complicated networks to easily learned routines.

The loop equations of a network can be obtained without first converting all sources to potential sources, and the node equations can be obtained without first converting all sources to current sources. However, then the general methods of Secs. 11-9 and 11-10 do not apply, and each set of equations is obtained by applying Kirchhoff's laws in a manner dictated by the needs of the problem. The choice of method in such cases depends on intangible factors, and so no rules can be given for making a decision. The following numerical examples may help to clarify these statements. The examples are purposely made rather complicated, in order to emphasize the rather subtle points under consideration in this section.

**Example 11-4.** Use the loop method of analysis to obtain $\mathbf{I}_C$ in Fig. 11-24.

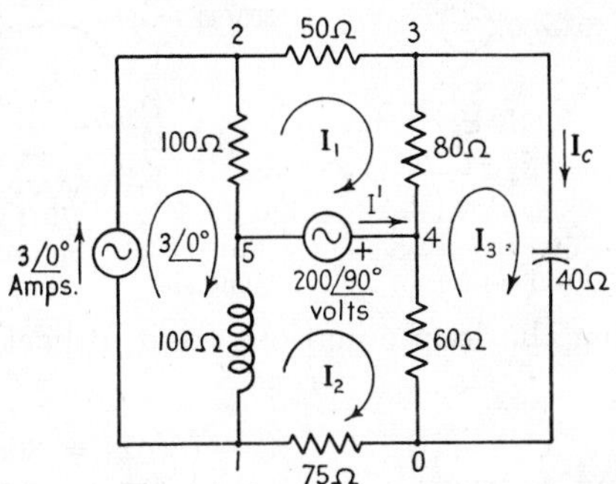


FIG. 11-24. A network illustrating various special cases in the loop and node methods of network analysis.

*Solution.* First consider the network in its original form. Four loop currents are necessary to completely specify the network, but one of them is known. A Kirchhoff potential equation is written for each of the numbered loops, as follows:

$$100(\mathbf{I}_1 - 3) + 50\mathbf{I}_1 + 80(\mathbf{I}_1 - \mathbf{I}_3) = -j200$$
$$j100(\mathbf{I}_2 - 3) + 60(\mathbf{I}_2 - \mathbf{I}_3) + 75\mathbf{I}_2 = j200$$
$$80(\mathbf{I}_3 - \mathbf{I}_1) + (-j40)\mathbf{I}_3 + 60(\mathbf{I}_3 - \mathbf{I}_2) = 0$$

If the numerically known terms are all transposed to the right, and the other terms are regrouped, the result is

$$\begin{aligned}
(100 + 50 + 80)\mathbf{I}_1 \quad + \quad 0 \quad &- (80)\mathbf{I}_3 = 300 - j200 \\
0 + (60 + 75 + j100)\mathbf{I}_2 \quad &- (60)\mathbf{I}_3 = j(200 + 300) \\
(-80)\mathbf{I}_1 \quad - (60)\mathbf{I}_2 (80 + 60 &- j40)\mathbf{I}_3 = 0
\end{aligned} \tag{11-50}$$

The terms $-300$ and $-j300$ were transposed to the right-hand side. They arise from the known current source, but in Eqs. (11-50) they appear as parts of the loop potential sources.

Equations (11-50) can be solved directly. However, before solving them note that Sec. 11-11 provides a physical interpretation for the terms 300 and $j300$ on the right of Eqs. (11-50). The current source and the two branches nearest to it can be modified as shown in Fig. 11-25. The complete network then has the appearance of Fig. 11-26. It is now

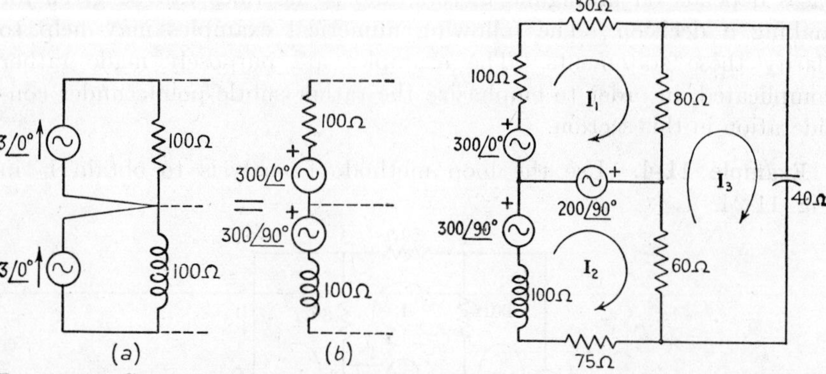


FIG. 11-25. Conversion of current source of Fig. 11-24 to two potential sources.

FIG. 11-26. Setup of Fig. 11-24 for loop analysis.

in a form for writing the loop equations from inspection by the rules of Sec. 11-9, *viz.:*

$$\begin{aligned} 230\mathbf{I}_1 \quad &+0 \quad &-(80)\mathbf{I}_3 &= 300 - j200 \\ 0 + (135 + j100)&\mathbf{I}_2 &-(60)\mathbf{I}_3 &= j200 + j300 \\ -(80)\mathbf{I}_1 \quad &-(60)\mathbf{I}_2 &+ (140 - j40)\mathbf{I}_3 &= 0 \end{aligned} \tag{11-51}$$

The set is identical with Eqs. (11-50) and provides a physical meaning for the modifications of the loop potential sources which automatically appeared in Eqs. (11-50).

Equations (11-51) can be solved for $\mathbf{I}_3$ by using determinants. Let

$$\mathbf{\Delta} = \begin{vmatrix} 230 & 0 & -80 \\ 0 & 135 + j100 & -60 \\ -80 & -60 & 140 - j40 \end{vmatrix}$$

$$= 230(135 + j100)(140 - j40) - (80)^2(135 + j100) - (60)^2(230)$$

$$= (3.58 + j1.34) \times 10^6$$

By Cramer's rule the solution is

$$\mathbf{I}_3 = \frac{\begin{vmatrix} 230 & 0 & 200 - j300 \\ 0 & 135 + j100 & j500 \\ -80 & -60 & 0 \end{vmatrix}}{\mathbf{\Delta}}$$

$$= \frac{(80)(135 + j100)(300 - j200) + (60)(j500)(230)}{(3.58 + j1.34) \times 10^6}$$

$$= \frac{4.84 + j7.14}{3.58 + j1.34} = \frac{8.63\underline{/55.9^\circ}}{2.26\underline{/35.4^\circ}} = 2.26\underline{/35.4^\circ} \text{ amp} \tag{11-52}$$

It is noted that $\mathbf{I}_3 = \mathbf{I}_C$, the required current.

**Example 11-5.** Solve the network of Fig. 11-24 for the current $\mathbf{I}_C$, using a node analysis.

*Solution.* Equations are written in terms of the node potentials $\mathbf{V}_{10}$, $\mathbf{V}_{20}$, $\mathbf{V}_{30}$, $\mathbf{V}_{40}$, and $\mathbf{V}_{50}$ (abbreviated $\mathbf{V}_1$, $\mathbf{V}_2$, $\mathbf{V}_3$, $\mathbf{V}_4$, and $\mathbf{V}_5$). The current $\mathbf{I}'$ in the potential source is not required but is temporarily introduced. The objective is to find $\mathbf{V}_3$, from which $\mathbf{I}_C = \mathbf{V}_3/(-j40)$ can be found. Equations can be obtained directly from Fig. 11-24 by writing a Kirchhoff current equation for each numbered node. The equations are

$$\begin{aligned}
\frac{1}{j100}(\mathbf{V}_1 - \mathbf{V}_5) + \frac{1}{75}\mathbf{V}_1 &= -3 \\
\tfrac{1}{100}(\mathbf{V}_2 - \mathbf{V}_5) + \tfrac{1}{50}(\mathbf{V}_2 - \mathbf{V}_3) &= 3 \\
\frac{1}{-j40}\mathbf{V}_3 + \frac{1}{50}(\mathbf{V}_3 - \mathbf{V}_2) + \frac{1}{80}(\mathbf{V}_3 - \mathbf{V}_4) &= 0 \\
\tfrac{1}{60}\mathbf{V}_4 + \tfrac{1}{80}(\mathbf{V}_4 - \mathbf{V}_3) &= \mathbf{I}' \\
\frac{1}{j100}(\mathbf{V}_5 - \mathbf{V}_1) + \frac{1}{100}(\mathbf{V}_5 - \mathbf{V}_2) &= -\mathbf{I}'
\end{aligned} \tag{11-53}$$

It is not necessary to keep both $\mathbf{V}_5$ and $\mathbf{V}_4$ in the equations because nodes 4 and 5 are joined by a potential source. Therefore the substitution

$$\mathbf{V}_5 = \mathbf{V}_4 - j200$$

can be made for $\mathbf{V}_5$. Also $\mathbf{I}'$ can be eliminated by adding the last two equations together. The result of making these two changes is the set of four equations

$$\begin{aligned}
-j0.01(\mathbf{V}_1 - \mathbf{V}_4 + j200) + 0.0133\mathbf{V}_1 &= -3 \\
0.01(\mathbf{V}_2 - \mathbf{V}_4 + j200) + 0.02(\mathbf{V}_2 - \mathbf{V}_3) &= 3 \\
j0.025\mathbf{V}_3 + 0.02(\mathbf{V}_3 - \mathbf{V}_2) + 0.0125(\mathbf{V}_3 - \mathbf{V}_4) &= 0 \\
0.0167\mathbf{V}_4 + 0.0125(\mathbf{V}_4 - \mathbf{V}_3) + (-j0.01)(\mathbf{V}_4 - \mathbf{V}_1 - j200) & \\
+ 0.01(\mathbf{V}_4 - \mathbf{V}_2 - j200) &= 0
\end{aligned}$$

All numerical terms can be transposed to the right, and terms can be regrouped on the left, to give

$$\begin{aligned}
(0.0133 - j0.01)\mathbf{V}_1 + 0 + 0 + j0.01\mathbf{V}_4 &= -3 - 2 \\
0 + (0.02 + 0.01)\mathbf{V}_2 - 0.02\mathbf{V}_3 - 0.01\mathbf{V}_4 &= 3 - j2 \\
0 - 0.02\mathbf{V}_2 + (0.02 + 0.0125 + j0.025)\mathbf{V}_3 - 0.0125\mathbf{V}_4 &= 0 \\
j0.01\mathbf{V}_1 - 0.01\mathbf{V}_2 - 0.0125\mathbf{V}_3 & \\
+ (0.0167 + 0.0125 + 0.01 - j0.01)\mathbf{V}_4 &= 2 + j2
\end{aligned} \tag{11-54}$$

The node current sources include the terms $-2$ and $-j2$, which are due to the potential source.

Before proceeding to the solution of these equations, consider the conversion of the potential source to a pair of current sources as shown in

Fig. 11-27. First it is replaced by two potential sources, and then each of these is combined with a series branch to give a current-source equivalent. With this change the original network takes on the form of Fig. 11-28. Note that node 5 has now disappeared. The node equations

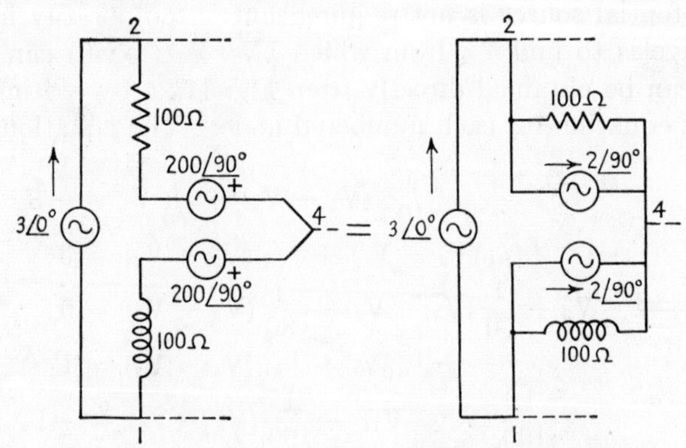


FIG. 11-27. Conversion of potential source of Fig. 11-27 to two current sources.

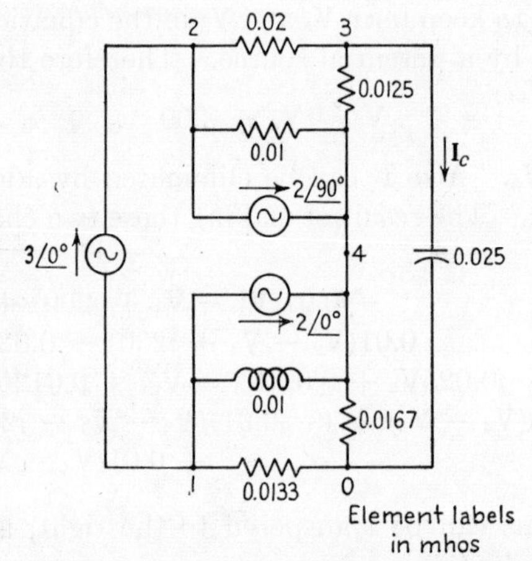


FIG. 11-28. Setup of Fig. 11-24 for node analysis.

for Fig. 11-28 can be written from inspection by applying the rules of Sec. 11-10, *viz.:*

$$
\begin{aligned}
(0.0133 - j0.01)\mathbf{V}_1 &+ 0 && + 0 && + j0.01\mathbf{V}_4 = -5 \\
0 &+ 0.03\mathbf{V}_2 && -0.02\mathbf{V}_3 && -0.01\mathbf{V}_4 = 3 - j2 \\
0 &- 0.02\mathbf{V}_2 && + (0.0325 + j0.025)\mathbf{V}_3 && -0.0125\mathbf{V}_4 = 0 \\
j0.01\mathbf{V}_1 &- 0.01\mathbf{V}_2 && -0.0125\mathbf{V}_3 && + (0.0392 - j0.01)\mathbf{V}_4 = 2 + j2
\end{aligned}
\tag{11-55}
$$

These equations are identical with Eqs. (11-54). Therefore Fig. 11-28 lends physical interpretation to the terms $-2$ and $-j2$ on the right of Eqs. (11-54).

It is noted that the node solution leads to four simultaneous equations instead of three obtained in Example 11-4. Therefore, it is not a preferred method for this particular problem. However, in many cases the node solution is the simpler.

Determinants are used to obtain the solution. Let

$$\mathbf{\Delta} = \begin{vmatrix} 0.0133 - j0.01 & 0 & 0 & j0.01 \\ 0 & 0.03 & -0.02 & -0.01 \\ 0 & -0.02 & 0.0325 + j0.025 & -0.0125 \\ j0.01 & -0.01 & -0.0125 & 0.0392 - j0.01 \end{vmatrix}$$

This is evaluated by expanding in terms of minors of the first column.

$$\begin{aligned} \mathbf{\Delta} &= (1.33 - j)[(3)(12.73 - 2.5) + j(3)(9.80 - 3.25) - 2.5 - 2.5 \\ &\qquad - 3.25 - j2.5 - 4.68 - 15.68 + j4] \times 10^{-8} \\ &\qquad\qquad - j[j(9.75 + j7.5) - j4] \times 10^{-8} \\ &= [(1.33 - j)(17.08 + j21.15) + 5.75 + j7.5] \times 10^{-8} \\ &= 49.7 + j18.6 \end{aligned}$$

By Cramer's rule the solution for $\mathbf{V}_3$ is

$$\mathbf{V}_3 = \frac{\begin{vmatrix} 0.0133 - j0.01 & 0 & -5 & j0.01 \\ 0 & 0.03 & 3 - j2 & -0.01 \\ 0 & -0.02 & 0 & -0.0125 \\ j0.01 & -0.01 & 2 + j2 & 0.0392 - j0.01 \end{vmatrix}}{\mathbf{\Delta}}$$

$$= \frac{[(1.33 - j)(3.75 - j2.5) + 4 + j4 + 7.5 + j7.5 + 23.52 - 4 - j15.68 - j6) - j(-8 + 6 + j4 - 15)] \times 10^{-6}}{\mathbf{\Delta}}$$

$$= \frac{[(1.33 - j)(34.77 - j12.68) + 6 + j24.75] \times 10^{-6}}{\mathbf{\Delta}}$$

$$= \frac{39.8 - j26.9}{0.497 + j0.186} = \frac{48.1\underline{/-34.1^\circ}}{0.53\underline{/-20.5^\circ}} = 90.7\underline{/-54.6^\circ}$$

Finally, the required current is

$$\mathbf{I}_C = j0.025\mathbf{V}_3 = 2.26\underline{/35.4^\circ} \text{ amp} \tag{11-56}$$

in agreement with Eq. (11-52)

These two examples show that there can be an appreciable difference in the amount of work required to solve a problem by different methods. They also show the significance of the adjustments described in Sec. 11-10 when a network is not in a natural form for either the loop or the node analysis. In order to emphasize the inadvisability of adhering strictly to stereotyped methods, the same problem is solved using the Helmholtz-Thévenin theorem in the following example.

**Example 11-6.** Obtain the current $\mathbf{I}_c$ of Fig. 11-24 by the use of the Helmholtz-Thévenin theorem.

*Solution.* The network, with the capacitor branch removed, is replaced by the Helmholtz-Thévenin equivalent. This is done by first going through Fig. 11-25, as in Example 11-4, to obtain the network on the left-hand side of Fig. 11-29. This is easy to solve because its two

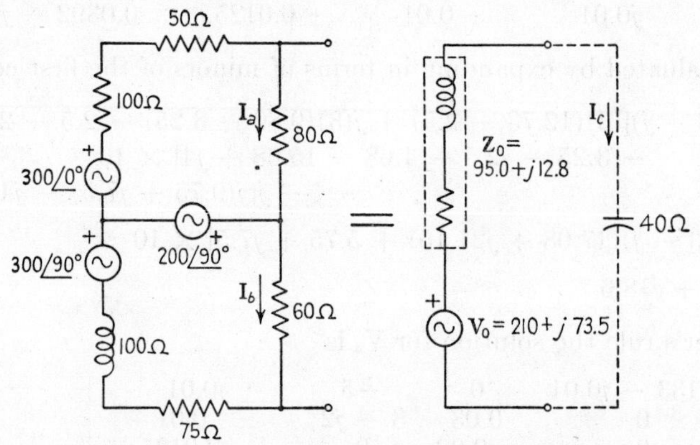


FIG. 11-29. Solution of Fig. 11-24 by Helmholtz-Thévenin theorem.

loops are independent of one another. The current $\mathbf{I}_a$ and $\mathbf{I}_b$ can be found directly.

$$\mathbf{I}_a = \frac{300 - j200}{230} = 1.30 - j0.87$$

$$\mathbf{I}_b = \frac{j500}{135 + j100} = \frac{j(500)(135 - j100)}{(135)^2 + (100)^2} = 1.77 + j2.38$$

It follows that

$$\mathbf{V}_0 = 80(1.30 - j0.87) + 60(1.77 + j2.38) = 210 + j73.5$$

The impedance of the equivalent source is the input impedance at the terminals of the network on the left of Fig. 11-29, with the sources shorted out. This is a series-parallel combination for which the impedance is

$$\begin{aligned}
\mathbf{Z}_0 &= \frac{(80)(150)}{80 + 150} + \frac{60(75 + j100)}{60 + 75 + j100} \\
&= 52.2 + \frac{60}{(135)^2 + (100)^2}(75 + j100)(135 - j100) \\
&= 52.2 + \frac{60}{28{,}220}(10{,}120 + 10{,}000 + j13{,}500 - j7{,}500) \\
&= 52.2 + 42.7 + j12.75 = 94.9 + j12.75
\end{aligned}$$

The right-hand circuit of Fig. 11-29 is now used to find $\mathbf{I}_C$. It is

$$\mathbf{I}_C = \frac{154.5 + j1.91}{94.4 + j12.75 - j40} = \frac{222\underline{/19.3°}}{98.8\underline{/-16.1°}}$$
$$= 2.26\underline{/35.4°} \text{ amp} \tag{11-57}$$

which agrees with the solutions obtained in Examples 11-4 and 11-5.

**11-12. Combination of Sources (Millman's Theorem).** The solution of a network having a number of potential-source equivalents in parallel can sometimes be simplified by first determining the common potential across the combination. Figure 11-30*a* is an illustration, using three

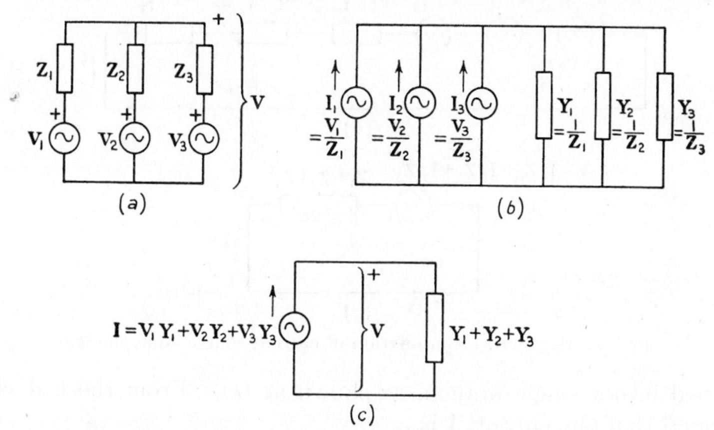


FIG. 11-30. Parallel combination of potential-source equivalents.

sources as an example. The method applies to any number of sources combined in the same way. Of course, the potential sources $\mathbf{V}_1$, $\mathbf{V}_2$, and $\mathbf{V}_3$ can be replacements, through the compensation theorem, for network potentials which were not originally sources.

Each of the potential sources with its series branch can be replaced by a current source in parallel with a branch, as shown in Fig. 11-30*b*. Then the three current sources can be combined into one, and the three branches can be combined into a single branch, as shown at (*c*). It follows that the potential $\mathbf{V}$ is

$$\mathbf{V} = \frac{\mathbf{V}_1\mathbf{Y}_1 + \mathbf{V}_2\mathbf{Y}_2 + \mathbf{V}_3\mathbf{Y}_3}{\mathbf{Y}_1 + \mathbf{Y}_2 + \mathbf{Y}_3} \tag{11-58}$$

This formula is an expression of Millman's theorem.

The dual of Millman's theorem is obtained from the series connection of current-source equivalents. A typical situation is shown in Fig. 11-31*a*. The objective is to find the current $\mathbf{I}$. Each of the current sources with its parallel branch can be replaced by a potential source in series with a branch, as shown in Fig. 11-31*b*. The potential sources can then be combined into a single source, and the branches can be

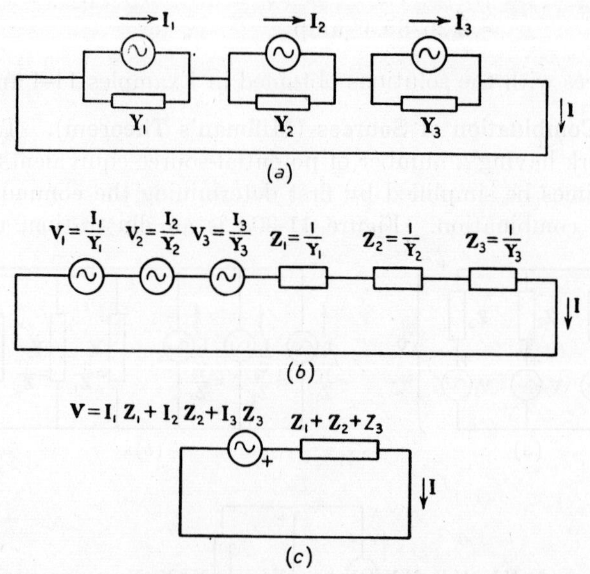


FIG. 11-31. Series combination of current-source equivalents.

combined into a single branch, as shown at (*c*). From the last circuit it is found that the current **I** is

$$\mathbf{I} = \frac{\mathbf{I}_1\mathbf{Z}_1 + \mathbf{I}_2\mathbf{Z}_2 + \mathbf{I}_3\mathbf{Z}_3}{\mathbf{Z}_1 + \mathbf{Z}_2 + \mathbf{Z}_3} \tag{11-59}$$

In the application of this theorem the current sources $\mathbf{I}_1$, $\mathbf{I}_2$, and $\mathbf{I}_3$ can be replacements, through the compensation theorem, for currents which were not originally source currents.

**11-13. Reciprocity Theorem.** Consider the network of Fig. 11-32*a*, all elements of which are linear. The solution for the current $\mathbf{I}_2$ is

$$\mathbf{I}_2 = \frac{\begin{vmatrix} \varrho_{11} & \mathbf{V}_s & \varrho_{13} \\ \varrho_{21} & 0 & \varrho_{23} \\ \varrho_{31} & 0 & \varrho_{33} \end{vmatrix}}{\Delta} = \frac{-\mathbf{V}_s \begin{vmatrix} \varrho_{21} & \varrho_{23} \\ \varrho_{31} & \varrho_{33} \end{vmatrix}}{\Delta} \tag{11-60}$$

where

$$\Delta = \begin{vmatrix} \varrho_{11} & \varrho_{12} & \varrho_{13} \\ \varrho_{21} & \varrho_{22} & \varrho_{23} \\ \varrho_{31} & \varrho_{32} & \varrho_{33} \end{vmatrix} \tag{11-61}$$

Figure 11-32*b* is the same circuit, with **V** placed in loop 2. The solution for $\mathbf{I}_1'$ is

$$\mathbf{I}_1' = \frac{\begin{vmatrix} 0 & \varrho_{12} & \varrho_{13} \\ \mathbf{V}_s & \varrho_{22} & \varrho_{23} \\ 0 & \varrho_{23} & \varrho_{33} \end{vmatrix}}{\Delta} = \frac{-\mathbf{V}_s \begin{vmatrix} \varrho_{12} & \varrho_{13} \\ \varrho_{23} & \varrho_{33} \end{vmatrix}}{\Delta} \tag{11-62}$$

From Eq. (11-34) it is known that $\varrho_{12} = \varrho_{21}$ and $\varrho_{13} = \varrho_{31}$. It follows that Eqs. (11-60) and (11-62) are identical, and therefore that $\mathbf{I}_2 = \mathbf{I}_1'$. The statement that a source and a current can be interchanged in this way is one form of the *reciprocity theorem.*

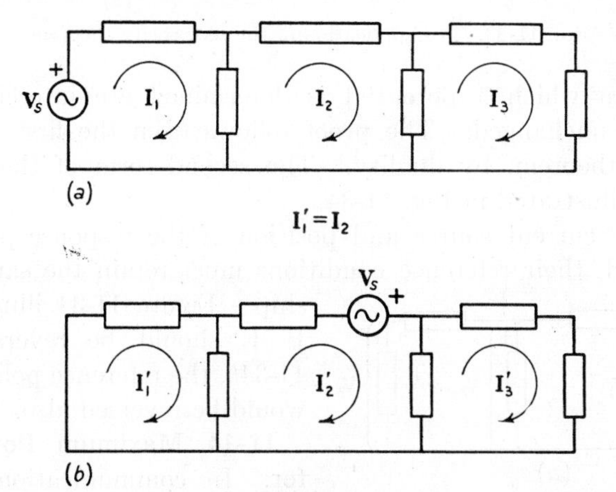


Fig. 11-32. Illustration of the reciprocity theorem, in terms of a loop analysis.

A similar property holds for networks of any complexity, as long as the network has only *one* source. The theorem was proved for interchange of a loop source and a loop current only, but it can also be proved for a branch source and a branch current. In words the theorem may be stated as follows. In any linear bilateral network the branches in which a potential source is applied and a response current determined may be interchanged, with no change in the response current.† In the application of this theorem the reference polarity of the potential source must bear the same relationship to the branch current in each of its positions.

The reciprocity theorem is useful in extending the scope of existing solutions. For example, consider the bridge circuit of Fig. 11-33. Suppose it is adjusted to give a balance ($I = 0$) when a source is con-

† The reciprocity theorem does not apply to nonlinear networks—networks having vacuum tubes or transitors, for example.

nected as shown at (*a*). The reciprocity theorem shows that the circuit is also balanced when the source is connected as shown at (*b*).

A second form of the reciprocity theorem can be proved for a circuit having a current source and a response potential between two nodes. If the pair of nodes between which a current source is applied and the

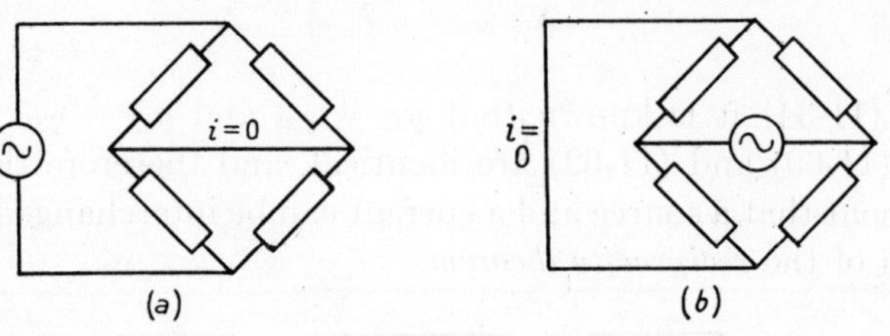


Fig. 11-33. An application of the reciprocity theorem.

pair between which a potential is determined are interchanged, the potential is unchanged. The proof follows from the first form of the reciprocity theorem, by duality. The second form of the reciprocity theorem is illustrated in Fig. 11-34.

When the current source and position of the response potential are interchanged, their reference conditions must retain the same relationship. Figure 11-34 illustrates this. If $\mathbf{I}_s$ should be reversed in Fig. 11-34*b*, the reference polarity for $\mathbf{V}_2'$ would be reversed also.

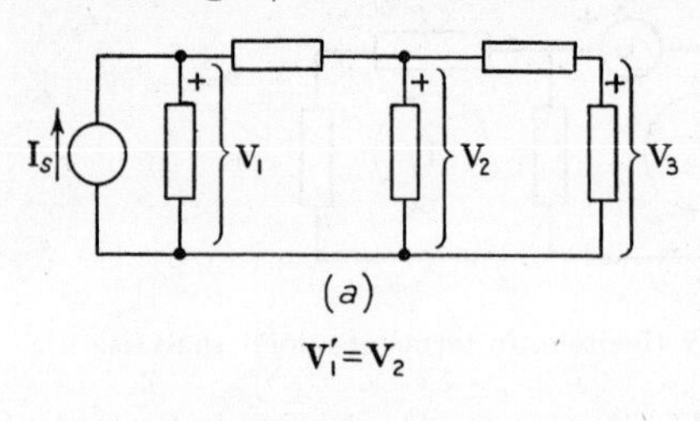


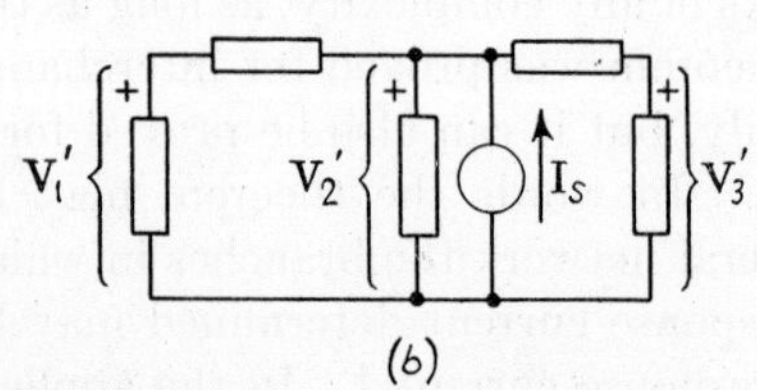


Fig. 11-34. Illustration of the reciprocity theorem in terms of a node analysis.

**11-14. Maximum Power Transfer.** In communication circuits in particular it is frequently necessary to adjust a load impedance so as to obtain maximum power from the network to which it is connected. Such a situation is represented in Fig. 11-35*a*. The problem is to find $\mathbf{Z}$ so that it will draw a maximum of power from the rectangle.

The rectangle can be replaced by its potential- or current-source equivalent. $\mathbf{V}_0$ and $\mathbf{Z}_0$ are found by the techniques of Sec. 11-5. The potential-source equivalent is shown in Fig. 11-35*b*. Let

$$\begin{aligned} \mathbf{Z}_0 &= Z_0\epsilon^{j\zeta_0} \\ \mathbf{Z} &= Z\epsilon^{j\zeta} \\ \mathbf{V}_0 &= V_0\epsilon^{j\alpha_0} \end{aligned} \tag{11-63}$$

The power to the load is

$$
\begin{aligned}
P &= \mathrm{Re}\,(\mathbf{VI}^*) \\
&= \mathrm{Re}\left(\frac{\mathbf{V}_0\mathbf{Z}}{\mathbf{Z}_0 + \mathbf{Z}}\right)\left(\frac{\mathbf{V}_0}{\mathbf{Z}_0 + \mathbf{Z}}\right)^* \\
&= \mathrm{Re}\left(\frac{\mathbf{V}_0\mathbf{Z}}{\mathbf{Z}_0 + \mathbf{Z}}\,\frac{\mathbf{V}_0^*}{\mathbf{Z}_0^* + \mathbf{Z}^*}\right) \\
&= \mathrm{Re}\left[\frac{V_0^2\mathbf{Z}}{Z_0^2 + Z^2 + ZZ_0(\epsilon^{j(\zeta-\zeta_0)} + \epsilon^{-j(\zeta-\zeta_0)})}\right] \\
&= \mathrm{Re}\left[\frac{V_0^2 Z\epsilon^{j\zeta}}{Z_0^2 + Z^2 + 2ZZ_0\cos(\zeta - \zeta_0)}\right] \\
&= \frac{V_0^2 Z\cos\zeta}{Z_0^2 + Z^2 + 2ZZ_0\cos(\zeta - \zeta_0)}
\end{aligned}
\tag{11-64}
$$

This is a function of the two variables $Z$ and $\zeta$. Equation (11-64) can be made a maximum in three ways, as follows:

1. $Z$ and $\zeta$ are allowed to vary at will.
2. $\zeta$ is held fixed, and $Z$ is allowed to vary.
3. $Z$ is held fixed, and $\zeta$ is allowed to vary.

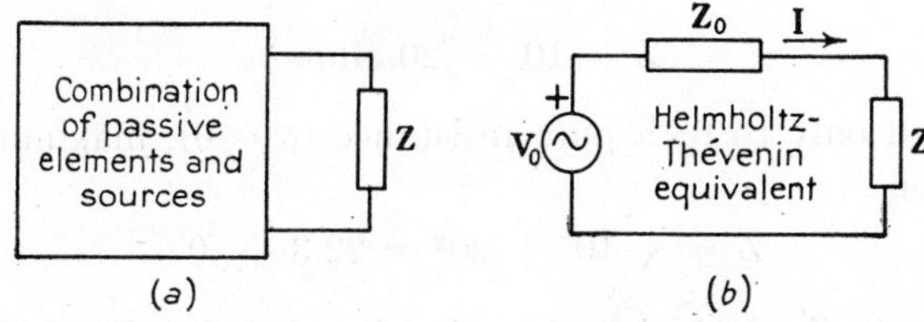


FIG. 11-35. Analysis of circuit for conditions of maximum power transfer to impedance **Z**.

Under (1) a maximum occurs when $\partial P/\partial Z = 0$ and $\partial P/\partial\zeta = 0$. It can be shown that this is true when

$$Z = Z_0 \tag{11-65}$$

$$\zeta = -\zeta_0 \tag{11-66}$$

That is, $\mathbf{Z} = \mathbf{Z}_0^*$ for maximum power transfer. This is equivalent to a condition of resonance, where the reactance of the load cancels the reactance of the source.

If only $Z$ is variable, as in (2), a maximum will be attained but it is smaller than the one obtained in (1). It occurs when $\partial P/\partial Z = 0$, and this is satisfied when

$$Z = Z_0 \tag{11-67}$$

Thus, when the angle of the load impedance is restricted, the maximum power is obtained when the magnitudes of the load and "internal" impedances are the same.

If $\zeta$ is variable but $Z$ is fixed, the maximum $P$ is obtained when $\partial P/\partial \zeta = 0$. This yields the formula

$$\sin \zeta = -\left(\frac{2ZZ_0}{Z^2 + Z_0^2}\right) \sin \zeta_0 \tag{11-68}$$

**Example 11-7.** For the circuit shown specify the load **Z** for maximum power transfer if: (*a*) **Z** is unrestricted; (*b*) **Z** is real; (*c*) $|\mathbf{Z}| = 15$ ohms.

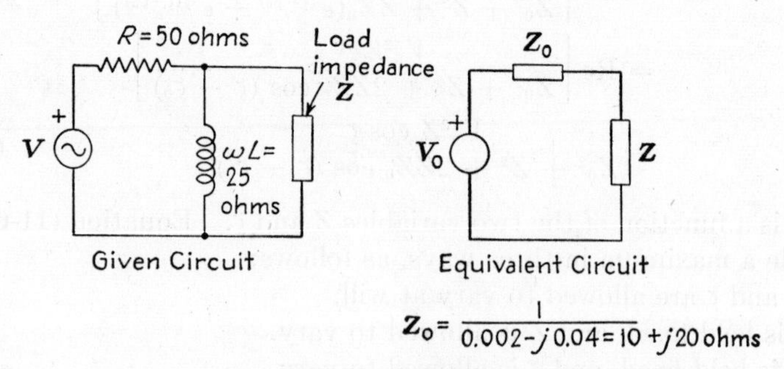


*Solution.* The maximum power obtainable occurs when

$$\mathbf{Z} = 10 - j20 \text{ ohms}$$

If **Z** is allowed only to be a pure resistance ($\zeta = 0$), maximum power is obtained when

$$\mathbf{Z} = \sqrt{10^2 + 20^2} = 22.3 + j0$$

Finally, suppose $|\mathbf{Z}| = 15$ ohms but that its angle is adjustable. Then

$$\zeta = -\sin^{-1} \frac{(2)(15)(22.3)(20)}{[(15)^2 + (22.3)^2](22.3)}$$

$$= -\sin^{-1} 0.833 = -56.3°$$

or

$$\mathbf{Z} = 15(\cos 56.3° - j \sin 56.3°) = 8.32 - j12.5 \text{ ohms}$$

**11-15. Summary.** Chapter 11 presents most of the techniques of general applicability for network analysis. There are other theorems available to the specialist, but these are omitted because of their limited field of use.

It is found that many circuits can be analyzed by a number of techniques. This invites a discussion of their comparative advantages and disadvantages. Since circuits can have so many different forms, it is impossible to give a general list of preferred methods of approach to stereotyped problems. In this study it is important to become familiar with all methods, in order to gain insight into their various advantages.

The material of this chapter should be read and digested with this idea in mind.

To a great extent the easiest method to apply in a given circuit depends not only on the circuit itself but also on the quantity to be found. For example, if a single current or potential is required in an extensive network, one of the theorems such as Helmholtz's equivalent-source theorem or the T-Π transformation is frequently useful. However, if all the currents in the network are needed, the general systematic loop solution is perhaps preferable. Likewise, if all the node potentials are required, the general node method possibly applies most easily.

In comparing the different methods, it is important to bear in mind that, in general, they lead to different portions of the complete analysis of a circuit. To make a just comparison between two methods, it is necessary to compare them on the basis of identical yield of results. This means that certain auxiliary calculations may be needed for some methods, and not for others.

## PROBLEMS

**11-1.** A load consisting of a resistor $R_L$ in series with an inductor $L$ is supplied with power from two sources, as shown in Fig. P11-1.

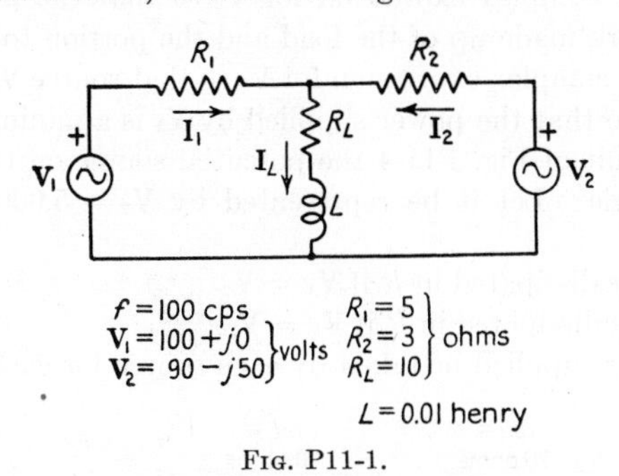


FIG. P11-1.

*a.* Using the branch current method of solution, determine the current in the load impedance and the current delivered by each of the two potential sources.

*b.* Write the sinusoidal time functions for each of the three currents specified in part *a* and for the source potentials.

*c.* Use complex notation to determine the power delivered to the load.

*d.* Determine the power lost in each of the feed lines.

*e.* Use complex notation to determine the power delivered by each source. Compare the sum of these with the sum of the power delivered to the load and lost in the feed lines.

**11-2.** Refer to the circuit of Fig. P11-2. The load takes 1,800 kw and operates with fixed potential $\mathbf{V}_2$. The power factor is 0.75, with the current lagging, and the frequency is 60 cps.

*a.* Determine the value of $C_a$ to be added across the load so that the generator will operate at unity power factor. Capacitors $C_b$ and $C_c$ are cut out for this case. The total power loss in the lines is to be a minimum.

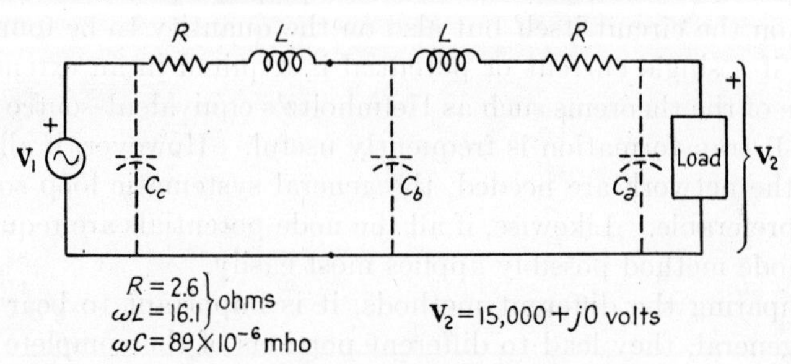


FIG. P11-2.

*b.* Determine the value of $C_b$ to give unity power factor at the generator when $C_a$ and $C_c$ are absent. The total power loss in the lines is to be a minimum.

*c.* Determine the value of $C_c$ to make the generator operate at unity power factor in the absence of $C_a$ and $C_b$.

**11-3.** Refer to the circuit of Fig. P10-15. Let $\mathbf{V}_1 = 5{,}000 + j0$ be constant and let $\mathbf{V}_2$ take or receive no power. $\mathbf{V}_L$ is not specified in this problem.

*a.* Determine the complex expression for $\mathbf{V}_2$ so that the power factor of the two-terminal network made up of the load and the portion to its right is unity.

*b.* Determine the complex expression for $\mathbf{V}_2$ so that source $\mathbf{V}_1$ operates at unity power factor, and so that the power supplied by $\mathbf{V}_1$ is a minimum.

**11-4.** In the circuit of Fig. P11-4 the potential source on the right is fixed in magnitude and angle. Let it be represented by $\mathbf{V}_2 = 5{,}000 + j0$ volts. Use superposition to:

*a.* Find the power dissipated in $R$ if $\mathbf{V}_1 = \mathbf{V}_2$.

*b.* Find the power dissipated in $R$ if $\mathbf{V}_1 = \mathbf{V}_2\epsilon^{j2\pi/3}$.

*c.* Find the power supplied or taken by each source for case (*b*).

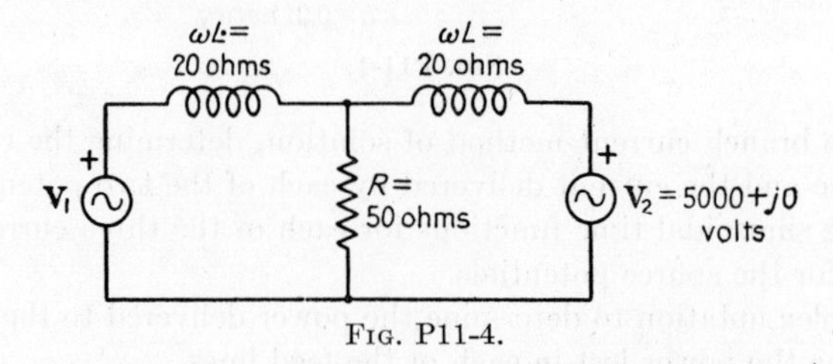


FIG. P11-4.

**11-5.** In Fig. P11-4 suppose the inductance on the left is replaced by a capacitor of 20 ohms reactance and that $\mathbf{V}_1 = \mathbf{V}_2\epsilon^{-j2\pi/3}$, where $\mathbf{V}_2 = 500 + j0$.

*a.* Use the superposition theorem to find the current in $R$.

*b.* Use the branch current method of solution to find the current in $R$.

*c.* Completely specify a current source and a potential source that could replace $R$ without disturbing the remainder of the network.

*d.* Specify $\mathbf{V}_a$ of Fig. P11-5 so that the entire branch shown in Fig. P11-5 can be substituted for $R$ without disturbing the remainder of the network.

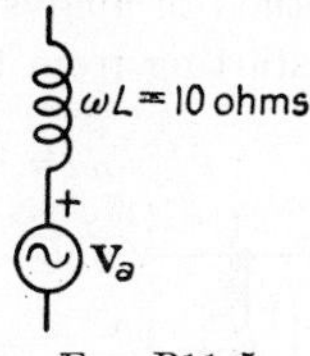


FIG. P11-5.

**11-6.** Two current generators (constant-current transformers) supply current to a series-connected street-lighting circuit. An approximate circuit is shown in Fig. P11-6. Use the method of branch currents to determine:

*a.* The current in each section of lamps.

*b.* The power delivered by each source and the power factor at which it operates.

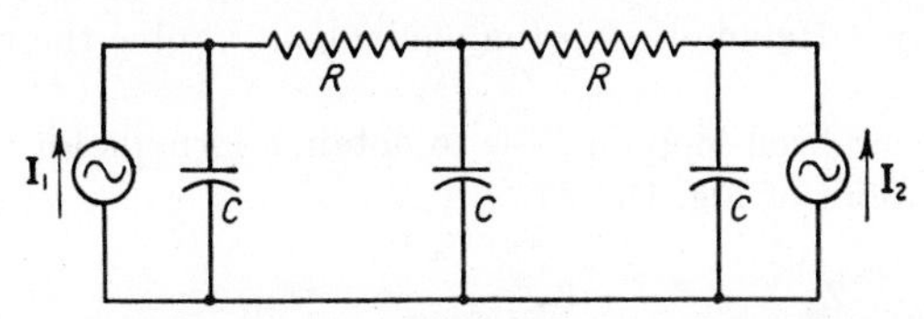


FIG. P11-6.

**11-7.** Refer to the circuit of Fig. P11-6. $\mathbf{I}_1$ is to remain as specified in the figure, and $\mathbf{I}_2$ is to be adjustable in magnitude but fixed in angle.

*a.* What specifications for $\mathbf{I}_2$ will make each source supply the same power?

*b.* What will be the current in each section of lights under this condition?

*c.* At what power factor will each source then operate?

**11-8.** Refer to the circuit of Fig. P11-6. $\mathbf{I}_1$ is to remain as specified in the figure, and $\mathbf{I}_2$ is to be adjustable. What are the specifications for $\mathbf{I}_2$ so that the current will be the same in each section of lamps and will be the maximum value attainable so long as $\mathbf{I}_1$ remains fixed?

**11-9.** Derive the equations given in Fig. 11-5 for $\mathbf{K}_i$, $\mathbf{K}_v$, and $\mathbf{Z}_0$.

**11-10.** Use the Helmholtz-Thévenin theorem to solve Prob. 11-6.

**11-11.** Use the Helmholtz-Thévenin theorem to find the current $\mathbf{I}_2$ or Prob. 11-1.

**11-12.** Use the Helmholtz-Norton theorem to find the current $\mathbf{I}_2$, Prob. 11-1.

**11-13.** Use the T-Π or Π-T transformation to determine the currents $\mathbf{I}_1$ and $\mathbf{I}_2$ of Prob. 11-1.

**11-14.** Use the generalized method of loop currents to solve for the currents of Prob. 11-1. That is, $\mathbf{I}_1$, $\mathbf{I}_2$, and $\mathbf{I}_L$ are eventually required, but loop currents are to be found first.

**11-15.** Determine the potentials of junctions (1) and (2) of the circuit of Fig. P11-15 by the following methods:

*a.* Apply the Helmholtz-Thévenin theorem to the section to the left of the dotted line (not the dashed line).

*b.* Use the generalized node method of analysis, after first making a suitable change in the form of the source, starting from the original circuit.

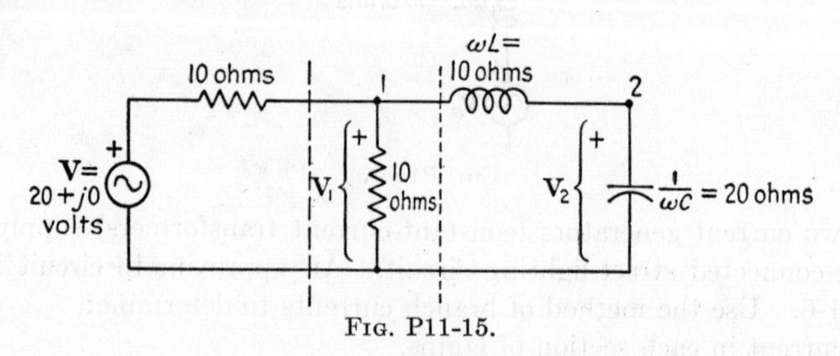


FIG. P11-15.

**11-16.** Replace the portion of the network to the left of the dashed (not dotted) line of Fig. P11-15 by a Helmholtz-Norton equivalent. Solve the resulting circuit for $\mathbf{V}_2$.

**11-17.** Use the generalized loop analysis to obtain a formula for the potential ratio $\mathbf{V}_2/\mathbf{V}_1$ for the circuit of Fig. P11-17.

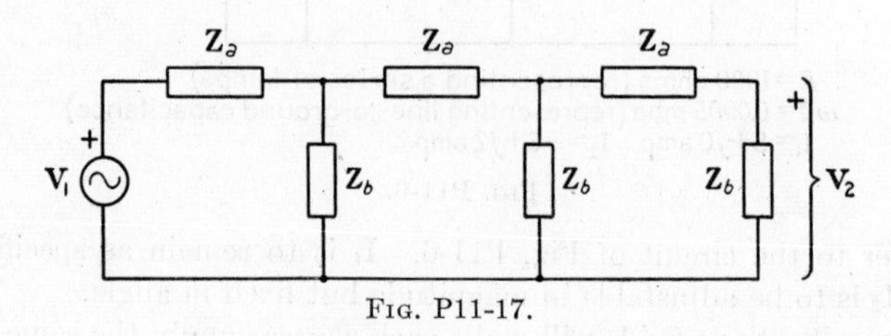


FIG. P11-17.

**11-18.** Use the generalized node analysis to obtain the formula specified in Prob. 11-17.

**11-19.** Use any method of analysis to find the impedance of the bridge circuit of Fig. P11-19.

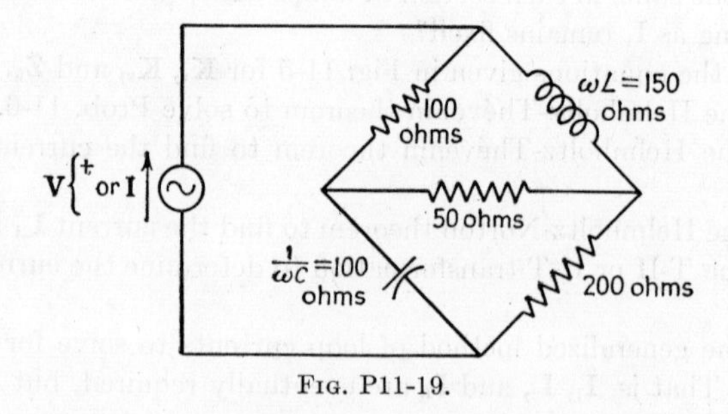


FIG. P11-19.

**11-20.** Use the loop method of analysis to find the current in each branch of the circuit of Fig. P11-19 if the source is a potential source $\mathbf{V} = 50 + j0$.

**11-21.** Use the node method of analysis to find the current in each branch of the circuit of Fig. P11-19 if the source is a current source $\mathbf{I} = 0.5 + j0$.

**11-22.** Repeat Prob. 11-20, using the node method of analysis.

**11-23.** Repeat Prob. 11-21, using the loop method of analysis.

**11-24.** Let the 50-ohm resistor in Fig. P11-19 be replaced by a current source $I_2 = 0.05 + j0.05$, with reference direction to the right. The source on the left is the potential source specified in Prob. 11-20. Find the current in each branch of the network, using any method of analysis.

**11-25.** Terminals 1 and 2 of the circuit of Fig. P11-25 are connected through a 50-ohm resistor. Determine the current in this resistor ($\mathbf{I}_{12}$):

*a.* Using a loop analysis.

*b.* Using a node analysis.

*c.* Using the Helmholtz-Thévenin equivalent for the given circuit between terminals 1 and 2.

*d.* Using the Helmholtz-Norton equivalent for the given circuit between 1 and 2.

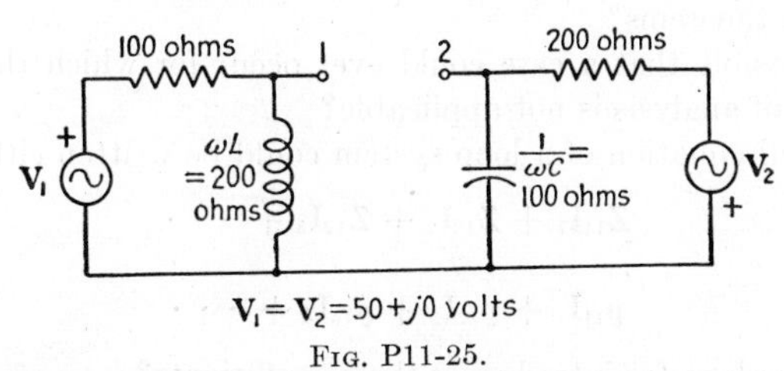


Fig. P11-25.

**11-26.** Use the generalized node method of analysis to solve Prob. 11-6.

**11-27.** Find the load impedance to be connected to terminals 1 and 2 of Fig. P11-25, to absorb maximum power and the power absorbed, under the conditions that

*a.* The load is a pure resistance.

*b.* The load impedance is of 100 ohms magnitude, with adjustable angle.

*c.* The load can be adjusted to any value.

**11-28.** Derive Eqs. (11-65), (11-66), (11-67), and (11-68) from Eqs. (11-64).

**11-29.** The 50-ohm resistor of Fig. P11-19 is replaced by a variable impedance $\mathbf{Z}_r$. Specify $\mathbf{Z}_r$ so that it takes maximum power when the source is $\mathbf{V} = 50 + j0$, and determine the power

*a.* When $\mathbf{Z}_r$ is real.

*b.* When $\mathbf{Z}_r$ has any angle but has a magnitude of 200 ohms.

*c.* When $\mathbf{Z}_r$ can be adjusted to any value.

**11-30.** Do Prob. 11-29, but use a current source $\mathbf{I} = 0.5 + j0$ amp.

**11-31.** Do Prob. 11-25, but replace $\mathbf{V}_1$ by a current source $\mathbf{I}_1 = 0.5 + j0$ amp with its reference direction downward.

**11-32.** Refer to Fig. P11-4, with $\mathbf{V}_2 = 5{,}000 + j0$ volts, and $\mathbf{V}_1$ adjustable.

*a.* Find $\mathbf{V}_1$ so that $R$ takes 480 kw and so that one-fourth of the power is supplied by $\mathbf{V}_2$.

*b.* Find the power factor at which each source operates.

## QUESTIONS

**11-1.** Name and discuss two ways in which complex algebra simplifies the solution of networks.

**11-2.** Are there any cases for which complex algebra makes a solution possible, whereas it would be impossible without the use of such algebra?

**11-3.** Does a Helmholtz equivalent source represent a two-terminal network internally as well as externally?

**11-4.** Show that the Helmholtz-Thévenin and Helmholtz-Norton equivalent sources are dually related.

**11-5.** Is there any difference between the Helmholtz equivalent-source theorems and the equivalent circuits for sources discussed previously?

**11-6.** Specify either a T (or a Π) network which cannot be transformed to the other form at one particular frequency.

**11-7.** Do you think the superposition theorem is more useful for obtaining a numerical solution for a specific network or for use in theoretical work, as in the proving of other theorems?

**11-8.** Is it possible that a case could ever occur for which the general loop-current method of analysis is not applicable?

**11-9.** A typical equation of a loop system could be written either

$$\mathbf{Z}_{11}\mathbf{I}_1 + \mathbf{Z}_{12}\mathbf{I}_2 + \mathbf{Z}_{13}\mathbf{I}_3 + \cdots$$

or

$$\boldsymbol{\varrho}_{11}\mathbf{I}_1 + \boldsymbol{\varrho}_{12}\mathbf{I}_2 + \boldsymbol{\varrho}_{13}\mathbf{I}_3 + \cdots$$

Can you give a reason for introducing the $\rho$ coefficients?

**11-10.** Describe what is meant by a *loop potential source.*

**11-11.** What change in the network setup would cause the sign to change in the formula for a copedance if it is a copedance off the main diagonal of the determinant?

**11-12.** Is it possible to arrange the network in such a way as to change the sign in the formula for the copedance if it is on the main diagonal of the determinant?

**11-13.** Can you think of a network for which at least two of the off-diagonal copedances must have positive signs in their formulas?

**11-14.** Suppose a network is given and its loop solution is set up. Discuss the difference between the dual of this network and the solution of the original network on a node basis.

**11-15.** Formulate a question similar to Question 9, but for the junction solution.

**11-16.** Describe what is meant by a *node current source.*

**11-17.** What change in the network setup would cause the sign to change in the formula for a comittance if it is not on the main diagonal of the determinant?

**11-18.** Is it possible to arrange a network in such a way as to change the sign of the comittance if it is on the main diagonal of the determinant?

**11-19.** Is it always possible to arrange a network, for analysis on the node basis, so that the formulas for the comittances off the main diagonal carry negative signs?

**11-20.** What precautions must be taken in the setting up of a circuit for solution if the determinant is to be symmetrical about the main diagonal, (*a*) for a loop solution, (*b*) for a node solution?

**11-21.** Do you get the same unknown quantities evaluated directly in both the loop and node solutions of a network?

**11-22.** Can either the loop or the node general solution of a network always be depended upon to give the simplest formulation of the solution?

**11-23.** Make up an example to illustrate reciprocity as it would be based on a node solution.

**11-24.** A potential source of 10 volts is connected in series with an impedance **Z** and a resistor $R = 2$ ohms. Specify **Z** so that $R$ will take the maximum power from the source.

# CHAPTER 12
# MAGNETIC COUPLING

**12-1. Introduction.** When two coils are sufficiently close and appropriately oriented, a changing current in one will produce an effect in the other. The effect can be explained in terms of a changing magnetic flux produced by the current. In circuit analysis the explanation in terms of flux is replaced by the concept of mutual inductance.

Mutual inductance is quite similar to self-inductance, being used to express the potential induced in one coil in terms of the changing current in another coil. It is possible to have any number of coils coupled magnetically, in which case there is a mutual inductance between each pair. For the sake of simplicity, the detailed treatment will be confined to the case of two coils.

The windings will, of course, have resistance in any practical case. As in the case of a single inductor, the resistance is considered to be external to the coil.

**12-2. Dot System of Winding Labeling.** Consider the pair of magnetically coupled coils of Fig. 12-1*a*. There may or may not be a common

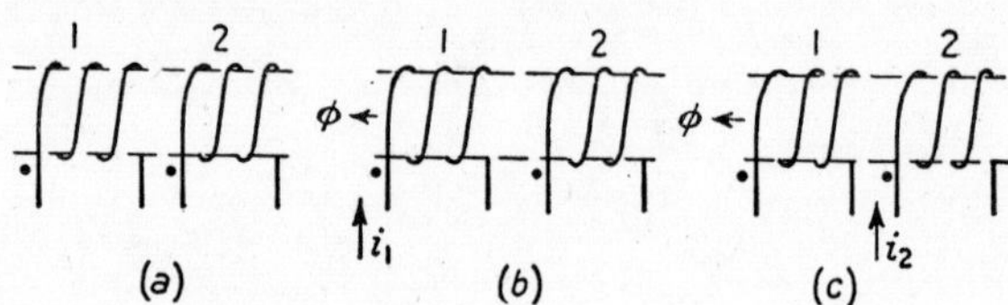


Fig. 12-1. Three views of a pair of magnetically coupled coils showing the meaning of the dot convention.

core of magnetic material. The dots placed at the winding ends have the following significance:

Suppose a test d-c current enters the dotted terminal of winding (1), as shown at (*b*) of the figure. It will produce flux in the direction shown. Now suppose a test d-c current enters the dotted terminal of the second coil. The dots are so placed that the flux will be in the same direction as before. This demonstrates the significance of the dots. When currents enter both dotted terminals (or if they leave both), their magnetic effects are aiding.

Dots do not usually appear on commercial transformers. However, the information leading to a knowledge of correct dot positions can always be obtained from direct observation of winding directions, from electrical tests or from some sort of letter markings on the terminals. The purpose of the dots is to clarify the meaning of circuit diagrams, without making it necessary actually to show winding directions.

If the currents $i_1$ and $i_2$ are varying quantities, which may become negative, the above directions, including the flux direction, are to be interpreted as *reference directions.*

**12-3. Definition of Mutual Inductance.** For the two coils of Fig. 12-2 assume that $i_2$ is constant and $i_1$ is varying. Coil 1 has a self-inductance $L_1$ such that

$$v_1 = L_1 \frac{di_1}{dt} \tag{12-1}$$

Now suppose that $i_1$ is constant and that $i_2$ is varying; then

$$v_2 = L_2 \frac{di_2}{dt} \tag{12-2}$$

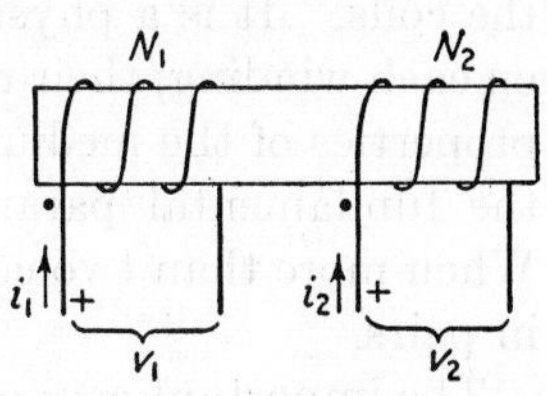


FIG. 12-2. Reference conditions for currents and potential differences with magnetically coupled coils.

for coil 2. $L_2$ is the self-inductance of coil 2.

Now return to the first condition. Any potential across coil 2 is due to the varying current $i_1$ and is proportional to $di_1/dt$. Thus, using the *positive* constant $M$ as a proportionality constant,

$$v_2 = M \frac{di_1}{dt} \tag{12-3}$$

It may be proved that Eq. (12-3) has the proper algebraic sign by noting that the direction of flux in coil 1 is the same whether it is due to $i_1$ or $i_2$. Therefore, an increasing $i_1$ (positive $di_1/dt$) and an increasing $i_2$ (positive $di_2/dt$) will make $v_2$ have the same polarity. It follows that Eqs. (12-2) and (12-3) should have the same sign if $L$ and $M$ are each positive. Similar reasoning leads to

$$v_1 = M \frac{di_2}{dt} \tag{12-4}$$

for the potential across winding 1 when there is a changing current in winding 2 only. It can be shown that $M$ has identical values in Eqs. (12-3) and (12-4).

It is not necessary for the reference conditions to be related to the dots as shown in Fig. 12-2. For example, a reversal of $i_2$ can be compensated for by a negative sign in Eq. (12-4) or by allowing $M$ to be algebraic and assume a negative sign. In this text $M$ is always positive, but there are some situations for which it is convenient to let $M$ become negative.

When there is a simultaneous current in both windings, the complete formulas for potentials $v_1$ and $v_2$ become, for Fig. 12-2,

$$\begin{aligned} v_1 &= L_1 \frac{di_1}{dt} + M \frac{di_2}{dt} \\ v_2 &= M \frac{di_1}{dt} + L_2 \frac{di_2}{dt} \end{aligned} \tag{12-5}$$

The proportionality constant $M$ is called the *mutual inductance* between the coils. It is a physical parameter depending on the number of turns on each winding, their relative position and orientation, and the magnetic properties of the medium around and inside the coils. $L_1$, $L_2$, and $M$ are the fundamental parameters for a pair of magnetically coupled coils. When more than two coils are magnetically coupled, they may be treated in pairs.

The important case of sinusoidal currents is to be considered. In that case the effect of the mutual inductance can be predicted by observing the similarity with self-inductance. Thus, $L\ di/dt$ is symbolized by $j\omega L\mathbf{I}$, and $M\ di/dt$ is symbolized by $j\omega M\mathbf{I}$. If the notation

$$\begin{aligned} &\mathbf{I}_1 \text{ symbolizes } i_1 \\ &\mathbf{I}_2 \text{ symbolizes } i_2 \\ &\mathbf{V}_1 \text{ symbolizes } v_1 \\ &\mathbf{V}_2 \text{ symbolizes } v_2 \end{aligned} \tag{12-6}$$

is employed, Eqs. (12-5) become

$$\begin{aligned} \mathbf{V}_1 &= j\omega L_1\mathbf{I}_1 + j\omega M\mathbf{I}_2 \\ \mathbf{V}_2 &= j\omega M\mathbf{I}_1 + j\omega L_2\mathbf{I}_2 \end{aligned} \tag{12-7}$$

Equations (12-7) can be incorporated in the general network loop equations.

**12-4. Coefficient of Coupling.** The magnitude of $M$ depends on the permeability of the magnetic medium, the size of the coils, the number of turns, and their physical relationship. In order to see how these effects are related, in Fig. 12-2 let $i_2$ be constant and let $i_1$ be varying. There are two formulas for the potential across coil 2, as follows:

$$\begin{aligned} v_2 &= N_2 \frac{d\phi_{21}}{dt} \\ v_2 &= M \frac{di_1}{dt} \end{aligned} \tag{12-8}$$

$N_1$ and $N_2$ are the respective numbers of turns on coils 1 and 2. The flux $\phi_{21}$ is the flux linking coil 2 due to the current in coil 1. It is related to

$i_1$ by the proportionality

$$\phi_{21} = K_{12}N_1 i_1 \tag{12-9}$$

where $K_{12}$ is a proportionality constant which depends on the magnetic path. The two forms of Eqs. (12-8) combine to give

$$M = N_2 \frac{d\phi_{21}}{di_1} \tag{12-10}$$

and Eq. (12-9) yields

$$\frac{d\phi_{21}}{di_1} = K_{12}N_1 \tag{12-11}$$

Equations (12-10) and (12-11) then give

$$M = K_{12}N_1N_2 \tag{12-12}$$

It is known that the self-inductance of a coil is proportional to the square of its number of turns. It follows that the product $N_1N_2$ is proportional to $\sqrt{L_1L_2}$ and hence that

$$M = k\sqrt{L_1L_2} \tag{12-13}$$

The factor $k$ is the *coefficient of coupling*. It is a product of $K_{12}$ and the proportionality factor between $N_1N_2$ and $\sqrt{L_1L_2}$. These factors need not be known individually because we are interested only in proving that $M$ is proportional to $\sqrt{L_1L_2}$. The coefficient of coupling may be regarded as an experimentally determined constant.

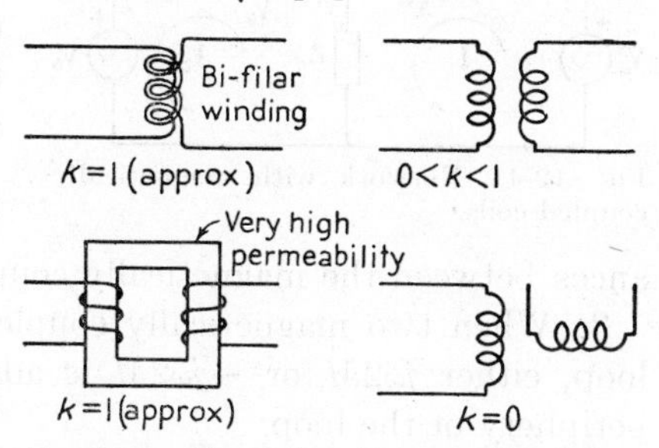


FIG. 12-3. Examples of how various values of coefficient of coupling can be obtained.

The magnitude of $k$ depends on the orientation of the coils and on the core material. A number of examples are given in Fig. 12-3. A pair of coils separated by a large distance can have a large value of $k$ if they are linked by a highly permeable magnetic circuit. When $M$ is restricted to positive values, as in this text, $k$ is a positive constant which always is less than 1.

**12-5. Circuits with Magnetically Coupled Coils.** Figure 12-4 can be used to illustrate the method of solving circuits when they include magnetic coupling. Kirchhoff potential equations can be written as follows:

$$\begin{aligned} (\mathbf{Z}_a + \mathbf{Z}_c)\mathbf{I}_1 - \mathbf{Z}_c\mathbf{I}_2 - \mathbf{Z}_a\mathbf{I}_3 + \mathbf{V}_1 &= \mathbf{V}_a \\ -\mathbf{Z}_c\mathbf{I}_1 + \mathbf{I}_2(\mathbf{Z}_b + \mathbf{Z}_c) - \mathbf{Z}_b\mathbf{I}_3 + \mathbf{V}_2 + \mathbf{V}_b &= 0 \\ -\mathbf{Z}_a\mathbf{I}_1 - \mathbf{Z}_b\mathbf{I}_2 - (\mathbf{Z}_a + \mathbf{Z}_d + \mathbf{Z}_b)\mathbf{I}_3 - \mathbf{V}_1 - \mathbf{V}_2 &= 0 \end{aligned} \tag{12-14}$$

The potentials $\mathbf{V}_1$ and $\mathbf{V}_2$ can be expressed in terms of the various currents in order to get Eqs. (12-14) into a form similar to Eqs. (11-29). Note that $\mathbf{V}_1$ is due to $\mathbf{I}_1$ and $\mathbf{I}_3$, in part, because $L_1$ is common to loops 1 and 3, and that $\mathbf{V}_1$ is also partly due to $\mathbf{I}_2$ and $\mathbf{I}_3$ because $L_1$ is magnetically coupled to $L_2$, and $L_2$ is common to loops 2 and 3. Thus

$$\mathbf{V}_1 = j\omega[L_1(\mathbf{I}_1 - \mathbf{I}_3) + M(\mathbf{I}_2 - \mathbf{I}_3)] = j\omega[L_1\mathbf{I}_1 + M\mathbf{I}_2 - (L_1 + M)\mathbf{I}_3]$$
$$\mathbf{V}_2 = j\omega[L_2(\mathbf{I}_2 - \mathbf{I}_3) + M(\mathbf{I}_1 - \mathbf{I}_3)] = j\omega[M\mathbf{I}_1 + L_2\mathbf{I}_2 - (M + L_2)\mathbf{I}_3]$$

which may be substituted into Eqs. (12-14) to give, after a rearrangement,

$$\begin{aligned}
&(\mathbf{Z}_a + \mathbf{Z}_c + j\omega L_1)\mathbf{I}_1 + (-\mathbf{Z}_c + j\omega M)\mathbf{I}_2 \\
&\qquad + (-\mathbf{Z}_a - j\omega L_1 - j\omega M)\mathbf{I}_3 = \mathbf{V}_a \\
&(-\mathbf{Z}_c + j\omega M)\mathbf{I}_1 + (\mathbf{Z}_b + \mathbf{Z}_c + j\omega L_2)\mathbf{I}_2 \\
&\qquad + (-\mathbf{Z}_b - j\omega L_2 - j\omega M)\mathbf{I}_3 = -\mathbf{V}_b \\
&(-\mathbf{Z}_a - j\omega L_1 - j\omega M)\mathbf{I}_1 + (-\mathbf{Z}_b - j\omega L_2 - j\omega M)\mathbf{I}_2 \\
&\qquad + [\mathbf{Z}_a + \mathbf{Z}_b + \mathbf{Z}_d + j\omega(L_1 + L_2 + 2M)]\mathbf{I}_3 = 0
\end{aligned} \tag{12-15}$$

If either dot position should be changed, each $M$ in Eq. (12-15) would be replaced by $-M$.

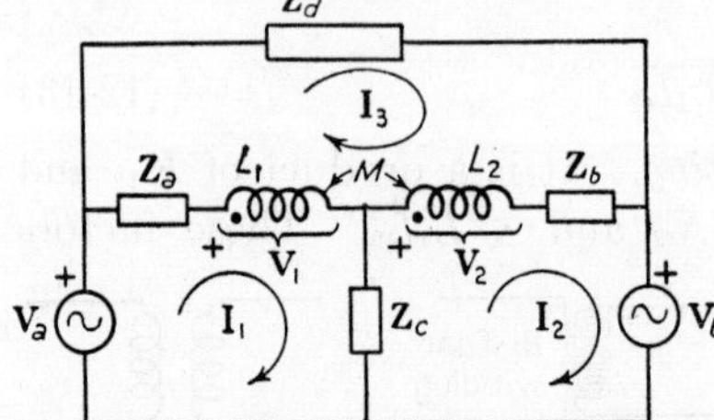

FIG. 12-4. Network with magnetically coupled coils.

Three important observations are to be made from Eqs. (12-15):

1. The reactances of the self inductances ($j\omega L_1$ and $j\omega L_2$) of magnetically coupled coils add to the total impedance on the periphery of a loop in the usual way.

2. Terms of the form $j\omega M$ or $-j\omega M$ add to the common impedances between the magnetically coupled loops.

3. When two magnetically coupled coils are on the periphery of one loop, either $j\omega 2M$ or $-j\omega 2M$ is added to the total impedance on the periphery of the loop.

These rules are easily illustrated by comparing Eqs. (12-15) and (11-29) for typical copedances. Thus,

$$\begin{aligned}
&\text{Rule 1:} \quad & \varrho_{11} &= \mathbf{Z}_a + \mathbf{Z}_c + j\omega L_1 \\
&\text{Rule 2:} \quad & \varrho_{12} &= -\mathbf{Z}_c + j\omega M \\
& & \varrho_{13} &= -\mathbf{Z}_a - j\omega L_1 - j\omega M \\
&\text{Rule 3:} \quad & \varrho_{33} &= \mathbf{Z}_a + \mathbf{Z}_b + \mathbf{Z}_d + j\omega(L_1 + L_2 + 2M)
\end{aligned} \tag{12-16}$$

The equations for $\varrho_{12}$ and $\varrho_{13}$ in Eq. (12-16) show that if in the two coupled loops one current reference direction is toward a dot and the other is away from a dot, then $-j\omega M$ appears in the copedance; and if the current directions are both toward (or away) from dots, then $+j\omega M$ appears in the copedance. The last equation of (12-16) shows that if two magnetically coupled coils are on one loop, the term $+j2\omega M$ is added if the loop current enters (or leaves) both dots; otherwise the term $-j2\omega M$ would be added.

Again it is stressed that $M$ may be regarded as an algebraic variable by writing all copedances including $M$ like $\mathfrak{z}_{12}$ in Eq. (12-16) and then allowing $M$ itself to be negative when necessary. However, it is possible to do this only when $M$ couples two loops. It could not be done in the example of Fig. 12-4, as evidenced by $\mathfrak{z}_{12}$ having a − sign and $\mathfrak{z}_{13}$ a + sign before $j\omega M$.

It is possible to have many coils magnetically coupled. When this is the case each pair of the group is treated by the techniques described above. It should be noted that a separate set of dots is required for each pair of coils.

**Example 12-1.** Find the current $\mathbf{I}_2$ in the accompanying circuit.

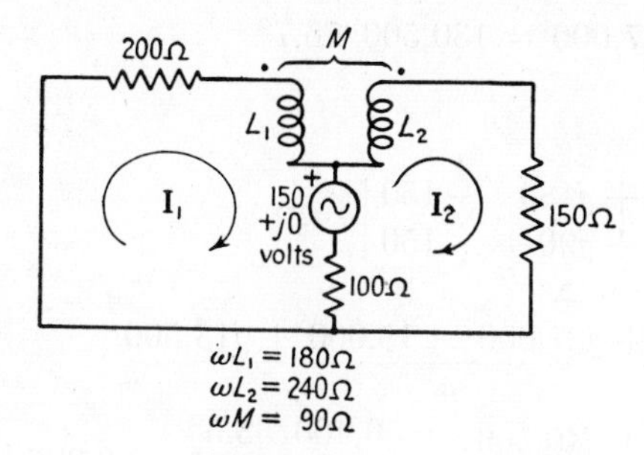


*Solution.* The network equations are

$$(200 + 100 + j180)\mathbf{I}_1 - (100 + j90)\mathbf{I}_2 = -150$$
$$-(100 + j90)\mathbf{I}_1 + (100 + 150 + j240)\mathbf{I}_2 = 150$$

The determinant is

$$\mathbf{\Delta} = \begin{vmatrix} 300 + j180 & -100 - j90 \\ -100 - j90 & 250 + j240 \end{vmatrix}$$
$$= (300 + j180)(250 + j240) - (100 + j90)^2$$
$$= 75{,}000 - 43{,}200 + j(45{,}000 + 72{,}000) - 10{,}000 + 8{,}100 - j18{,}000$$
$$= 29{,}900 + j99{,}000 = 103{,}200\underline{/73.2^\circ}$$

The solution for $\mathbf{I}_2$ is

$$\mathbf{I}_2 = \frac{\begin{vmatrix} 300 + j180 & -150 \\ -100 - j90 & 150 \end{vmatrix}}{\mathbf{\Delta}}$$
$$= \frac{45{,}000 + j27{,}000 - 15{,}000 - j13{,}500}{\mathbf{\Delta}}$$
$$= \frac{30{,}000 + j13{,}500}{\mathbf{\Delta}} = \frac{32{,}900\underline{/24.2^\circ}}{103{,}200\underline{/73.2^\circ}} = 0.319\underline{/-49^\circ} \text{ amp}$$

**Example 12-2.** Find the current $\mathbf{I}_2$ for the network of Example 12-1 but with the dot position changed on winding 2.

*Solution.* The equations are

$$(200 + 100 + j180)\mathbf{I}_1 - (100 - j90)\mathbf{I}_2 = -150$$
$$-(100 - j90)\mathbf{I}_1 + (100 + 150 + j240)\mathbf{I}_2 = 150$$

The determinant is

$$\boldsymbol{\Delta} = \begin{vmatrix} 300 + j180 & -100 + j90 \\ -100 + j90 & 250 + j240 \end{vmatrix}$$
$$= (300 + j180)(250 + j240) - (-100 + j90)^2$$
$$= 75{,}000 - 43{,}200 + j(45{,}000 + 72{,}000) - 10{,}000 + 8{,}100 + j18{,}000$$
$$= 29{,}900 + j127{,}000 = 130{,}500\underline{/76.7^\circ}$$

The current $\mathbf{I}_2$ is

$$\mathbf{I}_2 = \frac{\begin{vmatrix} 300 + j180 & -150 \\ -100 + j90 & 150 \end{vmatrix}}{\boldsymbol{\Delta}}$$
$$= \frac{45{,}000 + j27{,}000 - 15{,}000 + j13{,}500}{\boldsymbol{\Delta}}$$
$$= \frac{30{,}000 + j40{,}500}{\boldsymbol{\Delta}} = \frac{50{,}400\underline{/53.5^\circ}}{130{,}500\underline{/76.7^\circ}} = 0.386\underline{/-23.2^\circ} \text{ amp}$$

**12-6. Equivalent Circuit for Two Magnetically Coupled Coils.** It is possible to replace a pair of magnetically coupled coils by a network of three inductors which are not magnetically coupled. The method of doing this is conveniently given in terms of the pair of coils of Fig. 12-5. All potentials and currents are sinusoidal. The resistors shown replace the resistances of the coils. The following equations are written for $M$ positive.

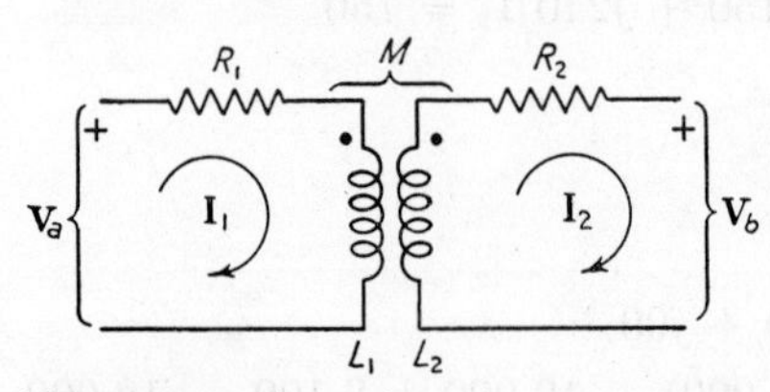


FIG. 12-5. A pair of magnetically coupled coils, with winding resistance shown separately.

The techniques of section 12-5 provide the equations

$$\begin{aligned} (R_1 + j\omega L_1)\mathbf{I}_1 - j\omega M\mathbf{I}_2 &= \mathbf{V}_a \\ -j\omega M\mathbf{I}_1 + (R_2 + j\omega L_2)\mathbf{I}_2 &= -\mathbf{V}_b \end{aligned} \qquad (12\text{-}17)$$

It is useful to define the additional quantities

$$\begin{aligned} L_1' &= L_1 - M \\ L_2' &= L_2 - M \end{aligned} \qquad (12\text{-}18)$$

In terms of these Eqs. (12-17) can be written

$$\begin{aligned} [R_1 + j\omega(L_1' + M)]\mathbf{I}_1 - j\omega M\mathbf{I}_2 &= \mathbf{V}_a \\ -j\omega M\mathbf{I}_1 + [R_2 + j\omega(L_2' + M)]\mathbf{I}_2 &= -\mathbf{V}_b \end{aligned} \tag{12-19}$$

The last pair of equations are recognized as the loop equations of the circuit of Fig. 12-6. The center branch is a self-inductance of $M$ henrys. It is not magnetically coupled to any other coil.

It is possible to construct such a circuit if $L_1'$ and $L_2'$ are each positive. They are both positive if $L_1 = L_2$, because $M$ is then less than either $L_1$ or $L_2$. However, it is possible to have cases in which either $L_1'$ or $L_2'$ is negative. In that case an equivalent circuit that is good at all frequencies can exist on paper and be used in theoretical work, but it could not be constructed in the laboratory. There is no such thing physically as a

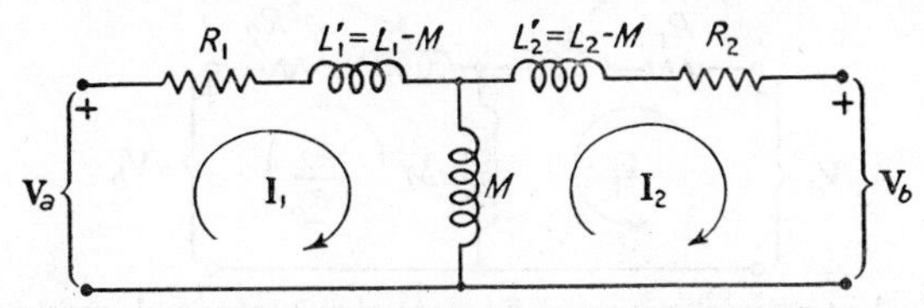


FIG. 12-6. A network which is equivalent to Fig. 12-5.

negative inductance, but at a fixed frequency the negative inductance can be replaced by a capacitance. Another equivalent circuit can be made by using the T-Π transformation on the circuit of Fig. 12-6.

It should be noted that if one of the dot positions were changed in Fig. 12-5, the central inductance would be $-M$ and Eqs. (12-18) would have a $+$ sign before each $M$.

If a circuit using magnetic coupling is to be analyzed on a node basis, an equivalent circuit can first be introduced. The node analysis then applies as in any network.

In order further to consider equivalent circuits for transformers, suppose the current $\mathbf{I}_2$ is multiplied by $1/a$ and that $\mathbf{V}_b$ is multiplied by $a$, where $a$ is some arbitrary positive real number. Equations (12-17) can be written

$$\begin{aligned} (R_1 + j\omega L_1)\mathbf{I}_1 - j\omega aM\frac{\mathbf{I}_2}{a} &= \mathbf{V}_a \\ -j\omega aM\mathbf{I}_1 + a^2(R_2 + j\omega L_2)\frac{\mathbf{I}_2}{a} &= -a\mathbf{V}_b \end{aligned} \tag{12-20}$$

To interpret these the auxiliary inductances,

$$\begin{aligned} L_1'' &= L_1 - aM \\ L_2'' &= L_2 - \frac{M}{a} \end{aligned} \tag{12-21}$$

are defined. It is possible to chose $a$ so as to make $L_1''$ and $L_2''$ each positive. They can be introduced into Eqs. (12-20) to give

$$[R_1 + j\omega(L_1'' + aM)]\mathbf{I}_1 - j\omega aM \frac{\mathbf{I}_2}{a} = \mathbf{V}_a$$

$$-j\omega aM\mathbf{I}_1 + a^2 \left[ R_2 + j\omega \left( L_2'' + \frac{M}{a} \right) \right] \frac{\mathbf{I}_2}{a} = -a\mathbf{V}_b \tag{12-22}$$

These equations represent the loop analysis of the circuit of Fig. 12-7. However, it is to be emphasized that it is not an exact equivalent of the original circuit, because $\mathbf{I}_2$ is replaced by $\mathbf{I}_2/a$ and $\mathbf{V}_b$ is changed to $a\mathbf{V}_b$.

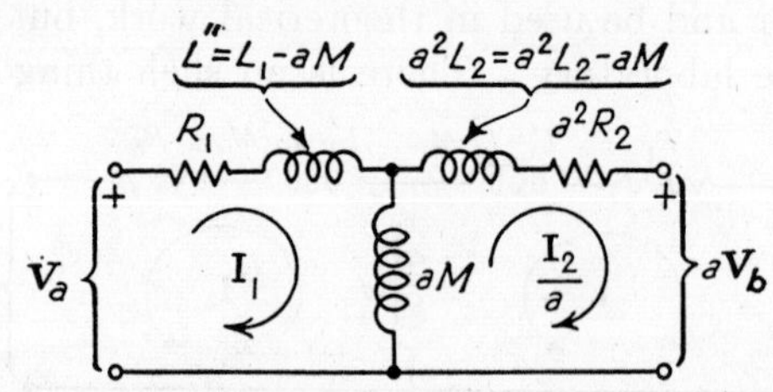


FIG. 12-7. Equivalent network with scaled potential difference and current on one winding.

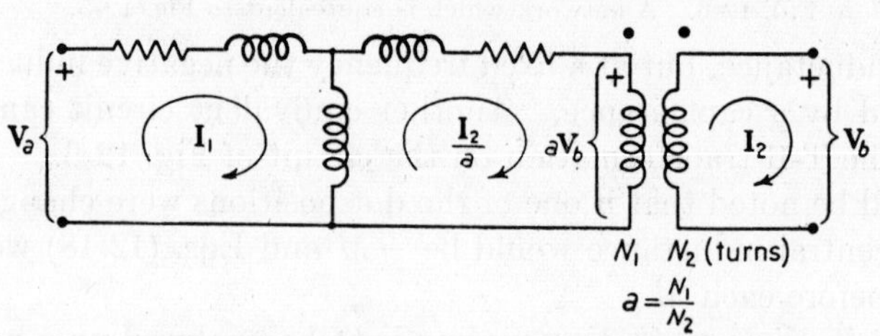


FIG. 12-8. Equivalent network with ideal transformer used to provide the scaling of current and potential on one side. Resistance and inductance values are the same as on Fig. 12-7.

In some cases this change is replaced on a circuit diagram by an *ideal* transformer, which is defined as a hypothetical two-winding device which transforms the potential by a certain ratio and the current by the inverse of that ratio. An ideal transformer is approximated by a pair of coils having near unity coefficient of coupling and a very large number of turns so that $M$ approaches infinity. An equivalent circuit, with ideal transformer included, is shown in Fig. 12-8.

So far the value of $a$ has been arbitrary. A number of values can always be chosen such that $L_1''$ and $L_2''$ are each nonnegative. One such value is

$$a = \sqrt{\frac{L_1}{L_2}} \tag{12-23}$$

Recalling that $M = k\sqrt{L_1L_2}$, the values

$$L_1'' = L_1 - \sqrt{\frac{L_1}{L_2}}\, k\sqrt{L_1L_2} = L_1(1-k)$$
$$L_2'' = L_2 - \sqrt{\frac{L_2}{L_1}}\, k\sqrt{L_1L_2} = L_2(1-k) \qquad (12\text{-}24)$$

are obtained. Each of these is positive because $k$ is always less than unity.

A similar treatment could have been followed by scaling the current and potential in winding 1.

**12-7. Impedance Changing.** In many applications a transformer is used to connect a load impedance to a source. Figure 12-9 shows such an arrangement. The currents $\mathbf{I}_1$ and $\mathbf{I}_2$ can be found by solving the loop equations

$$\begin{aligned} j\omega L_1\mathbf{I}_1 \pm j\omega M\mathbf{I}_2 &= \mathbf{V} \\ \pm j\omega M\mathbf{I}_1 + (\mathbf{Z}_r + j\omega L_2)\mathbf{I}_2 &= 0 \end{aligned} \qquad (12\text{-}25)$$

The net impedance attached to the source is $\mathbf{V}/\mathbf{I}_1$. From Eqs. (12-25)

$$\mathbf{I}_1 = \frac{(\mathbf{Z}_r + j\omega L_2)\mathbf{V}}{\omega^2(M^2 - L_1L_2) + j\omega L_1\mathbf{Z}_r} \qquad (12\text{-}26)$$

Thus the impedance is

$$\mathbf{Z} = \frac{\omega^2(M^2 - L_1L_2) + j\omega L_1\mathbf{Z}_r}{\mathbf{Z}_r + j\omega L_2} \qquad (12\text{-}27)$$

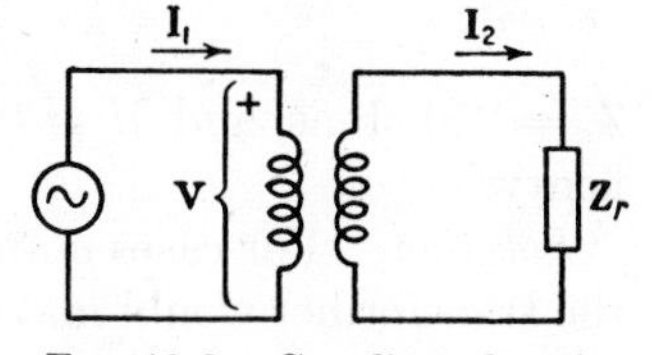


FIG. 12-9. Coupling of an impedance to a source through a transformer.

An important special case is the ideal transformer mentioned in Sec. 12-6. It is the limit obtained when the coefficient of coupling becomes unity and $L_1$ and $L_2$ approach infinity. In that case, $M^2 - L_1L_2$ approaches zero, and $\mathbf{Z}_r$ becomes negligible compared with $j\omega L_2$. Therefore, for the ideal transformer

$$\mathbf{Z} = \frac{L_1}{L_2}\mathbf{Z}_r \qquad (12\text{-}28)$$

Although $L_1$ and $L_2$ were each allowed to approach infinity, their ratio remains constant. The transformer effectively changes the impedance by the ratio of the winding inductances. In many practical cases Eq. (12-28) can be closely approximated, although it can never be attained exactly. It is useful as an engineering approximation.

Inductance is equal to the product of the permeance of the magnetic circuit by the square of the number of turns. Both coils have the same magnetic path when the coupling is unity. Therefore, for the ideal transformer, the ratio of the winding inductances is the ratio of the square of the number of turns. Equation (12-28) can be written

$$\mathbf{Z} = \left(\frac{N_1}{N_2}\right)^2 \mathbf{Z}_r \tag{12-29}$$

**Example 12-3.** In the accompanying figure assume that

$$\left(\frac{N_1}{N_2}\right)^2 = \frac{L_1}{L_2}$$

The frequency is 1,000 cps, and $L_1 = 4L_2 = 2$ henrys. Compare the impedance transforming performance of this transformer with the ideal, for the following cases: (*a*) $\mathbf{Z}_r = 250$ ohms, and $M = 0.98$ henry; (*b*)

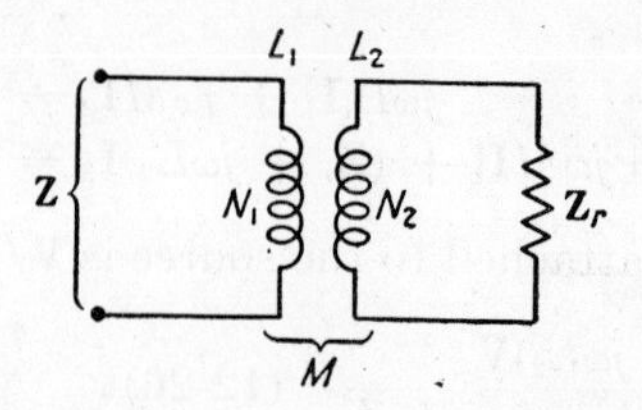


$\mathbf{Z}_r = 250$ ohms, and $M = 0.85$ henry; (*c*) $\mathbf{Z}_r = 2{,}500$ ohms, and $M = 0.98$ henry.

*Solution.* For cases *a* and *b* the ideal transformation ratio is 4, and so the transformer would make $\mathbf{Z} = 1{,}000$ ohms if it were ideal. The actual values of $\mathbf{Z}$ are obtained by substituting pertinent numerical values in Eqs. (12-27).

For case *a*

$$\mathbf{Z} = \frac{(6{,}280)^2(0.98^2 - 1) + j(6{,}280)(2)(250)}{250 + j(6{,}280)(0.5)} = \frac{-158 + j3{,}140}{0.25 + j3.14}$$

$$= \frac{(-158 + j3{,}140)(0.25 - j3.14)}{9.93} = \frac{9{,}830 + j1{,}281}{9.93}$$

$$= 989 + j129 = 1{,}000\underline{/7.4°} \text{ ohms}$$

In this application the transformer approaches the "ideal" fairly well.

For case *b*

$$\mathbf{Z} = \frac{(6{,}280)^2(0.85^2 - 1) + j(6{,}280)(2)(250)}{250 + j(6{,}280)(0.5)} = \frac{-1{,}095 + j3{,}140}{0.25 + j3.14}$$

$$= \frac{(-1{,}095 + j3{,}140)(0.25 - j3.14)}{9.93} = \frac{9{,}590 + j4{,}220}{9.93}$$

$$= 965 + j426 = 1{,}055\underline{/23.8°} \text{ ohms}$$

This transformer is further from the ideal than case *a*. The coefficient of coupling is too low, as indicated by the relatively large number 1,095 in the numerator on the right of the first line.

For case *c* the ideal transformer would give $\mathbf{Z} = 10{,}000$ ohms. The actual value is

$$\mathbf{Z} = \frac{(6{,}280)^2(0.98^2 - 1) + j(6{,}280)(2)(2{,}500)}{2500 + j(6{,}280)(0.5)} = \frac{-158 + j31{,}400}{2.5 + j3.14}$$
$$= \frac{(-158 + j31{,}400)(2.5 - j3.14)}{10.48} = \frac{98{,}200 + j79{,}000}{10.48}$$
$$= 9{,}370 + j7{,}550 = 10{,}020\underline{/38.8^\circ} \text{ ohms}$$

In this case the transformer is the same as in case *a*, but its performance deviates appreciably from the ideal. The reactances of the coils are too low in comparison with the load impedance, as indicated by the fact that 3.14 and 2.5 (in the denominator on the right of the first line) are nearly the same in size.

These examples emphasize the two conditions that must be satisfied by a transformer if it is to approximate an ideal transformer: it must have close coupling of the coils, and the coils must have reactances which are high in comparison with the load impedance.

**12-8. Summary.** Magnetic coupling can be interpreted in terms of the flux produced by one coil and linking another. However, for the circuit-analysis viewpoint it is treated in a manner analogous to the treatment of self-inductance. This leads to the definition of mutual inductance as a circuit parameter.

Mutual inductance lends itself readily to use in the loop equations of a network. When a node analysis is to be used, the magnetically coupled coils must be replaced by conductively connected equivalents. These equivalents may sometimes require negative inductances. This precludes the possibility of constructing such circuits but does not prevent their being used in theoretical work. Negative inductances can be eliminated by introducing ideal transformers.

Ideal transformers are useful because they represent limits which may be approached by actual transformers. With an ideal transformer the potential ratio is the turns ratio, and the current ratio is the inverse of the turns ratio. In actual transformers this simple relationship does not hold, and the actual current and potential ratios depend on the connected circuit as well as on the characteristics of the transformer.

## PROBLEMS

**12-1.** In the circuit of Fig. 12P-1, $i_1$ is the only current and is

$$i_1 = 1.5 \sin 5{,}000t \qquad \text{amp}$$

Sketch waves for $v_1$, $v_2$, and $v_3$, and write equations for them. Note the two pairs of dots, one pair being triangular.

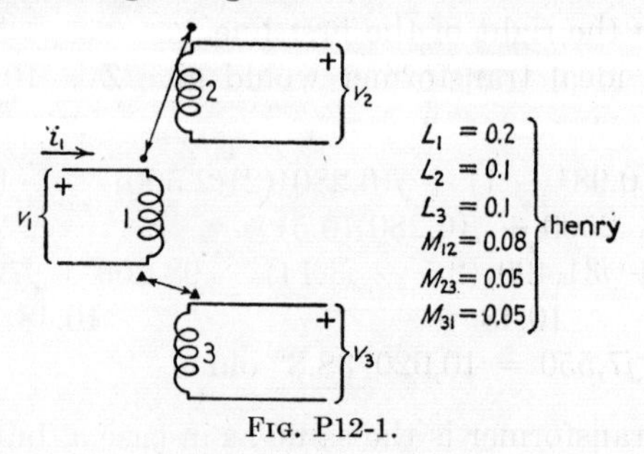


FIG. P12-1.

**12-2.** Refer to the circuit of Fig. P12-1.

*a.* Find the coefficient of coupling for each of the pairs of windings.

*b.* Is it possible to deduce the positions of a pair of dots relating coils 2 and 3? Explain your answer.

**12-3.** For the circuit of Fig. P12-3 do the following:

*a.* Find the currents $\mathbf{I}_1$ and $\mathbf{I}_2$.

*b.* Find the impedance presented to the potential source.

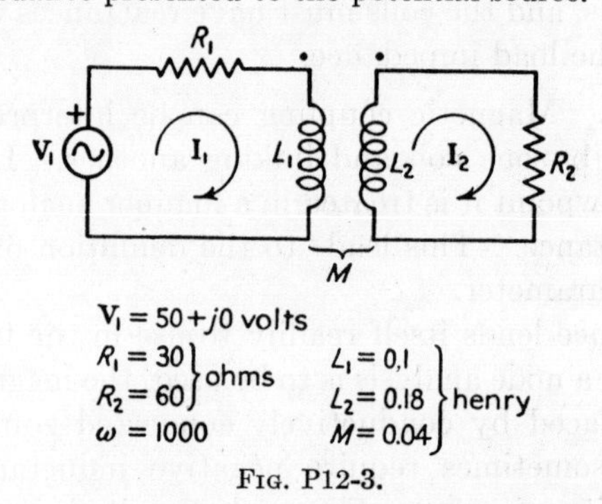


FIG. P12-3.

**12-4.** Refer to Fig. P12-4. The potential sources are as follows:

$$v_{ab} = 141.4 \sin 1{,}131t \quad \text{volts} \qquad \text{and} \qquad v_{dc} = 113.2 \cos 1{,}131t \quad \text{volts}$$

*a.* Find the mutual inductance.

*b.* Find the equations for $i_{ba}$ and $i_{cd}$ as functions of time.

*c.* Repeat part *b* for the case where the right-hand dot is on the bottom.

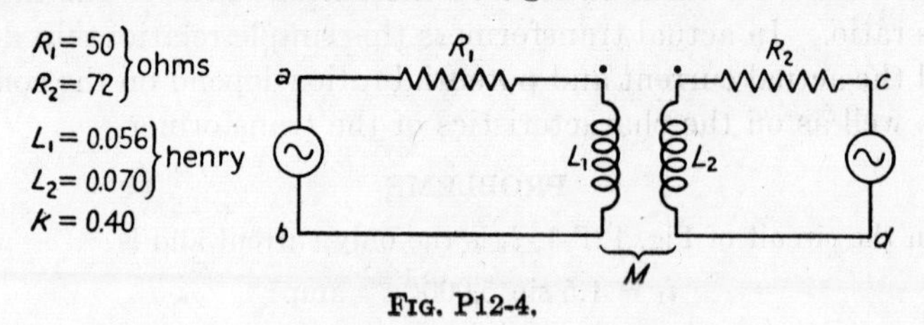


FIG. P12-4.

**12-5.** Figure P12-5 shows a three-winding transformer. Power is fed to winding (1) from the potential source $\mathbf{V}_1 = 250 + j0$ volts. Its frequency is 60 cps. The parameters of the transformer are $L_1 = 0.3$ henry, $L_2 = 0.5$ henry,

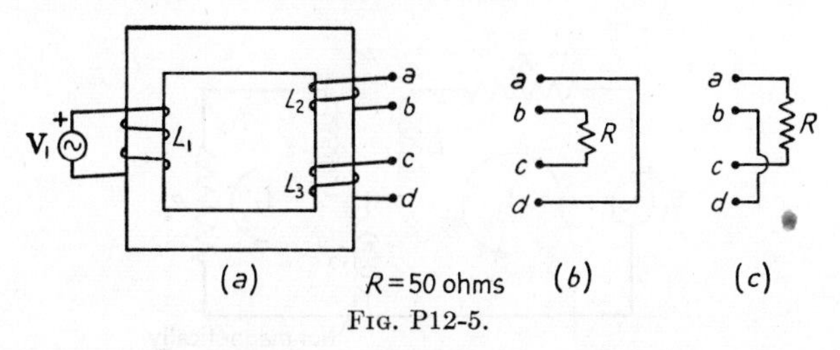


FIG. P12-5.

$L_3 = 0.8$ henry, $M_{12} = 0.35$ henry, $M_{23} = 0.6$ henry, $M_{31} = 0.4$ henry. The resistances of the windings are to be neglected. Winding directions are indicated on the diagram.

*a*. Find the power delivered to the resistor $R$ when it is connected as shown at (*b*) in the figure.

*b*. Find the power delivered to $R$ when it is connected as shown at (*c*) in the figure.

**12-6.** This problem deals with the transformer described in Fig. P12-5, but with coils 2 and 3 connected in parallel.

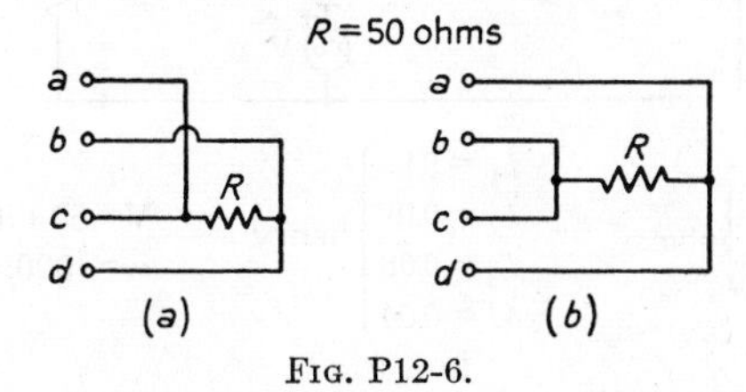


FIG. P12-6.

*a*. Compute the power delivered to the resistor when the windings are connected as shown in Fig. P12-6*a*.

*b*. Compute the power delivered to the resistor when the windings are connected as shown in Fig. P12-6*b*.

**12-7.** The following test is made in the laboratory, on two coils which are magnetically coupled. A potential source of 250 volts, a wattmeter, and two ammeters are available. When coil 1 is connected to this source, with coil 2 on open circuit, the current is 0.776 amp and the power taken by the coil is 75.2 watts. The second coil is then connected in series with the first coil, and the current is then 0.878 amp, and the power is 147 watts. Finally, coil 1 is connected to the same source, and coil 2 is short-circuited, and then the current in coil 1 is 1.17 amp. All tests are at 60 cps.

*a*. Determine $R_1$, $L_1$, $R_2$, $L_2$, and $M$ from the above data.

*b*. What would be the complex admittance of these two coils when connected in parallel, magnetically opposing?

*c*. What would be the complex impedance of these two coils when connected in series, magnetically aiding?

**12-8.** For the circuit of Fig. P12-8 determine

*a.* A literal expression for the current $\mathbf{I}_2$, when the coils are arranged as shown.

*b.* A literal expression for the current $\mathbf{I}_2$ if the left-hand dot is moved to the bottom.

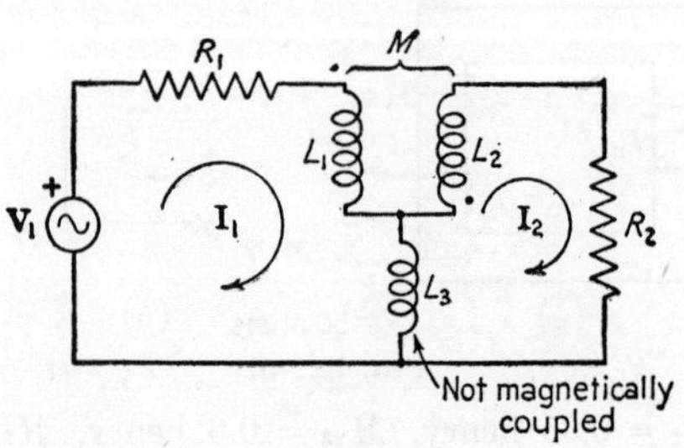


FIG. P12-8.

**12-9.** Refer to the circuit of Fig. P12-9, in which $L_3$ is not magnetically coupled.

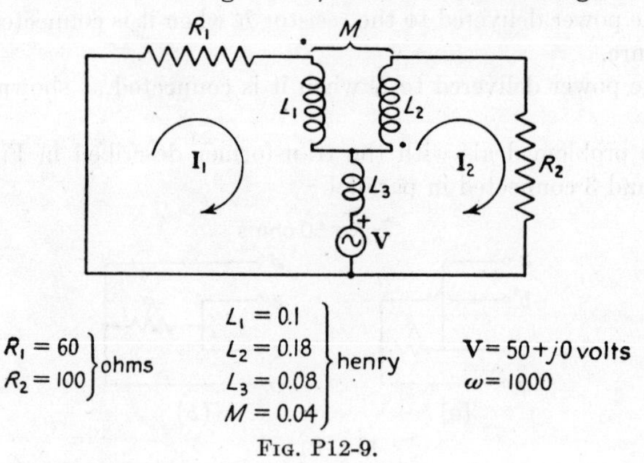


FIG. P12-9.

*a.* Find the currents $\mathbf{I}_1$ and $\mathbf{I}_2$.

*b.* What is the impedance seen by the source?

*c.* Assume $R_2$ is replaced by a variable impedance $\mathbf{Z}_2$. What value should it have to take the maximum possible power?

**12-10.** Consider the circuit of Fig. P12-10.

*a.* Use the generalized loop analysis to obtain a formula for the current $\mathbf{I}_3$.

*b.* Repeat the solution, with the right-hand dot at the bottom of the winding.

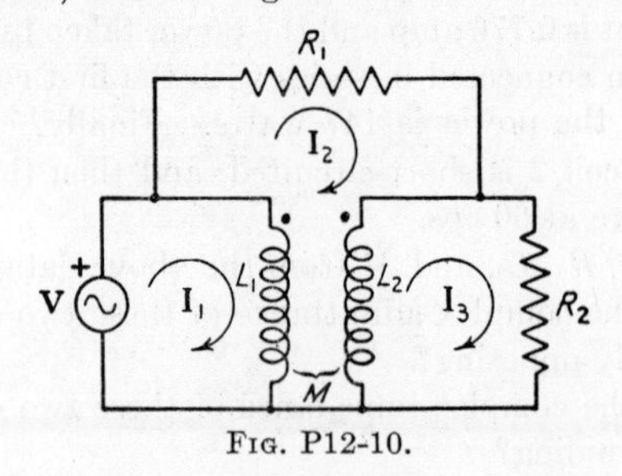


FIG. P12-10.

**12-11.** Refer to the circuit of Fig. P12-3.

*a.* Obtain the equivalent circuit of this transformer.

*b.* Find the impedance seen by the potential source, using this equivalent circuit.

**12-12.** Refer to the circuit of Fig. P12-3.

*a.* What is the largest value $M$ can have and still represent the transformer by an equivalent circuit of physically attainable form?

*b.* Admitting the possibility of an ideal transformer, show two equivalent circuits for this transformer if $M = 0.12$ henry. The circuit is to use only two inductors. Except for the ideal transformer, it is to be physically realizable.

**12-13.** Replace the transformer of Fig. P12-10 by a T equivalent. It need not be physically realizable. Use a node analysis on the resulting network to find the current $\mathbf{I}_3$.

**12-14.** In Fig. P12-9 the transformer is to be replaced by a T equivalent circuit.

*a.* Show how the circuit can be made up of real components if an ideal transformer is permitted.

*b.* Show how the circuit may be represented if negative inductance is allowed.

*c.* Apply a node analysis to the circuit obtained in (*c*), and from this obtain the solution for $\mathbf{I}_1$ and $\mathbf{I}_2$ of Fig. P12-9.

*d.* Use a step-by-step solution on the circuit obtained in part *c*, to find the currents $\mathbf{I}_1$ and $\mathbf{I}_2$ of Fig. P12-9.

**12-15.** Two one-to-one transformers are connected in cascade as shown in Fig. P12-15. Prove that the complex impedance $\mathbf{Z}$ is

$$\mathbf{Z} = \frac{R\omega^2(L_a^2 + L_aL_b - M_a^2) + j\omega^3(L_a^2L_b + L_aL_b^2 - L_aM_b^2 - L_bM_a^2)}{\omega^2(L_aL_b + L_b^2 - M_b^2) - j\omega R(L_a + L_b)}$$

Use the loop method of solving the network. Would it make any difference if any of the dot positions were changed?

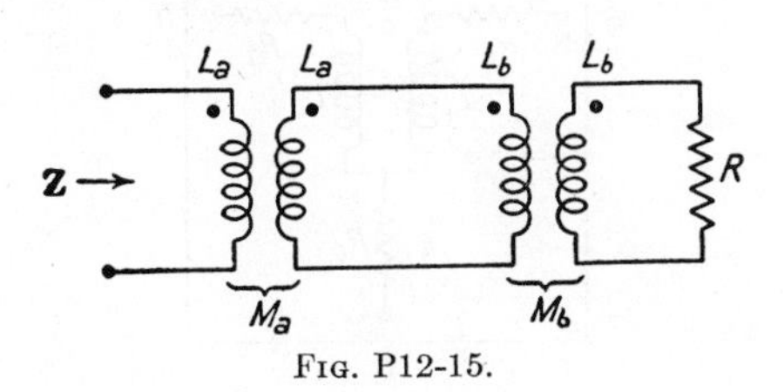


FIG. P12-15.

**12-16.** Do Prob. 12-15 by first replacing each transformer by an equivalent circuit and then using the step-by-step method of combining impedances.

**12-17.** The three coils specified in Prob. 12-1 are placed on a common core as shown in Fig. P12-17.

*a.* Appropriately place a set of dots showing the magnetic relationship between coils 2 and 3, and show actual winding directions.

*b.* Determine the complex impedance $\mathbf{Z}$, if $\omega = 2{,}500$ rad/sec.

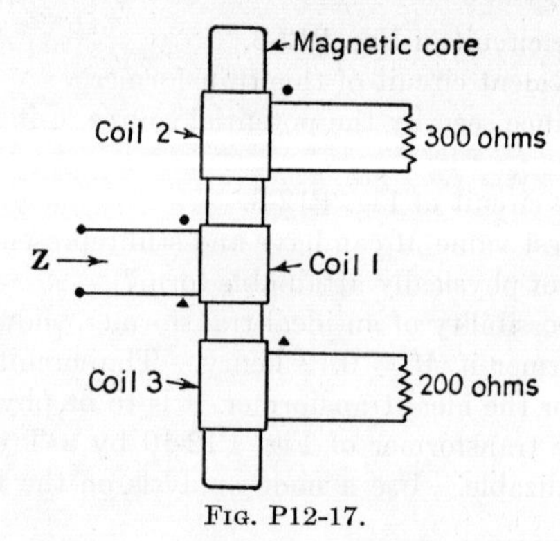


FIG. P12-17.

**12-18.** Do problem 12-17 for the arrangement of the coils shown in Fig. P12-18.

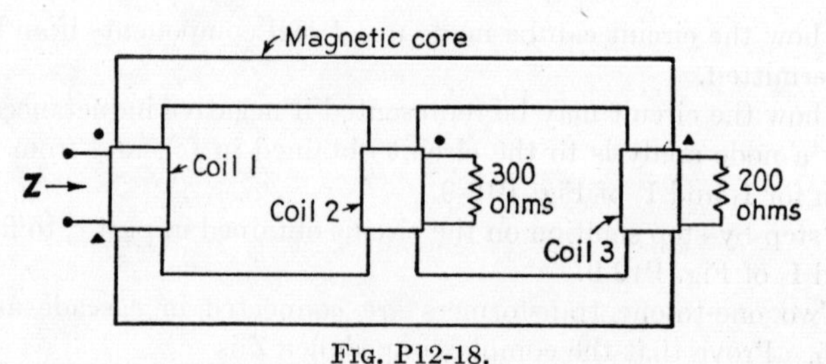


FIG. P12-18.

**12-19.** The dotted rectangle in Fig. P12-19 represents a box containing the elements shown. Terminals *a*, *b*, and *c* are the only ones available for making electrical measurements. A 250-volt 60-cps potential source, an ammeter, and a wattmeter are available for making measurements. The source is connected first

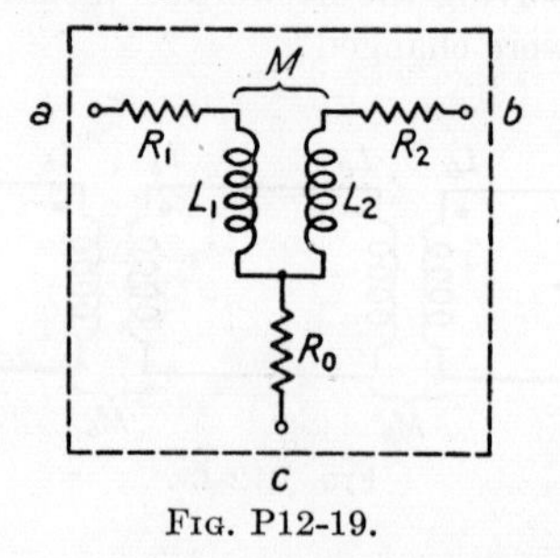


FIG. P12-19.

to terminals *a* and *c*, then to terminals *b* and *a*, and finally to terminals *c* and *b*. In each case the current and power are measured. For the three connections specified, the currents are, respectively, 0.824, 1.180, and 1.430 amp; and the powers are, respectively, 114, 278, and 284 watts. Compute values of $R_1$, $R_2$, $L_1$, $L_2$, $M$, and $R_0$, and decide how dots should be placed on the coils.

**12-20.** So-called "intermediate-frequency" amplifiers of radio receivers are often of the type shown in Fig. P12-20. The current source and the resistor $r_p$

comprise the current-source equivalent of the vacuum tube. For the conditions specified and at the angular frequency $\omega_0$, use a loop analysis to determine the potential **V**.

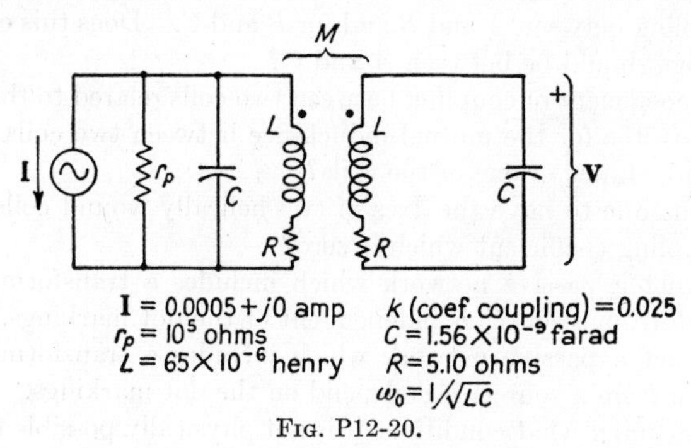


FIG. P12-20.

**12-21.** Do Prob. 12-20, but first replace the transformer by an equivalent T circuit. Then use a T-Π transformation to simplify the network, and finally use a node analysis to find **V**.

**12-22.** Refer to the circuit of Fig. P12-3. Replace the transformer by a T equivalent, and then use the T-Π transformation to obtain a Π equivalent. Finally, using a node analysis, solve the resulting network for the current $\mathbf{I}_2$.

**12-23.** In Fig. P12-10 let the resistor $R_1$ be replaced by a capacitor $C$. Obtain an expression for the value of $C$, in terms of the other parameters, which will cause the current $\mathbf{I}_3$ to be zero. Would it be possible to have zero $\mathbf{I}_3$ in such a network if one of the transformer dots had been on the bottom?

**12-24.** An inductor having inductance $L_1$ and resistance $R_1$ is connected in parallel with a second inductor having inductance $L_2$ and resistance $R_2$. Obtain formulas for the two possible impedances obtainable with this combination if the coils are magnetically coupled with mutual inductance $M$.

**12-25.** In Fig. P12-9 let $L_3$ be coupled to both $L_1$ and $L_2$ and let the mutual inductances be

$$M_{12} = 0.04 \text{ henry} \qquad M_{23} = 0.03 \text{ henry} \qquad M_{31} = 0.015 \text{ henry}$$

All other quantities are as specified in Fig. P12-9. The dots shown in Fig. P12-9 continue to show the relationship between $L_1$ and $L_2$. Solve for the currents $\mathbf{I}_1$ and $\mathbf{I}_2$:

*a.* If a pair of dots on the tops of $L_1$ and $L_3$ show their relationship, and a pair of dots on the top of $L_2$ and on the bottom of $L_3$ show their relationship.

*b.* If a pair of dots on the tops of $L_1$ and $L_3$ show their relationship, and a pair of dots on the bottoms of $L_2$ and $L_3$ show their relationship.

## QUESTIONS

**12-1.** If you were given a transformer without dot markings and if only the winding terminals were accessible, would it be possible to make measurements to establish a suitable set of markings?

**12-2.** Given a two-winding transformer; is there one and only one terminal on each winding on which a dot may be placed?

**12-3.** Three windings $A$, $B$, and $C$ are on a common magnetic core. Dots are known for coupling between $A$ and $B$ and for $B$ and $C$. Does this establish what the dot markings should be between $A$ and $C$?

**12-4.** Is the coefficient of coupling between two coils related to the turns ratio?

**12-5.** Is it possible for the mutual inductance between two coils to be greater than the self-inductance of one of the coils?

**12-6.** Is it possible to have the axes of two helically wound coils parallel and still have a coupling coefficient which is zero?

**12-7.** Construct a passive network which includes a transformer, such that the power taken from a source is independent of the dot markings.

**12-8.** Construct a passive network which includes a transformer, such that the power taken from a source does depend on the dot markings.

**12-9.** Discuss under what conditions it is not physically possible to construct a network which is the equivalent of a two-winding transformer, provided that the equivalent shall be valid for variable frequency.

**12-10.** Is it always possible to make an equivalent network for a transformer, at fixed frequency?

**12-11.** What change takes place in the equivalent network for a transformer as the coupling coefficient is reduced to zero?

**12-12.** Is there one and only one equivalent network possible for a given transformer?

**12-13.** What is an ideal transformer? What two conditions can never fully be met in attempting to construct an ideal transformer?

**12-14.** Would an ideal transformer absorb any energy?

**12-15.** A certain transformer couples a source to a resistor. At high frequency the transformer is near enough to the ideal to make the combination appear to be a pure resistance. Does the approximation become better or worse as the frequency is reduced?

**12-16.** Consider three coils labeled $A$, $B$, and $C$. Suppose $A$ is magnetically coupled to $B$ and $B$ is magnetically coupled to $C$. Is it possible that the coupling coefficient between $A$ and $C$ could be zero?

# CHAPTER 13

# POLYPHASE SYSTEMS

**13-1. Introduction.** The simplest possible system for a-c power transmission consists of a generator connected through a pair of wires to a load. This is called a *single-phase* system. In such a system power flows in pulses, a disadvantage in many applications. For example, a motor in such a system has an output torque which pulsates. The shaft is therefore subjected to fatigue loading and must be larger than if the torque were constant. Related to this is the fact that single-phase motors are not self-starting. Another disadvantage of single-phase systems is that space is used inefficiently in the construction of generators and motors.

The purpose of this chapter is to describe how these disadvantages are overcome with polyphase systems. The three-phase system is by far the most prevalent. Therefore, the treatment is confined almost exclusively to the three-phase case.

A precautionary word is in order in regard to the use of the term "phase," a much overworked term in electrical writing. It is used in this chapter in an entirely different sense from previously. Formerly it was used in specifying values of the time angle and in the expression "phase difference" as a measure of the separation of two waves. In this chapter it is used in a new meaning, both as an adjective and as a noun. This multiple usage of a single term is unfortunate, but the two meanings are so widely different as to minimize confusion.

**13-2. Power Flow.** A single-phase system is adequately described by Fig. 13-1. Power flow in such a system is discussed in Chap. 7. It is

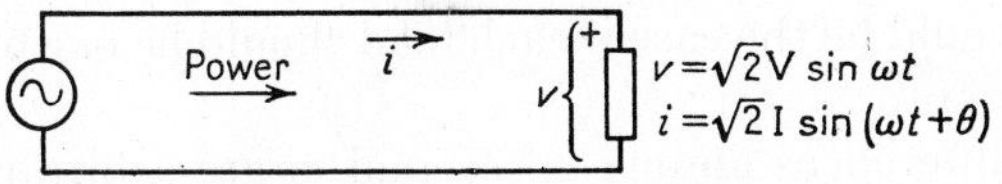

FIG. 13-1. Essential elements of a single-phase system.

found that the instantaneous power, for the reference direction indicated, is

$$p = VI \cos \theta - VI \cos (2\omega t + \theta) \qquad (13\text{-}1)$$

The above equation exhibits two terms, a constant component, and a sinusoidal component of twice the frequency of the potential and current waves. The combination of the two can be symbolically represented by the diagram of Fig. 13-2. The vertical line to the center of the circle represents the constant component, and the rotating line generates the double-frequency sinusoid. Its angular velocity is $2\omega$. The arrow on the right is a graphic representation of the instantaneous value.

Now consider the combination of three such systems, as illustrated in Fig. 13-3. The rotors of the three machines are attached to the same shaft, so that there are fixed phase differences among their potentials. Also, the loads are to be considered as a unit, such that the power received is the sum of the power received in each individual load impedance. In

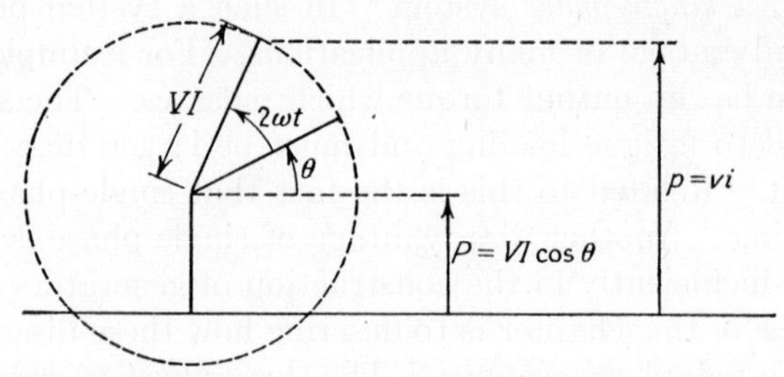


FIG. 13-2. Diagram representing instantaneous power in a single-phase system.

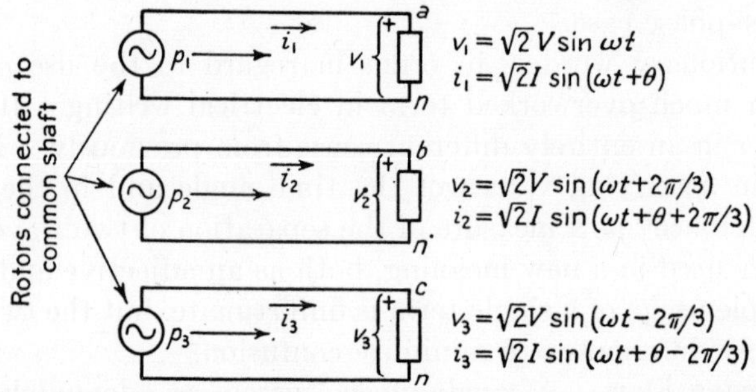


FIG. 13-3. Combination of three single-phase systems to form a six-wire three-phase system. All loads are identical.

practice, this would be the case if each load should be one of three separate windings on a motor.

The phase differences among $v_1$, $v_2$, and $v_3$ are arbitrarily set at 120°. The same is true of the currents. In similarity with Eq. (13-1), three power expressions are

$$\begin{aligned} p_1 &= VI \cos \theta - VI \cos (2\omega t + \theta) \\ p_2 &= VI \cos \theta - VI \cos \left(2\omega t + \theta + \frac{4\pi}{3}\right) \\ p_3 &= VI \cos \theta - VI \cos \left(2\omega t + \theta - \frac{4\pi}{3}\right) \end{aligned} \tag{13-2}$$

The total power is

$$p = p_1 + p_2 + p_3 \tag{13-3}$$

This sum is represented by Fig. 13-4. Three rotating lines represent the varying parts. Owing to their uniform spacing, in the sum the individual variations of $p_1$, $p_2$, and $p_3$ cancel out leaving the total power as the constant value

$$p = 3VI \cos \theta \tag{13-4}$$

The same result could be attained by analytically combining Eqs. (13-2). It is observed that this result is dependent upon having equal effective values of potential and current in each system.

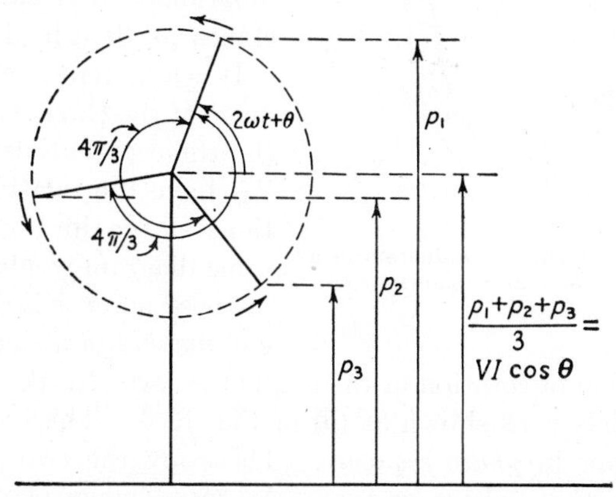


Fig. 13-4. Graphical combination of $p_1$, $p_2$, and $p_3$ as given in Eqs. (13-2).

The important observation is that the total power is a constant. The same situation can be attained with other numbers of individual systems. In all cases the phase difference among the potentials is adjusted so as to have the power rotating lines add up to zero as in Fig. 13.4. Three-phase systems have advantages over other systems when power transfer is the main consideration. Other numbers of phases are used in special cases, as when more than three are used in rectification. However, even in that case the additional phases are obtained from a three-phase system by suitable transformer connections. Two-phase systems have been used for power transmission, and are used in some servomechanism systems.

**13-3. Three-phase Generators.** The rotors of the three machines discussed in Sec. 13-2 are geared to the same shaft. It is possible to place two extra sets of windings on a single machine, to take the place of the second and third machines of the previous example. In rudimentary form such an arrangement is shown in Fig. 13-5. Each conductor is a symbol for a coil between the position of the conductor and a diametrically opposite slot (not shown) as in Fig. 2-3. The complete details are omitted to simplify the picture. Each of these windings is termed a *phase* of the machine.

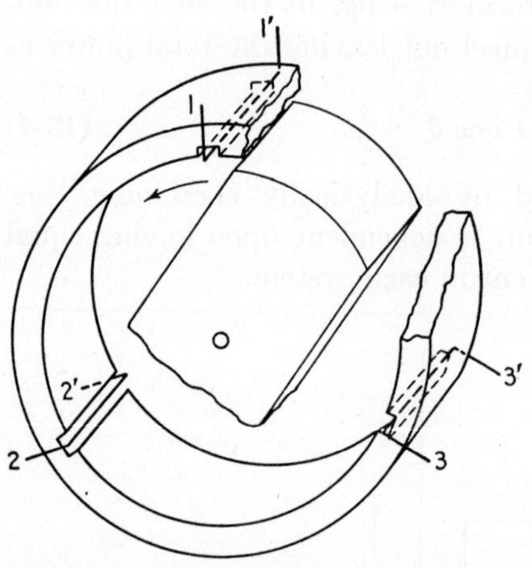


FIG. 13-5. Arrangement of conductors in a typical three-phase generator, showing position of one side of each coil.

The two additional phase windings do not appreciably increase the bulk of the machine because the space they occupy would be unused in a single-phase machine. For this reason a three-phase machine is preferable to the combination of three single-phase machines as described in Sec. 13-2.

It is apparent from the arrangement of the three conductors that the three potentials $\mathbf{V}_{11'}$, $\mathbf{V}_{22'}$, and $\mathbf{V}_{33'}$ have the relative phase positions shown in Fig. 13-6*a*. The same diagram would apply if each of these potentials were due to a coil instead of a single conductor.

If the direction of rotation of the magnet is reversed, the sinor diagram for the potentials is as shown at (*b*) of Fig. 13-6. The two diagrams of that figure differ in *phase sequence*. These are the two possible phase sequences in a three-phase system. An interchange of connections to

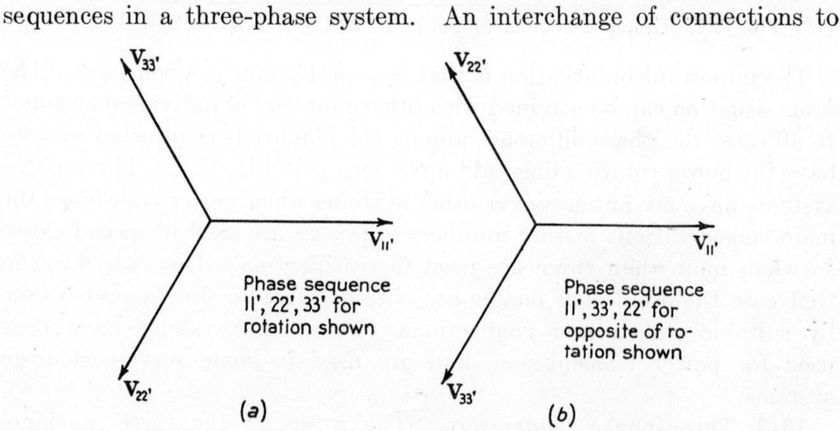


FIG. 13-6. Phase potentials for the generator of Fig. 13-5.

any two coils or a change in direction of rotation will reverse the phase sequence. Phase sequence must be known for the detailed solution of a three-phase problem.

**13-4. Three-phase Balanced Y-connected System.** *Four-wire System.* The system described in Sec. 13-3 is not practical because it requires six conductors. The three systems can be combined by making the bottom conductor common to all. The result is shown in Fig. 13-7, in a slightly rearranged form. The identifying letters *a*, *b*, *c*, and *n* are

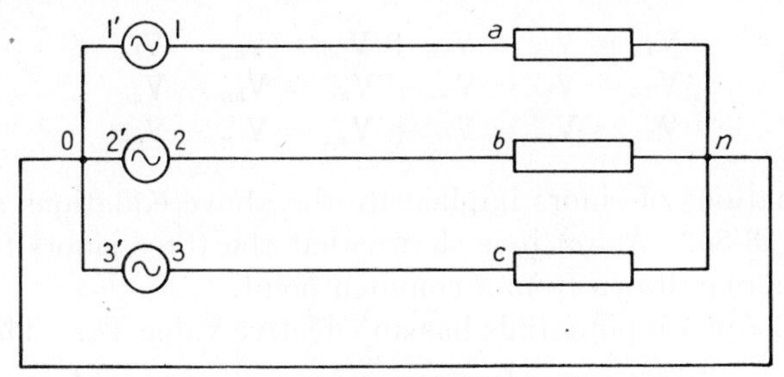


FIG. 13-7. A three-phase Y-Y four-wire system.

included on both diagrams to show how the transition is made. It is assumed that the individual impedances are identical and also that the individual sources of Fig. 13-3 are replaced, in Fig. 13-7, by the individual coils of Fig. 13-5. These are the conditions for a *balanced system.*

The conductors 1-*a*, 2-*b*, and 3-*c* are called *lines.* The conductor 0-*n* is called a neutral connection. The designation Y *connection* is used because

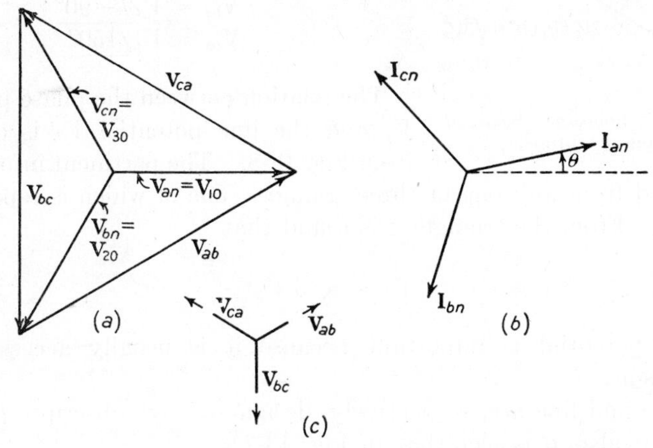


FIG. 13-8. Sinor diagrams for the system of Fig. 13-7.

the source and load diagrams are sometimes drawn with phases appearing in the form of a Y. The circles 1-1′, 2-2′, and 3-3′ are the *source phases,* and the rectangles *a*-*n*, *b*-*n*, and *c*-*n* are the *load phases.*

Sinor diagrams of potentials and currents are given in Fig. 13-8. The *phase potentials* $\mathbf{V}_{an}$, $\mathbf{V}_{bn}$, and $\mathbf{V}_{cn}$ are identical with Fig. 13-3. The current $\mathbf{I}_{an}$ is found from the potential $\mathbf{V}_{an}$ and the known characteristics of the branch connected between $a$ and $n$. Each of the other currents is determined similarly from a single potential and a single load branch.

Because the three phases are combined, three new potentials come into evidence. These are the *line potentials*

$$\begin{aligned} \mathbf{V}_{12} &= \mathbf{V}_{ab} = \mathbf{V}_{an} + \mathbf{V}_{nb} = \mathbf{V}_{an} - \mathbf{V}_{bn} \\ \mathbf{V}_{23} &= \mathbf{V}_{bc} = \mathbf{V}_{bn} + \mathbf{V}_{nc} = \mathbf{V}_{bn} - \mathbf{V}_{cn} \\ \mathbf{V}_{31} &= \mathbf{V}_{ca} = \mathbf{V}_{cn} + \mathbf{V}_{na} = \mathbf{V}_{cn} - \mathbf{V}_{an} \end{aligned} \tag{13-5}$$

The combinations of sinors implied by the above equations are carried out in Fig. 13-8*a*. At (*c*) it is shown that the three sinors for the line potentials can be drawn from a common point.

Each of the phase potentials has an effective value $V_p$. That is,

$$\begin{aligned} \mathbf{V}_{an} &= V_p\underline{/0} \\ \mathbf{V}_{bn} &= V_p\underline{/-120^\circ} \\ \mathbf{V}_{cn} &= V_p\underline{/120^\circ} \end{aligned} \tag{13-6}$$

Each of the potentials between lines has the same effective value $V_L$. The three line potentials are

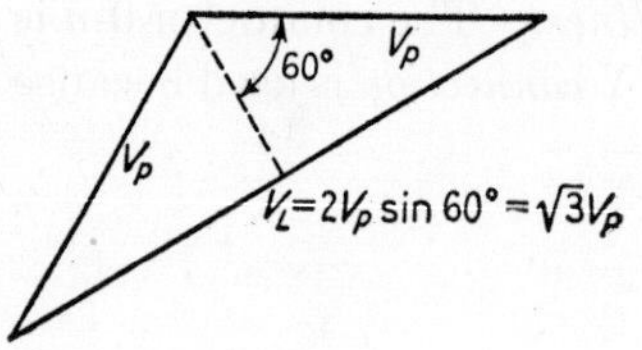

$$\begin{aligned} \mathbf{V}_{ab} &= V_L\underline{/30^\circ} \\ \mathbf{V}_{bc} &= V_L\underline{/-90^\circ} \\ \mathbf{V}_{ca} &= V_L\underline{/150^\circ} \end{aligned} \tag{13-7}$$



FIG. 13-9. Relation between phase and line potentials.

The relation between the phase potential $V_p$ and the line potential $V_L$ is obtained from Fig. 13-8. The pertinent information is obtained from any one of three triangles, one of which is repeated in Fig. 13-9. From the triangle it is found that

$$V_L = \sqrt{3}\, V_p \tag{13-8}$$

The line potential is important because it is usually accessible for measurement.

If phase and line are, respectively, designated by subscripts $P$ and $L$ for currents also, it is seen that in Fig. 13-7

$$I_P = I_L \tag{13-9}$$

*Three-wire System.* Continue to consider the system described in Fig. 13-7. The Kirchhoff current law for the junction $n$ is

$$\mathbf{I}_{n0} = \mathbf{I}_{an} + \mathbf{I}_{bn} + \mathbf{I}_{cn} \tag{13-10}$$

The above summation of sinors is obtainable from Fig. 13-8*b*. The result is zero. Since there is no current in the neutral connection between 0 and $n$, it may be removed with no effect on the potentials and currents. Therefore, the sinor diagrams of Fig. 13-8 are applicable to the circuit diagram of Fig. 13-10.

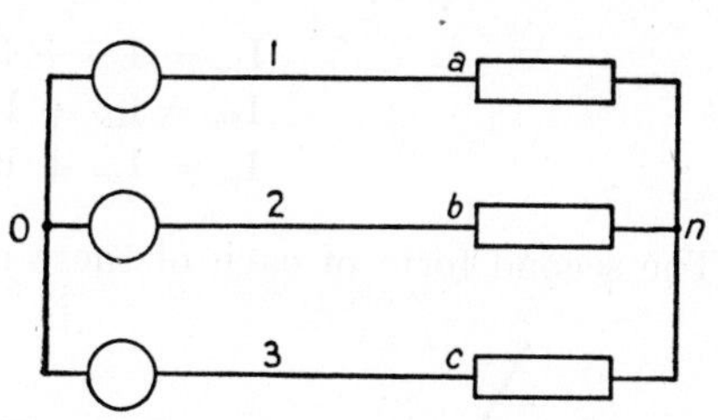


FIG. 13-10. Three-phase three-wire Y-Y system.

All the equations developed for the four-wire case apply to the three-wire case, because the sinor diagrams are identical. As will be pointed out later, when the load is not balanced, the two systems are no longer equivalent.

**13-5. Three-phase Balanced Δ-Δ System.** The three single-phase systems of Sec. 13-3 can be combined in a second way. One conductor serves as the top conductor of one system and the bottom conductor of the other. The result is the network shown in Fig. 13-11, where the sources are treated as potential sources. This puts the three source phases in series. However, owing to the 120° angle between all potentials, their sum is zero and this loop can be closed without having any circulating current.†

As in the previous cases, the coils of the source are called *source phases*, and the individual parts of the load are called *load phases*. The currents

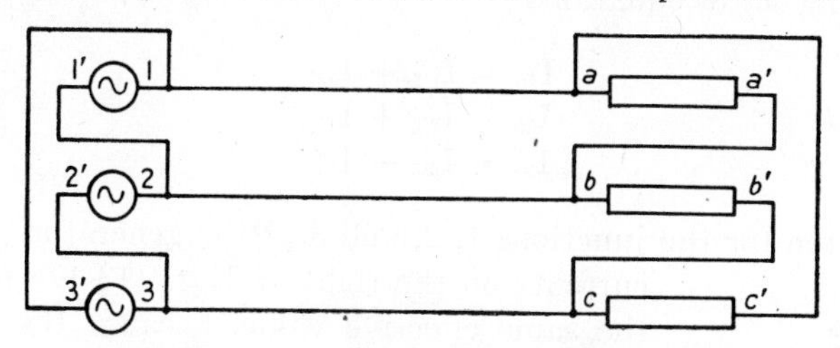


FIG. 13-11. A three-phase Δ-Δ connected system.

in the source phases are the source phase currents, and those in the load phases are called the load phase currents. The connections between source and load are called lines, as before.

Circuit diagrams using these connections are sometimes shown with the phases arranged in the form of a Δ. Hence, this is referred to as a Δ-Δ connection.

The three currents $\mathbf{I}_{aa'}$, $\mathbf{I}_{bb'}$, and $\mathbf{I}_{cc'}$ are obtained from the known source

† This is true only when the wave shape is sinusoidal. If the potentials of the sources have harmonics which are multiples of 3 (see Chap. 15), currents of these frequencies will flow in the closed loop.

potentials and the characteristics of the phases of the load. The line currents are obtained from the Kirchhoff current equations for the three junctions labeled $a$, $b$, and $c$. These equations are

$$\begin{aligned} \mathbf{I}_{1a} &= \mathbf{I}_{aa'} + \mathbf{I}_{c'c} = \mathbf{I}_{aa'} - \mathbf{I}_{cc'} \\ \mathbf{I}_{2b} &= \mathbf{I}_{bb'} + \mathbf{I}_{a'a} = \mathbf{I}_{bb'} - \mathbf{I}_{aa'} \\ \mathbf{I}_{3c} &= \mathbf{I}_{cc'} + \mathbf{I}_{b'b} = \mathbf{I}_{cc'} - \mathbf{I}_{bb'} \end{aligned} \tag{13-11}$$

The second form of each of these makes it clear that the constructions

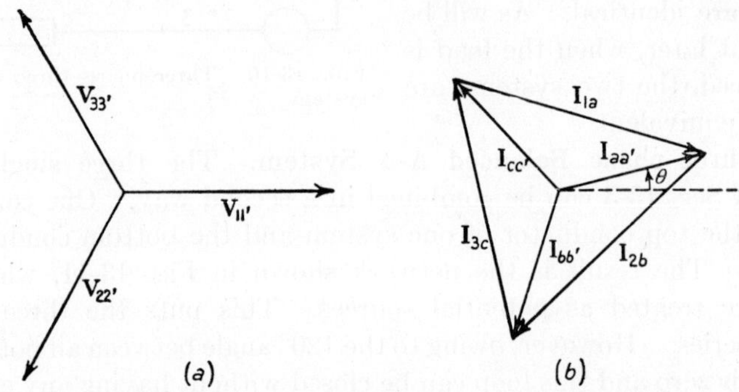


FIG. 13-12. Sinor diagrams for the system of Fig. 13-11.

indicated on sinor diagram ($b$) of Fig. 13-12 give the line currents. The corresponding set of equations

$$\begin{aligned} \mathbf{I}_{1a} &= \mathbf{I}_{1'1} + \mathbf{I}_{33'} \\ \mathbf{I}_{2b} &= \mathbf{I}_{2'2} + \mathbf{I}_{11'} \\ \mathbf{I}_{3c} &= \mathbf{I}_{3'3} + \mathbf{I}_{22'} \end{aligned} \tag{13-12}$$

can be written for the junctions 1, 2, and 3 at the generator. All three currents on the right of Eqs. (13-12) must have the same effective value, because the system is balanced. Figure 13-13 shows the arrangement of sinors meeting the required conditions. From a comparison with Fig. 13-12$b$ it follows that load and source currents are identical in corresponding phases of source and load. That is,

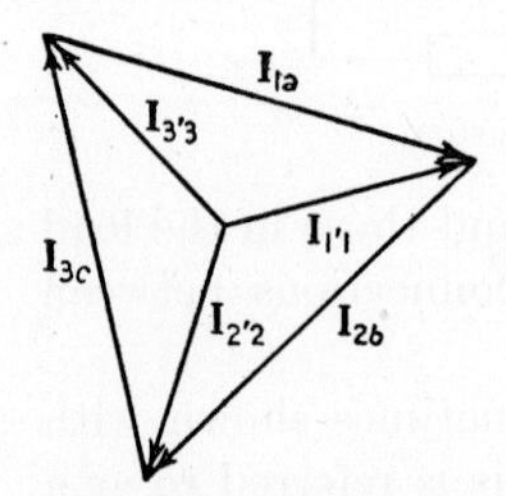


FIG. 13-13. Currents in the source of a balanced Δ-Δ three-phase system such as Fig. 13-11.

$$\begin{aligned} \mathbf{I}_{1'1} &= \mathbf{I}_{aa'} \\ \mathbf{I}_{2'2} &= \mathbf{I}_{bb'} \\ \mathbf{I}_{3'3} &= \mathbf{I}_{cc'} \end{aligned} \tag{13-13}$$

Each of the phase currents has an effective value $\mathbf{I}_p$, and each line current has an effective value $\mathbf{I}_L$. Thus, the three phase currents are

$$\begin{aligned} \mathbf{I}_{aa'} &= I_p/\underline{\theta} \\ \mathbf{I}_{bb'} &= I_p/\underline{\theta - 120°} \\ \mathbf{I}_{cc'} &= I_p/\underline{\theta + 120°} \end{aligned} \tag{13-14}$$

and the three line currents are

$$\begin{aligned} \mathbf{I}_{1a} &= I_L/\underline{\theta - 30°} \\ \mathbf{I}_{2b} &= I_L/\underline{\theta - 150°} \\ \mathbf{I}_{3c} &= I_L/\underline{\theta + 90°} \end{aligned} \tag{13-15}$$

Current relations in the Δ system are similar to the potential relations in the Y-Y system. The relation between $I_p$ and $I_L$ is obtained from a triangle similar to Fig. 13-9. It is

$$I_L = \sqrt{3}\, I_p \tag{13-16}$$

**13-6. Y-Δ and Δ-Y Systems.** The principles given for combining currents and potentials apply independently to each end of the network. It is therefore possible to use similar techniques when the load and source are connected differently.

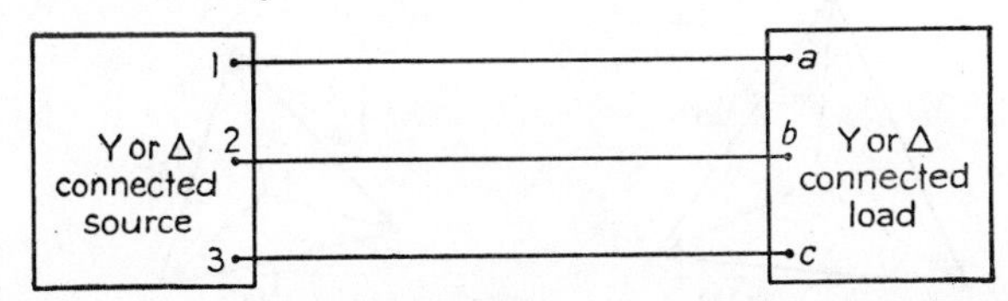


FIG. 13-14. Notation for the general balanced three-phase system.

The general situation is illustrated by the diagram of Fig. 13-14. The source and load have the same line potentials and the same line currents. Therefore, the sinor diagrams of these quantities are fundamental to the discussion. The sinor diagrams given at the top of Fig. 13-15 are general representations for the line potentials and currents. Alternate forms are given at the bottom of the figure. It is to be emphasized that the use of a single set of line potentials and currents does not mean that they will be the same for either Y or Δ connections. It means, rather, that in specific cases the actual potentials and currents can always be represented by these diagrams by suitable choice of positions and lengths.

If one end is Y-connected, the lower potential diagram is applicable because it puts phase potentials into evidence. Similarly, if one end is Δ-connected, the lower current diagram is used to put the phase currents into evidence. In each of the lower diagrams the phase quantities are indicated by the unlabeled dotted lines. Labels are omitted because a complete labeling which would be adequate for all cases would become cumbersome. When suitably labeled, these diagrams apply either to a source or to a load.

These diagrams serve only to summarize the possible relations among potentials and currents for the general balanced three-phase cases. In specific examples it is necessary to apply the given data in whatever way

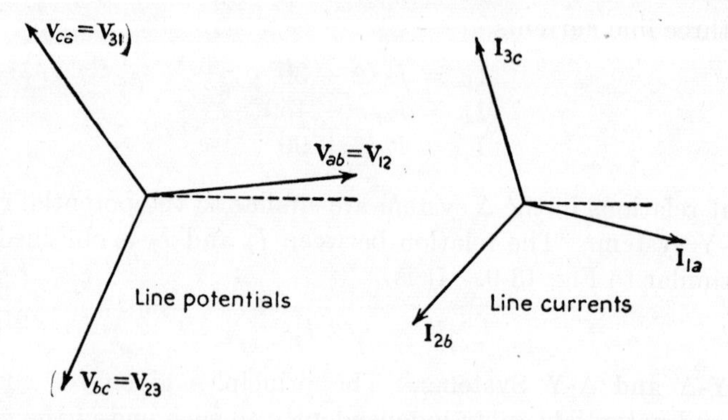


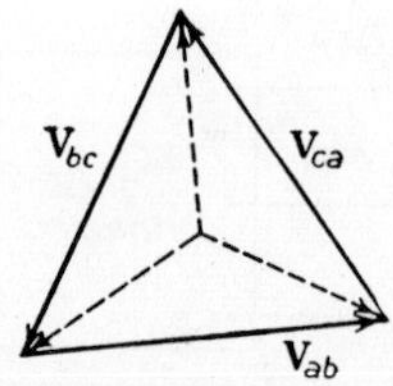


For Y-connection, phase potentials dotted

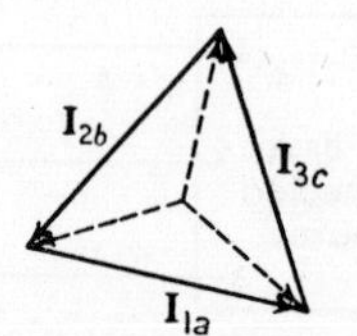


For Δ-connection, phase currents dotted

FIG. 13-15. Line and phase potentials and currents for balanced three-phase Y and Δ connections.

the situation demands. One general principle may be stated. The relationship between current and potential is always based on properties of the individual load phases. For example, if line potentials are given, the line current for a Y-connected load cannot be determined until the phase potentials are known. If the load is Δ-connected, the phase currents are first found and these are combined to give the line currents.

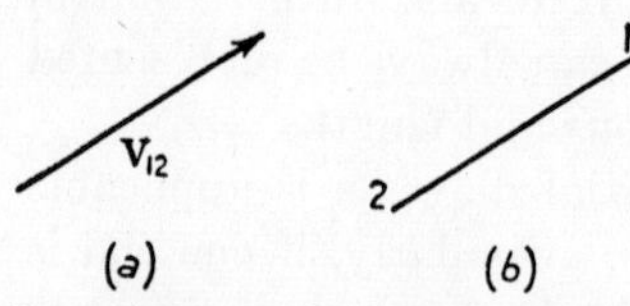


FIG. 13-16. Labeling of sinor for potential difference by placing symbols at the ends of the line.

**13-7. A Method of Labeling Sinor Diagrams.** In some instances the sinor diagrams for polyphase systems become so complex as to warrant a simplified method of labeling. If certain precautions are observed, it is possible to omit the arrowheads and labels from potential sinors, replacing them by symbols at the ends of the lines. Figure 13-16 is a case in point. The diagram shown at (*a*) is in the usual form. The same information is carried by the diagram at (*b*). The labels on diagram (*b*) are arrived at by referring to diagram (*a*) and placing the left-hand symbol of its subscript at the arrowhead end and the right-hand subscript at the tail end.† The (*b*) form represents either $\mathbf{V}_{12}$ or $\mathbf{V}_{21}$, whereas the (*a*) form represents only $\mathbf{V}_{12}$. When symbols are placed at the line ends, no other label or arrowhead is used.

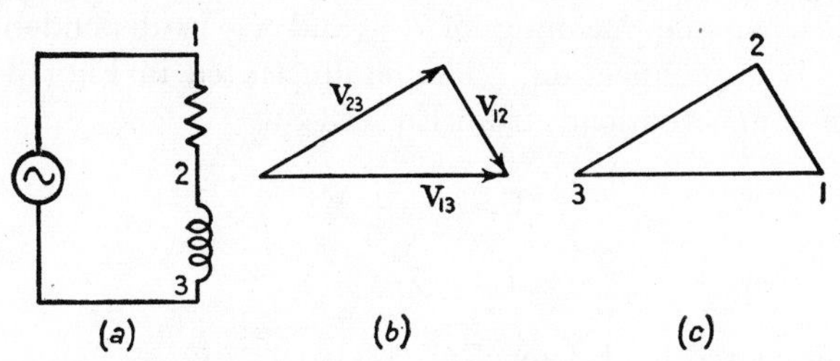


FIG. 13-17. Use of symbols at the ends of lines to simplify the labeling of a sinor diagram for potential differences.

An application of this system of notation is illustrated in Fig. 13-17. A circuit loop is shown at (*a*), and the conventional sinor diagram is shown at (*b*). By using the interpretation described above, the diagram in Fig. 13-17*c* is equivalent to the one at (*b*).

The diagram of Fig. 13-18*a* is equivalent to the diagram of Fig. 13-18*b*. However, when an attempt is made to replace the labels with numbers at the line ends, Fig. 13-18*b* results. It is not as simple as Fig. 13-17*c* because each apex acquires two designations. It is concluded that the new method is useful only when the order of placement is such that each apex requires a single symbol. Two conditions must be satisfied for this to be the case: adjacent sinors must represent potentials for adjacent branches, and they must be placed in such an order that the second subscript of one of them is the same as the first subscript of the one that precedes it.

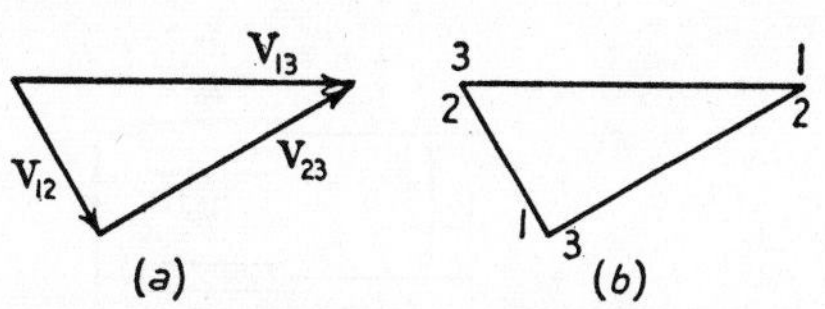


FIG. 13-18. Illustration of restrictions on the use of symbols at the line ends.

This method of labeling sinors does not apply to current sinors unless symbols are placed differently on circuit diagrams.

**13-8. Power in a Balanced System.** The power transmitted by a three-phase system is readily given in terms of the parameters of the system. Let each phase of the load be a branch having an angle $\theta$

† This rule is in agreement with frequent usage, but it is arbitrary. It would perhaps be more logical to reverse the order, so that subscripts would read from the tail to the head of the arrow.

between its potential and current. Thus, if Fig. 13-19 represents one phase, $\theta$ is the phase difference between $\mathbf{V}_{ab}$ and $\mathbf{I}_{ab}$. For either the Y or $\Delta$ connection the total average power going to the load is the sum of the powers going to the individual phases, *viz.*,

$$P = 3V_P I_P \cos\theta \tag{13-17}$$

FIG. 13-19. One phase of a three-phase balanced load, for the definition of power factor.

Although the formula is the same for either connection, the meaning of $V_P$ and $I_P$ is dependent upon the connection. This is illustrated in Fig. 13-20.

For the Y-connected load, from Eq. (13-8),

$$V_p = \frac{1}{\sqrt{3}} V_L \qquad I_P = I_L \tag{13-18}$$

For the $\Delta$-connected load, from Eq. (13-16),

$$V_P = V_L \qquad I_P = \frac{1}{\sqrt{3}} I_L \tag{13-19}$$

When either of these sets is substituted into Eq. (13-17), the result is

$$P = \sqrt{3}\, E_L I_L \cos\theta \tag{13-20}$$

The factor $\cos\theta$ is called the *power factor* of the three-phase load. It is important to note, however, that it is really the power factor of one of the

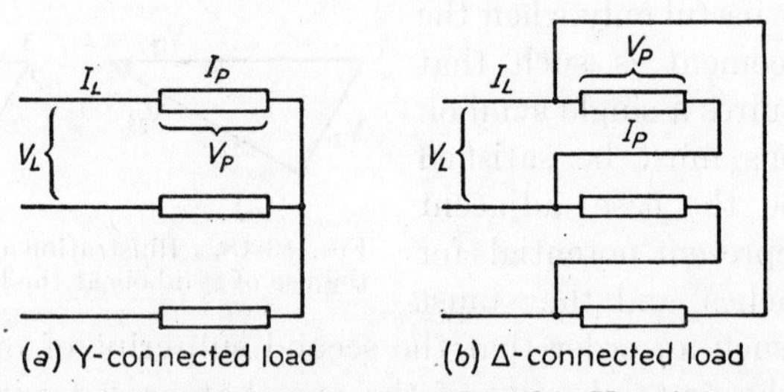


FIG. 13-20. General three-phase balanced load in Y or $\Delta$ connection.

phases of the *balanced load.* $\theta$ is not the angle between a line potential and a line current.

As in the single-phase case, if $|\theta|$ lies between $\pi/2$ and $\pi$, the algebraic power $P$ becomes negative. The device is then actually a power source.

**Example 13-1.** In a balanced three-phase system the source is Y-connected. The load is $\Delta$-connected, and each phase is a pure resistance of 160 ohms. Each line potential is 4,400 volts. Draw the sinor diagram for the system if $\mathbf{V}_{12} = 4{,}400 + j0$ and the phase sequence is $\mathbf{V}_{12}$, $\mathbf{V}_{23}$, $\mathbf{V}_{31}$. Show all line and phase currents and potentials. Also, find the power delivered by the source.

*Solution.* The diagram of source, line, and phase potentials is shown in the accompanying figure. The source phase potentials have the magnitude $4{,}400/\sqrt{3} = 2{,}540$ volts. From the known line potentials the load phase currents are found. Each has the magnitude $4{,}400/160 = 27.5$ amp. These phase currents are combined in accordance with Eqs.

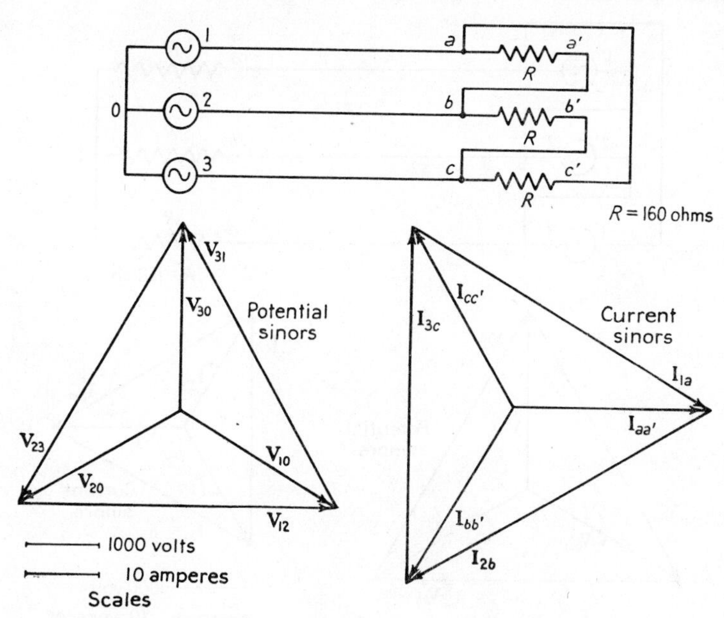


(13-11) to give the line current shown. The magnitude of each line current is $\sqrt{3}\,(27.5) = 47.6$ amp.

The power can be obtained from Eq. 13-20

$$P = \sqrt{3}\,(4{,}400)(47.6) = 362{,}000 \text{ watts}$$

It is instructive to consider the power delivered by each phase of the source. Note that for phase 1 the potential $\mathbf{V}_{10}$ and the current $\mathbf{I}_{1a}$ are in phase, indicating that source 1 operates at unity power factor. The same is true for all phases. If $P_1$ is the power with reference direction away from source, by Eq. 7-3 this power is

$$P_1 = V_{10}I_{01} = V_{10}I_{1a} = (2{,}540)(47.6) = 120{,}700 \text{ watts}$$

The total power is three times this because it is the same in each phase This checks the above result.

**Example 13-2.** A balanced three-phase system has a Δ-connected source, and the load is Y-connected. Each phase of the load is a resistance of 160 ohms. The line potential is 4,400 volts. Draw the sinor diagram for the system, choosing $\mathbf{V}_{12} = 4{,}400 + j0$ and the phase sequence $\mathbf{V}_{12}$, $\mathbf{V}_{23}$, and $\mathbf{V}_{31}$. Show all line currents and line and phase potentials for the load. Also, find the power delivered by the source.

*Solution.* The potential and current sinor diagrams are shown. The load phase potentials are obtained from the potential diagram, and from

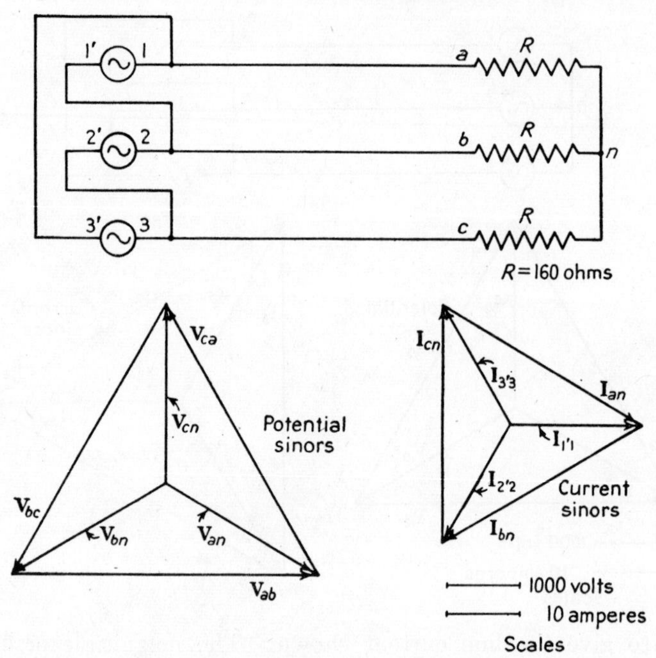


these the line currents can be obtained. The generator phase currents are determined as shown in the current sinor diagram.

The magnitude of the load phase potential is $4{,}400/\sqrt{3} = 2{,}540$ volts, and the magnitude of the line current is $2{,}540/160 = 15.9$ amp. The magnitude of the generator phase current is $15.9/\sqrt{3} = 9.17$ amp.

The power delivered can be obtained from $I^2R$ for each phase as

$$P = 3(15.9)^2(160) = 121 \text{ kw}$$

The same result would be obtained from Eq. 13-20. Source 1 has the potential $\mathbf{V}_{12} = \mathbf{V}_{11'}$, in phase with the current $\mathbf{I}_{1'1}$. Therefore it is an energy source operating at unity power factor. The power delivered by source 1 is

$$P_1 = V_{11'}I_{1'1} = (4{,}400)(9.17) = 40.3 \text{ kw}$$

Three times this value is in agreement with the power computed for the load.

**13-9. Equivalent Y and Δ Sources.** A knowledge of the nature of the source connections is not so important as may be implied by the earlier part of this chapter. In many cases problems dealing with loads are solvable without knowing what type of source connection is involved. The three-phase four-wire system is the only one for which the source connection is not arbitrary.

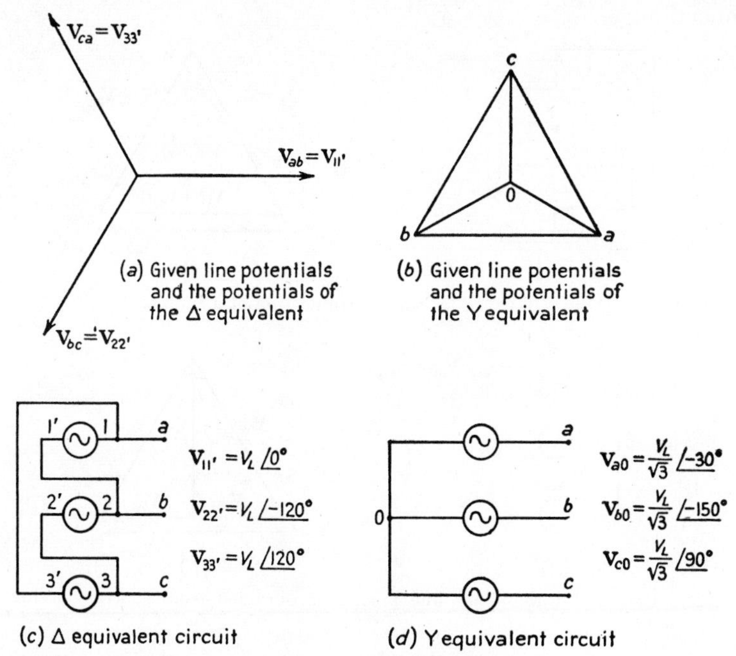


FIG. 13-21. Equivalent Δ and Y three-phase potential sources for a given set of line potentials.

The fact that the conditions at the load do not depend on the source connection suggests that either a Δ or a Y connection can be specified to give a prescribed set of line potentials. It then follows that a Δ connection can be the equivalent of a Y connection, as viewed from its terminals, or vice versa.

Two three-phase potential sources are defined as equivalent if their line potentials are identical. In Fig. 13-21*a* the balanced line potentials are assumed given. They are given in an alternate arrangement at (*b*). The diagram at (*a*) specifies the potential sources for the Δ connection, and the sinors within the triangle at (*b*) specify the potential sources for the Y connection.

Two other equivalent sources are of some importance. Suppose source $\mathbf{V}_{11'}$ is omitted from the $\Delta$ equivalent. The resulting circuit is shown at (*a*) of Fig. 13-22. The sinors for the remaining potential sources are shown at (*b*) of the figure. Kirchhoff's potential law for the circuit yields

$$\mathbf{V}_{ab} = -(\mathbf{V}_{22'} + \mathbf{V}_{33'}) \tag{13-21}$$

Therefore, $\mathbf{V}_{ab}$ is the same as if $\mathbf{V}_{11'}$ had been present. A similar conclusion follows if any one of the original sources should be omitted from the $\Delta$ connection.

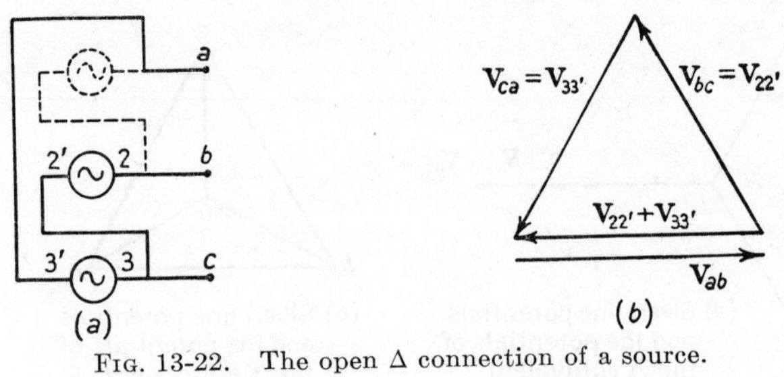


FIG. 13-22. The open $\Delta$ connection of a source.

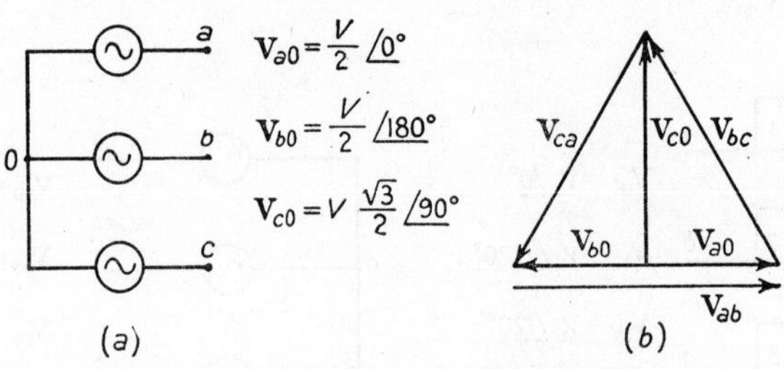


FIG. 13-23. Balanced three-phase line potentials obtained from sources having phase differences of 90°.

The connection of Fig. 13-22 is called an open $\Delta$, or V, connection. The arrangement is not efficient, for it wastes current capacity of the windings. However, it can be used to meet an emergency in the event of a failure of one phase of a three-phase $\Delta$ source.

The last equivalent source to be considered is obtained from potentials having phase differences of 90° and unequal magnitudes. The circuit is given in Fig. 13-23*a*. The sinor diagram of Fig. 13-23*b* shows that the line potentials form a balanced three-phase system.

The potentials $\mathbf{V}_{a0}$ and $\mathbf{V}_{b0}$ have a phase difference of 180°. This makes it possible to obtain them from a center-tapped transformer. It is then convenient to obtain the third potential source from a transformer also, as shown in Fig. 13-24*a*. If the primaries of the two transformers are supplied from a two-phase system (potentials differing in phase by 90°

and of equal effective values) as in Fig. 13-24*b*, the ratios of the two transformers must be different. Assuming ideal transformers, the sinors shown in Fig. 13-24*b* yield the set shown in Fig. 13-24*c*, which are also the ones shown in Fig. 13-23, where it is seen that they combine to give a

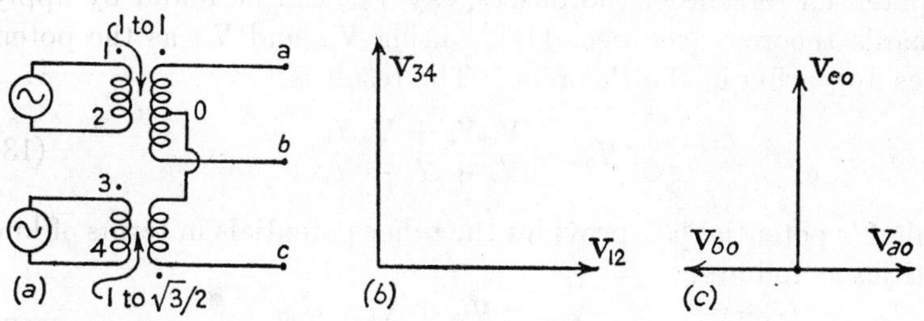


FIG. 13-24. The Scott connection for obtaining balanced three-phase line potentials from a balanced two-phase system.

balanced set of line potentials. The circuit of Fig. 13-24*a* is an arrangement for converting from a two-phase system to a three-phase system. It is called a Scott connection.

**13-10. Unbalanced Systems.** An unbalanced system is understood to be one in which the individual phases of the load are not all identical. The line potentials at the source may or may not be balanced. Usually they are kept nearly balanced at the source by potential-regulating devices. For this discussion the source line potentials are assumed to be balanced, and attention is concentrated on the unbalanced load. Three cases are considered: the four-wire Y, three-wire Y, and the Δ connection.

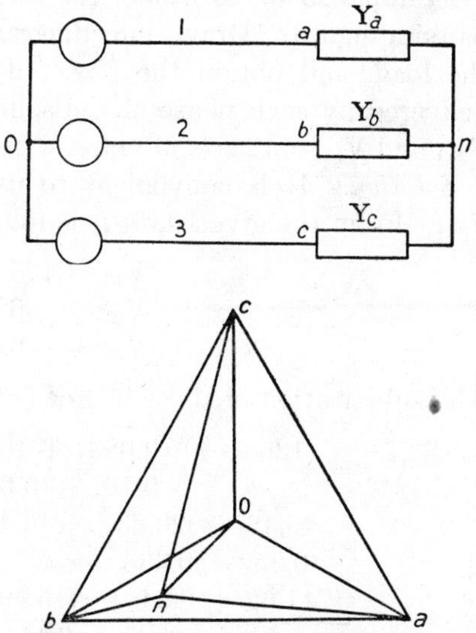


FIG. 13-25. Analysis of an unbalanced three-wire Y-Y system, including a sinor diagram of potentials labeled in accordance with Sec. 13-7.

*The Unbalanced Four-wire Y-connected Load.* The diagram of Fig. 13-7 applies to this case if each rectangle represents a different impedance. Because of the neutral connection each phase of the load is across one phase of the source. Accordingly, each load phase current can be found independently of the others. The current in the neutral is then obtained from Kirchhoff's current law at point *n*.

*The Unbalanced Three-wire Y-connected Load.* In the system of Fig. 13-25 it is assumed that the line potentials $\mathbf{V}_{ab}$, $\mathbf{V}_{bc}$, and $\mathbf{V}_{ca}$ are known. The solution consists of finding the phase potentials $\mathbf{V}_{an}$, $\mathbf{V}_{bn}$, and $\mathbf{V}_{cn}$, from which the currents can be found if the load impedances are known. The potential for one of the phases, say $\mathbf{V}_{an}$, can be found by applying Millman's theorem (see Sec. 11-12) using $\mathbf{V}_{ab}$ and $\mathbf{V}_{ac}$ as the potential sources appearing in the theorem. The result is

$$\mathbf{V}_{an} = \frac{\mathbf{V}_{ab}\mathbf{Y}_b + \mathbf{V}_{ac}\mathbf{Y}_c}{\mathbf{Y}_a + \mathbf{Y}_b + \mathbf{Y}_c} \tag{13-22}$$

Kirchhoff's potential law provides the other potentials in terms of known quantities as follows:

$$\begin{aligned} \mathbf{V}_{bn} &= \mathbf{V}_{ba} + \mathbf{V}_{an} \\ \mathbf{V}_{cn} &= \mathbf{V}_{ca} + \mathbf{V}_{an} \end{aligned} \tag{13-23}$$

It is interesting to note the properties of this system as they are exhibited on the sinor diagram of Fig. 13-25. The point $n$ does not necessarily lie within the triangle. When the load is balanced, points $n$ and 0 coincide because $\mathbf{V}_{0n}$ is then zero.

**Example 13-3.** Consider the three-phase system shown in the accompanying figure. Draw sinor diagrams for the potentials and currents at the load, and obtain the power delivered to the load and the power delivered by each phase of the source. The phase sequence is $\mathbf{V}_{12}$, $\mathbf{V}_{31}$, $\mathbf{V}_{23}$; and $\mathbf{V}_{12} = 125 + j0$ volts.

*Solution.* It is convenient to use Eq. (13-22) to find the potential $\mathbf{V}_{an}$. From the given data it is found that the line potentials are

$$\begin{aligned} \mathbf{V}_{12} &= 125 + j0 \\ \mathbf{V}_{23} &= -62.5 + j108.3 \\ \mathbf{V}_{31} &= -62.5 - j108.3 \end{aligned}$$

The substitution of these in Eq. (13-22) gives

$$\begin{aligned} \mathbf{V}_{an} &= \frac{(125 + j0)(0.083) + (62.5 + j108.3)(-j0.333)}{0.167 + 0.083 - j0.333} \\ &= \frac{46.48 - j20.83}{0.25 - j0.333} = \frac{(46.48 - j20.83)(0.25 + j0.333)}{(0.25)^2 + (0.333)^2} \\ &= \frac{11.62 + 6.94 + j(15.49 - 5.21)}{0.0625 + 0.1111} = 106.8 + j59.3 \text{ volts} \end{aligned}$$

From this the phase potentials of the load, in volts, are

$$\begin{aligned} \mathbf{V}_{an} &= 106.8 + j59.3 \text{ volts} \\ \mathbf{V}_{bn} &= \mathbf{V}_{ba} + \mathbf{V}_{an} = -125 + 106.8 + j59.3 = -18.2 + j59.3 \\ \mathbf{V}_{cn} &= \mathbf{V}_{ca} + \mathbf{V}_{an} = -62.5 - j108.3 + 106.8 + j59.3 = 44.3 - j49.0 \end{aligned}$$

The load phase currents, in amps, are

$$\mathbf{I}_{1a} = (106.8 + j59.3)(0.167) = 17.8 + j9.9 \text{ amp}$$
$$\mathbf{I}_{2b} = (-18.2 + j59.3)(0.083) = -1.5 + j4.80$$
$$\mathbf{I}_{3c} = (44.3 - j49.0)(-j0.333) = -16.3 - j14.7$$

As a check it is noted that $\mathbf{I}_{an} + \mathbf{I}_{bn} + \mathbf{I}_{cn} = 0$.

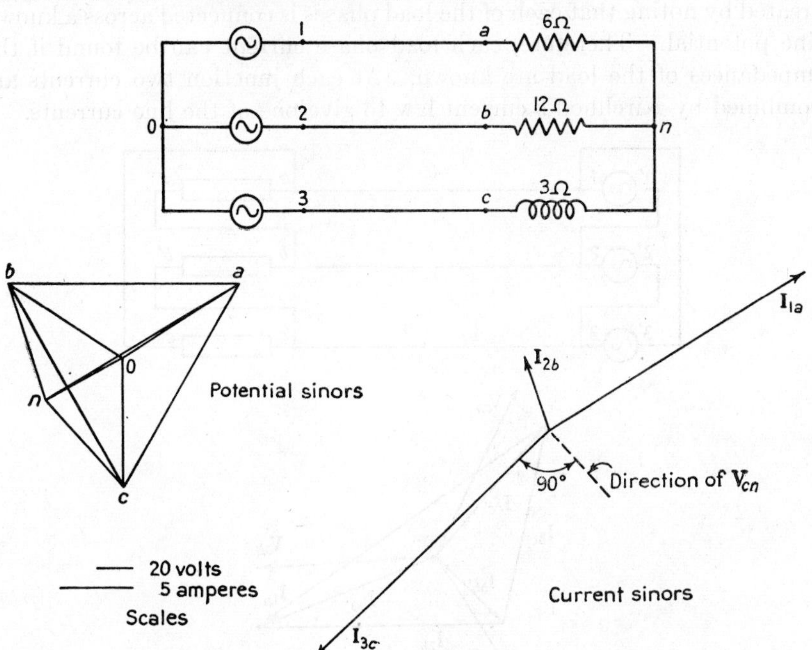


The power delivered to the load is the sum of the power into the two resistors, *viz.*:

$$\begin{aligned} P &= [(17.8)^2 + (9.9)^2](6) + [(1.5)^2 + (4.80)^2](12) \\ &= (370 + 98.0)(6) + (2.25 + 23.5)(12) \\ &= 2{,}490 + 308 = 2{,}798 \text{ watts} \end{aligned}$$

The power delivered by the individual sources can be found as follows:

$$\begin{aligned} P_{S1} = \text{Re}\,(\mathbf{V}_{10}\mathbf{I}_{1a}{}^*) &= \text{Re}\,[(62.5 + j36.1)(17.8 - j9.9)] \\ &= (62.5)(17.8) + (36.1)(9.9) \\ &= 1{,}111 + 357 = 1{,}468 \text{ watts} \\ P_{S2} = \text{Re}\,(\mathbf{V}_{20}\mathbf{I}_{2b}{}^*) &= \text{Re}\,[(-62.5 + j36.1)(-1.5 - j4.85)] \\ &= (-62.5)(-1.5) + (36.1)(4.85) \\ &= 94 + 175 = 269 \text{ watts} \\ P_{S3} = \text{Re}\,(\mathbf{V}_{30}\mathbf{I}_{3c}{}^*) &= \text{Re}\,[(-j72.7)(-16.3 + j14.7)] \\ &= (72.2)(14.7) = 1{,}061 \text{ watts} \end{aligned}$$

The sum of these is 2,798 watts, in agreement with the previous value obtained from a consideration of the load. Note that there is no correspondence between the powers in individual phases for the source and the load. Only the totals are the same.

*Unbalanced Δ-connected Load.* The Δ-connected unbalanced load is treated by noting that each of the load phases is connected across a known line potential. Therefore, each load phase current can be found if the impedances of the load are known. At each junction two currents are combined by Kirchhoff's current law to give one of the line currents.

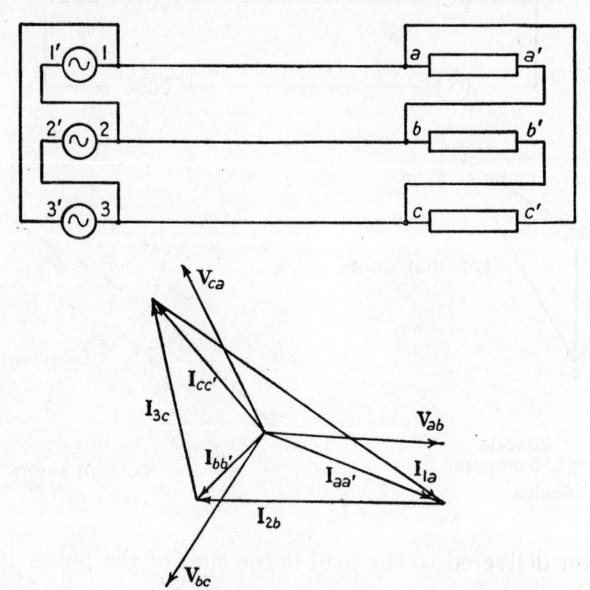


FIG. 13-26. Analysis of an unbalanced Δ-connected load.

A typical sinor diagram is shown in Fig. 13-26. The phase currents are

$$
\begin{aligned}
\mathbf{I}_{aa'} &= \frac{\mathbf{V}_{ab}}{\mathbf{Z}_{aa'}} \\
\mathbf{I}_{bb'} &= \frac{\mathbf{V}_{bc}}{\mathbf{Z}_{bb'}} \\
\mathbf{I}_{cc'} &= \frac{\mathbf{V}_{ca}}{\mathbf{Z}_{cc'}}
\end{aligned}
\tag{13-24}
$$

and they are combined in accordance with the equations

$$
\begin{aligned}
\mathbf{I}_{1a} &= \mathbf{I}_{aa'} - \mathbf{I}_{cc'} \\
\mathbf{I}_{2b} &= \mathbf{I}_{bb'} - \mathbf{I}_{aa'} \\
\mathbf{I}_{3c} &= \mathbf{I}_{cc'} - \mathbf{I}_{bb'}
\end{aligned}
\tag{13-25}
$$

**Example 13-4.** Consider the unbalanced three-phase system shown in the accompanying figure. The source potentials are obtained from a balanced source, and the loads are as specified in the diagram. Draw sinor diagrams showing the load phase and line currents and the line potentials and source phase potentials. The line potentials are balanced, and each is 125 volts. Take $\mathbf{V}_{ab} = 125 + j0$ and a phase sequence $\mathbf{V}_{ab}$, $\mathbf{V}_{ca}$, $\mathbf{V}_{bc}$. Find the power taken by the load and the power delivered by the source.

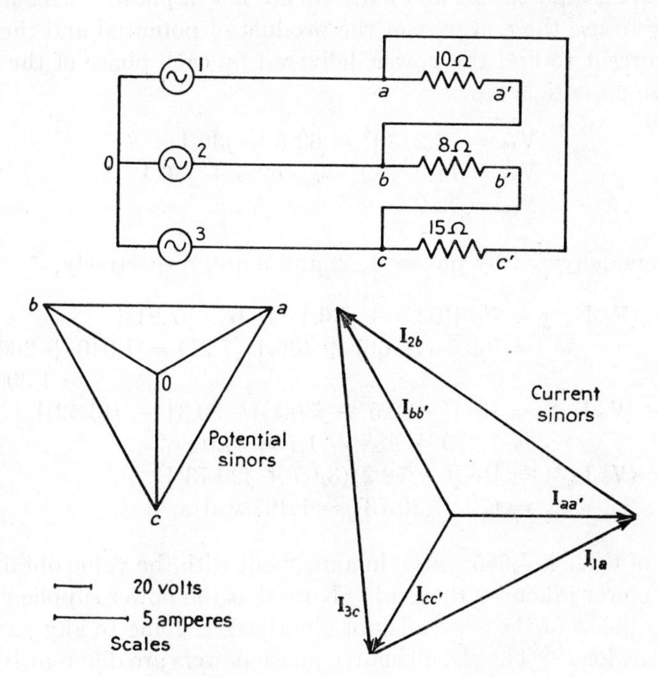


*Solution.* The potential sinor diagram can be constructed from the given data. The load-phase and line-current sinors can then be constructed. The phase currents are symbolically represented, in amp, by

$$\mathbf{I}_{aa'} = 12.50\underline{/0°} = 12.5 + j0$$
$$\mathbf{I}_{bb'} = 15.62\underline{/120°} = -7.81 + j13.52$$
$$\mathbf{I}_{cc'} = 8.33\underline{/-120°} = -4.16 - j7.21$$

The line currents are

$$\mathbf{I}_{1a} = \mathbf{I}_{aa'} + \mathbf{I}_{c'c} = 12.50 + 4.16 + j7.21 = 16.66 + j7.21$$
$$\mathbf{I}_{2b} = \mathbf{I}_{bb'} + \mathbf{I}_{a'a} = -7.81 + j13.52 - 12.50 = -20.31 + j13.52;$$
$$\mathbf{I}_{3c} = \mathbf{I}_{cc'} + \mathbf{I}_{b'b} = -4.16 - j7.21 + 7.81 - j13.52 = 3.65 - j20.73;$$

The powers in the load phases are

$$P_{L1} = (125)(12.5) = 1{,}562 \text{ watts}$$
$$P_{L2} = (125)(15.62) = 1{,}952 \text{ watts}$$
$$P_{L3} = (125)(8.33) = 1{,}041 \text{ watts}$$

The total power is 4,555 watts.

Note that in this case, although the load consists of pure resistance, the generator phase potentials and currents are not in phase. This makes it necessary to use the real part of the product of potential and the conjugate of current to find the power delivered by each phase of the source. The phase potentials are

$$\mathbf{V}_{10} = 72.2\underline{/30^\circ} = 62.5 + j36.1$$
$$\mathbf{V}_{20} = 72.2\underline{/150^\circ} = -62.5 + j36.1$$
$$\mathbf{V}_{30} = 72.2\underline{/-90^\circ} = -j72.2$$

The powers delivered by phases 1, 2, and 3 are, respectively,

$$P_{S1} = \text{Re}\,(\mathbf{V}_{10}\mathbf{I}_{1a}^*) = \text{Re}\,[(62.5 + j36.1)(16.6 - j7.21)]$$
$$= (62.5)(16.66) + (36.1)(7.21) = 1{,}040 + 260$$
$$= 1{,}300 \text{ watts}$$
$$P_{S2} = \text{Re}\,(\mathbf{V}_{20}\mathbf{I}_{2b}^*) = \text{Re}\,[(-62.5 + j36.1)(-20.31 - j13.52)]$$
$$= 1{,}270 + 488 = 1{,}758 \text{ watts}$$
$$P_{S3} = \text{Re}\,(\mathbf{V}_{30}\mathbf{I}_{3c}^*) = \text{Re}\,[(-j72.2)(3.65 + j20.73)]$$
$$= (72.2)(20.73) = 1{,}497 \text{ watts}$$

The sum of these is 4,555 watts, in agreement with the value obtained for the total power taken by the load. Note that the power supplied by one particular phase of the source is not identified as going to any particular phase of the load. That is, all source phase powers are different from the load phase powers.

**13-11. Unbalanced Sources.** In Sec. 13-10 all discussions of unbalanced conditions are confined to the load, on the assumption that line potentials remain balanced at the source. If the source potentials are not balanced but are known, the same methods apply. However, when the source is not a true potential source, an unbalanced load will cause the line potentials to be unbalanced by an amount which depends on the load. Therefore, the network must be solved as a whole.

To do this, one would expect to replace each phase source by a potential-source equivalent or a current-source equivalent. The network could then be solved by one of the techniques of Chap. 11. The situation is not as simple as this, however, when the phase sources are all combined in a single machine, as in Fig. 13-5. All the windings share a common magnetic path which introduces magnetic coupling among them. This could be handled by introducing mutual inductances, as in Chap. 12, if it were not for the fact that the magnetic path includes a rotating member. Because of these complications it is necessary to use a special type of circuit analysis, the method of *symmetrical components*. A brief sketch of the method is given.

It is possible to resolve an unbalanced system of three-phase potentials or currents into the sum of three balanced systems, the symmetrical component systems. One component system has three potentials (or currents) which are equal and *in phase*, and the other two are balanced three-phase systems, one having the *same phase sequence* as the original system, and the other having the *opposite phase sequence*. These are called, respectively, the *zero-*, *positive-*, and *negative-sequence* systems.

The relationships between potentials and currents in the machine are handled by defining a set of sequence impedances (zero, positive, and negative) to correspond with the three sequence components of potentials and currents. The zero-sequence impedance has no effect on the positive- or negative-sequence potentials and currents, and so forth. This reduces the unbalanced case to the sum of three balanced systems. The positive- and negative-sequence impedances of any machine having a rotating member (generator or motor) are different. In this way the effect of the rotating system is taken into account.

The subject of symmetrical components treats the finding of the component systems to describe given unbalanced systems, the finding of unbalanced systems when component systems are given, the effect of various unbalanced impedance conditions on the component systems of potential and current, and methods of determining the sequence components of impedance for a rotating machine. It is particularly useful for analyzing the behavior of power conditions under abnormal conditions of an unbalanced short circuit (*i.e.*, not a three-phase short circuit). It is the purpose of this brief discussion to acquaint the reader with the problems arising in unbalanced systems and to make known the existence of a technique for solving them. The details of the method do not fall within the scope of this text, and so for further information the texts listed in the bibliography should be consulted.

**13-12. The Effect of Series Line Impedance.** In many practical situations there is an impedance between the generator and the load, due to the connecting transmission line. The simplest case to analyze is the Y-connected load. In the event a load is Δ-connected, it can be replaced by its Y equivalent (see Sec. 11-6) to make the following analysis applicable.

It is assumed that the line currents are found by an appropriate method. This may always be done by temporarily considering the line impedances as part of the load. The technique of Sec. 13-10, the unbalanced three-wire Y-connected load, can then be used to find each line current.

An unbalanced case is illustrated in Fig. 13-27. The line impedance consisting of a series connection of $R$ and $L$ is typical of short transmission lines. Longer lines involve capacitance between lines.

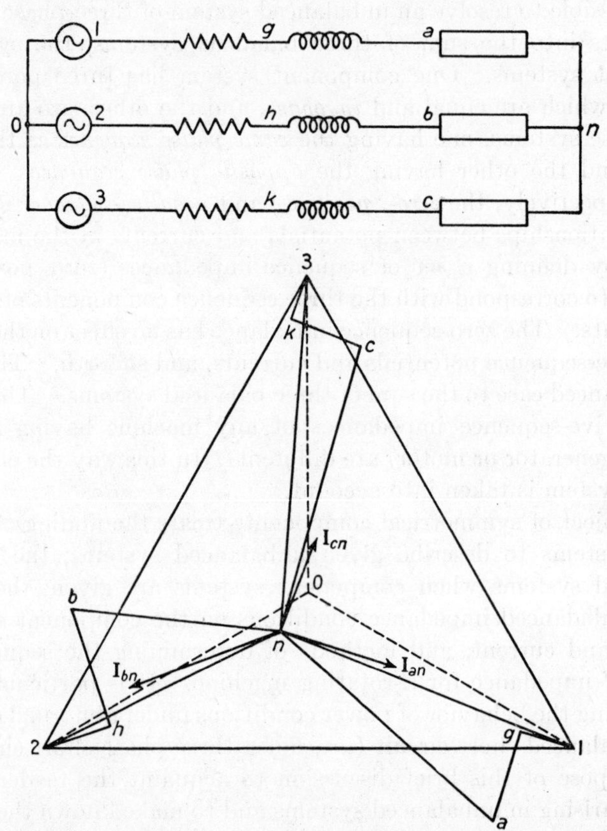


**Fig. 13-27.** Analysis of the Y-Y system with unbalanced load and series line impedances.

In the example of Fig. 13-27 all line impedances are the same. The unequal currents flowing in these impedances result in an unbalanced system of line potentials at the load. In the balanced case points 0 and $n$ would coincide, and potentials across the line impedances, the currents, and the load line potentials would become balanced. If that were the case, only one-third of the diagram would be needed. The constructions shown in the diagram are governed by the equations

$$\begin{aligned} \mathbf{V}_{1n} &= \mathbf{V}_{1g} + \mathbf{V}_{ga} + \mathbf{V}_{an} \\ \mathbf{V}_{2n} &= \mathbf{V}_{2h} + \mathbf{V}_{hb} + \mathbf{V}_{bn} \\ \mathbf{V}_{3n} &= \mathbf{V}_{3k} + \mathbf{V}_{kc} + \mathbf{V}_{cn} \end{aligned} \qquad (13\text{-}26)$$

**13-13. Measurement of Power by the Two-wattmeter Method.** In Sec. 13-8 power is shown to be the sum of the power delivered to all phases of the load. In a balanced system it is sufficient to measure the power in one phase and multiply by 3. However, loads are not always balanced, so a more general method must be considered. It is found that the sum of the indications of the two wattmeters of Fig. 13-28 is the total power

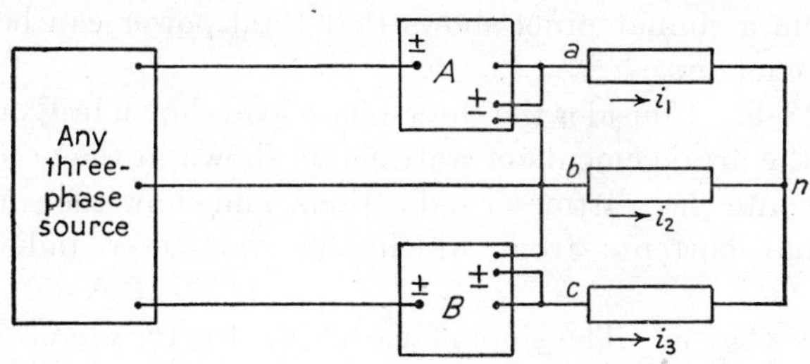


FIG. 13-28. Connections for the two-wattmeter method of measuring power.

delivered to any load, except for an unbalanced Y load with neutral connection.

Wattmeters $A$ and $B$ are connected so as to indicate the averages of the following instantaneous products:

$$\begin{aligned} p_A &= v_{ab} i_1 \quad \text{for wattmeter } A \\ p_B &= v_{cb} i_3 \quad \text{for wattmeter } B \end{aligned} \qquad (13\text{-}27)$$

From the circuit diagram it is found that

$$\begin{aligned} v_{ab} &= v_{an} - v_{bn} \\ v_{cb} &= v_{cn} - v_{bn} \\ i_2 &= -(i_1 + i_3) \end{aligned} \qquad (13\text{-}28)$$

The result of substituting these in Eqs. (13-27) is

$$\begin{aligned} p_A + p_B &= (v_{an} - v_{bn}) i_1 + (v_{cn} - v_{bn}) i_3 \\ &= v_{an} i_1 - v_{bn}(i_1 + i_3) + v_{cn} i_3 \\ &= v_{an} i_1 + v_{bn} i_2 + v_{cn} i_3 \end{aligned} \qquad (13\text{-}29)$$

Thus, it is proved that the sum of the indications of wattmeters $A$ and $B$ gives the total power delivered to the load. Three important observations are to be made.

1. The third equation of (13-28) would not be true if there were a fourth wire (neutral) carrying a current.

2. The proof does not require that potentials and currents should be sinusoids.

3. Although the average power delivered to each phase of the load is positive, it is possible for one of the wattmeters to give a negative indication.

The last statement is not self-evident, but it will be found to be true in subsequent discussions.

It would be possible to give a similar proof using a Δ-connected load. To do so Eqs. (13-28) are replaced by another set of three equations, two current equations and one potential equation. Also, in an $N$-phase $N$-wire system a similar proof shows that total power can be measured with $N$-1 wattmeters.

**Example 13-5.** Consider the three-phase load shown in Example 13–3. For each of the arrangements of wattmeters shown in the accompanying diagram compute the wattmeter indications, and show the sinors for the potentials and currents from which the wattmeter indications are computed.

*Solution for Case a.* The sinors for each wattmeter are obtained from Example 13–3. Numerically they are, in volts and amperes,

$$\mathbf{V}_{ab} = 125\underline{/0^\circ}$$
$$\mathbf{I}_{1a} = 17.8 + j9.9 = 20.4\underline{/29^\circ}$$

for wattmeter $A$ and

$$\mathbf{V}_{cb} = 125\underline{/-60^\circ}$$
$$\mathbf{I}_{3c} = -16.3 - j14.7 = 22.0\underline{/-138^\circ}$$

for wattmeter $B$. From these the wattmeter indications are

$$P_A = (125)(20.4) \cos 29^\circ = 2{,}225 \text{ watts}$$
$$P_B = (125)(22) \cos 78^\circ = 573 \text{ watts}$$

Note that the sum of these is 2,798, in agreement with the result obtained in Example 13–3.

*Solution for Case b.* For this case the pertinent sinors obtained from Example 13–3 are

$$\mathbf{V}_{ba} = 125\underline{/180^\circ}$$
$$\mathbf{I}_{2b} = -1.5 + j4.80 = 5.08\underline{/107.2^\circ}$$

for wattmeter $A$ and

$$\mathbf{V}_{ca} = 125\underline{/-120^\circ}$$
$$\mathbf{I}_{3c} = -16.3 - j14.7 = 22.0\underline{/-138^\circ}$$

for wattmeter $B$. The wattmeter indications are

$$P_A = (125)(5.08) \cos 72.8° = 188 \text{ watts}$$
$$P_B = (125)(22) \cos 18° = 2{,}610 \text{ watts}$$

Again the sum is 2,798 watts.

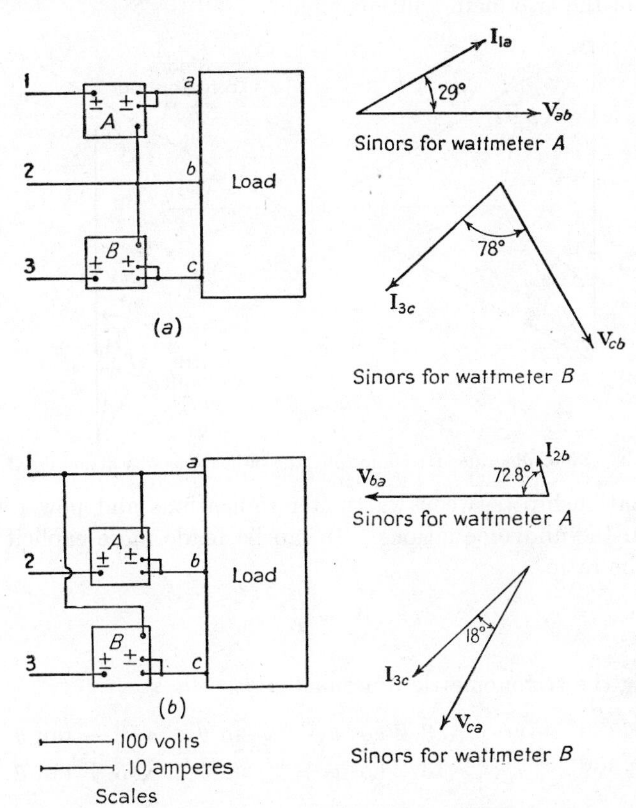


**13-14. Power Factor by the Two-wattmeter Method.** Power factor is not defined for the unbalanced three-phase load. Only the power factors of the individual phases can be specified. Therefore, there is no loss of generality in considering only balanced loads in the present discussion. It is also assumed that sinusoidal conditions prevail.

Let $V_p$ be the effective value of each phase potential and $I_L$ the effective value of each line current of Fig. 13-28. $\theta$ is the angle by which the current lags the potential of a phase, considering each phase as an algebraic load. Figure 13-29 shows a typical sinor diagram.

From the auxiliary diagram on the right it can be seen that the average powers indicated by wattmeters $A$ and $B$ are, respectively,

$$\begin{aligned} P_A &= \sqrt{3}\, V_P I_P \cos\,(30° + \theta) \\ P_B &= \sqrt{3}\, V_P I_P \cos\,(30° - \theta) \end{aligned} \tag{13-30}$$

The meters have equal indications only if the power factor is unity. When $\theta = 60°$, $P_A$ is zero and for larger values of $\theta$ the indication of $A$ is negative. If $\theta$ is itself negative, as when current leads the potential, the roles of the two meters interchange.

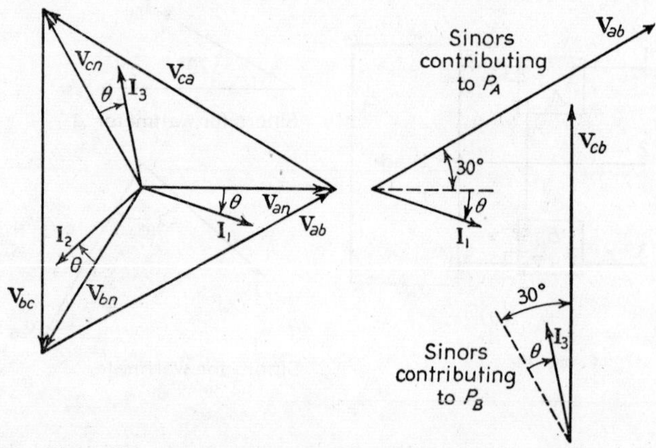


FIG. 13-29. Sinor diagrams for computing the indications of wattmeters $A$ and $B$.

The relationship between wattmeter indications and power factor is implicit in the above equations. It can be made more explicit by considering the ratio

$$W = \frac{P_A}{P_B} \tag{13-31}$$

Expanding the trigonometric functions gives

$$W = \frac{\cos\,(30° + \theta)}{\cos\,(30° - \theta)} = \frac{\sqrt{3}/2 \cos\theta - \frac{1}{2}\sin\theta}{\sqrt{3}/2 \cos\theta + \frac{1}{2}\sin\theta} = \frac{\sqrt{3} - \tan\theta}{\sqrt{3} + \tan\theta} \tag{13-32}$$

This can be solved for $\tan\theta$, giving

$$\tan\theta = \sqrt{3}\left(\frac{1 - W}{1 + W}\right) \tag{13-33}$$

This implies a relationship between power factor and $W$, because power factor is $\cos\theta$, which is related to $\tan\theta$. A plot of power factor as a function of $W$, obtained from Eq. (13-33), is given in Fig. 13-30.

As the problem was set up, this would not apply for negative values of $\theta$, because $W$ then becomes greater than unity. However, the same curve can be used by redefining $W$ as $P_B/P_A$ and bearing in mind that the angle has changed sign. Both cases are included by defining

$$W = \frac{P_{\text{small}}}{P_{\text{large}}} \tag{13-34}$$

When this is done, the curve has significance only for magnitude of power factor. The sign information is lost. This is no detriment, because the sign can be determined from a knowledge of which meter indicates the larger. It is possible to give rules for determining the sign of the angle, but there are two rules, depending on the phase sequence, so it is best to rely on the sinor diagram in specific cases.

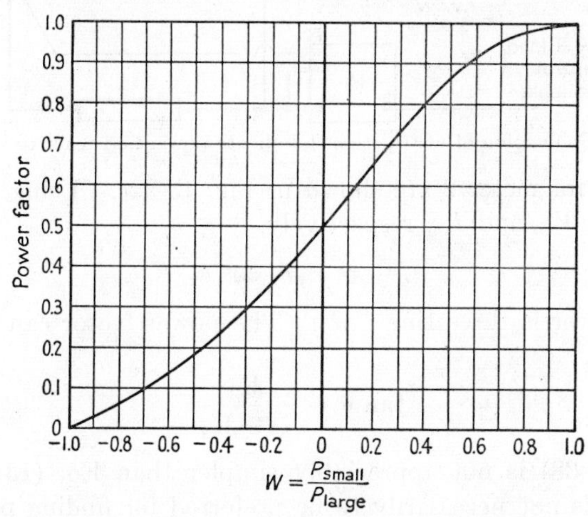


FIG. 13-30. Power factor as a function of ratio of wattmeter indications.

**13-15. Direct Measurement of Reactive Volt-amperes.** It has been shown that power and power factor can be found by the use of two wattmeters. Power is obtained directly, as the sum of two meter indications, and power factor is obtained either from Eq. (13-33) or from Fig. 13-30. The same information can be obtained by connecting two wattmeters in another way, so that one of them indicates power and the other indicates reactive volt-amperes. The connections are shown in Fig. 13-31, for a Y-connected load (omitting the dotted portion). We are assuming that the load is balanced.

The indication $M_1$ of meter 1 is determined by the sinors shown in Fig. 13-32*b*. It is

$$M_1 = V_{bc}I_{an} \cos (90° - \theta) = V_{bc}I_{an} \sin \theta \tag{13-35}$$

However, if $V_p$ and $I_p$ are phase magnitudes, the above becomes

$$M_1 = \sqrt{3}\, V_pI_p \sin \theta \tag{13-36}$$

which is $\sqrt{3}$ times the reactive volt-amperes of the phase.

It is important to note that Eq. (13-36) can be used only with a balanced load. This is not a serious restriction, however, because power factor and reactive volt-amperes are defined only for the balanced case.

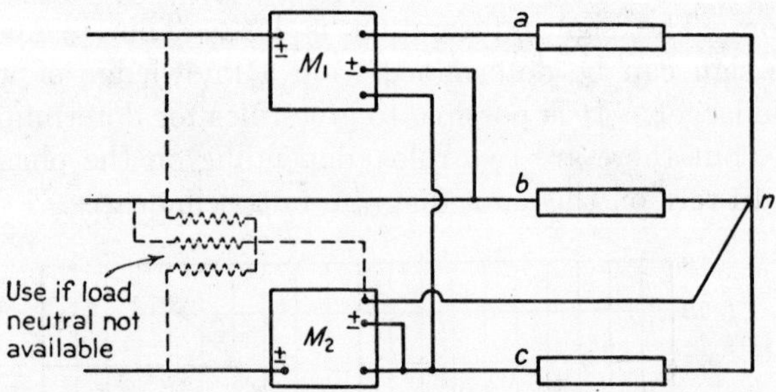


FIG. 13-31. Connection of wattmeters to indicate power and reactive volt-amperes.

The sinors for meter 2 are shown in Fig. 13-32*c*. Using the notation $V_p$ and $I_p$ for $V_{cn}$ and $I_{cn}$, respectively,

$$M_2 = V_pI_p \cos \theta. \tag{13-37}$$

The total power is three times $M_2$. The power factor can be obtained from

$$\tan \theta = \frac{M_1}{\sqrt{3}\, M_2} \tag{13-38}$$

Equation (13-38) is not appreciably simpler than Eq. (13-33), and so this method is not necessarily to be preferred for finding power factor.

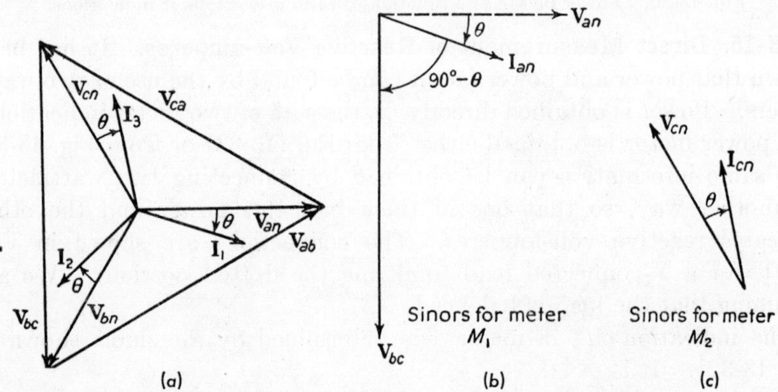


FIG. 13-32. Sinor diagrams for computing the indications of meters $M_1$ and $M_2$ of Fig. 13-31.

However, this method does have the advantage of a single meter indication which is directly proportional to reactive volt-amperes, a convenience in adjusting power systems.

If the neutral of the load is not available for connection or if the load is connected in delta, a substitute neutral can be obtained with three equal resistors. Such an arrangement is shown by the dotted portion of Fig. 13-31.

**13-16. Summary.** Polyphase systems are important because they eliminate pulsations in power flow that otherwise occur with alternating currents. They also utilize winding space more efficiently in motors and generators. The number of phases in a polyphase system can be any number greater than one. However, except for a few very special applications, three are universally used.

In the analysis of three-phase systems each portion of the generator which is called a phase is considered as a separate generator. These three generators can be interconnected in two different ways. The potential available in each phase is a function of the design of a generator and is a constant. The line potentials obtained from the two connections are related by the factor $\sqrt{3}$. Therefore, the type of connection to be used may be determined by the line potential desired.

As with the generators, three-phase loads are broken up into phases and can be connected in two different ways. When the load is balanced, the potential appearing across a phase impedance differs by the factor $\sqrt{3}$ for the two connections. It is higher for the $\Delta$ connection. Therefore, a set of impedances connected in $\Delta$ will take more power than a set connected in Y, when connected to the same lines.

An attempt is usually made to maintain a balance in three-phase systems. A motor is constructed with three identical windings and is therefore inherently balanced. Other loads, such as lighting, are not inherently balanced. At times, systems must operate with considerable unbalance. Another cause of unbalance occurs during periods of temporary disturbance. It is therefore necessary to be able to analyze unbalanced systems.

When a system is balanced, its power factor is the power factor of a phase, no matter whether the connection is Y or $\Delta$. If it is not balanced, power factor is not defined for the combined three-phase load.

For all loads, except the four-wire Y connection, power can be measured by two suitably connected wattmeters. The sum of the wattmeter indications is the total power regardless of wave shape or degree of balance. When the waves are sinusoidal and the load is balanced, the power factor can be determined from the ratio of the wattmeter indications.

## PROBLEMS

**13-1.** Prove that the total instantaneous power is a constant for a system like Fig. 13-3, in which there are two sources and two loads if the potentials across the two sources are separated by a phase difference of $\pi/2$ rad.

**13-2.** The three coils of a three-phase generator give the potentials

$$v_{11'} = 170 \sin \omega t \qquad \text{volts}$$
$$v_{22'} = 170 \sin \left(\omega t - \frac{2\pi}{3}\right) \qquad \text{volts}$$
$$v_{33'} = 170 \sin \left(\omega t + \frac{2\pi}{3}\right) \qquad \text{volts}$$

which may be considered to be potential sources. A three-phase load is made up by the interconnection of three impedances each of which is $\mathbf{Z}_p = 8 + j5$ ohms. The source phases and load phases are each connected in Y, as in Fig. P13-2.

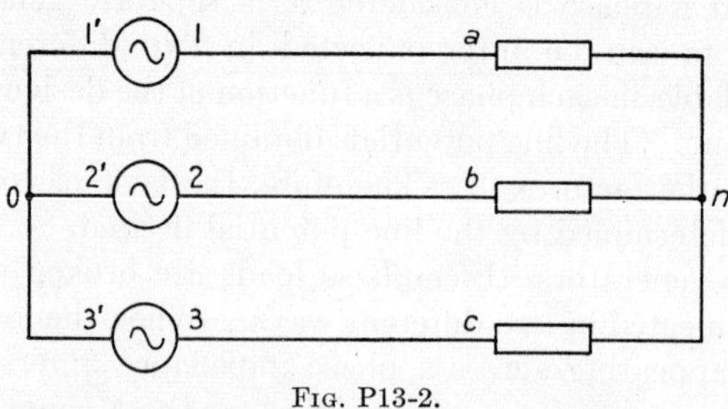


FIG. P13-2.

*a.* Specify the sinors for the load phase and line potentials and currents. Sketch sinor diagrams.

*b.* Determine the total average power delivered to the load.

**13-3.** The source and load phases specified in Prob. 13-2 are connected as shown in Fig. P13-3.

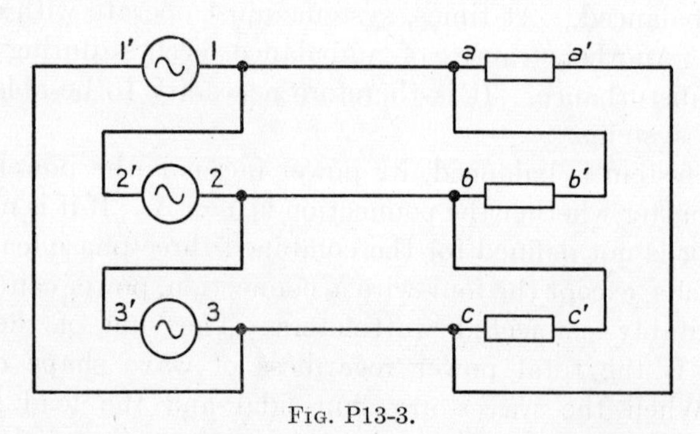


FIG. P13-3.

*a.* Specify the sinors for the load phase and line potentials and currents. Sketch sinor diagrams.

*b.* Determine the total average power delivered to the load.

**13-4.** The source and load phases specified in Prob. 13-2 are connected as shown in Fig. P13-4.

*a.* Specify the sinors for the load phase and line potentials and currents. Sketch sinor diagrams.

*b.* Determine the total average power delivered to the load.

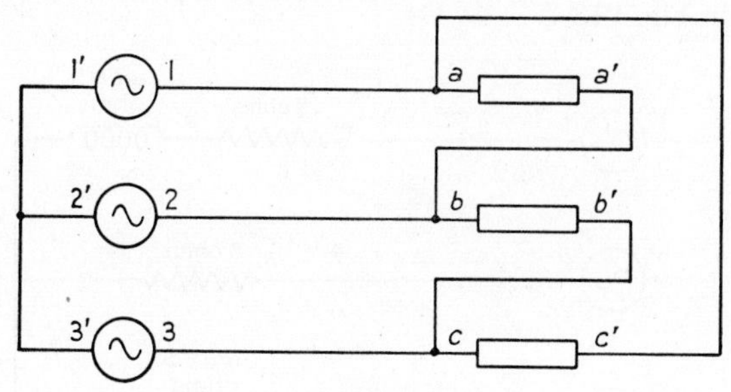


FIG. P13-4.

**13-5.** The source and load phases specified in 13-2 are connected as shown in Fig. P13-5.

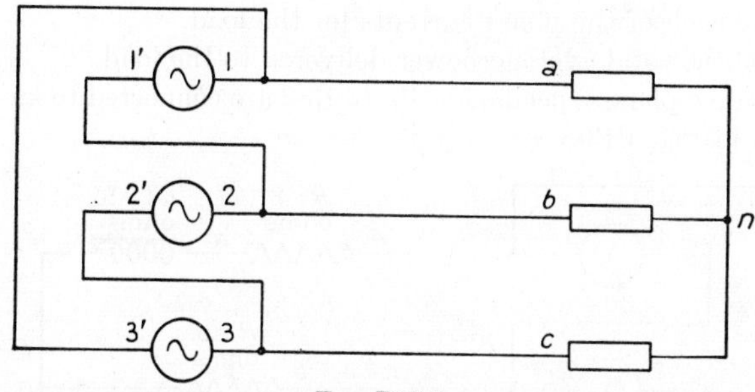


FIG. P13-5.

*a.* Specify and sketch the sinors for the load phase and line potentials and currents.

*b.* Determine the total average power delivered to the load.

**13-6.** In Fig. P13-6 the source phases are the ones specified in Prob. 13-2.

*a.* Determine the equivalent $\Delta$ source for the source shown at (*a*). Show the circuit and specify its parameters.

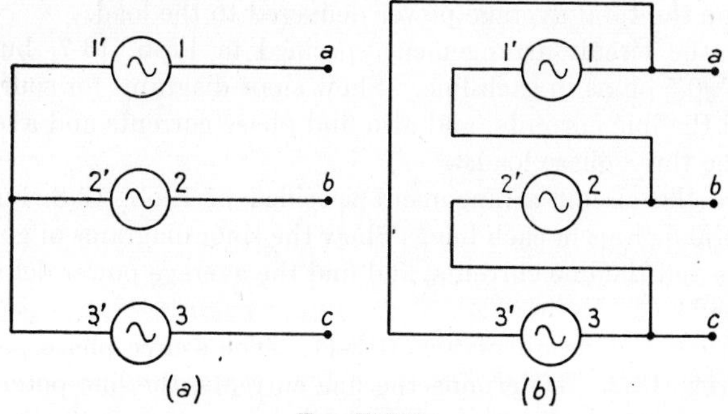


FIG. P13-6.

*b*. Determine the equivalent Y source for the source shown at (*b*). Show the circuit and specify its parameters.

**13-7.** The source phases specified in Prob. 13-2 are connected to an unbalanced load, as shown in Fig. P13-7.

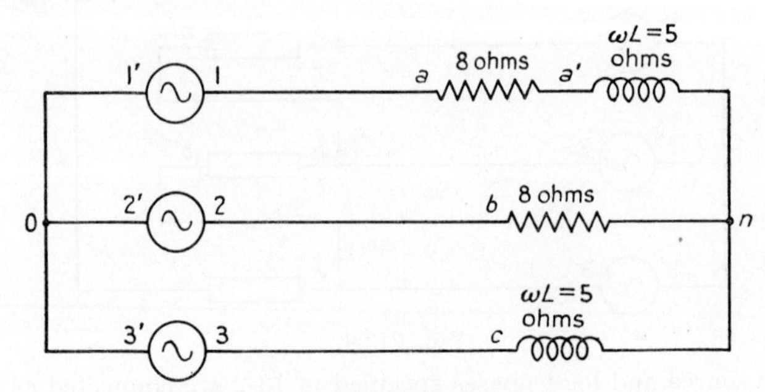


Fig. P13-7.

*a*. Determine each of the phase currents for the load.

*b*. Determine the total average power delivered to the load.

**13-8.** The source phases specified in Prob. 13-2 are connected to an unbalanced load, as shown in Fig. P13-8.

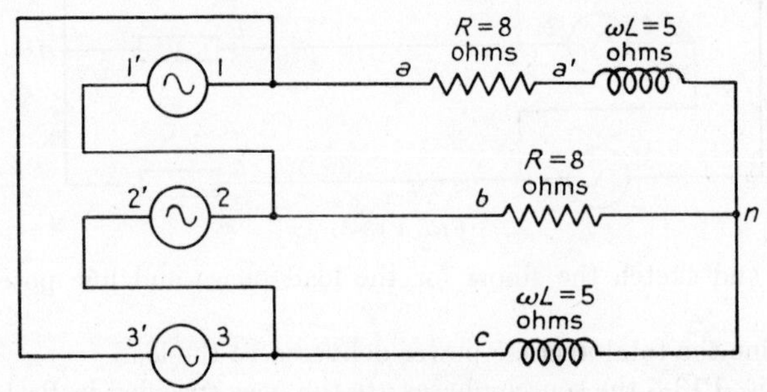


Fig. P13-8.

*a*. Determine the currents in each of the load phases.

*b*. Determine the total average power delivered to the load.

**13-9.** Solve the circuit arrangement specified in Prob. 13-7, but with line impedances of $j0.5$ ohms in each line. Show sinor diagrams for source and load potentials and the line currents, and also find phase currents and average power delivered to the three-phase load.

**13-10.** Solve the circuit arrangement specified in Prob. 13-8, but with line impedances of $j0.5$ ohms in each line. Show the sinor diagrams of generator and load potentials and the line currents, and find the average power delivered to the three-phase load.

**13-11.** Consider the circuit of Fig. P13-11. The source phase potentials are specified in Prob. 13-2. Determine the line currents, the line potentials at the load, and the power in each phase of the load.

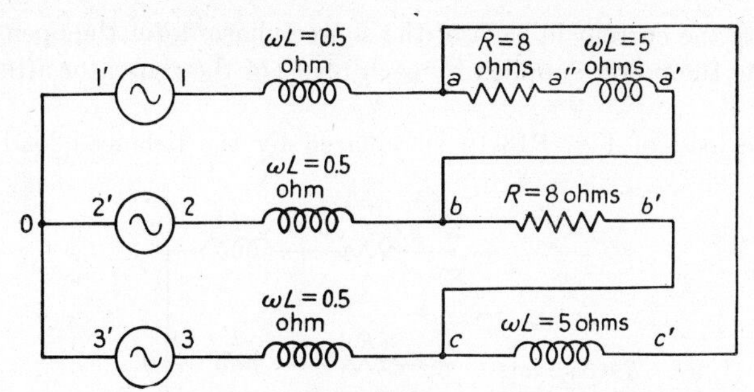


FIG. P13-11.

**13-12.** A pair of wattmeters is connected to indicate the average power delivered to the load specified in Prob. 13-2. Conventional wattmeter connections are used, as illustrated in Fig. 13-28. Find the following:

*a.* The indication of each wattmeter.

*b.* The power factor, from the ratio of the wattmeter indications.

**13-13.** Do Prob. 13-12, but assume the opposite phase sequence.

**13-14.** A pair of wattmeters is connected to indicate the power delivered to the load of Prob. 13-3. Conventional wattmeter connections are used, as illustrated in Fig. 13-28. Find:

*a.* The indication of each wattmeter.

*b.* The power factor, from the ratio of the two wattmeter indications.

**13-15.** A pair of wattmeters is connected to indicate the average power delivered to the load specified in Prob. 13-7. Conventional wattmeter connections are used, as illustrated in Fig. 13-28. Find the indication of each wattmeter and compare the sum of these indications with the total power in the phases.

**13-16.** A three-phase 15-kw generator is supplying full-load power to a balanced Y-connected resistance load. An open then occurs in one of the generator

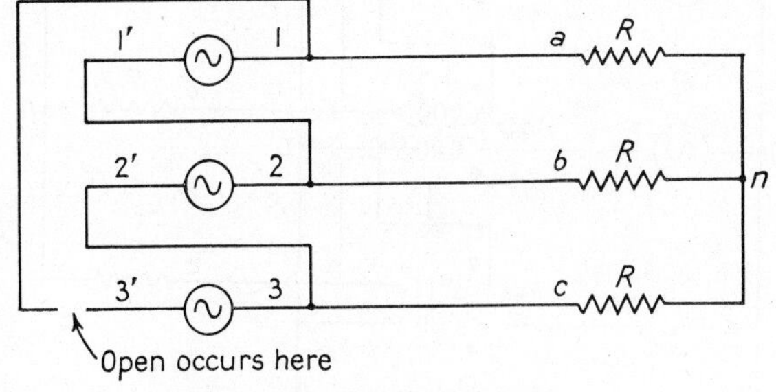


Line potential = 440 volts
Phase sequence : $\mathbf{V}_{11'}$ $\mathbf{V}_{22'}$ $\mathbf{V}_{33'}$

FIG. P13-16.

phases so that the circuit takes on the appearance of Fig. P13-16. Assume that the potentials of the two phases which remain are unchanged.

*a.* Compute the resistance of each of the load phases.

*b.* Compute the current in each of the source phases before the open occurs.

*c.* Compute the current in each of the source phases after the open occurs.

*d.* Compute the power supplied by each phase of the generator after the open occurs.

**13-17.** The load of Fig. P13-16 is replaced by the balanced load shown in Fig. P13-17.

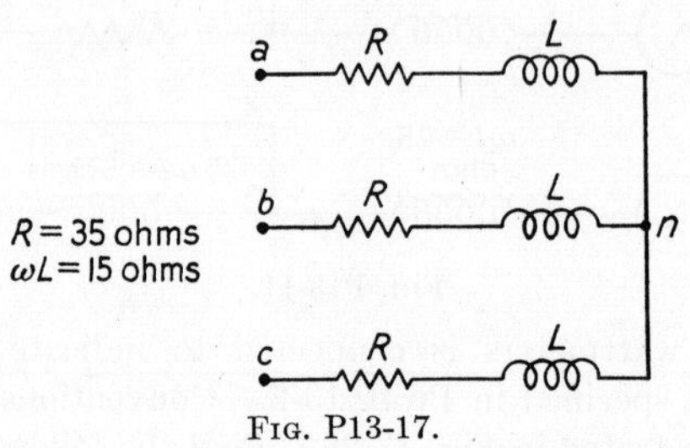


FIG. P13-17.

*a.* Compute the current in each phase of the source before the open occurs in phase 3 of the source.

*b.* Compute the current in each phase of the source after the open occurs in phase 3 of the source.

*c.* Compute the power supplied by each phase of the source, after the open occurs.

**13-18.** In Fig. P13-18 a bank of three transformers is connected between a three-phase potential source and a Y-connected load. The transformers are connected in Y on the source side and in Δ on the load side. Each transformer is to be regarded as an ideal transformer (see Sec. 12-6) with ratio such that the line potentials at the load are 220 volts and at the source are 2,200 volts.

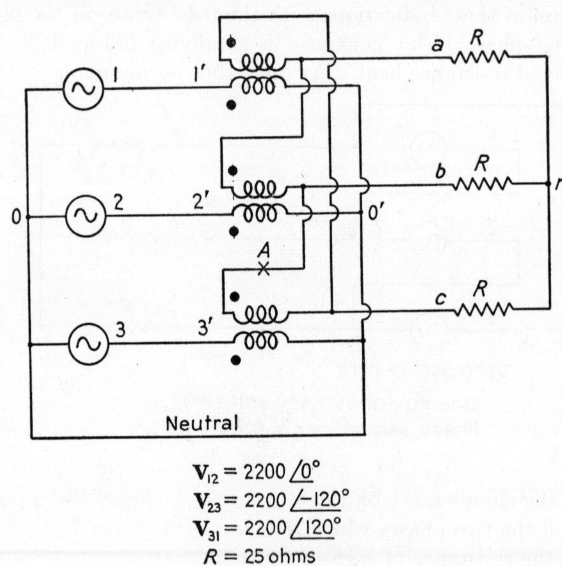


FIG. P13-18.

*a.* What is the turns ratio of the ideal transformers?

*b.* Find the currents $\mathbf{I}_{an}$, $\mathbf{I}_{bn}$, and $\mathbf{I}_{cn}$.

*c.* An open occurs at point $A$, making the transformers operate in open $\Delta$ on the load side. Find the currents asked for in part *a* and also the current $\mathbf{I}_{00'}$.

*d.* In addition to the open at point $A$, let the neutral connection be open. Find the currents asked for in part *a* and also the power delivered by each phase of the source in the load phases.

**13-19.** In the system of Fig. P13-18, instead of treating each transformer as ideal, let the self inductances of the high and low potential windings be $L_1$ and $L_2$ respectively, and let $k$ be the coupling coefficient. Prove that the ratio of the power transmitted under these conditions to the power transmitted with ideal transformers of the same turns ratio is given by the expression

$$\frac{9k^2R^2}{\omega^2L_2^2(1-k^2)+9R^2}$$

**13-20.** In Fig. P13-20 the circle on the right represents an induction motor, and each of the resistors $R$ connected in Y is 18 ohms. The inductors in the lines to

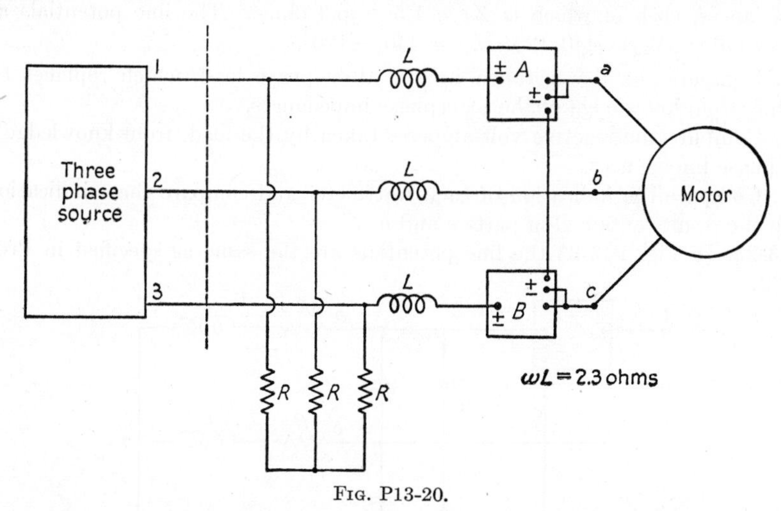


FIG. P13-20.

the induction motor represent line inductances. The power taken by the induction motor is measured by the two-wattmeter method with the results as follows:

$$P_A = 2{,}510 \text{ watts} \qquad P_B = 5{,}220 \text{ watts}$$

and the current in the lines to the motor is 25.1 amp. It is known that an induction motor is an inductive load.

*a.* Find the phase sequence of the system.

*b.* Compute the line potentials at the terminals of the source.

*c.* Compute the indications of the wattmeters if they should be moved to the position of the dotted line.

**13-21.** Fig. P13-21 shows a three-phase line for which the phase sequence is not known.

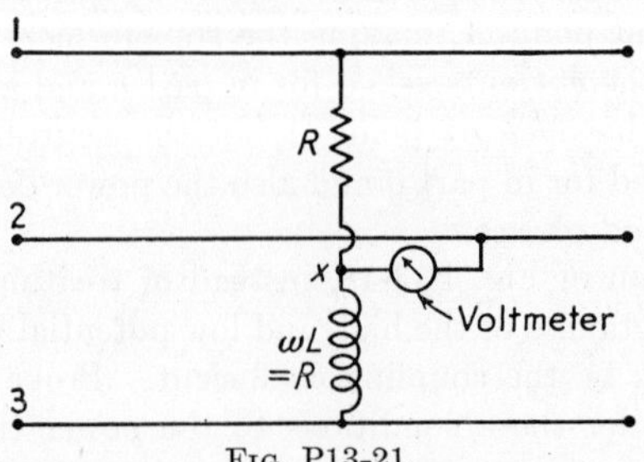


Fig. P13-21.

*a.* Obtain a literal expression for the potential $V_{2x}$ for each of the two possible phase sequences, in terms of the line potential $V_{12}$.

*b.* Repeat part *a* for the situation where the resistor and inductor are interchanged.

**13-22.** In Fig. P13-20 let the motor be replaced by a delta connection of impedances, each of which is $Z_T = 7.5 - j6.3$ ohms. The line potentials are $\mathbf{V}_{12} = 440\underline{/0°}$, $\mathbf{V}_{23} = 440\underline{/120°}$, $\mathbf{V}_{31} = 440\underline{/-120°}$.

*a.* Compute the power taken by the three-phase load, which replaces the motor, from knowledge of the load phase impedances.

*b.* Compute the reactive volt-amperes taken by the load, from knowledge of the phase impedances.

*c.* Compute the indication of each wattmeter and compare these indications with the results obtained in parts *a* and *b*.

**13-23.** In Fig. P13-23 the line potentials are the same as specified in Prob. 13-22.

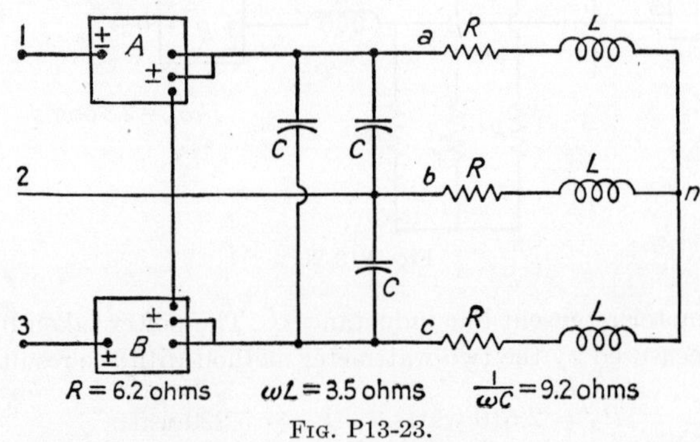


Fig. P13-23.

*a.* Compute the power dissipated in each phase.

*b.* Compute the indication of each wattmeter.

*c.* Compute the power factor of the combined load from the wattmeter indications.

*d.* Either convert the Y load to a Δ load, or the Δ capacitor connection to an equivalent Y, and obtain an equivalent load of known impedances in either Y or

Δ connection. Obtain the power factor from the parameters of this equivalent circuit and compare with the results obtained in part *c*.

*e.* Obtain a literal formula for $C$, in terms of $R$, $L$, and $\omega$, so that the combined load would operate at unity power factor.

**13-24.** In Fig. P13-24 the line potentials are the same as specified in Problem 13-22. Compute the power supplied by each phase of the source, assuming that the line potentials remain balanced in spite of the unbalance in the load.

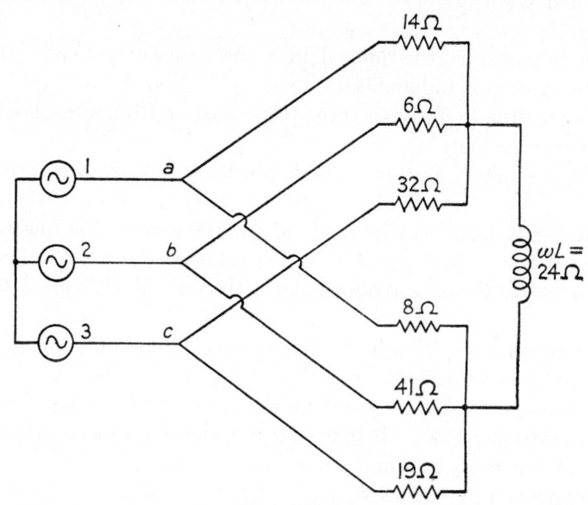


Fig. P13-24.

**13-25.** A three-phase induction motor is taking 6.5 kw at a power factor of 0.81 at a line potential of 220 volts. Each conductor to the motor has a resistance of 1.2 ohms.

*a.* Compute the power supplied by the source.

*b.* What is the power factor of the load connected to the source (*i.e.*, the line plus the motor)?

## QUESTIONS

**13-1.** What is the reason for the use of polyphase power?

**13-2.** Would it be possible to obtain constant power flow with any angle other than 120° between potentials of successive phases in a three-phase system?

**13-3.** Why is it that a three-phase generator is not three times the size of a single-phase generator of one-third the power capacity? Is the three-phase generator larger or smaller?

**13-4.** Explain what is meant by *phase sequence.*

**13-5.** How can the phase sequence at the terminals of the three-phase generator be changed? Give two methods.

**13-6.** A three-phase generator is first connected in Y and then in delta. How do the line potentials compare for these two cases? Is there any difference in the available power output for the two cases?

**13-7.** A Y-connected generator is connected to a balanced resistor load, connected in Y. The generator is then connected in delta, and the load is connected in delta. Does this make any change in the total average power delivered to the load? Explain your answer.

**13-8.** A Y-connected generator is connected to a Y-connected resistor load. Discuss any expected change in power delivered to the load

*a.* If the generator connection is changed from Y to delta.

*b.* If the load connection is changed from Y to delta (the generator being Y-connected).

**13-9.** How is power factor defined in a three-phase system? Does it have meaning if the system is unbalanced?

**13-10.** Is it possible to obtain a three-phase system from a single-phase system by the use of transformers?

**13-11.** Is it possible to obtain a single-phase system from a three-phase system?

**13-12.** What statement can be made about the sum of the line currents of a three-phase system in which there is no neutral connection?

**13-13.** What sort of source arrangement is the dual of a Y-connected potential source?

**13-14.** Is a set of capacitors in Δ connection the dual of a set of inductors in Y connection, without neutral?

**13-15.** A three-phase Y-connected potential source is to have balanced line potentials separated by 120°. Is it necessary to have balanced phase potentials?

**13-16.** Label the potential sinor diagrams of Examples 13-1 and 13-2, using the method described in Sec. 13-7.

**13-17.** A balanced load consisting of resistors in Δ is connected to a three-phase constant-potential line. They take a power $W$. What power will they take from the same line if they are reconnected in Y?

**13-18.** Suppose a given unbalanced three-phase load is supplied from three single-phase generators driven by the same shaft. Assuming the potential-source equivalent for each source is known, could this unbalanced network be completely solved by known methods of circuit analysis?

**13-19.** Can the two-wattmeter method of measuring three-phase power always be used in the Y-Y four-wire system?

**13-20.** Can the direction of power flow be determined from the indications of the wattmeters in the two-wattmeter method of power measurement?

**13-21.** Three-phase power, to a balanced load, is being measured by the two-wattmeter method. What information is needed to determine whether the load current in a phase of the load is leading or lagging the potential?

**13-22.** Suppose power is being measured by the two-wattmeter method for a variety of load conditions, all of which are balanced. Will both meters always give positive (upscale) indications?

**13-23.** Power in a balanced three-phase system is being measured by the two-wattmeter method. What happens to the indications of the two meters if the phase sequence is reversed (*a*) if the load has unity power factor, (*b*) if the load is not unity power factor?

**13-24.** Power is being measured by the two-wattmeter method. The load consists of pure resistances, but it is unbalanced. Will the indications of the two-wattmeters be the same?

**13-25.** In the arrangement of Fig. 13-31, what change, if any, would be needed to have meter $M_1$ continue to indicate $\sqrt{3}$ Im $(\mathbf{V}_p\mathbf{I}_p{}^*)$ if the phase sequence is reversed?

**13-26.** From the information given in Figs. 13-31 and 13-32, what will the indication of meter 1 do if the phase current leads the phase potential when the system is balanced?

# CHAPTER 14

# VARIABLE-RESPONSE NETWORKS

**14-1. Introduction.** The response of a network can be variable either because one or more of the circuit parameters vary or because the frequency varies. The changing impedance of a resonant circuit in which a capacitor is varied, as in the tuning of a radio receiver, is an example of the former. Another example is the induction motor when variable resistance is inserted in the rotor circuit for speed control. The various circuits of an audio-frequency amplifier can be cited as examples of circuits whose behavior must be known for variable-frequency operation. They must transmit signals having frequencies between 50 and 15,000 cps. Other applications involve different frequency ranges. For example, a broadcast radio set tuned to a frequency of 1 Mc should pass frequencies between 0.995 and 1.005 Mc and reject frequencies outside this band. The video amplifier of a television system must pass frequencies between 0 and 4 Mc.

The earlier chapters provide means for finding solutions for the networks to be considered. It is only necessary to carry through a solution with the variable parameter in literal form. In fact, in Sec. 6-11 this is done for the important cases of series and parallel resonant circuits. The present purpose is to emphasize interpretation of solutions, rather than the mechanics of obtaining them. Graphical interpretations are emphasized because many networks yield simple geometric shapes when the response functions are plotted as complex functions of the variable parameter. Such plots are sometimes useful in arriving at an estimate of a network performance.

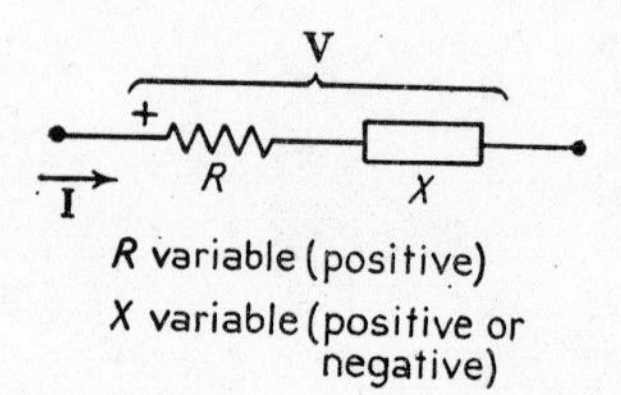

FIG. 14-1. The general series circuit with variable parameters.

**14-2. Locus Diagrams (Series Circuit).** Any network response can be described by plotting a phasor (complex quantity) in two dimensions. With the variation of the parameter, the phasor changes position and size, and its tip traces out a locus in the complex plane. In this chapter the term *response* is used broadly to include impedance and admittance. For example, an admittance is the current response to the potential $1 + j0$. Therefore, the plot may be a sinor representing a sinusoidal potential or current, or it may be an impedance or admittance phasor.

Consider the series circuit shown in Fig. 14-1. The rectangle is a pure reactance. It is variable and may be positive (inductive) or negative (capacitive).

$R$ = *Constant.* $X$ may vary either because an element varies or because of changing frequency. In either case the point $P$ of Fig. 14-2 moves along the vertical line as a locus. The vertical line can be marked off in a graduated scale of values of the variable parameter. An example is given in Fig. 14-3, where the reactance is the series combination of $L$ and $C$. As the frequency varies from zero to infinity, $P$ moves from a remote point below to one infinitely remote above the real axis.

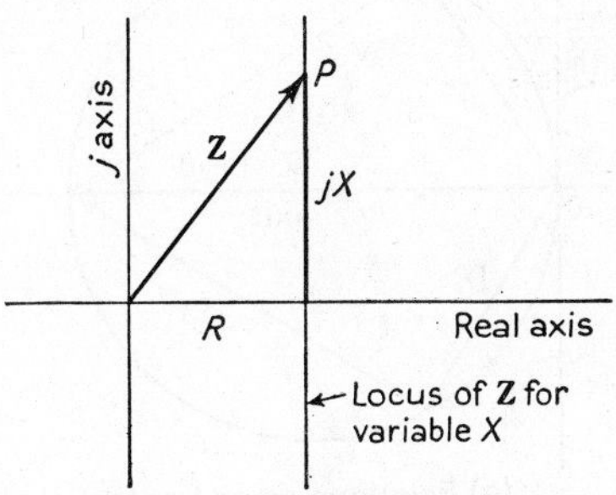


FIG. 14-2. Impedance locus of a series circuit with variable $X$.

The locus of Fig. 14-3 could be used as the source of data for the response curves of Fig. 6-21. It shows clearly how a change in $R$ affects the response. If $R$ is halved, for example, the vertical line of Fig. 14-3 moves to the dotted position, thereby causing the impedance to go through a smaller minimum and to change more rapidly when near the minimum.

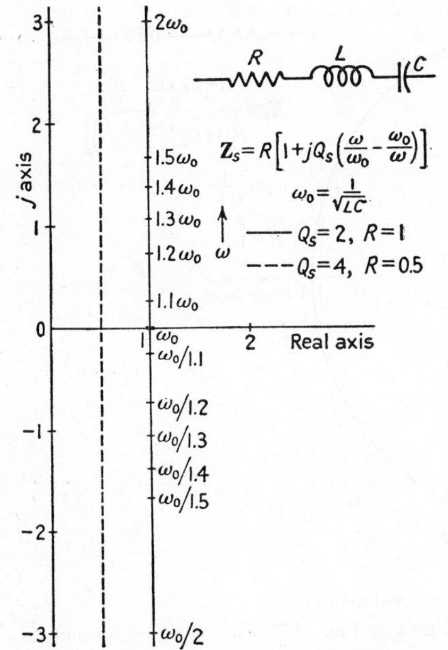


Labels on the vertical line are values of $\omega$.

FIG. 14-3. Impedance locus of series $R$-$L$-$C$ circuit with variable frequency.

Now, to treat the admittance of Fig. 14-1, suppose $\mathbf{V} = 1 + j0$ volts. The diagram of the current is also the diagram of the admittance. The locus for this case is easily obtained by referring to the auxiliary diagram of Fig. 14-4$a$, in which the solid lines are typical for a positive reactance. The sinor $j\mathbf{I}X$ for the reactance is drawn in a convenient position for adding to the sinor $\mathbf{I}R$ for the resistor. They are at right angles, and their sum is always unity. Therefore, the locus of the end of the $\mathbf{I}R$ sinor is a circle. The dotted construction is typical if the reactance is negative.

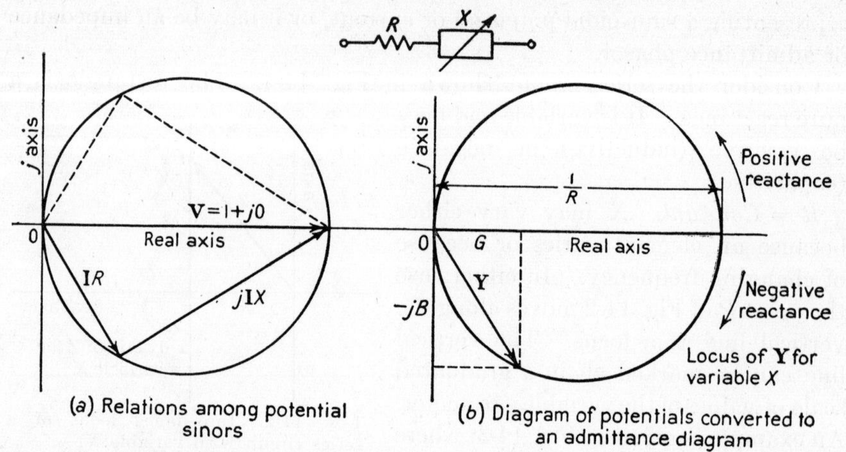


FIG. 14-4. Development of admittance locus for the general series circuit of Fig. 14-1, with variable $X$.

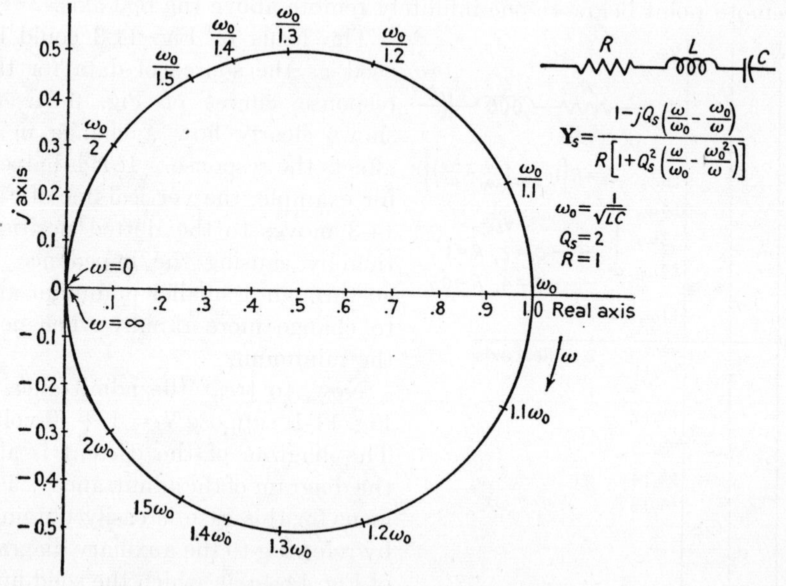


$$\mathbf{Y}_s = \frac{1 - jQ_s\left(\frac{\omega}{\omega_0} - \frac{\omega_0}{\omega}\right)}{R\left[1 + Q_s^2\left(\frac{\omega}{\omega_0} - \frac{\omega_0^2}{\omega}\right)\right]}$$

$$\omega_0 = \frac{1}{\sqrt{LC}}$$

Labels on the circle are values of $\omega$.

FIG. 14-5. Admittance locus for same series circuit as Fig. 14-3, with variable frequency.

The locus described above is for the **I**$R$ sinor. However, $R$ is a constant, so the locus of the current sinor (or admittance phasor) is similar, as shown in Fig. 14-4$b$.

The horizontal and vertical coordinates of **Y** are the same as those given by Eqs. (10-41). The admittance locus shown in Fig. 14-5 is an important special case. In Fig. 14-5 $\omega$ is the variable, but either $L$ or $C$ or both could be the variable and the locus would still be a circle.

$X$ = *Constant.* A similar treatment can be applied when $R$ is variable and $X$ remains constant. In this case the impedance locus is a horizontal line as shown in Fig. 14-6.

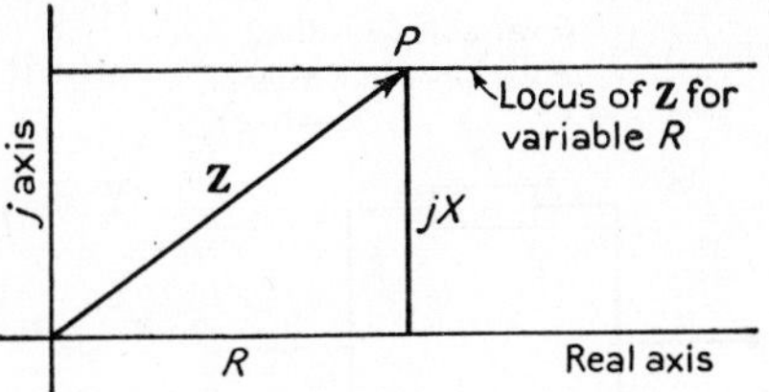


FIG. 14-6. Impedance locus of a series circuit with variable $R$.

The admittance diagram for variable $R$ is developed in Fig. 14-7$a$ for a positive $X$. (The result depends on whether $X$ is positive or negative.) Again it is assumed that the potential is $\mathbf{V} = 1 + j0$ volts. The locus of the $j\mathbf{I}X$ sinor is proved to be a semicircle by observing that it is perpendicular to $\mathbf{I}R$ and that their sum is unity. Dividing $jX\mathbf{I}$ by $jX$, to get the locus of $\mathbf{I}$, rotates the circle clockwise through 90° and changes its dimensions. The result, shown in Fig. 14-7$b$, is labeled $\mathbf{Y}$, since $\mathbf{I} = \mathbf{Y}$ when $\mathbf{V} = 1$.

With negative reactance the semicircle in Fig. 14-7$a$ would be below the horizontal axis. To get the admittance diagram, this circle is rotated

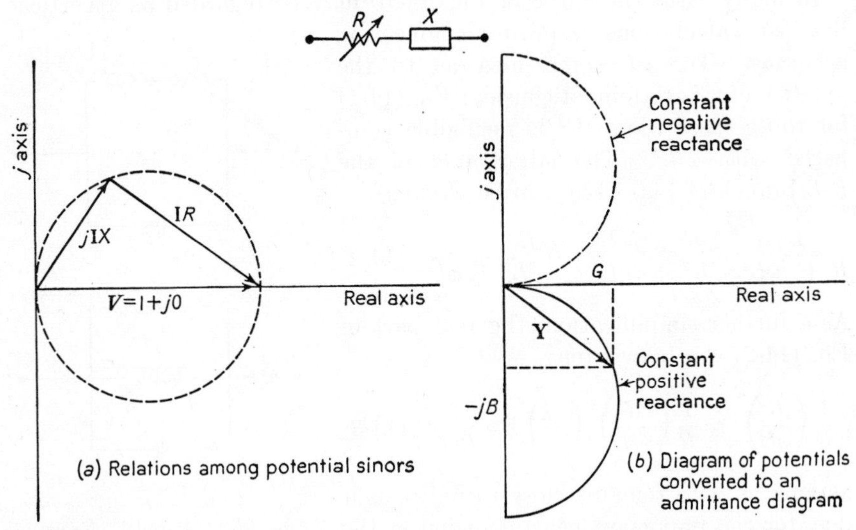


FIG. 14-7. Development of admittance locus for the general series circuit of Fig. 14-1, with variable $R$.

90° counterclockwise, as shown dotted in Fig. 14-7$b$. The $G$ and $B$ coordinates of the loci of Fig. 14-7$b$ are given by Eqs. (10-41).

**14-3. Locus Diagrams (Parallel Circuit).** The case of a susceptance $B$

in parallel with a conductance $G$, shown in Fig. 14-8, can be referred to its series circuit dual.

An important parallel circuit is shown in Fig. 14-9$a$. It is important because it represents the practical case, in which there always is some resistance in the inductive branch. The admittance is

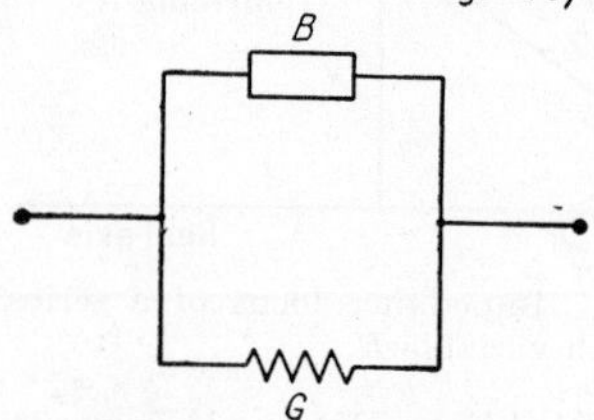


FIG. 14-8. General parallel circuit (dual of Fig. 14-1).

$$\mathbf{Y} = \frac{1}{R + j\omega L} + j\omega C$$
$$= \frac{R + j(\omega R^2 C - \omega L + \omega^3 L^2 C)}{R^2 + \omega^2 L^2} \qquad (14\text{-}1)$$

A plot of Eq. (14-1), with frequency as the variable, is shown in Fig. 14-10. For purposes of comparison the locus for the network of Fig. 14-9$b$ is also shown. The parameters are so adjusted that both networks have the same admittance at unity power factor. The smaller the dissipation (higher the $Q$), the more nearly the curve approaches the vertical line. For Fig. 14-9$a$ $Q$ is defined as if the elements were all connected in series.

In many cases the curve of Fig. 14-10 may be regarded as a vertical line for calculations requiring engineering accuracy. To get some idea as to the validity of this statement consider Eq. (14-1) for those cases where $R^2$ is negligible compared with $\omega^2 L^2$. The admittance of the $R$-$L$ branch of Fig. 14-9$a$ can be written

$$\frac{1}{R + j\omega L} = \frac{R - j\omega L}{R^2 + \omega^2 L^2} \approx \frac{R}{\omega^2 L^2} - \frac{j}{\omega L} \qquad (14\text{-}2)$$

As a further simplification, the real part of Eq. (14-2) can be written

$$\frac{1}{R}\left(\frac{R}{\omega L}\right)^2 = \frac{1}{R}\left(\frac{R}{\omega_0 L}\right)^2 \left(\frac{\omega_0}{\omega}\right)^2 \approx \frac{1}{RQ^2} \qquad (14\text{-}3)$$

as long as $\omega_0/\omega$ remains close to unity, as it does for the important central region of the admittance locus. (The $Q$ appearing in Eq. (14-3) is defined for the circuit in a series connection, and $\omega_0 = 1/\sqrt{LC}$). Using these approximations it is concluded that when $\omega$ is near $\omega_0$ and when the circuit $Q$ is sufficiently high,

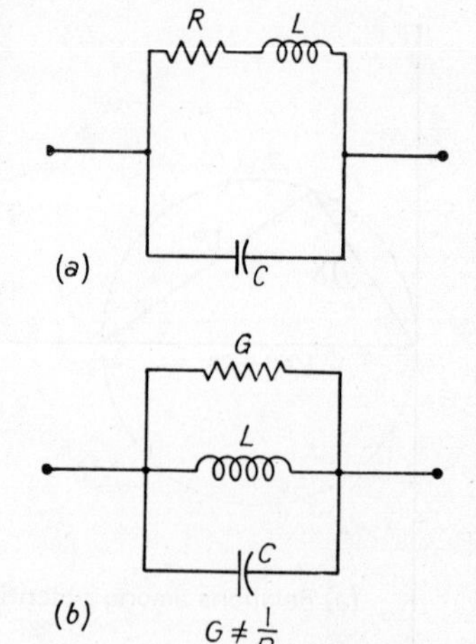


FIG. 14-9. Parallel circuit in which the inductor has series resistance.

$$\mathbf{Y} \approx \frac{1}{RQ^2} + j\left(\omega C - \frac{1}{\omega L}\right) \tag{14-4}$$

Equation (14-4) is recognized as the admittance of Fig. 14-9*b*. Thus, within the above limitations on $\omega$ and $Q$, the two networks of Fig. 14-9 are equivalent. This proves that with a high $Q$ the curve and the

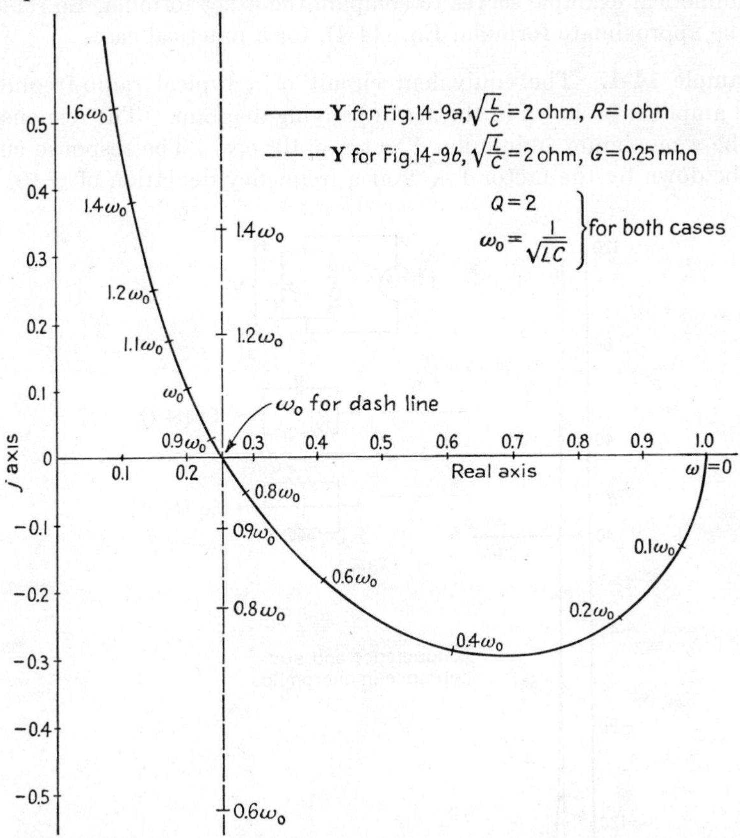


FIG. 14-10. Typical admittance curves for circuits of Fig. 14-9, with variable frequency.

vertical line of Fig. 14-10 are nearly the same when $\omega$ is near $\omega_0$. In Fig. 14-10, the $Q$ is purposely made so low that the approximation is not good, in order to emphasize the difference between the two curves.

Let us further assume that $\omega$ is near enough to $\omega_0$ to make relation (6-50) an acceptable approximation. Then, as shown in Sec. 6-11, Eq. (14-4) can be written

$$\mathbf{Y} = \frac{1}{RQ^2}\sqrt{1 + Q\left(2\frac{\omega - \omega_0}{\omega_0}\right)^2} \;\Big/ \tan^{-1} 2Q\left(\frac{\omega - \omega_0}{\omega_0}\right) \tag{14-5}$$

Since this is the quantity plotted in the universal resonance curve of Fig. 6-21, it follows that when $Q$ is high Fig. 6-21 can be a good approximate curve for **Y** of Fig. 14-9$a$, when $\omega$ is near $\omega_0$. If Figs. 9$a$ and $b$ are equivalent near $\omega = \omega_0$, it can be shown that the $Q$ of Fig. 14-9$a$ (considered as a series circuit) is the same as the $Q$ of Fig. 14-9$b$.

A numerical example serves to compare the exact formula, Eq. (14-1), and the approximate formula, Eq. (14-4), for a practical case.

**Example 14-1.** The equivalent circuit of a typical radio-frequency tuned amplifier is shown in the accompanying diagram. The response $V$ is to be a maximum (minimum $Y$) at $f = 10^6$ cps. The response curve is to be down by the factor $1/\sqrt{2}$ at a frequency deviation of $\pm 10^4$ cps

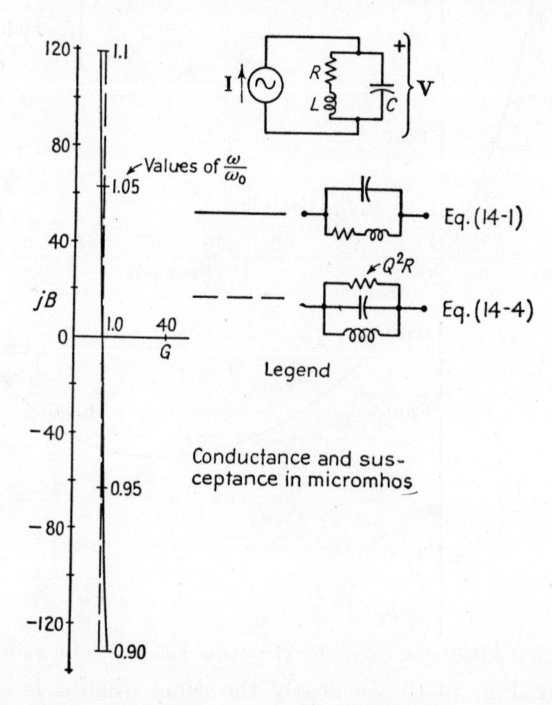


from $f = 10^6$ cps.. The value of $C$ is $10^{-10}$ farad. Specify $L$ and $R$, assuming the universal resonance formulas are applicable, and then compare the complex admittance function as it is portrayed by plots of Eqs. (14-1) and (14-4).

*Solution.* Equation (6-56) gives

$$Q = \frac{10^6}{2 \times 10^4} = 50$$

Also

$$L = \frac{1}{\omega_0^2 C} = \frac{1}{(2\pi)^2 \times 10^{12}(10^{-10})} = 2.54 \times 10^{-4} \text{ henry}$$

and

$$R = \frac{2\pi \times 10^6(2.54) \times 10^{-4}}{50} = 31.9 \text{ ohms}$$

For the exact formula Eq. (14-1) gives

$$\mathbf{Y} = \frac{31.9 + j(\omega/\omega_0)[0.64 + 1{,}600(\omega/\omega_0)^2 - 1{,}600]}{1{,}020(2.56 \times 10^6 + (\omega/\omega_0)^2}$$

Equation (14-4) gives the approximate formula

$$\mathbf{Y} \approx \left[12.5 + j628\left(\frac{\omega}{\omega_0} - \frac{\omega_0}{\omega}\right)\right] \times 10^{-6}$$

The complex plots of these two functions are shown. It is seen that the two networks are nearly identical, within the limits of usual engineering accuracy, when $f$ is between $0.95 \times 10^6$ and $1.05 \times 10^6$ Mc.

Many other impedance or admittance functions can be represented similarly. The diagrams all share certain common characteristics, when frequency is the variable. Statements of these characteristics are listed below, without proofs. These properties are sometimes useful in estimating how a locus will behave, without computing it completely.

1. If the locus is assumed to extend into the range of "negative" as well as positive frequencies, the portion obtained when $\omega$ is negative is a reflection in the real axis of the portion for positive $\omega$. In view of the definition of frequency as the number of cycles per second, the concept of a negative frequency is unnatural. It may be regarded as having meaning only as a mathematical quantity. Figure 14-11 shows the locus originally given in Fig. 14-10 for the complete range of $\omega$ from $-\infty$ to $+\infty$.

2. When the frequency is either zero or infinite, the imaginary part of a response function can have no value other than zero or infinity. Figure 14-3 is a case for which the imaginary part is infinite at both extremes of frequency. In Fig. 14-5 the imaginary part is zero at each extremity, and in Fig. 14-10 the imaginary part is zero at one extremity and infinite at the other.

3. When the frequency is either zero or infinite, a tangent to the locus curve must be parallel to either the real or imaginary axis. All the examples that have been given have the tangent parallel to the imaginary axis at zero and infinite frequencies.

4. When the complete range of frequencies from $-\infty$ to $+\infty$ is considered, the locus forms one or more closed loops. With increasing $\omega$ a point on the locus moves in a clockwise direction around the enclosed area. In some cases, as in Figs. 14-3 and 14-10, the locus does not close at $\omega = -\infty$ and $+\infty$. Therefore, for at least part of the curve, there is no enclosed area apparent. However, the theorem is made to fit all

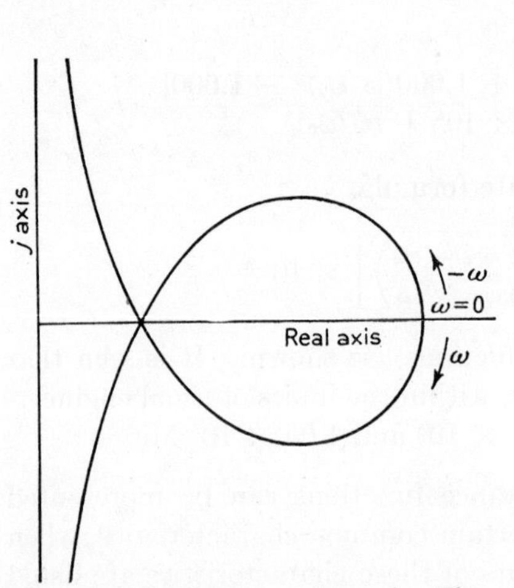


FIG. 14-11. Admittance locus for Fig. 14-9, showing variation for positive and negative frequencies.

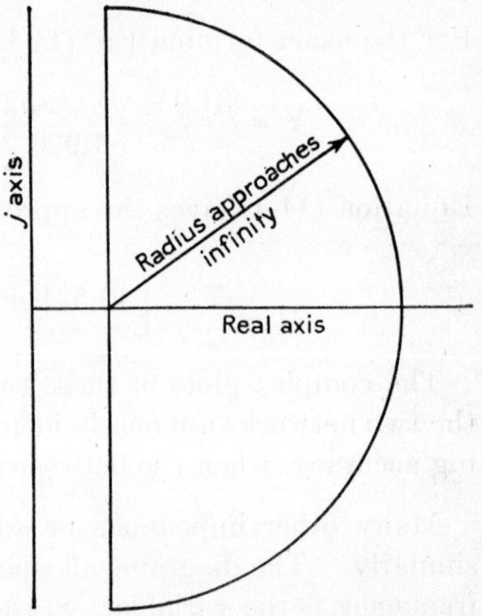

FIG. 14-12. Method of completing the locus with a circular arc to form an enclosed area, for cases like Figs. 14-2 and 14-11.

cases by imagining that the locus is completed by a very large circular arc to the right (of radius approaching infinity), as in Fig. 14-12.

**14-4. The Parallel-T Null Network.** A network of considerable importance is the parallel-T combination shown in Fig. 14-13*a*. It has

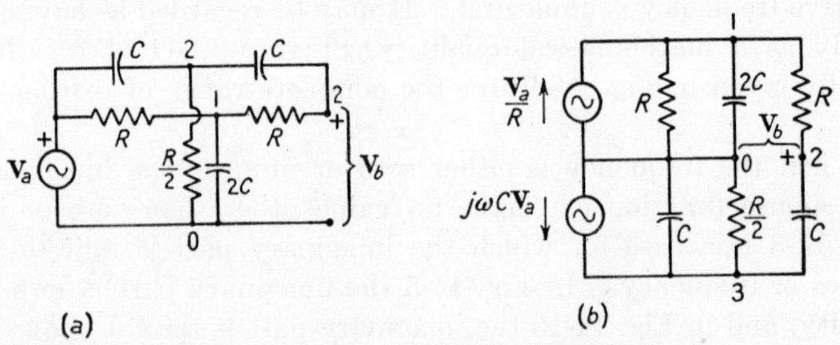


FIG. 14-13. The parallel-T null network.

the unique property that $\mathbf{V}_b$ is zero at one frequency. This network falls into one of the special cases discussed in Sec. 11-11. The solution is easily obtained by the node analysis. The source is replaced by two current-source equivalents, as in Fig. 14-13*b*.

The determinant of the network is

$$\mathbf{\Delta} = \begin{vmatrix} 2(G + j\omega C) & -G & 0 \\ -G & G + j\omega C & -j\omega C \\ 0 & -j\omega C & 2(G + j\omega C) \end{vmatrix}$$

$$= G^3\left(1 + j\frac{\omega}{\omega_0}\right)\left[2 - 2\left(\frac{\omega}{\omega_0}\right)^2 + j8\frac{\omega}{\omega_0}\right]$$

where $G = 1/R$ and $\omega_0 = 1/RC$. The cofactors $\mathbf{\Delta}_{12}$ and $\mathbf{\Delta}_{32}$ are needed.† They are

$$\mathbf{\Delta}_{12} = 2G(G + j\omega C)$$
$$\mathbf{\Delta}_{32} = j2\omega C(G + j\omega C)$$

The potential $\mathbf{V}_b$ is

$$\mathbf{V}_b = \frac{\mathbf{\Delta}_{12}(\mathbf{V}_a/R) + \mathbf{\Delta}_{32}(j\omega C\mathbf{V}_a)}{\mathbf{\Delta}}$$

The steps following the substitution of formulas for the determinants are omitted. Expressed as the ratio $\mathbf{V}_b/\mathbf{V}_a$, the response is

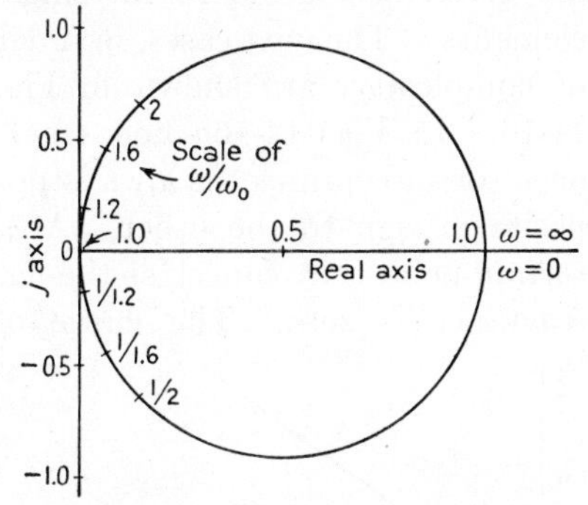


FIG. 14-14. Locus of $\mathbf{V}_b/\mathbf{V}_a$ for the parallel-T network of Fig. 14-13.

$$\frac{\mathbf{V}_b}{\mathbf{V}_a} = \frac{1 - (\omega/\omega_0)^2}{1 - (\omega/\omega_0)^2 + j4(\omega/\omega_0)} \tag{14-6}$$

We are to determine the shape of the locus of this complex ratio as $\omega$ varies. To simplify the ensuing manipulations, let $u = \omega/\omega_0$. The form of the locus is found by considering the new function

$$\frac{\mathbf{V}_b}{\mathbf{V}_a} - \frac{1}{2} = \frac{1 - u^2}{1 - u^2 + j4u} - \frac{1}{2}$$
$$= \frac{1 - u^2 - j4u}{2(1 - u^2 + j4u)}$$
$$= \frac{(1 - u^2)^2 + (4u)^2/\tan^{-1} -4u/(1 - u^2)}{2[1 - u^2)^2 + (4u)^2]/\tan^{-1} 4u/(1 - u^2)}$$
$$= \frac{1}{2}\Big/ -2\tan^{-1}\frac{4u}{1 - u^2} \tag{14-7}$$

Equation (14-7) describes a circle of radius ½. However, because it is the locus of $\mathbf{V}_b/\mathbf{V}_a$ − ½, the circle is displaced to the right by the amount ½ when plotted in the $\mathbf{V}_b/\mathbf{V}_a$ plane. The locus is shown in Fig. 14-14.

† A *cofactor* of row $m$ and column $n$ of a determinant is $(-1)^{m+n}$ times the minor of that row and column.

**14-5. Reactance Curves.** When there is no dissipation in a circuit containing $L$ and $C$ the impedance reduces to a reactance, or the admittance to a susceptance. Therefore, the locus is reduced to the imaginary axis, and there is no information gained by plotting it.

The behavior of such circuits is most conveniently plotted as a curve of reactance or susceptance. The variable parameter is usually $\omega$. Reactance and susceptance curves are given in Fig. 14-15 for single elements. The next cases, in order of complexity, are shown in Fig. 14-16. In Fig. 14-16*a* one reactance (or susceptance) is always opposite in sign to the other. At a certain point they cancel, so the net reactance is zero. The curve of Fig. 14-16*b* is the negative reciprocal of (*a*). The sign is changed when a reciprocal is taken because, with no dissipation,

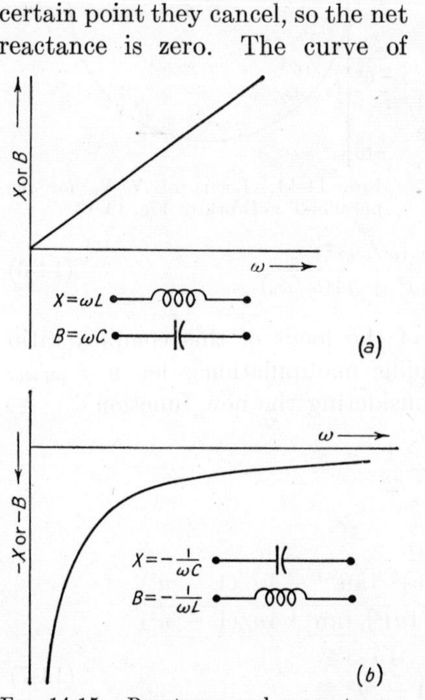


FIG. 14-15. Reactance and susceptance curves for a single element.

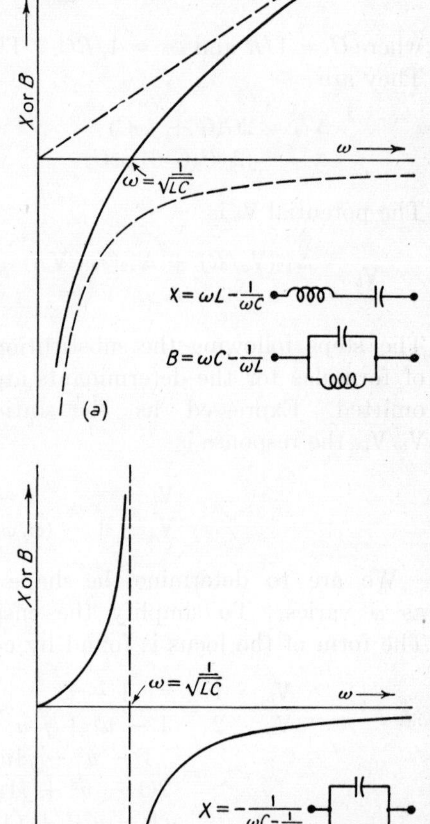


FIG. 14-16. Reactance and susceptance curves for pairs of elements.

$$
\begin{aligned}
\mathbf{Z} &= jX \\
\mathbf{Y} &= jB
\end{aligned} \tag{14-8}
$$

and if

$$\mathbf{Z} = \frac{1}{\mathbf{Y}} \tag{14-9}$$

$$X = -\frac{1}{B} \tag{14-10}$$

Another pair of curves is given in Fig. 14-17, for one element more than in the previous cases. A logical justification of the shapes is obtained by

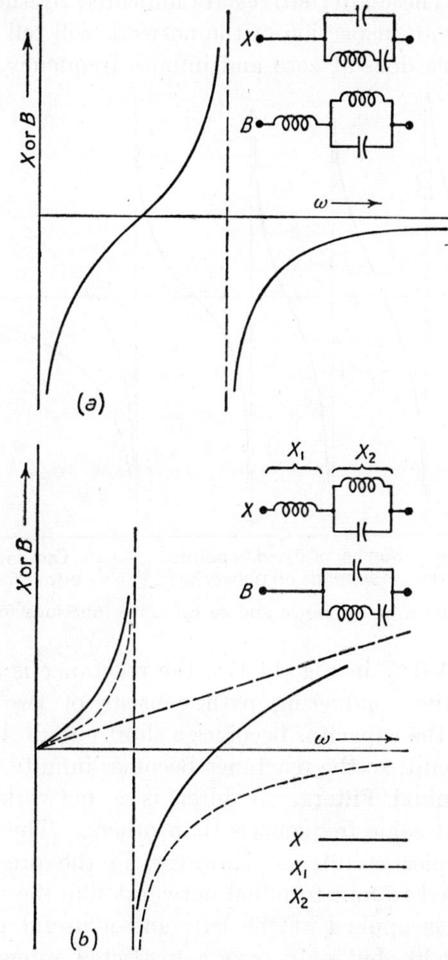


FIG. 14-17. Reactance and susceptance functions.

first considering curve (*b*). It is the combination of curves 14-15*a* and 14-16*b*, as indicated by the dotted curves. Then curve 14-17*a* is obtained by taking the negative reciprocal of curve 14-17*b*.

As networks of nondissipative elements become more extensive, their reactance or susceptance curves have more *zeros* (points at which they become zero) and *poles* (points at which they become infinite). It can be proved that these functions always have one of the forms shown in Fig. 14-18. The number of poles and zeros is indefinite, depending on the number of elements. At each end of the frequency scale the function can behave in either of two ways. It can be zero, or it can become infinite. These alternatives are indicated by the dotted curves.

In specific cases an inspection of the network will tell what the reactance or susceptance does at zero and infinite frequency. For example,

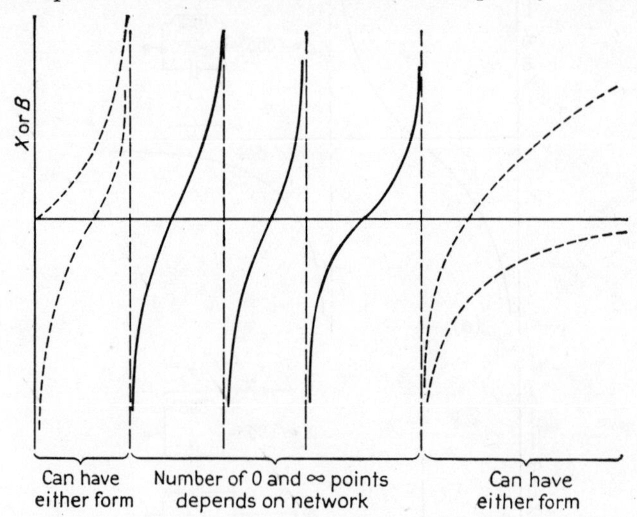


FIG. 14-18. General form of reactance and susceptance functions for all nondissipative networks.

in the circuit labeled $X$ in Fig. 14-17*b*, the reactance is zero at zero frequency because the conducting path consists of two inductors. At infinite frequency the capacitor becomes a short circuit, but one inductor remains in the circuit, so the reactance becomes infinite.

**14-6. Four-terminal Filters.** A filter is a network that responds more vigorously at some frequencies than others. The simple resonant circuits are examples of filters. However, in the present section the term *filter* is applied to four-terminal networks like the examples of Fig. 14-19. A source is applied at the left, and a useful power output is received at the right, but only over a restricted range of frequencies. Those frequencies for which there is no appreciable loss in the network constitute the *pass bands*. The networks of Fig. 14-19 show the essential features of filters having the pass bands indicated, but practical designs may differ in details from the ones shown.

Filters are used for many purposes, particularly in the field of communications. Their use makes it possible to operate many adjacent communication channels on a common transmission system. Of course, to do this it is necessary to change the frequencies of the information signal to put them within the appropriate band. Fortunately, this is

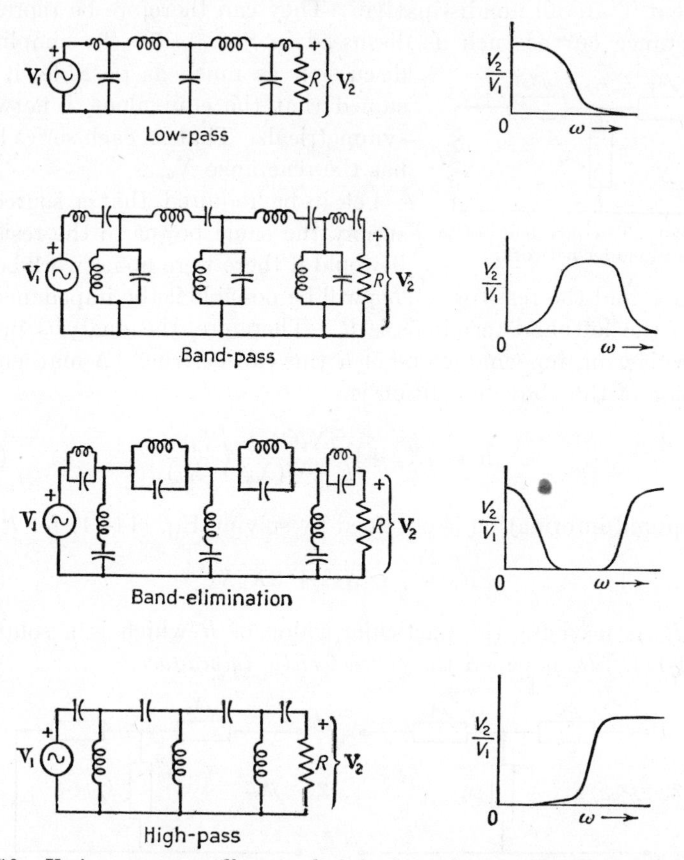


FIG. 14-19. Various common filters and their approximate response functions. The number of sections to and the filter network values of components vary with specific designs.

relatively easy to do. A number of band-pass filters, with their pass bands placed side by side, are used in such an application.

There are many techniques of designing filters, all of which are approximations. Filter design is one of the most difficult in the study of circuits. Accordingly, it is possible to give only a sketchy review of the subject, indicating something of what determines the pass band of a filter. In fact, the filters described in this section are not typical of the most erudite designs available, but they do illustrate principles; it is for this purpose that they are presented.

Through the repeated application of the T-Π and Π-T transformations it is possible to reduce a ladder network to the form of Fig. 14-20.* If there are no dissipative elements in the network, the branches of the equivalent T are all nondissipative. They can therefore be represented by reactance curves such as discussed in Sec. 14-5. To simplify the discussion as much as possible, it is assumed that the equivalent T network is symmetrical. That is, each series branch has the reactance $X_a$.

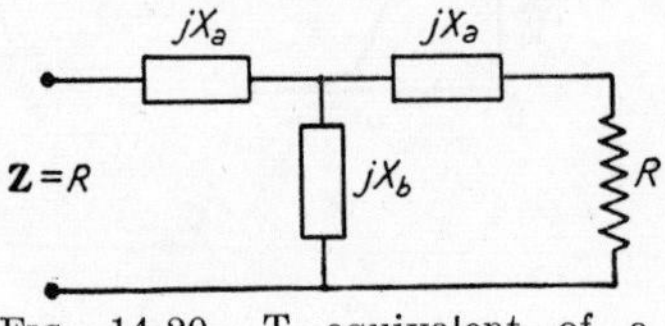


Fig. 14-20. T equivalent of a symmetrical ladder network.

Let it be required that a source shall supply the same power to the resistor as it would if there were no network between the source and the resistor. This will be possible if the impedance looking into the lefthand terminals is $R$. Therefore, the analysis proceeds by investigating for what value of $R$ this can be true. A mathematical expression of the above condition is

$$R = jX_a + \frac{jX_b(R + jX_a)}{R + j(X_a + X_b)} \tag{14-11}$$

The required information is obtained by solving Eq. (14-11) for $R$, thus:

$$R_0 = j\sqrt{X_a^2 + 2X_aX_b} \tag{14-12}$$

where $R_0$ is used for the particular value of $R$ which is a solution of Eq. (14-11). $R_0$ is called the *characteristic impedance.*

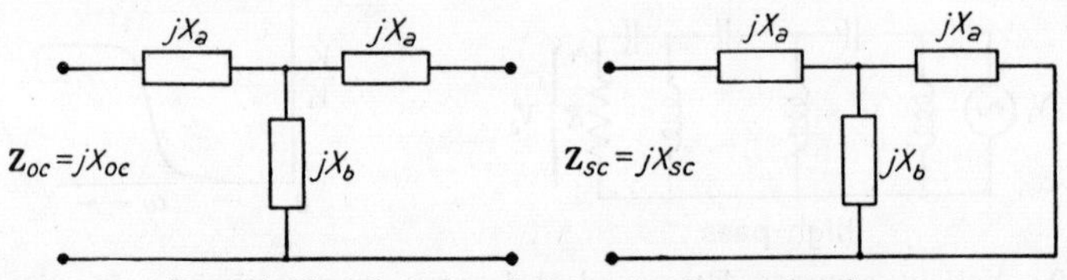


Fig. 14-21. Open- and short-circuit terminations.

Note that for the conditions indicated at (a) and (b) of Fig. 14-21

$$\mathbf{Z}_{oc} = jX_{oc} = j(X_a + X_b)$$

$$\mathbf{Z}_{sc} = jX_{sc} = jX_a + \frac{jX_a jX_b}{j(X_a + X_b)} = \frac{j\,X_a^2 + 2X_aX_b}{X_a + X_b} \tag{14-13}$$

and that

$$\mathbf{Z}_{oc}\mathbf{Z}_{sc} = -(X_a^2 + 2X_aX_b) \tag{14-14}$$

* See footnote, p. 231, relevant to the use of Eqs. (11-25) and (11-26).

Comparing with Eq. (14-12) yields

$$R_0 = \sqrt{\mathbf{Z}_{oc}\mathbf{Z}_{sc}} = \sqrt{-X_{oc}X_{sc}} \tag{14-15}$$

The stipulation was made that power must be transmitted by the system. Therefore, $R_0$ must be real. Equation (14-15) shows that $R_0$ can be real only if $X_{oc}$ and $X_{sc}$ have opposite signs. Each of these is a reactance function which may cross the axis many times, in the manner of Fig. 14-18. Whenever $X_{oc}$ and $X_{sc}$ are on the same side of the axis, the network cannot transmit power without attenuation; but when they are on opposite sides of the axis the network can transmit power without attenuation. Frequencies for which the network can transmit power without attenuation constitute the *pass band* (or *bands*).

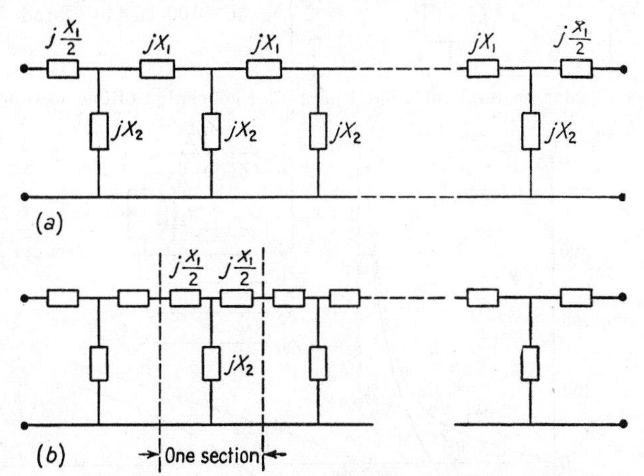


FIG. 14-22. A filter structure built up of T or Π sections.

Equation (14-15) shows that the value of $R_0$ for which power can be transmitted without attenuation is a *variable*. If $R$ is fixed, there will not always be complete transmission in the pass band. Filters designed along these lines always involve a compromise in the choice of a value of $R$ which will serve moderately well over the pass band. Thus it is seen that the pass band is an idealized concept, which is never exactly attained.

There are several methods of designing filter networks. All of them give networks which somewhat resemble those of Fig. 14-19. Filter design is a subject which involves complicated mathematics. The present discussion is limited to a brief analysis of one method of design which yields moderately good performance with comparatively little difficulty, although it is not the best method if the best possible performance is desired.

The method to be discussed is based on Fig. 14-22*a*. The network can be regarded as a *cascade* connection of T sections as shown in Fig. 14-22*b*. It is then postulated that

$$X_1 X_2 = -K^2 \qquad (14\text{-}16)$$

where $K$ is a constant real number and is a design parameter of the filter. A filter meeting this condition is called a *constant-K* filter. Each of the networks shown in Fig. 14-19 can be built up of constant-$K$ sections by proper choice of the $L$ and $C$ parameters. A similar design can be based on the cascade connection of Π sections.

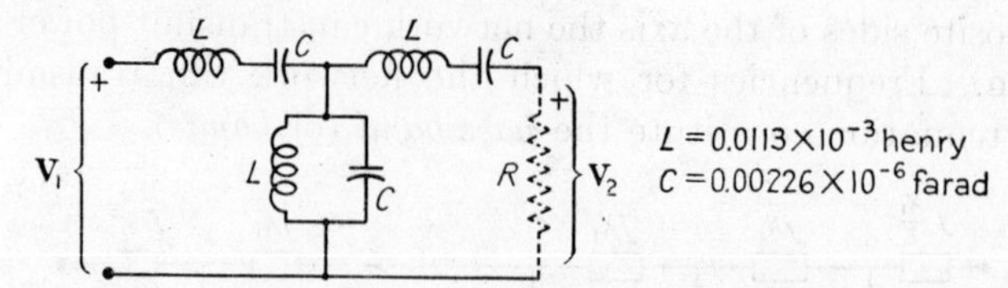


FIG. 14-23. Example of a band-pass filter consisting of one section.

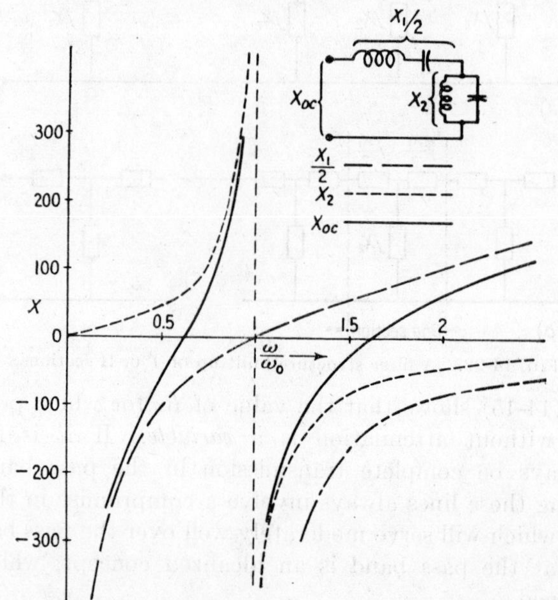


FIG. 14-24. Plots of $X_1/2$, $X_2$, and $X_{oc}$ for Fig. 14-23.

**14-7. Illustrative Example.** Figure 14-23 shows a constant-$K$ band-pass $T$ filter section. The reactances $X_1$ and $X_2$ are

$$\frac{X_1}{2} = 70.7\left(\frac{\omega}{\omega_0} - \frac{\omega_0}{\omega}\right) \qquad (14\text{-}17)$$

$$X_2 = -70.7\,\frac{1}{(\omega/\omega_0) - (\omega_0/\omega)}$$

where

$$\omega_0 = \frac{1}{\sqrt{LC}} \tag{14-18}$$

They are plotted as functions of $\omega/\omega_0$ in Fig. 14-24. The figure also includes a plot of

$$X_{oc} = \frac{X_1}{2} + X_2 \tag{14-19}$$

The short-circuit characteristic is obtained in Fig. 14-25. It is the sum of $X_1$ and $X_A$, where $X_A$ is the reactance indicated in Fig. 14-25. The

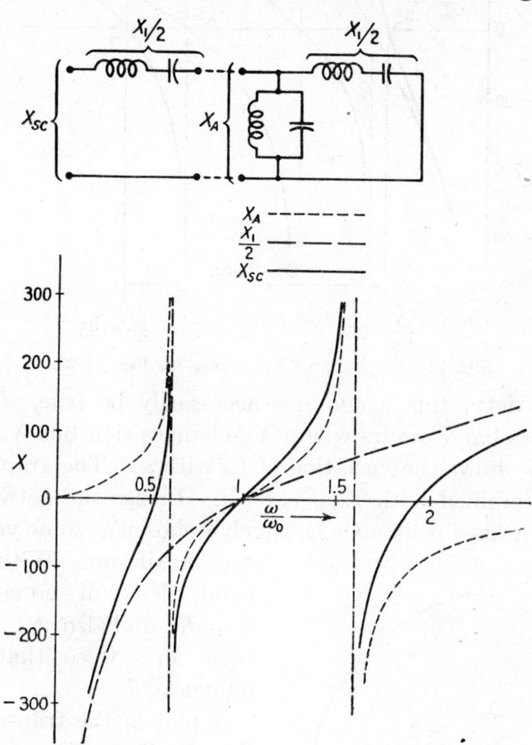


FIG. 14-25. Plots of $X_1/2$, $X_A$, and $X_{sc}$ for Fig. 14-23.

curve of $X_A$ in Fig. 14-25 is proportional to the negative reciprocal of the $X_{oc}$ curve of Fig. 14-24, since

$$jX_A = (jX_1/2)(jX_2)/[j(X_1/2) + jX_2] = -jK^2/2X_{oc}.$$

The $X_{sc}$ curve is given by

$$X_{sc} = X_1 + X_A \tag{14-20}$$

Finally, the $X_{oc}$ and $X_{sc}$ curves are superimposed in Fig. 14-26. It is seen that although $X_{oc}$ and $X_{sc}$ change sign three times each, within the pass band, they do so at the same points. If the design were not of the

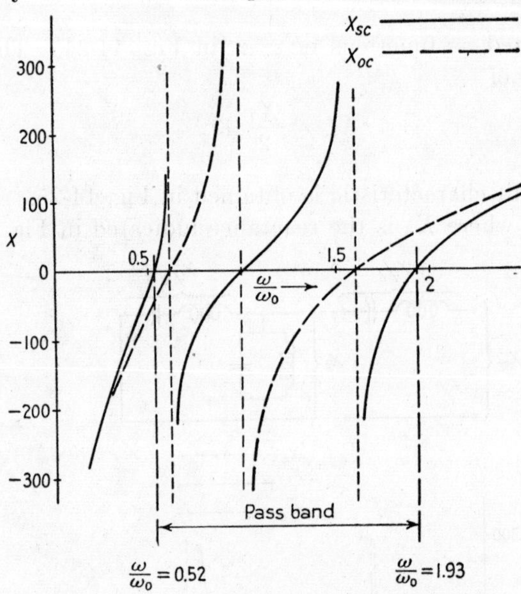


FIG. 14-26. $X_{oc}$ and $X_{sc}$ curves for Fig. 14-23.

constant-$K$ variety, this would not necessarily be true. The nominal edge of the pass band occurs where $X_{sc}$ changes sign but $X_{oc}$ does not.

Figure 14-27 shows the variation of $R_0$ with $\omega$. The graph is a plot of Eq. (14-12) combined with Eqs. (14-17). In use the network must be terminated in a fixed resistance $R$, which is chosen as some value less than the maximum. Within the pass band, $V_2$ will equal $V_1$ where $R = R_0$, and also at $\omega = \omega_0$ because then $X_1 = 0$ so that $R_0$ has no influence.

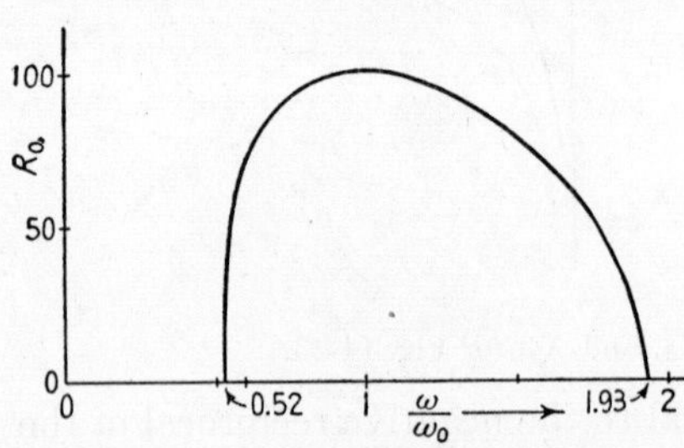


FIG. 14-27. Variation of $R_0$ for Fig. 14-23.

A plot of the transmission function $\mathbf{V}_2/\mathbf{V}_1$ is given in Fig. 14-28. It is given in two parts, as a magnitude function and as an angle function. The magnitude function is given for two values of terminating resistance. These curves are plots of the magnitude and angle of the complex function

$$\frac{\mathbf{V}_2}{\mathbf{V}_1} = \frac{jRX_2}{-(X_1^2 + 2X_1X_2) + jR(X_1 + X_2)} \tag{14-21}$$

which may be obtained by solving the network by one of the methods described in Chap. 11. The curve is by no means flat within the pass band, because $R \neq R_0$. However, it is seen that the edges of the band agree quite closely with those predicted by Fig. 14-26. The peaks occurring near the band edges are due to resonance effects which are not adequately controlled because $R$ is too large. The response function

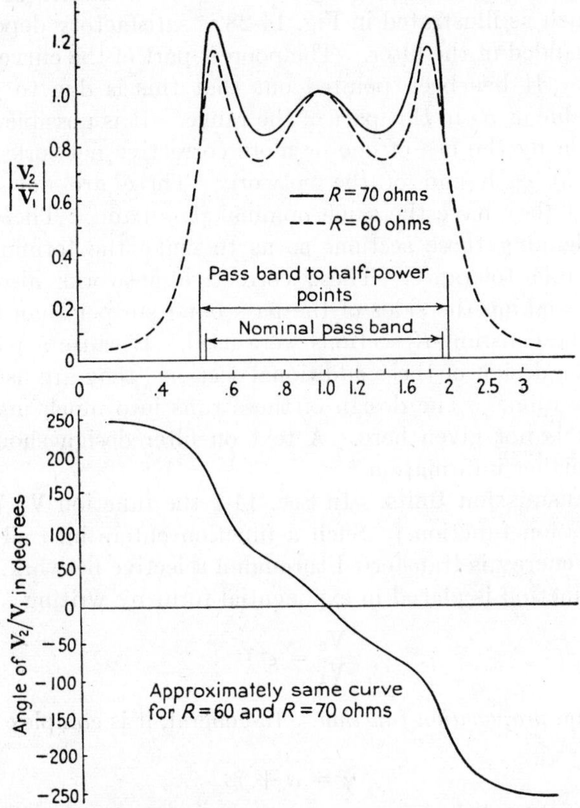


FIG. 14-28. Plots of magnitude and angle of the complex response function $V_2 V_1$ for Fig. 14-23. The horizontal scale is $\omega/\omega_0$.

would be different for a filter consisting of more than one section because each successive section would act as a termination for the preceding section.

The response of a constant-$K$ band-pass filter is symmetrical about $\omega_0$ in the sense that the magnitude of response obtained at some frequency $\omega$ is also obtained at frequency $\omega_0^2/\omega$. This follows from Eqs. (14-17). Suppose the edge of the band is defined as the point where the power transfer is reduced to one-half the value obtained at $\omega_0$. The magnitude of the potential ratio is then 0.707. For the $R = 60$ curve the frequencies $\omega_a$ and $\omega_b$ at these band edges occur at

$$\omega_a = 0.491\omega_0$$

and

$$\omega_b = 2.04\omega_0 \tag{14-22}$$

**14-8. Matching of Terminating Resistance.** Whether or not a performance such as illustrated in Fig. 14-28 is satisfactory depends on the service demanded of the filter. The poorest part of the curve is near the band edges. It has been pointed out that this is due to the rapidly changing value of $R_0$ in this part of the range. It is possible to improve this situation by the use of one or more corrective networks in cascade connection at each end of the network. These are not constant-$K$ sections, but they have the same nominal pass band. There is a technique for defining these sections so as to make the termination meet any reasonable tolerance. These corrective networks also have the property of making the sides of the pass band steeper than they would be if only the constant-$K$ sections were used. Because a parameter $m$ is used in the design of these additional sections, they are usually called $m$-derived sections. The design of these runs into much mathematical detail, so it is not given here. A text on filter design should be consulted for further information.*

**14-9. Transmission Units.** In Sec. 14-7 the function $\mathbf{V}_2/\mathbf{V}_1$ is called the transmission function.† Such a function enters into all considerations where energy is transferred through a selective network. In many cases this function is placed in exponential form by writing

$$\frac{\mathbf{V}_2}{\mathbf{V}_1} = \epsilon^{-\gamma} \tag{14-23}$$

$\gamma$ is called the *propagation function*. In general, it is complex and can be written

$$\gamma = \alpha + j\beta \tag{14-24}$$

whence

$$\frac{\mathbf{V}_2}{\mathbf{V}_1} = \epsilon^{-\alpha}\epsilon^{-j\beta} \tag{14-25}$$

The factor $\epsilon^{-\alpha}$ is the magnitude of the complex number. Equation (14-24) serves to define $\alpha$, the *attenuation function*, and $\beta$, the *phase*

* See W. R. LePage and S. Seely, "General Network Analysis," Chap. 7, McGraw-Hill Book Company, Inc., New York, 1952.

† The potential ratio may be considered as typical of any transmission function. Other transmission functions would be: current ratio, current-to-potential ratio, or potential-to-current ratio.

*function* (or *angle function*). The unit of $\alpha$ is the *neper*, and the unit of $\beta$ is the *radian*.

The exponential form for $\mathbf{V}_2/\mathbf{V}_1$ is convenient for at least three reasons. From Eq. (14-25) it follows that

$$\alpha = -\ln \frac{V_2}{V_1} = \ln V_1 - \ln V_2 \tag{14-26}$$

For fixed input, $\alpha$ is proportional to the negative of the logarithm of the output magnitude. For those devices which ultimately are to excite

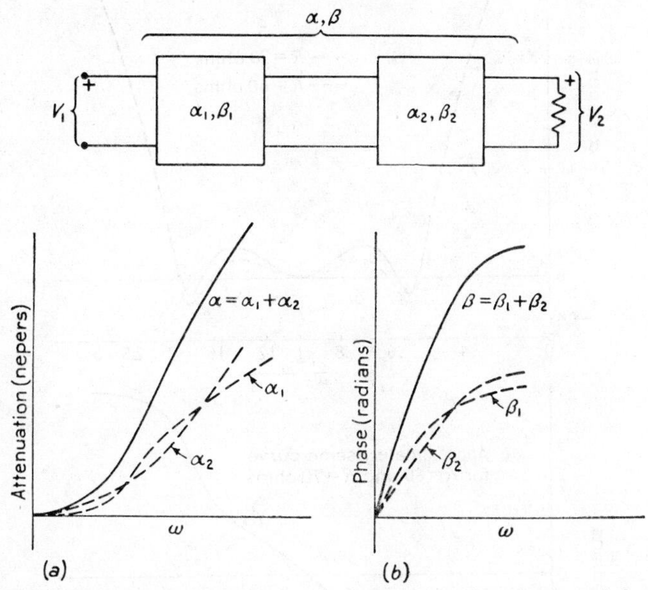


FIG. 14-29. Combination of attenuation and phase functions for cascaded networks.

the senses of sight or hearing (an audio amplifier, for example) this is a natural unit, because these senses are themselves approximately logarithmic. That is, $\alpha$ then becomes a rough measure of the perceived response.

The propagation function is convenient to use when the over-all characteristics of two or more cascaded networks are to be considered. An example of this is given in Fig. 14-29. The two networks have propagation functions $\gamma_1$ and $\gamma_2$. Each is a function of frequency as shown by the accompanying graphs. The over-all response is

$$\frac{\mathbf{V}_1}{\mathbf{V}_2} \epsilon^{-\gamma_1}\epsilon^{-\gamma_2} = \epsilon^{-\gamma} \tag{14-27}$$

Therefore

$$\begin{aligned} \gamma &= \gamma_1 + \gamma_2 \\ \alpha &= \alpha_1 + \alpha_2 \\ \beta &= \beta_1 + \beta_2 \end{aligned} \qquad (14\text{-}28)$$

The attenuation and phase functions are combined by addition. When this is to be done graphically, as in Fig. 14-29, it is simpler to add the attenuation functions than to multiply the magnitude functions.

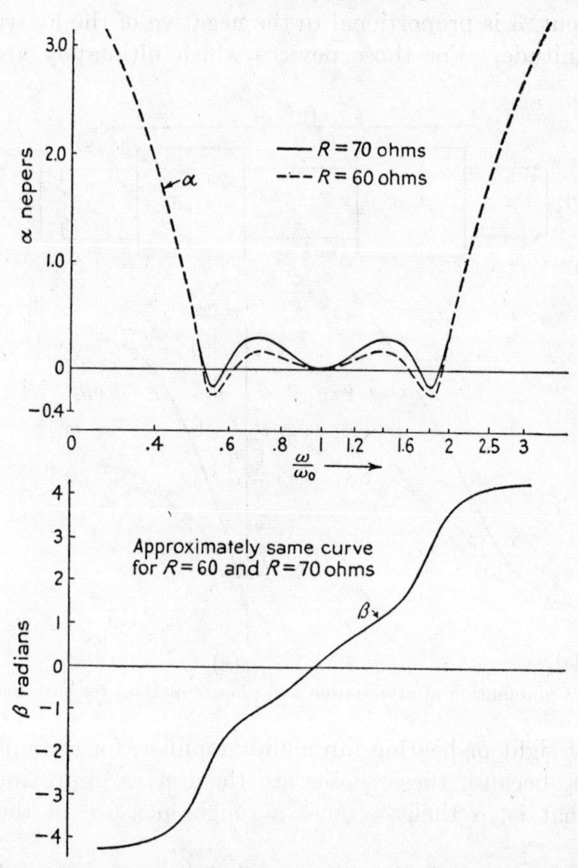


FIG. 14-30. Plots of the components of the attenuation function of Fig. 14-23.

The third advantage of the use of $\alpha$ is that a very wide range of magnitudes of the transmission can be shown on one graph. This is a well-known characteristic of logarithmic scales, and the use of $\alpha$ amounts to nothing more than the introduction of a logarithmic scale.

It is important to note that the introduction of the minus sign in Eq. (14-23) causes $\alpha$ to be large in the region of low transmission. Therefore, a graph of $\alpha$ has an inverted appearance when compared with a graph of the magnitude of the transmission function. Also, the angle function defined by Eqs. (14-23) and (14-24) is the negative of the angle of $\mathbf{V}_2/\mathbf{V}_1$. This choice of signs is entirely arbitrary and is in agreement with common practice. Plots of $\alpha$ and $\beta$, for the network of Fig. 14-23, are given in Fig. 14-30. It is instructive to compare with them Fig. 14-28.

In many considerations power transfer is important. In that case, the logarithm is taken of the ratio of the power input to the power output.

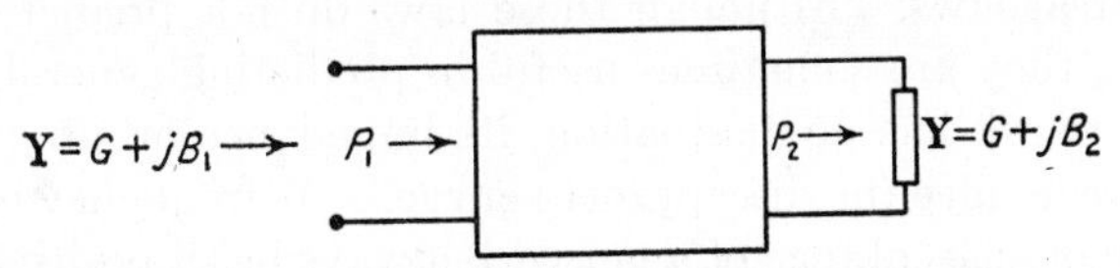


FIG. 14-31. Power transmission in a four-terminal network when the terminating admittance has the same real part as the input admittance.

Logarithms to the base 10 are used, and to give more convenient-sized units, a factor 10 is introduced. Thus, the power *gain* in a system is

$$D = 10 \log \frac{P_2}{P_1} \tag{14-29}$$

The unit of $D$ is the *decibel*. Under conditions of a network having the *same input conductance as the termination*, as in Fig. 14-31, the decibel is proportional to $\alpha$. The powers are

$$\begin{aligned} P_1 &= V_1^2 G \\ P_2 &= V_2^2 G \end{aligned} \tag{14-30}$$

Hence

$$D = 10 \log \left(\frac{V_1}{V_2}\right)^2 = 20 \log \frac{V_1}{V_2} \tag{14-31}$$

This is similar to Eq. (14-26) except for a sign, the factor 10, and the base of the logarithm. However, for any number $x$,

$$\ln x = (\ln 10)(\log x) = 2.3 \log x \tag{14-32}$$

Therefore,

$$\alpha = -0.23D \tag{14-33}$$

where $\alpha$ is in nepers and $D$ in decibels. The decibel unit is generally used in practical work. It is sometimes used in situations where input and output impedances are not identical. It then loses meaning in terms of power but still has meaning as the logarithm of a ratio of potentials or currents. The neper is more useful in analysis because it is based on natural logarithms.

**14-10. Summary.** In many applications it is important to know how the response of a circuit varies with one of the circuit parameters or with frequency. This is particularly true of frequency-selective networks, as used in communications. Information about the response is conveniently given by plotting the response function in the complex plane. When this is done, the scale of the variable parameter is carried on the locus curve itself. For many networks these curves are straight lines or circles.

Impedance and admittance plots in the complex plane all obey a few simple universal laws. Although these laws do not predict the details of the curves, they are sometimes useful in predicting general trends.

When a network has no dissipation, its impedance or admittance plot is given as a reactance (or susceptance) curve. As frequency is increased, the reactance or susceptance of a network always has a positive slope and alternately becomes zero and infinite. At zero and infinite frequencies the reactance or susceptance may be either zero or infinite.

When a frequency-selective system must pass (or reject) frequencies over a relatively large band of frequencies, it is usually called a filter. Filters are usually four-terminal networks, in which a signal is applied at one pair of terminals and a response is obtained at the other pair. One technique of filter design is based on a cascading of T or Π sections to form a ladder. Series and shunt branches are chosen so that their product is a real constant. Such a network is called a constant-$K$ filter. It can be designed to act as a low-pass, band-pass, band-elimination, or high-pass device. The essential characteristics of a filter are derivable from impedance considerations at one pair of terminals when the other pair are alternately on open circuit and short circuit.

The transmission properties of a four-terminal network are expressed in terms of the propagation function, a complex quantity. Its real part (the attenuation function) is the natural logarithm of the magnitude of the ratio of input to output signal. Its imaginary part (the phase function) is the phase difference between the input and output signals. Properties of filters can be plotted as curves of attenuation and propagation functions vs. frequency.

## PROBLEMS

NOTE: In those problems calling for locus curves, label each computed data point with the corresponding value of the variable parameter. Unless specified otherwise, allow the variable parameter to cover enough range to show the essential features of the locus.

**14-1.** A resistor of 300 ohms is connected in series with an inductor $L$.

*a.* Plot the locus of the complex impedance of the circuit, if $L = 0.25$ henry, with the frequency varying between 200 and 2000 cps.

*b.* Plot the locus of the impedance, with $L$ variable and $f$ constant at 100 cps. $L$ is variable between the limits of 0.2 and 1.6 henrys.

**14-2.** Repeat Prob. 14-1, plotting the admittance of the circuit in each case.

**14-3.** A resistor $R$ is connected in series with an inductor of 0.06 henry. The frequency is 500 cps. $R$ varies between the limits 60 and 600 ohms.

*a.* Plot the locus of the complex impedance of the circuit, showing several values of $R$ on the locus.

*b.* Plot the locus of the complex admittance of the circuit, showing several values of $R$ on the locus.

**14-4.** The locus of the complex impedance of a series circuit of $R$, $L$, and $C$ is to be plotted under the various conditions specified below.

*a.* Let $R = 1{,}000$, $C = 0.5 \times 10^{-6}$ farad, and $f = 100$ cps. $L$ is variable.

*b.* Let $R = 1{,}000$, $C = 0.5 \times 10^{-6}$ farad, and $L = 0.8$ henry. Frequency is variable.

*c.* Let $R = 1{,}000$, $L = 0.8$ henry, $f = 100$ cps. $C$ is variable.

**14-5.** Plot the admittance loci for the circuits and conditions specified in Prob. 14-4.

**14-6.** A circuit consists of a resistor, a perfect inductor, and a perfect capacitor in parallel. The locus of its complex admittance is to be plotted for the various conditions specified below.

*a.* Let $R = 2{,}000$ ohms, $L = 0.003$ henry, and $f = 10^5$ cps. $C$ is variable.

*b.* Let $R = 2{,}000$ ohms, $L = 0.003$ henry, and $C = 10^{-9}$ farad. The frequency is variable.

*c.* Let $R = 2{,}000$, $C = 10^{-9}$ farad, and $f = 10^5$ cps. $L$ is variable.

**14-7.** Plot the impedance loci for the circuits and conditions specified in Prob. 14-6.

**14-8.** A circuit consists of a capacitor connected in parallel with an inductor. The inductor has a resistance $R_L = 30$ ohms. The capacitance is $0.883 \times 10^{-6}$ farad, and the inductance is 0.00715 henry. For this condition

*a.* Plot the locus of the admittance of this circuit, with $\omega$ as the variable parameter.

*b.* From the curve plotted in part (*a*) estimate the frequency of minimum admittance and the frequency at which the admittance is real. From the formulas given in Probs. 10-19 and 10-20 obtain alternate values for these frequencies, and compare with the graphically obtained values.

*c.* Compute the constants of a pure parallel circuit having the same admittance as the original circuit, at the frequency for which the original circuit operates at minimum admittance.

**14-9.** Refer to the circuit specified in Prob. 14-8.

*a.* Plot the locus of the impedance of the circuit, with $\omega$ as the variable parameter.

*b.* Plot the impedance locus of the circuit specified in part *c* of Prob. 14-8.

**14-10.** Refer to the circuit specified in Prob. 14-8. Let $\omega_1$ be the angular frequency for maximum impedance and $\omega_2$ the angular frequency for unity power factor. Both of these are for the given set of parameter values. In each of the following cases plot loci of the admittance:

*a.* Let the angular frequency be fixed at $\omega_1$, and let $C$ be the variable.

*b.* Let the angular frequency be fixed at $\omega_2$, and let $C$ be the variable.

*c.* In case (*a*) suppose $C$ is adjusted to the value which gives minimum admittance. Show the locus of admittance if $C$ is then held constant and $\omega$ is allowed to vary.

**14-11.** Refer to the circuit specified in Prob. 14-8. Let $\omega_1$ be the angular frequency for maximum impedance and $\omega_2$ the angular frequency for unity power factor. Both of these are for the given set of parameter values. Plot loci of the admittance for the following conditions:

*a.* Let the angular frequency be fixed at $\omega_1$, and let $L$ be variable.

*b.* Let the angular frequency be fixed at $\omega_2$, and let $L$ be variable.

*c.* In case (*a*) suppose $L$ is adjusted to the value which gives minimum admittance. Show the locus of admittance if $L$ is then held constant, and $\omega$ is allowed to vary.

**14-12.** Plot the locus of $\mathbf{V}_2/\mathbf{I}_1$ for the circuit specified in Prob. 10-7. Show data points at the frequencies

| | | |
|---|---|---|
| 0 | 1,000,000 | 3,000,000 |
| 500,000 | 2,000,000 | 4,000,000 |

**14-13.** Plot the locus of $\mathbf{V}_2/\mathbf{V}_1$ for the circuit specified in Prob. 10-10, but with the 500-ohm resistor changed to 2,500 ohms. Show data points for the frequencies

| | | |
|---|---|---|
| 1,000 | 3,600 | 5,000 |
| 2,700 | 4,000 | 5,500 |
| 3,200 | 4,500 | 7,000 |

**14-14.** Plot the locus of $\mathbf{V}_2/\mathbf{V}_0$ for the circuit specified in Prob. 10-11 with $R = 10{,}000$ ohms and $C = 10^{-8}$ farad. Show data points at the frequencies

| | | | |
|---|---|---|---|
| 150 | 500 | 1,200 | 3,500 |
| 300 | 800 | 2,000 | 6,000 |

**14-15.** Plot the locus of $\mathbf{V}_2/\mathbf{V}_0$ for the circuit specified in Prob. 10-12. Show data points at the frequencies

| | | |
|---|---|---|
| 1,500 | 7,500 | 18,000 |
| 4,500 | 11,000 | 30,000 |

**14-16.** Plot the locus of $\mathbf{V}_2/\mathbf{I}_0$ for the circuit specified in Prob. 10-13. Show data points for the frequencies

| | | |
|---|---|---|
| 5 | 15 | 50 |
| 10 | 25 | 200 |

**14-17.** A circuit consists of an inductor of 0.005 henry in parallel with a capacitor of $0.001 \times 10^{-6}$ farad.

*a.* Plot the curve of the susceptance of this network as a function of frequency.

*b.* Plot the curve of the reactance of this network as a function of frequency.

**14-18.** A capacitor of $0.002 \times 10^{-6}$ farad is connected in series with the network specified in Prob. 14-17.

*a.* Plot the curve of the reactance of the new network as a function of frequency.

*b.* Plot the curve of the susceptance of the new network as a function of frequency.

**14-19.** An inductor of 0.002 henry is connected in series with the network specified in Prob. 14-17.

*a.* Plot the curve of the reactance of the new network as a function of frequency.

*b.* Plot the curve of the susceptance of the new network as a function of frequency.

**14-20.** A circuit consists of an inductor of 0.005 henry in series with a capacitor of $0.001 \times 10^{-6}$ farad.

*a.* Plot the curve of the reactance of this network as a function of frequency.

*b.* Plot the curve of the susceptance of this network as a function of frequency.

**14-21.** An inductor of 0.0025 henry is connected in parallel with the network specified in Prob. 14-20.

*a.* Plot the curve of the susceptance of the new network as a function of frequency.

*b.* Plot the curve of the reactance of the new network as a function of frequency.

**14-22.** A capacitance of $0.0025 \times 10^{-6}$ farad is connected in parallel with the network specified in Prob. 14-20.

*a.* Plot the curve of the susceptance of the new network as a function of frequency.

*b.* Plot the curve of the susceptance of the new network as a function of frequency.

**14-23.** A low-pass filter is to be of the constant-$K$ type, with maximum characteristic impedance $R_0$ of 500 ohms. The cutoff frequency is 5,000 cps.

*a.* Determine the constants of a T section of such a filter.

*b.* Plot the variation of the actual $R_0$, as a function of frequency, throughout the pass band.

*c.* Plot the attenuation and phase functions ($\alpha$ and $\beta$) of one section, as functions of frequency, when the section is terminated in a pure resistance of 400 ohms. The frequency range should extend to twice the cutoff value.

**14-24.** A high-pass filter is to be of the constant-$K$ type with maximum characteristic impedance $R_0$ of 500 ohms. The cutoff frequency is 500 cps.

*a.* Determine the constants of a T section of such a filter.

*b.* Plot the variation of the actual $R_0$, as a function of frequency, from cutoff up to a frequency beyond which there is no appreciable change.

*c.* Plot the attenuation and phase functions ($\alpha$ and $\beta$) of one section, as functions of frequency, when the section is terminated in a pure resistance of 400 ohms. The frequency range should extend from half cutoff value to the point beyond which there is no appreciable change.

## QUESTIONS

**14-1.** Consider the impedance locus of a series $R$-$L$-$C$ circuit. What changes does it undergo as (*a*) the resistance is changed, (*b*) $\sqrt{L/C}$ is changed while $\sqrt{LC}$ remains constant? Frequency is the variable parameter.

**14-2.** Answer Question 14-1 for the admittance locus of the same circuit.

**14-3.** What is the shape of the locus of the impedance of $G$ and $L$ in parallel (*a*) for variable $G$, (*b*) for variable frequency?

**14-4.** Specify the constants of a circuit for which the curved locus in Fig. 14-10 would be an impedance locus.

**14-5.** What happens to the right-hand intercept on the real axis of the curve of Fig. 14-10 as the resistance in the inductance branch approaches zero?

**14-6.** Suppose Fig. 14-1 is an $R$-$L$ circuit. In an actual case, using a physical inductor which has some resistance, what does the point $P$ do as the frequency becomes infinite?

**14-7.** Why is it not convenient to show the properties of reactance networks as plots in the complex plane?

**14-8.** Sketch the general shape of the net reactance and net susceptance functions for the network formed by the series connection of an inductor, a capacitor, and a parallel combination of a second capacitor and a second inductor. For what network would these be the general susceptance and reactance curves, respectively?

**14-9.** From a knowledge of the properties of a network impedance or admittance function how must its angle be varying as the magnitude passes through (*a*) a minimum, (*b*) a maximum? Assume the locus does not encircle the origin.

**14-10.** Is it necessary that an impedance or admittance function be real when it is a minimum or a maximum?

**14-11.** What is the distinguishing feature of a constant-$K$ filter?

**14-12.** Can a constant-$K$ filter have any one of the following forms: low pass, band pass, band elimination, high pass?

**14-13.** Why is it impossible for a filter of the constant-$K$ type to give uniform performance over the transmission range?

**14-14.** How are $\alpha$ and $\beta$ related to the complex function that represents the response (or transmission) of a network?

**14-15.** What values of $\alpha$ correspond to transmission functions of magnitudes 0, 0.5, and 1?

# CHAPTER 15

# NONSINUSOIDAL PERIODIC WAVES

**15-1. Introduction.** No wave met in practice is exactly sinusoidal. The waves are always somewhat distorted, although in many cases the distortion is negligible. In all the preceding chapters except Chap. 3, the assumption was made that the waves were sinusoidal. The purpose of this chapter is to show how linear* circuits behave under the influence of nonsinusoidal periodic waves.

**15-2. Sources of Nonsinusoidal Periodic Waves.** As pointed out in the introduction to this chapter, all sources provide nonsinusoidal waves to some extent, although the deviation may sometimes be negligible. Some sources, as in power systems, are made as nearly sinusoidal as practicable. In other cases, nonsinusoidal conditions are inherently necessary, as in music and speech transmission. The waves obtained from microphones and phonograph pickups are nonsinusoidal. In a strict sense they are also nonperiodic, but considered over relatively small time intervals they are periodic but nonsinusoidal.

Many vacuum-tube circuits behave like nonsinusoidal sources. Typical of these is the "multivibrator" circuit, which produces a square-wave output, and the relaxation oscillator, which produces a saw-tooth wave.

In addition to these sources, nonsinusoidal waves can be obtained by the excitation of nonlinear elements by sinusoidal sources. A simple illustration of this is shown in Fig. 15-1. It can represent a wide variety of nonlinear devices, such as a vacuum tube under nonlinear conditions of operation. Either the current or the potential can be a sinusoidal wave, but not both, as illustrated in the figure.

Another important case is shown in Fig. 15-2. It approximately shows the effect of having a ferromagnetic core in an inductor. Hysteresis is neglected. The flux is related to the current by a nonlinear magnetization curve. Neglecting coil resistance, if the induced potential is a sinusoidal wave, the flux is also sinusoidal, since the potential is the time derivative of the flux. The current wave is dictated by the shape of the magnetization curve, as shown in the figure. In a similar way, the device could generate a nonsinusoidal potential if the current were sinusoidal.

* It is recalled that a linear circuit is one in which the $R$, $L$, and $C$ parameters are constant, being independent of current magnitude or direction.

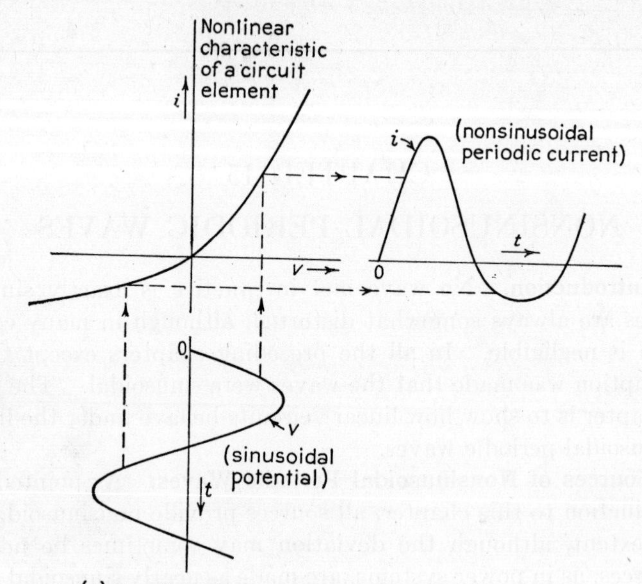


(a) Nonsinusoidal current from a sinusoidal potential

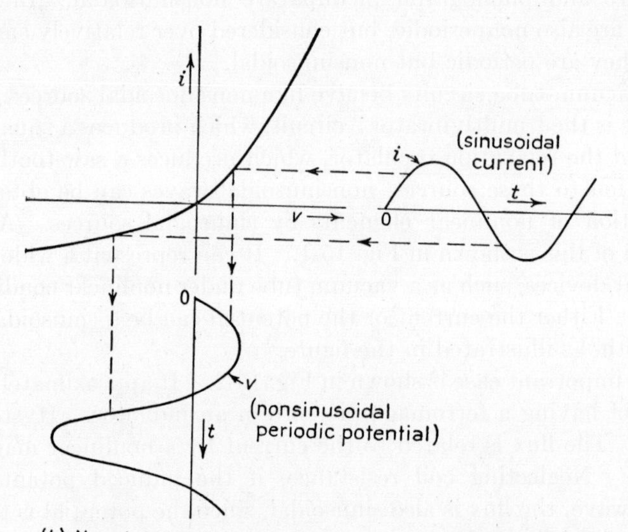


(b) Nonsinusoidal potential from a sinusoidal current

FIG. 15-1. Generation of nonsinusoidal wave by a nonlinear element.

In many cases the nonsinusoidal current or potential generated in a nonlinear element is impressed on a linear circuit. Thus the problem is reduced to one of finding the response of a linear network to a nonsinusoidal wave. To fall within the scope of this chapter, all networks to which the nonsinusoidal functions are applied must be linear. Nonlinear elements are admitted only as sources, and then only if they are approximate current or potential sources.

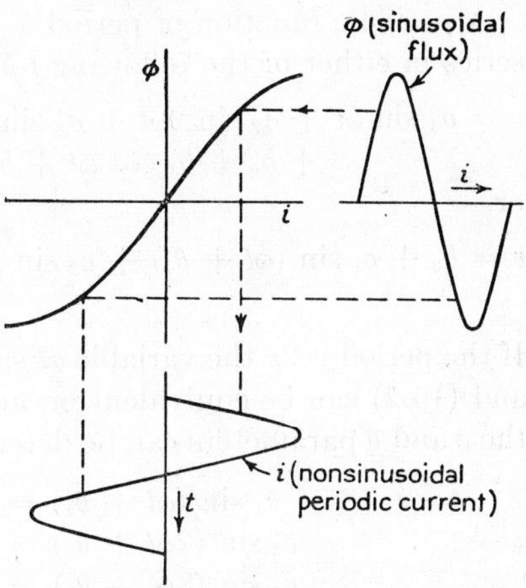

FIG. 15-2. Effect of nonlinearity in a magnetic circuit.

Figure 15-3 illustrates how a nonlinear element may impress a nonsinusoidal wave on a linear network. It shows the equivalent circuit of a vacuum-tube amplifier. The circle represents the nonlinear relation between potential on the control grid of the tube and the current in the plate circuit. Thus, although the potential $v_1$ may be sinusoidal, the current $i_p$ is nonsinusoidal. This current flows into a circuit which is linear. (This is somewhat in error, because in practice the resistor $r_p$ can be considered linear only to a first approximation.) The potential $v_2$ is then the response of a linear network to a nonsinusoidal excitation.

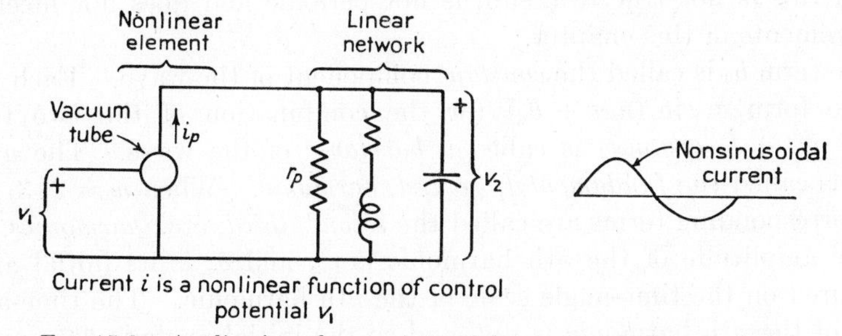

FIG. 15-3. Application of a nonsinusoidal current to a linear network.

**15-3. Examples of Harmonic Synthesis.** Any periodic function arising in practical examples can be represented by an infinite series of sinusoidal components whose frequencies are integral multiples of the lowest one. Such a sum of sinusoidal components is called a *Fourier series*. Usually a finite number of sinusoidal components will give a good approximation, the number required depending on the function to be represented. The method used to find the magnitudes and initial angles of the components, the technique of *harmonic analysis,* is the subject of Chap. 16. Present considerations deal with the problem of synthesis, showing how the addition of a number of harmonically related sinusoidal components leads to a nonsinusoidal periodic wave.

A periodic function of period $T = 2\pi/\omega$ can be expressed as a Fourier series in either of the following forms:

$$v = a_1 \sin \omega t + a_2 \sin 2\omega t + a_3 \sin 3\omega t + \cdots + b_0 + b_1 \cos \omega t + b_2 \cos 2\omega t + b_3 \cos 3\omega t + \cdots \quad (15\text{-}1)$$

or

$$v = b_0 + c_1 \sin (\omega t + \theta_1) + c_2 \sin (2\omega t + \theta_2) + c_3 \sin (3\omega t + \theta_3) + \cdots \quad (15\text{-}2)$$

If the period is $2\pi$ the variable $\omega t$ can be replaced by $x$. Equations (15-1) and (15-2) can be equivalent because, given a set of $a$ and $b$ parameters, the $c$ and $\theta$ parameters can be determined from the equations

$$\begin{aligned} c_1 \sin (\omega t + \theta_1) &= a_1 \sin \omega t + b_1 \cos \omega t \\ c_2 \sin (2\omega t + \theta_2) &= a_2 \sin 2\omega t + b_2 \cos 2\omega t \\ c_3 \sin (3\omega t + \theta_3) &= a_3 \sin 3\omega t + b_3 \cos 3\omega t \\ &\text{etc.} \end{aligned} \quad (15\text{-}3)$$

The same set of equations will serve to determine the $a$ and $b$ parameters if the $c$ and $\theta$ parameters are given.

It is said that the frequencies in the terms of Eq. (15-1) are *harmonically* related because they are all integral multiples of the lowest frequency. When this is not true, the sum is not periodic and does not meet the requirements of this chapter.

The term $b_0$ is called the *constant* component of the wave. Each term of the form $c_n \sin (n\omega t + \theta_n)$ (or the combination of the two terms $a_n \sin n\omega t + b_n \cos n\omega t$) is called a *harmonic* of the wave. The $n = 1$ term is called the *fundamental,* or *first, harmonic.* When $n = 2, 3,$ etc., the corresponding terms are called the *second, third,* etc., *harmonics.*

The amplitude of the $n$th harmonic is $c_n$, and $\theta_n$ is its initial angle, measured on the time-angle scale of the $n$th harmonic. The time-angle scale of the $n$th harmonic is $n\omega t$, and so the initial angle is $\theta_n/n$ on the time-angle scale of the fundamental.

The forms illustrated in Eqs. (15-1) and (15-2) will recur repeatedly. It is therefore convenient to have names for them. The form given in Eq. (15-1) will be called the *sine-cosine* form, and the one given in Eq. (15-2) will be called the *sine* form. Still another form consisting of all cosine terms is useful in many applications but is omitted from consideration here, in the interest of simplicity.

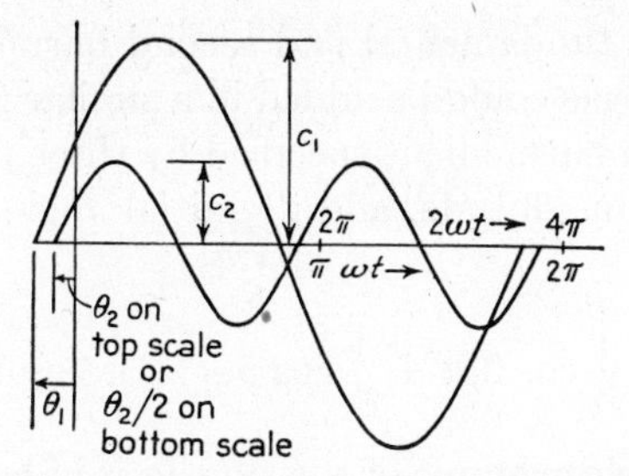


Fig. 15-4. Comparison of timeangle scales of the fundamental and second harmonic.

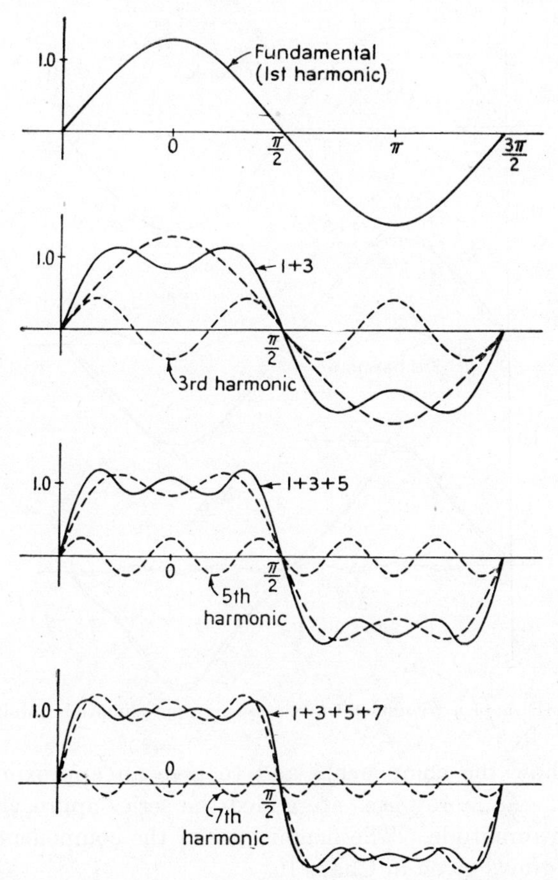


Fig. 15-5. Synthesis of a square wave, showing approximation obtained with four terms.

A comparison of a fundamental and second harmonic is shown in Fig. 15-4. Additional terms could be added in a similar manner. This figure emphasizes that each harmonic is specified by three parameters, the order of the harmonic, its magnitude, and its initial angle.

The series

$$v = \frac{4}{\pi}\left(\cos \omega t - \frac{1}{3}\cos 3\omega t + \frac{1}{5}\cos 5\omega t - \frac{1}{7}\cos 7\omega t + \cdots\right) \qquad (15\text{-}4)$$

can be used as a simple example of the synthesis of harmonic components. It is a special case of Eq. (15-1) in which all $a$ terms are zero. Figure

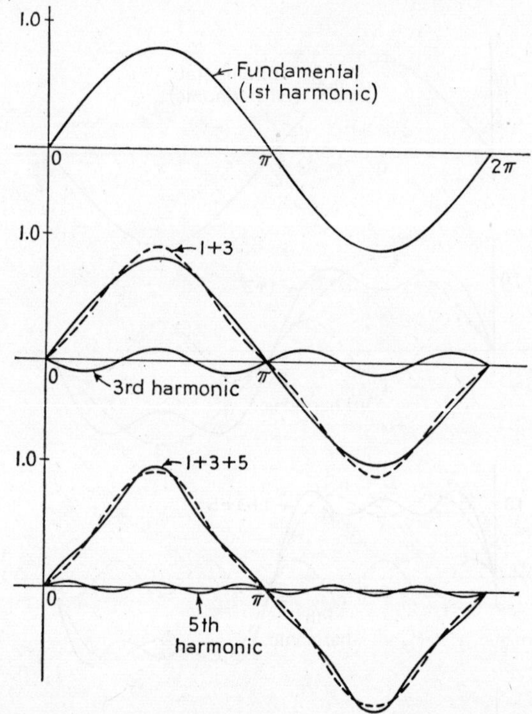


Fig. 15-6. Synthesis of a triangular wave, showing approximation obtained with three terms.

15-5 shows how the components add to give an approximation for a square wave. As more terms are added the series approaches a square wave of unit amplitude. The magnitudes of the components are determined by methods given in Chap. 16.

As another example consider the series

$$v = \frac{8}{\pi^2}\left(\sin \omega t - \frac{1}{9}\sin 3\omega t + \frac{1}{25}\sin 5\omega t - \frac{1}{49}\sin 7\omega t + \cdots\right) \qquad (15\text{-}5)$$

It is graphically represented in Fig. 15-6. As more and more terms are added, the series approaches a triangular wave having a peak value of unity.

**15-4. Effect of Choice of Origin on the Form of the Series.** The form of a series for a given wave depends on the position of the wave on the time axis. For example, suppose that Eq. (15-2) is used to represent a given wave and the origin is then shifted to the right an amount $t_0$ on the time scale. Recalling the meaning of initial angle, as shown in Fig. 2-27, it follows that such a shift of origin will cause $\theta_n$ to increase by an amount $n\omega t_0$. Thus, a change in origin affects all the initial angles, but

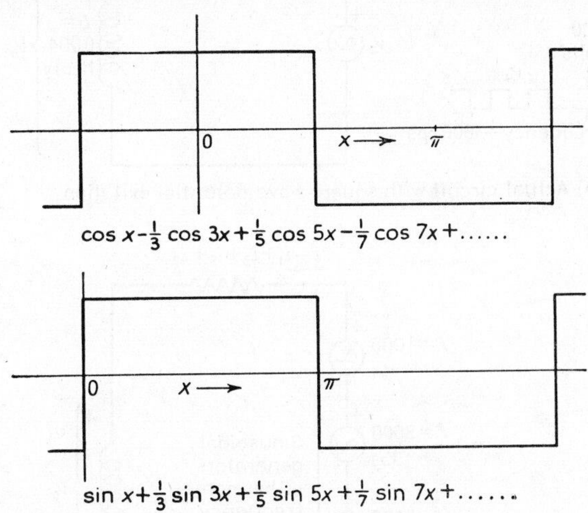


FIG. 15-7. An example of the effect of choice of origin on form of the series formula for a wave.

not the amplitudes. However, the $a$ and $b$ coefficients of Eq. (15-1) both change if the origin is shifted.

This can be illustrated by applying Eqs. (15-3) to the $n$th harmonic to give

$$c_n \sin (n\omega t + \theta_n) = (c_n \cos \theta_n) \sin n\omega t + (c_n \sin \theta_n) \cos n\omega t \quad (15\text{-}6)$$

from which it follows that

$$a_n = c_n \cos \theta_n$$
$$b_n = c_n \sin \theta_n \quad (15\text{-}7)$$

Equation (15-7) shows that $a_n$ and $b_n$ are both functions of $\theta_n$ and therefore depend on the position of the origin on the time axis.

In Fig. 15-7 two positions of the origin are shown, using the square wave as an illustration. The corresponding expressions for the series are included. Some positions of the origin may yield simpler series than others. Since the choice of origin is usually arbitrary, it is well to choose it appropriately.

**15-5. Response of Linear Networks to Nonsinusoidal Periodic Waves.** The specific example of Fig. 15-8*a* is used as an illustration of an analysis of a linear network in which currents and potentials are periodic but nonsinusoidal. The principle of superposition applies because the circuit is

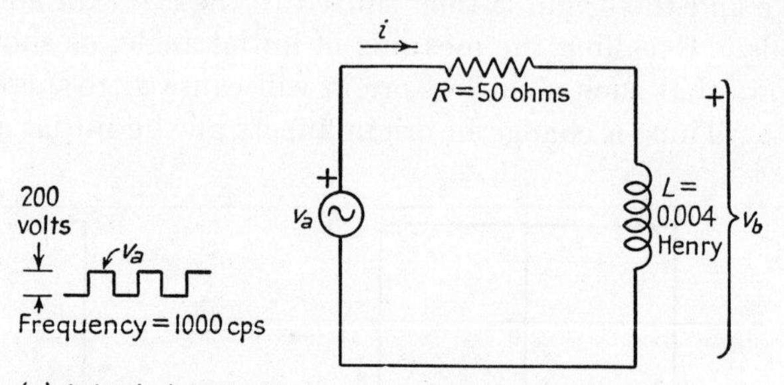


(a) Actual circuit with square wave potential exitation

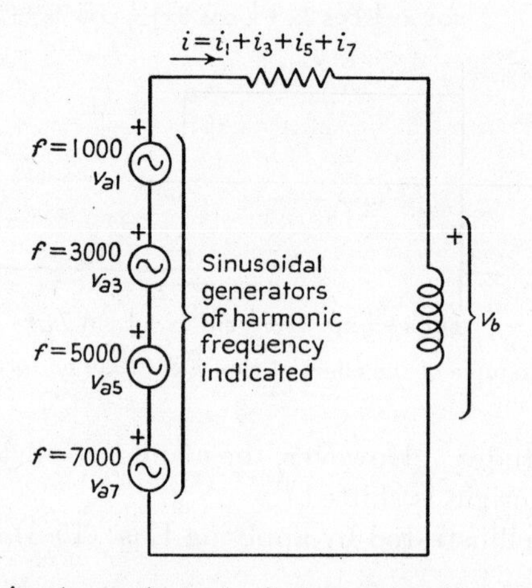


(b) Approximate equivalent of above circuit

FIG. 15-8. Illustration of superposition of harmonic components.

linear. Thus, the square-wave potential source can be replaced by the series of sinusoidal sources of odd harmonic frequencies, shown in Fig. 15-8*b*. The potential $v_{a1}$ will give a sinusoidal response $i_1$, $v_{a3}$ will give a response $i_3$, etc. The total response current is then

$$i = i_1 + i_3 + i_5 + \cdots \tag{15-8}$$

Each component of current is sinusoidal and can be found from the known circuit parameters by the *steady-state circuit theory*. The concept of sinor representation for sinusoids, and complex algebra, can be applied to each component.* For example, let

$$\begin{array}{ll} \mathbf{V}_{a1} \text{ symbolize } v_{a1} & \mathbf{I}_1 \text{ symbolize } i_1 \\ \mathbf{V}_{a3} \text{ symbolize } v_{a3} & \mathbf{I}_3 \text{ symbolize } i_3 \\ \text{etc.} & \end{array} \tag{15-9}$$

each current sinor $\mathbf{I}_n$ is related to its corresponding potential sinor $\mathbf{V}_{an}$ by

$$\mathbf{I}_n = \frac{\mathbf{V}_{an}}{\mathbf{Z}_n} \tag{15-10}$$

where

$$\mathbf{Z}_n = \sqrt{R^2 + (n\omega L)^2} \Big/ \tan^{-1} \frac{n\omega L}{R} \tag{15-11}$$

The index $n$ is allowed to take on enough values to represent the waves of $v_a$ and $i$ with sufficient accuracy. Tabulated numerical values for the case of Fig. 15-8 are given below, for four values of $n$. The numerical values for the $\sqrt{2}\,\mathbf{V}_{an}$ column of the table are obtained from Eq. (15-4) after it has been multiplied by 100, because the peak value of $v_a$ is 100 volts.

| $n$ | $\sqrt{2}\,\mathbf{V}_{an}$ volts | $\mathbf{Z}_n$ ohms | $\sqrt{2}\,\mathbf{I}_n = \frac{\sqrt{2}\,\mathbf{V}_{an}}{\mathbf{Z}_n}$ amp | $i_n$ amp |
|---|---|---|---|---|
| 1 | $127 \underline{/90°}$ | $56 \underline{/26.5°}$ | $2.26 \underline{/73.5°}$ | $2.26 \sin(\omega t + 73.5°)$ |
| 3 | $42.4 \underline{/-90°}$ | $90.3 \underline{/56.4°}$ | $0.47 \underline{/146.4°}$ | $0.47 \sin(3\omega t - 146.4°)$ |
| 5 | $25.4 \underline{/90°}$ | $135 \underline{/68.3°}$ | $0.188 \underline{/31.7°}$ | $0.188 \sin(5\omega t + 31.7°)$ |
| 7 | $18.1 \underline{/-90°}$ | $182.5 \underline{/74°}$ | $0.10 \underline{/164°}$ | $0.10 \sin(7\omega t - 164°)$ |

The resulting equation for the current is

$$i = 2.26 \sin(\omega t + 73.5°) + 0.47 \sin(3\omega t - 146.4°) + 0.188 \sin(5\omega t + 31.7°) + 0.10 \sin(7\omega t - 164°) \tag{15-12}$$

It is noted that this series converges more rapidly than the series for the applied potential. The coil has the effect of suppressing the higher harmonics. A plot of the current, obtained from Eq. (15-12) is given in Fig. 15-9.

Another response of interest is the potential $v_b$. It is the sum of sinusoidal components $v_{b1}$, $v_{b3}$, etc., which are symbolically represented by sinors as follows:

$$\begin{array}{l} \mathbf{V}_{b1} \text{ symbolizes } v_{b1} \\ \mathbf{V}_{b3} \text{ symbolizes } v_{b3} \\ \text{etc.} \end{array} \tag{15-13}$$

* It must be realized that complex numbers which symbolically represent sinusoids of *different frequencies* cannot be added. Only the time functions themselves can be added when the frequencies differ.

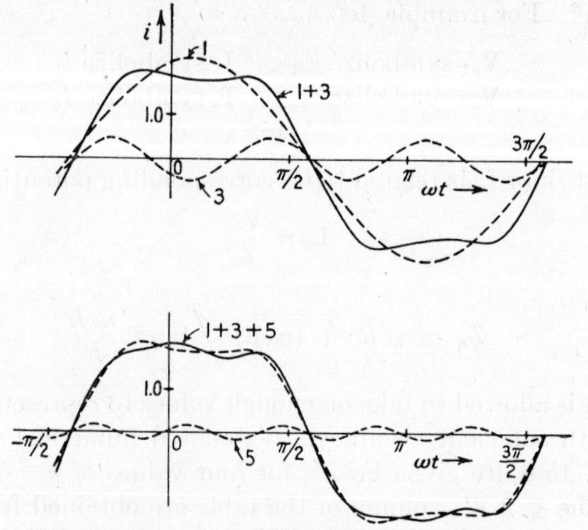


(a) Synthesis of current from components of Eq. (15-12). Seventh harmonic omitted

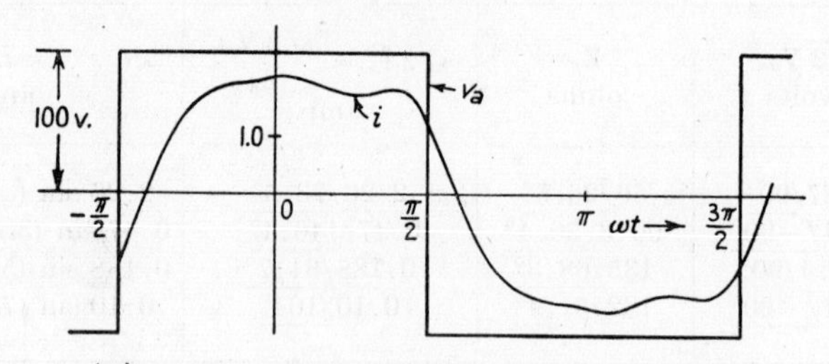


(b) Curves of potential and current in Fig. 15-8

FIG. 15-9. Analysis of current in Fig. 15-8 in terms of harmonic components.

For each value of $n$, the steady-state analysis of the network gives

$$\mathbf{V}_{bn} = \frac{jn\omega L(\mathbf{V}_{an})}{\mathbf{Z}_n} \tag{15-14}$$

where $\mathbf{Z}_n$ is given by Eq. (15-11). The computations for four values of $n$ are given in the tabulation below.

| $n$ | $\frac{j\omega L}{\mathbf{Z}_n}$ | $\sqrt{2}\,\mathbf{V}_{bn} = j\omega L \frac{\sqrt{2}\,\mathbf{V}_{an}}{\mathbf{Z}_n}$ | $v_{bn}$ |
|---|---|---|---|
| 1 | $.448\underline{/73.5^\circ}$ | $56.8\underline{/163.5^\circ}$ | $56.8 \sin(\omega t + 163.5^\circ)$ |
| 3 | $.835\underline{/43.6^\circ}$ | $35.4\underline{/-46.4^\circ}$ | $35.4 \sin(3\omega t - 46.4^\circ)$ |
| 5 | $.930\underline{/31.7^\circ}$ | $23.6\underline{/121.7^\circ}$ | $23.6 \sin(5\omega t + 121.7^\circ)$ |
| 7 | $.962\underline{/26^\circ}$ | $17.4\underline{/-64^\circ}$ | $17.4 \sin(7\omega t - 64^\circ)$ |

The equation for the potential $v_b$ is

$$v_b = 56.8 \sin(\omega t + 163.5°) + 35.4 \sin(3\omega t - 46.4°) + 23.6 \sin(5\omega t + 121.7°) + 17.4 \sin(7\omega t - 64°) \quad (15\text{-}15)$$

This series converges less rapidly than the one for $v_a$. The increasing reactance of the coil, with increasing frequency, causes the potential

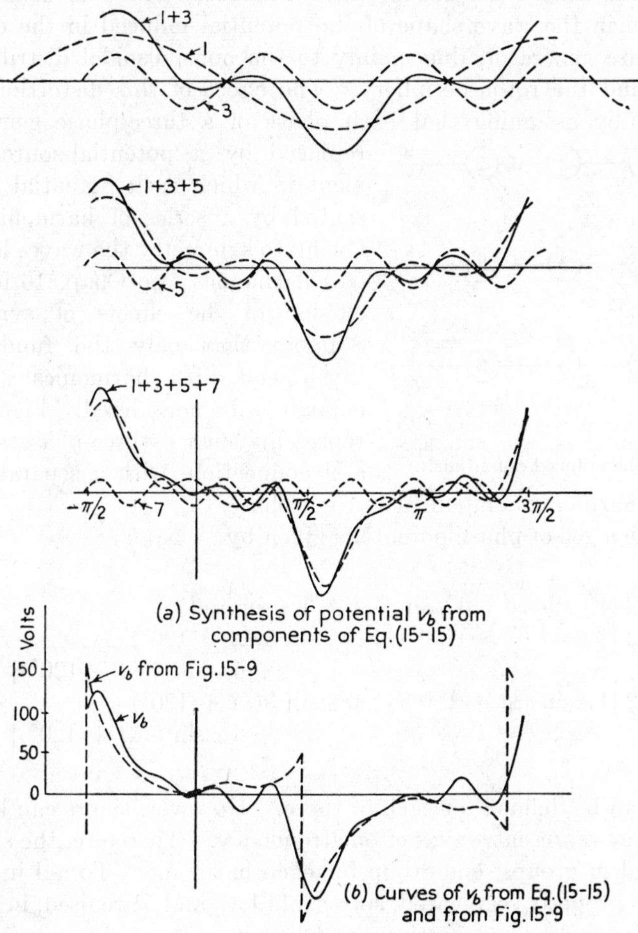


FIG. 15-10. Analysis of potential $v_b$ in Fig. 15-8 in terms of harmonic components. ($v_b$ from Fig. 15-9 is a plot of $v_a - iR$.)

across it to accentuate the higher harmonics. For this reason Eq. (15-15) would not be considered a good engineering approximation of $v_b$. More terms are needed to give a good approximation. A plot of Eq. (15-15) is given in Fig. 15-10; also included is a graph of $v_a - iR$, in which $i$ has been obtained from Fig. 15-9, which is a more accurate graph of $v_b$.

The reader is warned that superposition of responses due to harmonic components cannot be used if the circuit changes during a cycle. This excludes any circuit employing an ideal rectifier (which is alternately an open circuit and a short circuit) if the rectifier causes the circuit to open at any time during the cycle.

**15-6. Harmonics in Three-phase Sources.** There is usually some distortion in the wave shape of the potential induced in the coils of a three-phase generator, due mainly to the nonsinusoidal distribution of flux around the rotor periphery. The effect of this distortion can be analyzed by assuming that each phase of a three-phase generator is replaced by a potential-source equivalent in which each potential is represented by a series of harmonic terms. Owing to symmetry the waves have only odd harmonics (see Chap. 16 for a discussion of the effects of symmetry). Suppose that only the fundamental, third, and fifth harmonics are large enough to be considered. Figure 15-11 represents such a three-phase source in a Y connection, with a separate source for each harmonic component in each phase.

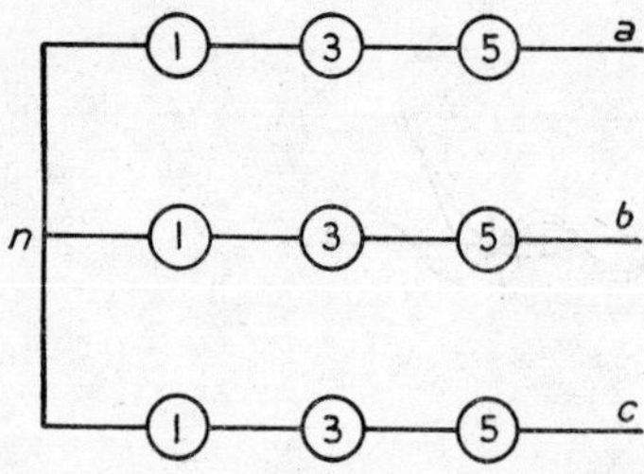


FIG. 15-11. Potential sources representing a three-phase generator with fundamental, third, and fifth harmonics in the induced potentials.

Assume a set of phase potentials given by

$$
\begin{aligned}
v_{an} &= \sqrt{2}\,[V_1 \sin \omega t + V_3 \sin 3\omega t + V_5 \sin 5\omega t] \\
v_{bn} &= \sqrt{2}\,[V_1 \sin (\omega t - 120°) + V_3 \sin 3(\omega t - 120°) \\
&\qquad + V_5 \sin 5(\omega t - 120°)] \qquad (15\text{-}16) \\
v_{cn} &= \sqrt{2}\,[V_1 \sin (\omega t + 120°) + V_3 \sin 3(\omega t + 120°) \\
&\qquad + V_5 \sin 5(\omega t + 120°)]
\end{aligned}
$$

A sinor can be defined for each of these. However, sinors can be added only if they represent waves of one frequency. Therefore, the sinors are considered in groups, one group for each harmonic. To aid in keeping the sinors properly segregated, subscripts 1, 3, and 5 are used, in addition to the regular double subscripts, as follows:

Fundamental frequency:

$\mathbf{V}_{an1}$ symbolizes $\sqrt{2}\, V_1 \sin \omega t$
$\mathbf{V}_{bn1}$ symbolizes $\sqrt{2}\, V_1 \sin (\omega t - 120°)$
$\mathbf{V}_{cn1}$ symbolizes $\sqrt{2}\, V_1 \sin (\omega t + 120°)$

Third harmonic:

$$
\begin{aligned}
&\mathbf{V}_{an3} \text{ symbolizes } \sqrt{2}\, V_3 \sin 3\omega t \\
&\mathbf{V}_{bn3} \text{ symbolizes } \sqrt{2}\, V_3 \sin 3(\omega t - 120°) = \sqrt{2}\, V_3 \sin 3\omega t \\
&\mathbf{V}_{cn3} \text{ symbolizes } \sqrt{2}\, V_3 \sin 3(\omega t + 120°) = \sqrt{2}\, V_3 \sin 3\omega t
\end{aligned}
\qquad (15\text{-}17)
$$

Fifth harmonic:

$$
\begin{aligned}
&\mathbf{V}_{an5} \text{ symbolizes } \sqrt{2}\, V_5 \sin 5\omega t \\
&\mathbf{V}_{bn5} \text{ symbolizes } \sqrt{2}\, V_5 \sin 5(\omega t - 120°) = \sqrt{2}\, V_5 \sin (5\omega t + 120°) \\
&\mathbf{V}_{cn5} \text{ symbolizes } \sqrt{2}\, V_5 \sin 5(\omega t + 120°) = \sqrt{2}\, V_5 \sin (5\omega t - 120°)
\end{aligned}
$$

Typical diagrams of these sinors are shown in Fig. 15-12. In each group they can be combined to obtain the line potentials for one harmonic.

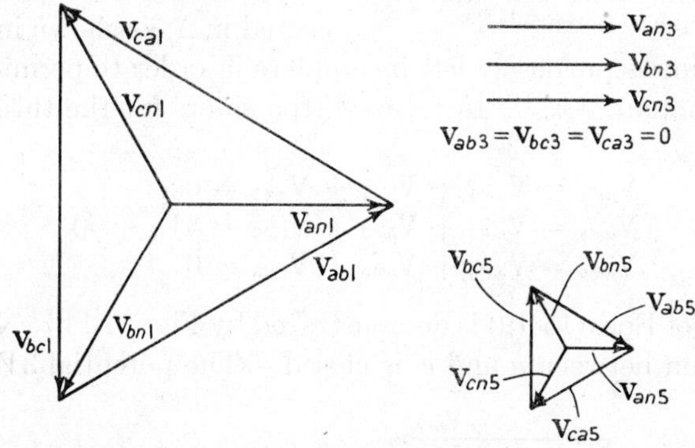


FIG. 15-12. Sinors for the various potentials for each of the three frequency components of Fig. 15-11.

No sinor representation is possible for the complete line potentials because they are nonsinusoidal.

Important observations can be made from Fig. 15-12. The fundamental- and fifth-harmonic components each form a balanced three-phase system. The fifth-harmonic system has the opposite phase sequence from the fundamental. All the components of the third-harmonic system are in phase. Since $\mathbf{V}_{ab3} = \mathbf{V}_{an3} - \mathbf{V}_{bn3}$, etc., it follows that all third-harmonic components of the line potentials are zero. Converting the sinors of Fig. 15-12 to time functions yields the line potentials,

$$
\begin{aligned}
v_{ab} &= \sqrt{6}\,[V_1 \sin (\omega t + 60°) + V_5 \sin (5\omega t - 60°)] \\
v_{bc} &= \sqrt{6}\,[V_1 \sin (\omega t - 90°) + V_5 \sin (5\omega t + 90°)] \\
v_{ca} &= \sqrt{6}\,[V_1 \sin (\omega t + 120°) + V_5 \sin (5\omega t - 120°)]
\end{aligned}
\qquad (15\text{-}18)
$$

If such a machine is connected to a balanced load of linear elements, the currents can be determined by superimposing solutions due to each of the systems of harmonic components. If there is no neutral connection, so that the load is acted upon only by line potentials, there will be no third-harmonic component of current anywhere in the network. If the load is Y-connected, however, third-harmonic potentials will appear between the neutrals. If there is a neutral connection, each phase of the load is connected across a phase of the source and there will be third-harmonic currents throughout the system.

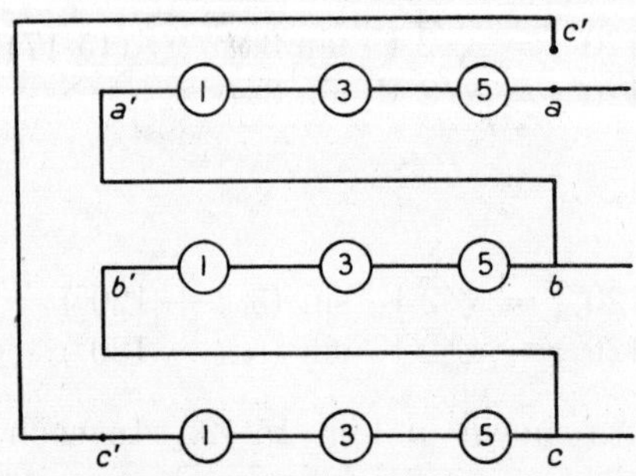


FIG. 15-13. The Δ connection of a generator with fundamental, third, and fifth harmonics in the induced potentials.

Now suppose the machine is connected in Δ, as shown in Fig. 15-13. The connection is purposely left incomplete in order to permit consideration of the potential $v_{ac'}$. In terms of the sinors for the three harmonic components:

$$
\begin{aligned}
\mathbf{V}_{ac'1} &= \mathbf{V}_{aa'1} + \mathbf{V}_{bb'1} + \mathbf{V}_{cc'1} = 0 \\
\mathbf{V}_{ac'3} &= \mathbf{V}_{aa'3} + \mathbf{V}_{bb'3} + \mathbf{V}_{cc'3} = 3V_3 + j0 \\
\mathbf{V}_{ac'5} &= \mathbf{V}_{aa'5} + \mathbf{V}_{bb'5} + \mathbf{V}_{cc'5} = 0
\end{aligned}
\qquad (15\text{-}19)
$$

The validity of Eqs. (15-19) is demonstrated by Fig. 15-14. Now suppose the connection between $a$ and $c'$ is closed. The potential $3V_3$ will cause

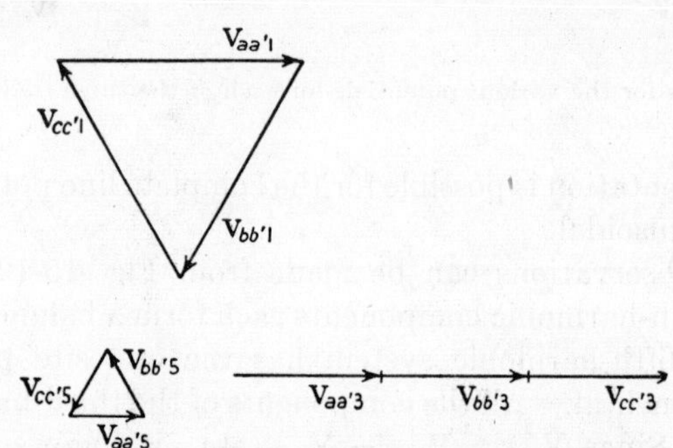


FIG. 15-14. Sinors for the various potentials for each of the three frequency components of Fig. 15-13.

a third-harmonic current to circulate within the windings of the machines. The effect of this current will be to cause the suppression of the third harmonic of the potentials. To understand this, consider Fig. 15-15, which applies only to the third harmonic.* Up to this point, there was

* This is somewhat of an oversimplification because it neglects mutual effects between windings. However, if mutual effects were included, the same conclusion would be reached, provided the phases have balanced currents and potentials.

no need to consider source impedances. However, the third-harmonic current is limited by the impedances of the windings, and so the impedances must be included in the consideration. The circulating current is

$$\mathbf{I}_3 = \frac{\mathbf{V}_{ac'3}}{3\mathbf{Z}_3} = \frac{\mathbf{V}_{aa'}}{\mathbf{Z}_3} = \frac{\mathbf{V}_{bb'3}}{\mathbf{Z}_3} = \frac{\mathbf{V}_{cc'3}}{\mathbf{Z}_3} \tag{15-20}$$

The line potentials are

$$\begin{aligned} \mathbf{V}_{ab3} &= \mathbf{V}_{aa'3} - \mathbf{I}_3\mathbf{Z}_3 = 0 \\ \mathbf{V}_{bc3} &= \mathbf{V}_{bb'3} - \mathbf{I}_3\mathbf{Z}_3 = 0 \\ \mathbf{V}_{ca3} &= \mathbf{V}_{cc'3} - \mathbf{I}_3\mathbf{Z}_3 = 0 \end{aligned} \tag{15-21}$$

It is found that in both the Y connection without neutral and the Δ connection there are no third harmonics in the line potentials. Further investigation would show that the line potentials have no components of frequencies which are multiples of the third. From the standpoint of efficiency the Y connection is somewhat preferable, because with the Δ connection the third harmonic current causes heating of the machine windings.

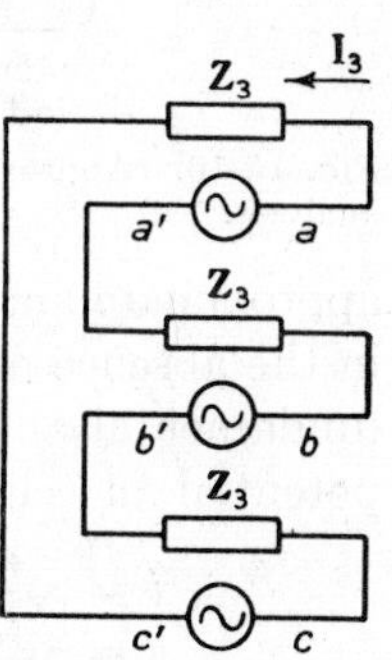

FIG. 15-15. Internal circuit to third harmonic in Δ-connected source.

For two cases (the balanced Y-connected source without neutral and the balanced Δ-connected source) it has been shown that all third-harmonic components of the line currents must be zero. This conclusion can be obtained directly from the fact that there is no neutral connection, without regard for the type of source or load connection. To proceed with a proof, let $i_a$, $i_b$, and $i_c$ be the line currents of a balanced three-phase three-wire system (with all their reference directions the same). Since there are only three wires,

$$i_a + i_b + i_c = 0 \tag{15-22}$$

Suppose each current is the sum of a fundamental and a third harmonic:

$$\begin{aligned} i_a &= \sqrt{2}\,[I_1 \sin \omega t + I_3 \sin 3\omega t] \\ i_b &= \sqrt{2}\,[I_1 \sin (\omega t - 120°) + I_3 \sin (3\omega t - 360°)] \\ i_c &= \sqrt{2}\,[I_1 \sin (\omega t + 120°) + I_3 \sin (3\omega t + 360°)] \end{aligned} \tag{15-23}$$

The sum of the fundamental components is zero, so Eq. (15-22) becomes $3I_3 \sin \omega t = 0$. This is possible only if $I_3 = 0$, confirming the previous conclusion.

**15-7. Harmonics Due to Iron-core Transformers in Three-phase Networks.** In Fig. 15-2 it is shown that current and flux (or potential) in a coil with an iron core cannot both be sinusoidal at the same time. If the current is sinusoidal, the potential will be nonsinusoidal, and vice versa. It is impossible to account for this accurately in a linear-network analysis, but the circuit of Fig. 15-16 is a first-order approximation. It should be appraised with the understanding that there is no one value of $L$ which describes the coil (hence the quotation marks on the diagram) and that it can no longer be considered as a passive element. In this

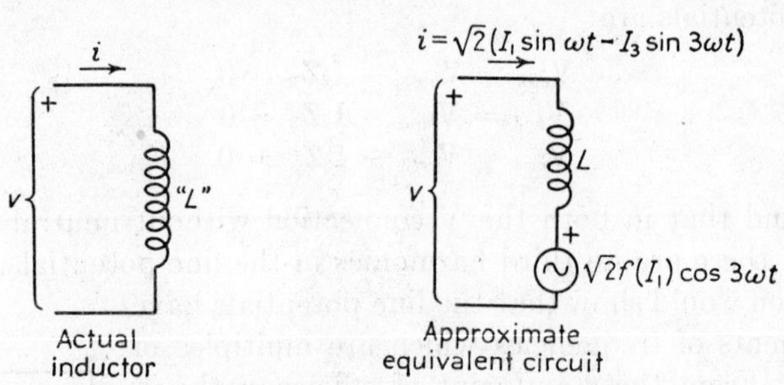


FIG. 15-16. Approximate equivalent for an iron-core inductor for use in linear-network analysis.

approximate analysis $L$ may be thought of as the inductance of the coil in the absence of magnetic saturation. Consideration is confined to the fundamental and third harmonic. Accordingly, it is assumed that the potential and current can be written

$$\begin{aligned} i &= \sqrt{2}\,(I_1 \sin \omega t - I_3 \sin 3\omega t) \\ v &= \sqrt{2}\,[\omega L I_1 \cos \omega t - 3\omega L I_3 \cos 3\omega t + f(I_1) \cos 3\omega t] \end{aligned} \qquad (15\text{-}24)$$

The third harmonic of potential source is written $f(I_1)$ to indicate it as a function of the fundamental of current. It is a hypothetical potential

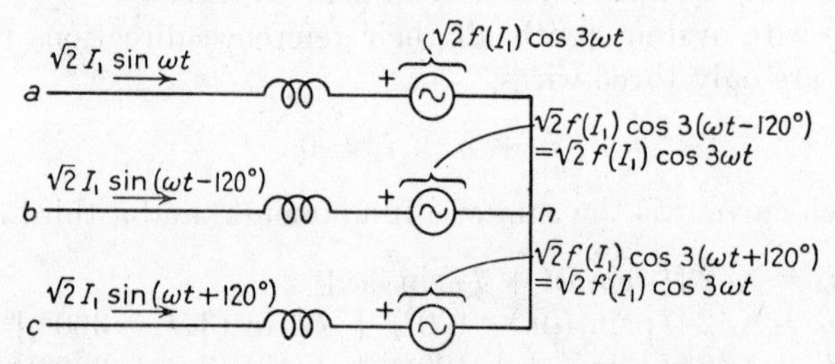


FIG. 15-17. Approximate equivalent network for nonlinear inductor in a Y connection.

source which approximately takes into account the third-harmonic generating effects of magnetic saturation. The function $f(I_1)$ is zero when $I_1$ is zero and increases with $I_1$, but not linearly.

Now suppose three identical inductors (or transformers) are connected in Y to a balanced three-phase source having no harmonics, as indicated in Fig. 15-17. There is no neutral connection. The fundamental components of current form a balanced system, as shown. From the conclusions of Sec. 15-6, it is known that no third-harmonic currents will flow. Therefore, no compensating third-harmonic potentials appear across the inductance of the equivalent circuit ($j\omega LI_3 = 0$), and so the line-to-neutral potential includes a third-harmonic component.

This phenomenon must be heeded in choosing transformer connections. For example, if a three-phase line is converted to three single-phase lines by three transformers, the arrangement shown in Fig. 15-18 would not be satisfactory. The third-harmonic potential would appear across the secondaries and therefore would be in the line potentials of the single-phase systems. However, if the three secondaries are connected in delta, the third harmonics will be suppressed, as described in Sec. 15-6. The third-harmonic current which will then flow in the Δ-connected secondaries provides the needed third-harmonic component of magnetizing force.

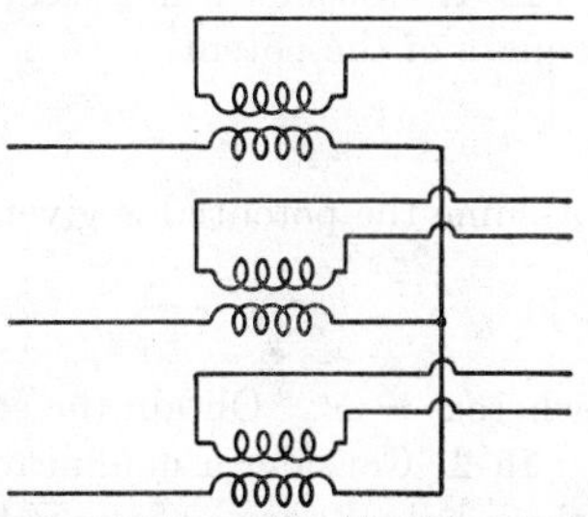

FIG. 15-18. Arrangement that gives distorted output potentials due to saturation of iron in transformers, when obtaining three single-phase lines from a three-phase system.

If the primaries and secondaries are connected in Y also, each transformer will operate with a distorted potential and a sinusoidal current. This is not advisable, even if phase potentials are not used directly, because when operated with a sinusoidal current and a distorted potential there is more power loss in the iron. For this reason, Y connections on both primary and secondary are not advisable. In cases where such a connection is required, from other considerations, the transformers are provided with small auxiliary windings which are connected in delta. They do not supply any load, their only purpose being to provide a path for a third-harmonic circulating current. Such windings are called *tertiary windings*.

**15-8. Summary.** A periodically varying quantity can be treated by considering it to be the sum of a number of sinusoidal components. The frequencies of the components are integral multiples of the lowest (fundamental) frequency. An infinite number of components is required to give an exact representation of a general periodic function. However, for an engineering approximation it is usually sufficient to consider a relatively few terms.

The possibility of representing nonsinusoidal periodic functions by sinusoidal components is useful when analyzing a liner network. Steady-state circuit theory applies to each harmonic component. Thus, the steady-state sinusoidal solutions, which take up the bulk of this text, can be extended to the nonsinusoidal case.

Harmonics may be due to deviations from the sinusoidal wave shape in a source, or they may be due to nonlinear circuit elements. The iron-core transformer (or inductor) and vacuum tubes are common sources of harmonics. In linear circuit analysis the effects of nonlinear elements are approximately accounted for by replacing the elements by equivalent circuits. This equivalent includes the element itself as a passive device and one or more sources (potential or current) at the various harmonic frequencies. The network can be analyzed by the standard methods of sinusoidal circuit analysis, sinors and complex quantities, but final results must be in terms of time functions because sinors cannot be combined if they symbolize sinusoids of different frequencies.

## PROBLEMS

**15-1.** Consider a nonlinear device in which the current is proportional to the square of the potential, *viz.*,

$$i = 0.005(v)^2$$

Assume the potential is given by

$$v = 2 + 2 \sin x$$

where $x = \omega t$. Obtain the series for the current.

**15-2.** Consider a nonlinear device in which the current is proportional to the three-halves power of the potential, *viz.*,

$$i = 0.01(v)^{3/2}$$

Assume the potential is the same as in Prob. 15-1. Use three terms in the binomial expansion of $(2 + 2 \sin x)^{3/2}$ and suitable trigonometric identities to show that the first four terms in the series for the current are approximately

$$i \approx \sqrt{8}\left[\frac{19}{1{,}600} + \frac{93}{6{,}400} \sin x - \frac{3}{1{,}600} \cos 2x + \frac{1}{6{,}400} \sin 3x\right]$$

**15-3.** Let the wave of a potential be expressed by the four terms

$$v = 50 + 80 \sin\left(x + \frac{\pi}{6}\right) + 25 \sin 2\left(x + \frac{\pi}{10}\right) + 4 \sin 3x$$

*a.* Write this in the sine-cosine form.
*b.* Write this as a series employing cosine terms only.
*c.* For each component determine the position of the principal zero nearest to the origin. Specify this in radians on the scale of the fundamental.

**15-4.** Consider the wave given by

$$i = 2 \sin \omega t + \sin\left(\frac{3\omega t}{2} + \frac{\pi}{3}\right)$$

in which $\omega = 2\pi(100)$.

*a.* What is the frequency of the wave?

*b.* What is the amplitude of the fundamental component of this wave?

*c.* On the time-angle scale of the fundamental what is the location of the closest intercept to the origin of the second harmonic? What is the similar intercept for the third harmonic?

**15-5.** Suppose the distribution of flux density in the air gap of a four-pole a-c generator, such as shown in Fig. 2-6, is given by the equation

$$B = B_0 (\sin 2\theta + 0.14 \sin 6\theta + 0.06 \sin 10\theta)$$

$\theta$ is the mechanical angle measured clockwise around the rotor from a point midway between two poles.

*a.* Carry out the necessary graphical construction to obtain the shape of the curve of flux distribution over the face of one pole.

*b.* Suppose this rotor rotates with an angular velocity of 1,800 rpm. What is the equation for the potential induced in a single conductor of length $l$, as a function of time? Take $\theta = 0$ when $t = 0$.

**15-6.** Refer to the data given in Prob. 15-2.

*a.* Plot a graph of the function relating current and potential, and from it determine the shape of the current wave as a function of time angle $x$. This is to be done graphically, in the manner shown in Fig. 15-1.

*b.* Graphically combine the components specified in Prob. 15-2 over one cycle of the fundamental, and compare the result with the wave obtained in part *a*.

**15-7.** In the wave specified in Prob. 15-3, let $x = 2\pi ft$, where $f = 1{,}000$ cps.

*a.* Write the equation of another potential $v'$, where $v'$ leads $v$ by 0.0003 sec. Write it as a series of sine functions.

*b.* Write the same function as a sine-cosine series.

*c.* Write the same function, using cosine terms only.

**15-8.** Consider the situation described in Prob. 15-5. A second conductor (2) is placed on the stator, 30 mechanical degrees in the direction of rotation from the first conductor (1), where conductor (1) is the one specified in Prob. 15-5. Let the potentials induced in these conductors be $v_1$ and $v_2$, where the subscripts correspond to the conductor numbers.

*a.* Write the series for the potential $v_2$ as a series of cosine functions.

*b.* Write the above function in the sine-cosine form.

*c.* Write a series for $v_2$ as a series of sine functions.

*d.* Conductors (1) and (2) are connected in series in such a way as to give the largest possible maximum in the resulting potential wave. Write the series for this wave as a sine series and as a sine-cosine series.

**15-9.** A potential source has a potential described by the series given in Prob. 15-3. The frequency is 100 cps. It is applied to a capacitor of $0.2 \times 10^{-6}$ farad. What is the equation for the current.

*a.* Expressed as a cosine series.

*b.* Expressed as a sine-cosine series.

*c.* Expressed as a sine series.

**15-10.** Let the potential

$$v = 50 \sin 377t + 20 \cos 774t + 5 \sin 1{,}131t$$

be applied to an inductor of 0.02 henry. What is the equation for the current

*a.* Expressed as a sine series.

*b.* Expressed as a sine-cosine series.

*c.* Expressed as a cosine series.

**15-11.** An inductor of 0.02 henry and a resistor of 15 ohms are connected in series across the potential source specified in Prob. 15-10. Obtain an equation for the current through the combination, as a series of sine terms.

**15-12.** A capacitor of $80 \times 10^{-6}$ farad is in series with a resistor of 15 ohms, and the combination is connected across the potential specified in Prob. 15-10. Obtain an equation for the current, expressing it as a series of sine terms.

**15-13.** An inductor of 0.02 henry, a capacitor of $80 \times 10^{-6}$ farad, and a resistor of 15 ohms are connected in series across the potential specified in Prob. 15-10. Write an equation for the current, expressing it as a series of sine terms.

## QUESTIONS

**15-1.** Is it possible to have sinusoidal currents in a circuit even though the source provides a pure sinusoidal potential on open circuit?

**15-2.** Would it be possible to write a trigonometric series for any periodic function using nothing but cosine functions?

**15-3.** How are the frequencies of the different terms in the trigonometric series for a periodic function related to one another?

**15-4.** Suppose a given periodic function passes through the origin. Can it be concluded that its series has no cosine terms?

**15-5.** In general an infinite number of terms are required to accurately represent a periodic wave. How is it that in many cases engineering calculations can be based on a finite number of terms?

**15-6.** What property must a network have if its response to a nonsinusoidal periodic function is to be analyzed by the superposition of the responses to the components in the series for the excitation?

**15-7.** When the responses to various harmonic components are added to find a complete response, why is it necessary to use time functions, rather than symbolic representations in terms of sinors?

**15-8.** Suppose Fig. 15-11 included a seventh and ninth harmonic. Draw the sinor diagrams which correspond with Fig. 15-12, for these harmonics.

**15-9.** Specify and show an approximate equivalent circuit for an iron-core inductor, employing a current source for the third harmonic.

# CHAPTER 16
# FOURIER SERIES

**16-1. Introduction.** In Chap. 15 it is shown that the combination of a series of sinusoidal components, with harmonically related frequencies, results in a nonsinusoidal periodic function. It is the purpose of this chapter to show how it is possible to find the magnitudes and initial angles of the harmonic components of a given nonsinusoidal periodic function. The ability to do this is very important. It makes it possible to apply the principle of superposition when an arbitrary nonsinusoidal periodic wave is applied to a linear circuit. Chapter 15 demonstrates how the principle of superposition is used when the series for the function is known, and Chap. 16 shows how the series is obtained from a given wave shape.

**16-2. Formulas for the Coefficients.** Formulas are to be obtained for the coefficients of the sine-cosine form of the series, when the shape of the wave is specified by some means other than the series. Let

$$v = a_1 \sin x + a_2 \sin 2x + a_3 \sin 3x + \cdots \\ + b_0 + b_1 \cos x + b_2 \cos 2x + b_3 \cos 3x + \cdots \quad (16\text{-}1)$$

This is the same as Eq. (15-1) except that, for simplicity, $\omega t$ is replaced by $x$, so that the wave will have a period $2\pi$ in the variable $x$. It is relatively simple to obtain formulas for the $a$ and $b$ coefficients if the assumption is made that the given function can be represented by the series. From the purely mathematical standpoint the ability to represent a periodic function by a series requires proof, but the findings of experience are taken as sufficient proof for this engineering analysis.

Let it be required to find the coefficient $a_n$, where $n$ has any integer value. Multiply both sides of Eq. (16-1) by $\sin nx$, and integrate from 0 to $2\pi$. Thus, a few typical terms are written

$$\int_0^{2\pi} v(x) \sin nx\, dx = \int_0^{2\pi} a_1 \sin x \sin nx\, dx + \int_0^{2\pi} a_2 \sin 2x \sin nx\, dx \\ + \cdots + \int_0^{2\pi} a_n \sin^2 nx\, dx + \cdots + \int_0^{2\pi} b_0 \sin nx\, dx \\ + \int_0^{2\pi} b_1 \cos x \sin nx\, dx + \int_0^{2\pi} b_2 \cos 3x \sin nx\, dx + \cdots \quad (16\text{-}2)$$

It is possible to prove that

$$\int_0^{2\pi} \sin nx \sin kx \, dx = 0 \qquad n \neq k$$

and (16-3)

$$\int_0^{2\pi} \cos nx \sin kx \, dx = 0 \qquad \text{all } n \text{ and } k$$

This being the case, Eq. (16-2) reduces to

$$\int_0^{2\pi} v(x) \sin nx \, dx = a_n \int_0^{2\pi} \sin^2 nx \, dx \tag{16-4}$$

The integral of $\sin^2 nx$ from 0 to $2\pi$ is $\pi$, so the formula for $a_n$ is

$$a_n = \frac{1}{\pi} \int_0^{2\pi} v(x) \sin nx \, dx \tag{16-5}$$

The coefficient $b_n (n \neq 0)$ is found by a similar procedure. Both sides of Eq. (16-1) are multiplied by $\cos nx$ and integrated from 0 to $2\pi$, as follows:

$$\begin{aligned} \int_0^{2\pi} v(x) \cos nx \, dx &= \int_0^{2\pi} a_1 \sin x \cos nx \, dx + \int_0^{2\pi} a_2 \sin 2x \cos nx \, dx \\ &\quad + \cdots + \int_0^{2\pi} b_0 \cos nx \, dx + \int_0^{2\pi} b_1 \cos x \cos nx \, dx \\ &\quad + \int_0^{2\pi} b_2 \cos 2x \cos nx \, dx + \cdots + \int_0^{2\pi} b_n \cos^2 nx \, dx + \cdots \end{aligned} \tag{16-6}$$

It can be shown that

$$\int_0^{2\pi} \cos nx \cos kx \, dx = 0 \qquad n \neq k \tag{16-7}$$

This is used, with the second equation of (16-3), to show that all terms but one on the right of Eq. (16-6) are zero. Therefore

$$\int_0^{2\pi} v(x) \cos nx \, dx = b_n \int_0^{2\pi} \cos^2 nx \, dx \tag{16-8}$$

The integral of $\cos^2 nx$ between the limits 0 and $2\pi$ is $\pi$; hence

$$b_n = \frac{1}{\pi} \int_0^{2\pi} v(x) \cos nx \, dx \qquad n \neq 0 \tag{16-9}$$

The case $n = 0$ is a special one. To find $b_0$, integrate both sides of Eq. (16-1) from 0 to $2\pi$, as it stands. The integral from 0 to $2\pi$ of any term of the form $\sin nx$ or $\cos nx$ is zero. Hence

$$\begin{aligned} \int_0^{2\pi} v(x) \, dx &= b_0 \int_0^{2\pi} dx \\ b_0 &= \frac{1}{2\pi} \int_0^{2\pi} v(x) \, dx \end{aligned} \tag{16-10}$$

Equations (16-5), (16-9), and (16-10) are sufficient to specify a Fourier series when $v(x)$ is known, provided that the necessary integrals can be evaluated. All terms are included by allowing $n$ to have successive integral values. These results are important and are summarized as follows:

$$\begin{aligned} a_n &= \frac{1}{\pi}\int_0^{2\pi} v(x)\sin nx\,dx \qquad n \geq 1 \\ b_0 &= \frac{1}{2\pi}\int_0^{2\pi} v(x)\,dx \\ b_n &= \frac{1}{\pi}\int_0^{2\pi} v(x)\cos nx\,dx \qquad n \geq 1 \end{aligned} \tag{16-11}$$

The sine series form

$$v = b_0 + c_1 \sin(\omega t + \theta_1) + c_2 \sin(2\omega t + \theta_2) + c_3 \sin(3\omega t + \theta_3) + \cdots \tag{16-12}$$

can be obtained from Eqs. (16-11) through the relations

$$c_n\underline{/\theta_n} = a_n + jb_n$$

or

$$\begin{aligned} c_n &= \sqrt{a_n^2 + b_n^2} \\ \theta_n &= \tan^{-1}\frac{b_n}{a_n} \end{aligned} \tag{16-13}$$

which follow from Eqs. (15-3).

The Fourier series represents a function by an infinite sum. If the representation is to be useful, the series must converge. That is, the succeeding coefficients must eventually become small at such a rate that for each value of $x$ the infinite sum will be finite. The subject of convergence is not treated in detail because of the mathematical acumen it requires. However, it can safely be said that the Fourier series for most functions met in engineering practice are convergent.

**16-3. Effect of Symmetry.** A wave can be symmetrical in a number of ways. Three types of symmetry are to be considered, as illustrated in Fig. 16-1. These symmetries are important because, when present, the series are simplified.

A wave having point symmetry is unchanged if it is rotated 180° about an axis perpendicular to the paper at the point of symmetry. A wave having axis symmetry is unchanged if it is rotated 180° about the axis of symmetry. These two types of symmetry are considered first.

If a wave has point or axis symmetry, it is convenient to choose an origin at the position of the point or axis of symmetry, even though the point or axis of symmetry of the original wave may have been positioned elsewhere. By this choice of origin the series expression for the wave is simplified. To see why, note that a sine function has point symmetry (but not axis symmetry) about the origin, and that a cosine function has axis symmetry (but not point symmetry) about the origin. A series made up of sine terms only will therefore have point symmetry about the origin, but this symmetry will be destroyed if one or more cosine terms should be added. Similarly, if a series has cosine terms only, it will have axis symmetry about the origin, which will be destroyed if any sine terms should be added. Thus, the most general forms are

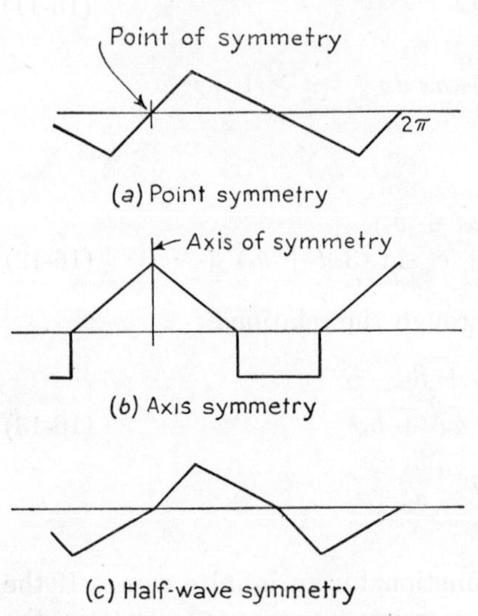


FIG. 16-1. Examples of three types of symmetries.

$$v = a_1 \sin \omega t + a_2 \sin 2\omega t + a_3 \sin 3\omega t + \cdots$$

for point symmetry and (16-14)

$$v = b_0 + b_1 \cos \omega t + b_2 \cos 2\omega t + b_3 \cos 3\omega t + \cdots$$

for axis symmetry.

Half-wave symmetry is illustrated in Fig. 16-1*c*. Such a wave is unchanged if it is rotated 180° about the horizontal axis and then shifted horizontally a half period.

For a consideration of half-wave symmetry refer to Fig. 16-2. At (*a*) two examples of sine and cosine waves of odd order (1 and 3) are shown. All of them exhibit half-wave symmetry. Other odd harmonics would do the same. None of the waves of Fig. 16-2*b* have half-wave symmetry, as may be seen by applying the above test with $\pi$ used as the half period. Therefore, a wave with half-wave symmetry cannot have even harmonics, and so a general expression for its series is

$$v = a_1 \sin x + a_3 \sin 3x + a_5 \sin 5x + \cdots + b_1 \cos x + b_3 \cos 3x + b_5 \cos 5x + \cdots \quad (16\text{-}15)$$

It is seen that knowledge of symmetry simplifies the computation of coefficients by showing that certain terms are absent.

When symmetry prevails, the formulas for the nonzero coefficients can be reduced to forms slightly simpler than Eqs. (16-11). It can be shown that for any wave having point or axis symmetry at the origin, or half-wave symmetry,

$$
\begin{aligned}
\int_0^{2\pi} v(x) \sin nx \, dx &= 2 \int_0^{\pi} v(x) \sin nx \, dx && \text{half-wave or point} \\
\int_0^{2\pi} v(x) \, dx &= 2 \int_0^{\pi} v(x) \, dx && \text{axis} \qquad (16\text{-}16) \\
\int_0^{2\pi} v(x) \cos nx \, dx &= 2 \int_0^{\pi} v(x) \cos nx \, dx && \text{half-wave or axis}
\end{aligned}
$$

for all nonvanishing coefficients. It is necessary to make a change of variable of integration to prove these relations. In view of Eqs. (16-16), for the symmetries specified above,

$$
\begin{aligned}
a_n &= \frac{2}{\pi} \int_0^{\pi} v(x) \sin nx \, dx \\
b_0 &= \frac{1}{\pi} \int_0^{\pi} v(x) \, dx \qquad (16\text{-}17) \\
b_n &= \frac{2}{\pi} \int_0^{\pi} v(x) \cos nx \, dx
\end{aligned}
$$

for all nonzero coefficients. Equations (16-14) and (16-15) must be consulted to see what terms are missing in specific cases, because Eqs. (16-17) will not give the correct result for the vanishing terms.

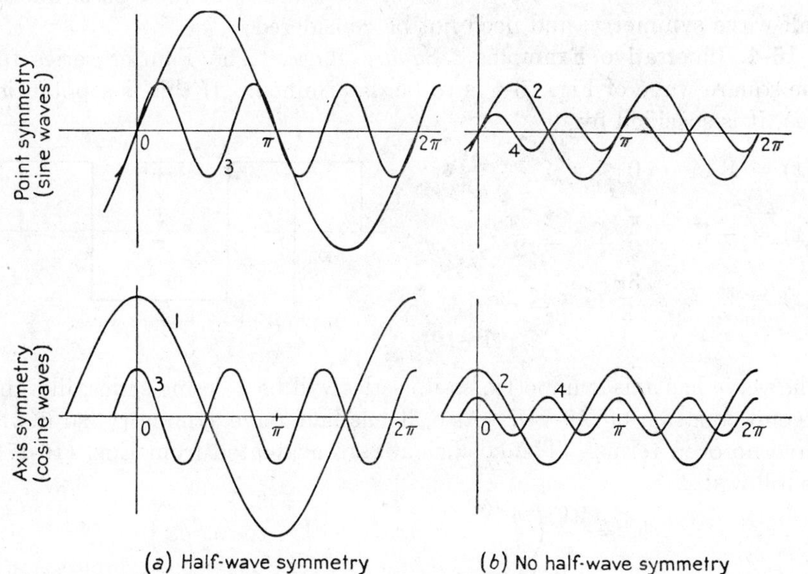


FIG. 16-2. Symmetry properties of sine and cosine waves. Numbers on the waves are orders of the harmonics.

Equations (16-17) offer a very useful simplification when $v(x)$ is made up of a number of sections each of which is given by a different equation. Such a case is illustrated in Fig. 16-3. In this case the third equation of

(16-11) leads to the two integrals

$$b_n = \frac{1}{\pi}\left(\int_0^{\pi/2} \cos x \cos nx \, dx + \int_{3\pi/2}^{2\pi} \cos x \cos nx \, dx\right)$$

but the third equation of (16-17) leads to (16-18)

$$b_n = \frac{2}{\pi}\int_0^{\pi/2} \cos x \cos nx \, dx$$

The smaller range of integration is also an advantage when graphical methods of integration are necessary.

If a wave simultaneously has half-wave symmetry and one of the other symmetries at the origin, it can be shown that Eqs. (16-11) for the nonzero $a_n$ and $b_n$ coefficients can be simplified still further. It is found that the limits of integration can be changed to 0 and $\pi/4$, if the multiplying factor is changed to $4/\pi$. Note that $b_0$ is then zero, due to half-wave symmetry, and need not be considered.

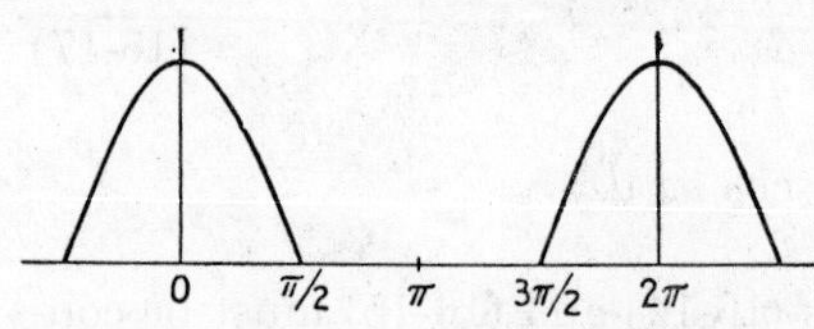

Fig. 16-3. Example of case where formulas for the coefficients can be simplified by employing the effects of symmetry.

**16-4. Illustrative Examples.** *Square Wave.* The Fourier series for the square wave of Fig. 16-4 is to be determined. If this is a potential $v(x)$, it is specified by

$$v(x) = V \qquad 0 \leq x \leq \frac{\pi}{2}$$
$$v(x) = -V \qquad \frac{\pi}{2} \leq x \leq \frac{3\pi}{2}$$
$$v(x) = V \qquad \frac{3\pi}{2} \leq x \leq 2\pi \tag{16-19}$$

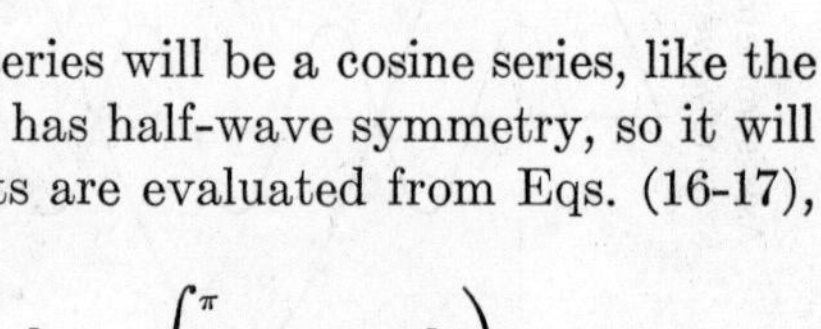

Fig. 16-4. Square wave.

The wave has axis symmetry, so its series will be a cosine series, like the second equation of (16-14). Also, it has half-wave symmetry, so it will have no even terms. The coefficients are evaluated from Eqs. (16-17), as follows:

$$b_n = \frac{2V}{\pi}\left(\int_0^{\pi/2} \cos nx \, dx - \int_{\pi/2}^{\pi} \cos nx \, dx\right)$$
$$= \frac{2V}{\pi n}\left(\sin \frac{n\pi}{2} - \sin 0 - \sin n\pi + \sin \frac{n\pi}{2}\right)$$
$$= \frac{4V}{\pi n}(-1)^{(n-1)/2} \qquad n \text{ odd} \qquad (16\text{-}20)\dagger$$

† These formulas would have been much simpler if full advantage had been taken

This is the general term for the $n$th harmonic. The factor $(-1)^{(n-1)/2}$ enters because $\sin(n\pi/2)$ is alternately $+1$ and $-1$ as $n$ takes on successive odd values. The series is

$$v = \frac{4V}{\pi}\left(\cos x - \frac{1}{3}\cos 3x + \frac{1}{5}\cos 5x - \frac{1}{7}\cos 7x + \cdots\right) \quad (16\text{-}21)$$

Equation (16-20) gives the same information as Eq. (16-21), in slightly more concise form. Except for the multiplying factor $V$, Eq. (16-21) is the same as the series specified in Eq. (15-4).

*Triangular Wave.* Consider the triangular wave of Fig. 16-5. It can be written

$$v(x) = \frac{2V}{\pi}x \qquad 0 \le x \le \frac{\pi}{2}$$

$$v(x) = \frac{2V}{\pi}(\pi - x) \qquad \frac{\pi}{2} \le x \le \pi \quad (16\text{-}22)$$

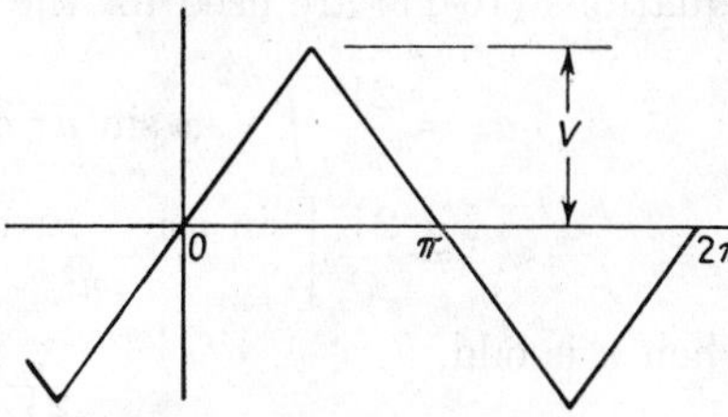

FIG. 16-5. Triangular wave.

The wave has point symmetry and half-wave symmetry. Therefore, it has no even harmonics, and all terms must be sine terms, like the first equation of (16-14). Using Eqs. (16-17) for the coefficients,

$$\begin{aligned} a_n &= \frac{4V}{\pi^2}\left[\int_0^{\pi/2} x \sin nx\,dx + \int_{\pi/2}^{\pi} (\pi - x)\sin nx\,dx\right] \\ &= \frac{4V}{\pi^2}\left\{\left[\frac{\sin nx - nx\cos nx}{n^2}\right]_0^{\pi/2} - \left[\frac{\pi\cos nx}{n}\right]_{\pi/2}^{\pi} - \left[\frac{\sin nx - nx\cos nx}{n^2}\right]_{\pi/2}^{\pi}\right\} \\ &= \frac{4V}{\pi^2}\left[\frac{(-1)^{\frac{n-1}{2}}}{n^2} + \frac{\pi}{n} - \frac{n\pi}{n^2} + \frac{(-1)^{\frac{n-1}{2}}}{n^2}\right] \\ &= \frac{8V}{(\pi n)^2}(-1)^{(n-1)/2} \qquad n \text{ odd} \end{aligned} \quad (16\text{-}23)\dagger$$

From this general term it follows that the series is

$$v = \frac{8V}{\pi^2}\left(\sin x - \frac{1}{9}\sin 3x + \frac{1}{25}\sin 5x - \frac{1}{49}\sin 7x + \cdots\right) \quad (16\text{-}24)$$

This is the same as Eq. (15-5), except for the amplitude factor $V$.

---

of the two symmetries in each case, whereby each integration would have been from 0 to $\pi/4$, as noted in the last paragraph of Sec. 18-3.

*Nonsymmetrical Wave.* An example of a nonsymmetrical wave is given in Fig. 16-6. Sine and cosine components must be considered for all harmonics. The function can be analytically expressed as follows:

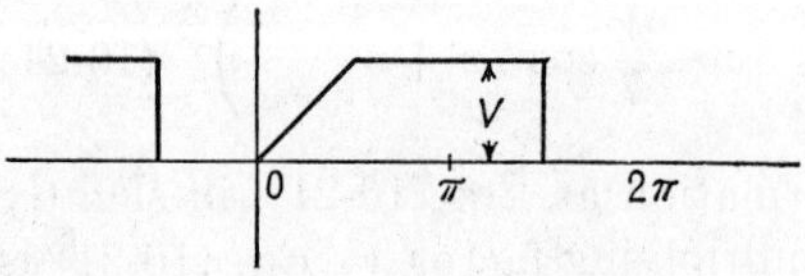

FIG. 16-6. Wave shape having no symmetry.

$$v(x) = \frac{2V}{\pi}x \qquad 0 \le x \le \frac{\pi}{2}$$
$$v(x) = V \qquad \frac{\pi}{2} \le x \le \frac{3\pi}{2}$$
$$v(x) = 0 \qquad \frac{3\pi}{2} \le x \le 2\pi \tag{16-25}$$

Equations (16-11) are used for the coefficients. For the $a$ coefficients

$$a_n = \frac{2V}{\pi^2}\int_0^{\pi/2} x \sin nx\, dx + V\int_{\pi/2}^{3\pi/2} \sin nx\, dx$$
$$= \frac{2V}{\pi^2}\left[\frac{\sin nx - nx \cos nx}{n^2}\right]_0^{\pi/2} - \frac{V}{\pi}\cos nx\Big|_{\pi/2}^{3\pi/2} \tag{16-26}$$

When $n$ is odd,

$$a_n = \frac{2V}{\pi^2 n^2}(-1)^{(n-1)/2}$$

When $n$ is even, (16-27)

$$a_n = -\frac{V}{\pi n}(-1)^{n/2}$$

For the $b$ coefficients

$$b_0 = \frac{2V}{2\pi^2}\int_0^{\pi/2} x\, dx + \frac{V}{2\pi}\int_{\pi/2}^{3\pi/2} dx$$
$$= \frac{V}{\pi^2}\frac{\pi^2}{8} + \frac{V}{2\pi}(\pi) = \frac{5V}{8}$$
$$b_n = \frac{2V}{\pi^2}\int_0^{\pi/2} x \cos nx\, dx + \frac{V}{\pi}\int_{\pi/2}^{3\pi/2} \cos nx\, dx \tag{16-28}$$
$$= \frac{2V}{\pi^2}\left[\frac{\cos nx + nx \sin nx}{n^2}\right]_0^{\pi/2} + \frac{V}{\pi}\left[\frac{\sin nx}{n}\right]_{\pi/2}^{3\pi/2}$$

When $n$ is odd, this becomes

$$b_n = \frac{2V}{\pi^2}\frac{\pi}{2n}(-1)^{\left(\frac{n-1}{2}\right)} - \frac{V}{\pi}\frac{2}{n}(-1)^{\left(\frac{n-1}{2}\right)}$$
$$= -\frac{V}{\pi n}(-1)^{(n-1)/2}$$

When $n$ is even, the result is (16-29)

$$b_n = \frac{2V}{\pi^2 n^2}(-1)^{n/2}$$

The sine-cosine form of the series can be written from these as follows:

$$v = V\left(\frac{2}{\pi^2}\sin x + \frac{1}{2\pi}\sin 2x - \frac{2}{9\pi^2}\sin 3x - \frac{1}{4\pi}\sin 4x + \frac{2}{25\pi^2}\sin 5x + \frac{1}{6\pi}\sin 6x \cdots + \frac{5}{8} - \frac{1}{\pi}\cos x - \frac{2}{4\pi^2}\cos 2x + \frac{1}{3\pi}\cos 3x + \frac{2}{16\pi^2}\cos 4x - \frac{1}{5\pi}\cos 5x - \frac{2}{36\pi^2}\cos 6x \cdots\right) \tag{16-30}$$

With numerical coefficients Eq. (16-30) becomes

$$\begin{aligned} v = \tfrac{5}{8} &+ (0.202 \sin x - 0.318 \cos x) \\ &+ (0.159 \sin 2x - 0.051 \cos 2x) \\ &+ (-0.0225 \sin 3x + 0.106 \cos 3x) \\ &+ (-0.0795 \sin 4x + 0.0126 \cos 4x) \\ &+ (0.0081 \sin 5x - 0.0635 \cos 5x) \\ &+ (0.053 \sin 6x - 0.0056 \text{ soc } 6x) + \cdots \end{aligned} \tag{16-31}$$

The function can be converted to a sine series by combining sine and cosine terms of each harmonic, in accordance with Eqs. (16-13). Thus, using complex numbers to represent the individual harmonics,

$$\begin{aligned} 0.202 - j0.318 &= 0.376\underline{/-57.6^\circ} = 0.376\underline{/-1.01 \text{ rad}} \\ 0.159 - j0.051 &= 0.167\underline{/-17.7^\circ} = 0.167\underline{/-0.309 \text{ rad}} \\ -0.0225 + j0.106 &= 0.108\underline{/102^\circ} = 0.108\underline{/1.78 \text{ rad}} \\ -0.0795 + j0.0126 &= 0.0805\underline{/171^\circ} = 0.0805\underline{/2.98 \text{ rad}} \\ 0.0081 - j0.0635 &= 0.064\underline{/-82.8^\circ} = 0.064\underline{/-1.45 \text{ rad}} \\ 0.053 - j0.0056 &= 0.0533\underline{/6^\circ} = 0.0533\underline{/0.11 \text{ rad}} \end{aligned} \tag{16-32}$$

With these values it is possible to replace Eq. (16-31) by the sine form

$$\begin{aligned} v = \tfrac{5}{8} &+ 0.376 \sin (x - 1.01) + 0.167 \sin (2x - 0.309) \\ &+ 0.108 \sin (3x + 1.78) + 0.0805 \sin (4x + 2.98) \\ &+ 0.064 \sin (5x - 1.45) + 0.0533 \sin (6x + 0.11) \end{aligned} \tag{16-33}$$

The last form is useful because it puts the amplitude and initial angle of each harmonic in evidence. The same information can be conveniently plotted as a "line spectrum" of amplitude and phase, as a function of frequency. An example is given in Fig. 16-7. Lines are used, rather than a continuous curve, because the amplitude and phase have meaning only at integral values of the abscissa. Each initial angle is to the scale of the corresponding harmonic.

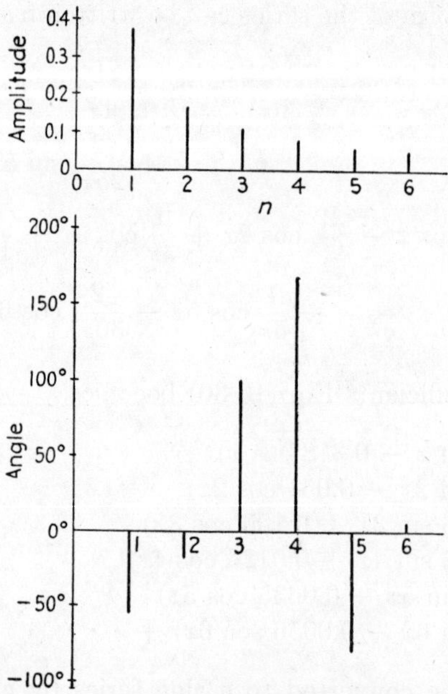


FIG. 16-7. Harmonic amplitude and initial angle spectra for wave of Fig. 16-6.

**16-5. Change of Scale.** The functions so far considered have a period, $2\pi$, in the variable $x$. However, as pointed out in Sec. 16-2, $x$ can represent $\omega t$, so that the function can have a general period $T$ in the variable $t$. From Eq. (2-4), $x$ and $t$ are also related by

$$x = \frac{2\pi}{T} t \qquad (16\text{-}34)$$

which puts the period $T$ into evidence.

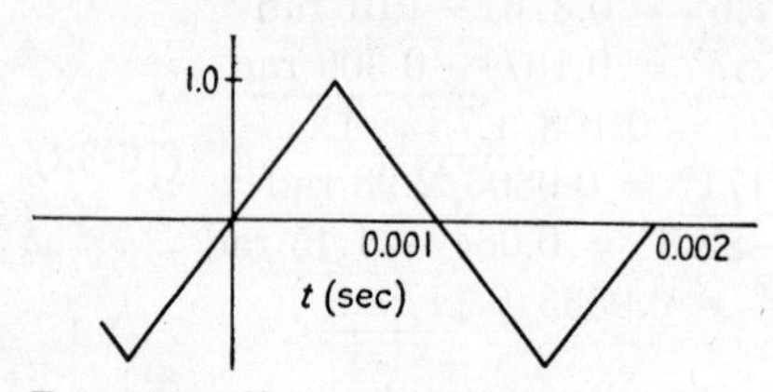


FIG. 16-8. Triangular wave shown on a time scale.

When the period is not $2\pi$, Eqs. (16-11) or (16-17) do not apply. The function can be changed to one in $x$, however, and then these formulas can be used. The series is written in the form

$$v = a_1 \sin \omega t + a_2 \sin 2\omega t + a_3 \sin 3\omega t + \cdots + b_0 + b_1 \cos \omega t + b_2 \cos 2\omega t + b_3 \cos 3\omega t + \cdots \qquad (16\text{-}35)$$

This is illustrated by the triangular wave of Fig. 16-8. On the $t$ axis its period is 0.002 sec. The analytical expression for the function is

$$\begin{aligned} v &= 2{,}000t & 0 \le t \le 0.0005 \\ v &= 2 - 2{,}000t & 0.0005 \le t \le 0.001 \end{aligned} \qquad (16\text{-}36)$$

In order to use Eq. (16-17) for the coefficients, it is observed that

$$\omega = \frac{2\pi}{0.002} = 3{,}142$$

and (16-37)

$$t = \frac{x}{3{,}142}$$

Therefore

$$\begin{aligned} v(x) &= 0.636x \qquad & 0 \le x \le \frac{\pi}{2} \\ v(x) &= 2 - 0.636x \qquad & \frac{\pi}{2} \le x \le \pi \end{aligned} \tag{16-38}$$

which could be used in Eqs. (16-17) to find the coefficients. However, this particular wave has already been treated, in Sec. 16-4, with Eq. (16-23) as the result, so for the present numerical case the series is

$$v = 0.81(\sin x - \tfrac{1}{9} \sin 3x + \tfrac{1}{25} \sin 5x \cdot \cdot \cdot) \tag{16-39}$$

Finally $3{,}142t$ can be substituted for $x$, giving

$$v = 0.810(\sin 3{,}142t - \tfrac{1}{9} \sin 9{,}426t + \tfrac{1}{25} \sin 15{,}710t \cdot \cdot \cdot) \tag{16-40}$$

**16-6. Shift of Origin.** In Sec. 15-4, it is pointed out that the form of the Fourier series of a wave depends on the position of the origin. The Fourier series of a function may be known for one location of origin but be required for a different origin. For example, let it be required to find the series for the square wave of Fig. 16-9. It is noted that if $O'$ were the origin and $x'$ the variable, the wave would be identical with Fig. 16-4. Therefore, Fig. 16-9 is represented by

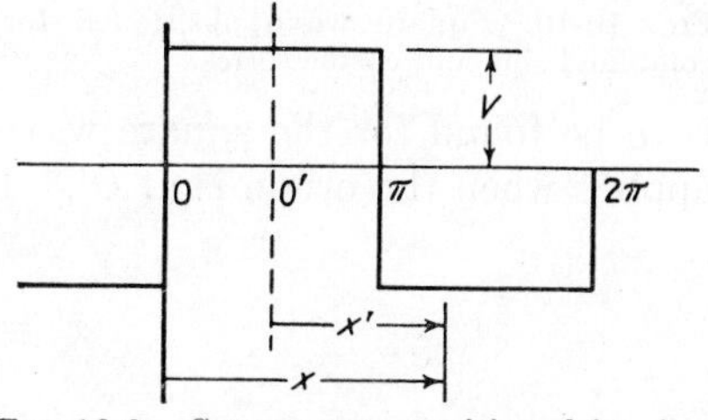


Fig. 16-9. Square wave positioned for sine series.

$$v = \frac{4V}{\pi}\left(\cos x' - \frac{1}{3}\cos 3x' + \frac{1}{5}\cos 5x' - \frac{1}{7}\cos 7x' \cdot \cdot \cdot\right) \tag{16-41}$$

However,

$$x' = x - \frac{\pi}{2}$$

and (16-42)

$$\cos\left(x - \frac{\pi}{2}\right) = \sin x$$

$$\cos\left(3x - \frac{3\pi}{2}\right) = -\sin 3x$$

$$\cos\left(5x - \frac{5\pi}{2}\right) = \sin 5x$$

etc.

Therefore, in terms of $x$ the series is

$$v = \frac{4V}{\pi}\left(\sin x + \frac{1}{3}\sin 3x + \frac{1}{5}\sin 5x + \frac{1}{7}\sin 7x + \cdots\right) \qquad (16\text{-}43)$$

This technique is usually advantageous if a point of symmetry is located at a point other than the origin. A new origin can be put at the point of symmetry, and the simplifications due to symmetry can be realized. A change of variable, such as Eqs. (16-42), then yields the required series with respect to the original origin.

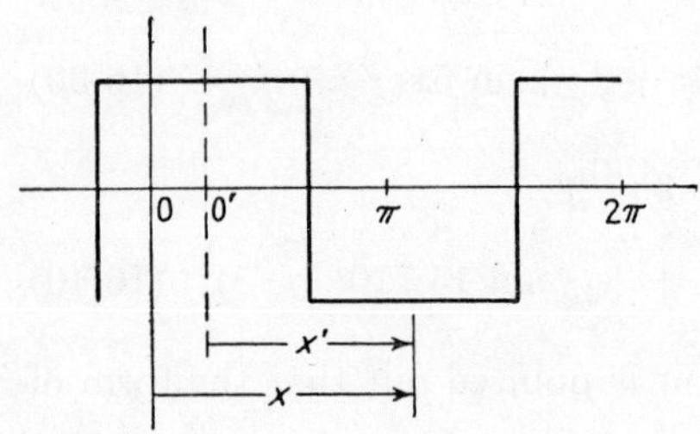

FIG. 16-10. Square wave positioned for combined sine and cosine series.

Figure 16-10 illustrates the process for another case. The series is to be found for the square wave in the variable $x$. Equation (16-41) applies when the origin is at $O'$. In this case

$$x' = x - \frac{\pi}{4}$$

and (16-44)

$$\cos\left(x - \frac{\pi}{4}\right) = \frac{1}{\sqrt{2}}(\cos x + \sin x)$$

$$\cos\left(3x - \frac{3\pi}{4}\right) = \frac{1}{\sqrt{2}}(-\cos 3x + \sin 3x)$$

$$\cos\left(5x - \frac{5\pi}{4}\right) = \frac{1}{\sqrt{2}}(-\cos 5x - \sin 5x)$$

$$\cos\left(7x - \frac{7\pi}{4}\right) = \frac{1}{\sqrt{2}}(\cos 7x - \sin 7x)$$

In terms of $x$ the sine-cosine series for Fig. 16-10 is

$$v = \frac{4V}{\pi\sqrt{2}}\left(\sin x - \frac{1}{3}\sin 3x - \frac{1}{5}\sin 5x + \frac{1}{7}\sin 7x + \cdots \right.$$
$$\left. + \cos x + \frac{1}{3}\cos 3x - \frac{1}{5}\cos 5x - \frac{1}{7}\cos 7x + \cdots \right) \qquad (16\text{-}45)$$

It can also be given as a sine series, like Eq. (16-12), by observing that

$$\begin{aligned} \cos\left(x - \frac{\pi}{4}\right) &= \sin\left(x + \frac{\pi}{4}\right) \\ -\cos\left(3x - \frac{3\pi}{4}\right) &= \sin\left(3x + \frac{3\pi}{4}\right) \\ \cos\left(5x - \frac{5\pi}{4}\right) &= \sin\left(5x - \frac{3\pi}{4}\right) \\ -\cos\left(7x - \frac{7\pi}{4}\right) &= \sin\left(7x - \frac{\pi}{4}\right) \end{aligned} \qquad (16\text{-}46)$$

from which

$$v = \frac{4V}{\pi}\left[\sin\left(x + \frac{\pi}{4}\right) + \frac{1}{3}\sin\left(3x + \frac{3\pi}{4}\right) + \frac{1}{5}\sin\left(5x - \frac{3\pi}{4}\right)\right.$$
$$\left. + \frac{1}{7}\sin\left(7x - \frac{\pi}{4}\right) + \cdots \right] \qquad (16\text{-}47)$$

The origin can also be shifted along the vertical axis to effect a change in the $b_0$ term. For example, the series for $v'$ in Fig. 16-11 is the same as

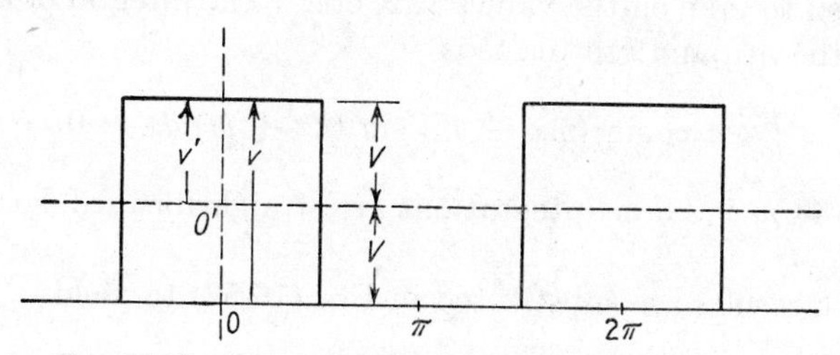

Fig. 16-11. Square wave with a constant component.

Eq. (16-21). Thus,

$$v' = \frac{4V}{\pi}\left(\cos x - \frac{1}{3}\cos 3x + \frac{1}{5}\cos 5x - \frac{1}{7}\cos 7x \cdots \right) \qquad (16\text{-}48)$$

and

$$v' = v - V \qquad (16\text{-}49)$$

Therefore

$$v = \frac{4V}{\pi}\left(\frac{\pi}{4} + \cos x - \frac{1}{3}\cos 3x + \frac{1}{5}\cos 5x - \frac{1}{7}\cos 7x \cdots\right) \tag{16-50}$$

**16-7. Effective Values.** Let the function $i(x)$ be given by the Fourier series

$$i(x) = b_0 + c_1 \sin(x + \theta_1) + c_2 \sin(2x + \theta_2) + c_3 \sin(3x + \theta_3) + \cdots \tag{16-51}$$

From Eq. (3-13) its effective value is known to be

$$I_{\text{eff}} = \sqrt{\frac{1}{2\pi}\int_0^{2\pi} i^2(x)\,dx} \tag{16-52}$$

The series of Eq. (16-51) can be squared, giving

$$i^2(x) = b_0^2 + c_1^2 \sin^2(x + \theta_1) + c_2^2 \sin^2(2x + \theta_2) + c_3^2 \sin^2(3x + \theta_2) + \cdots + \text{sum of terms of the form } c_m c_k \sin(nx + \theta_n)\sin(kx + \theta_k) \tag{16-53}$$

where $m \neq k$. The effective value of $i(x)$ is found by integrating Eq. (16-53) term by term. For $b_0$ we have

$$\int_0^{2\pi} b_0^2\,dx = 2\pi b_0^2 \tag{16-54}$$

Each of the other squared terms is taken care of by the formula

$$\int_0^{2\pi} c_n^2 \sin^2(nx + \theta_n)\,dx = \pi c_n^2 \tag{16-55}$$

if $n$ is allowed to take on the values 1, 2, etc. The integral of the general product of the $n$th and $k$th terms is

$$\int_0^{2\pi} c_m c_k \sin(mx + \theta_m)\sin(kx + \theta_k)\,dx = 0 \tag{16-56}$$

as long as $k \neq m$. These integrations are straightforward, so the details are omitted.

The above results are substituted in Eq. (16-52) to yield

$$I_{\text{eff}} = \sqrt{b_0^2 + \frac{c_1^2}{2} + \frac{c_2^2}{2} + \frac{c_3^2}{2} + \cdots} \tag{16-57}$$†

The amplitudes of the harmonics are $c_1$, $c_2$, etc. Each term within the square root in Eq. (16-57) is therefore the square of the effective value of an individual harmonic component. The effective value of the con-

† In mathematics Eq. (10-57) is known as Parseval's relation.

stant term is $b_0$. Thus it has been proved that the effective value of a periodic nonsinusoidal wave is the square root of the sum of the squares of the effective values of the harmonic components.

**16-8. Fourier Series in Complex Form.** In Eq. (16-1) the trigonometric terms can be replaced by exponentials, in accordance with the identities

$$\sin x = \frac{\epsilon^{jx} - \epsilon^{-jx}}{2j} \qquad \cos x = \frac{\epsilon^{jx} + \epsilon^{-jx}}{2} \tag{16-58}$$

which are obtained from Eqs. (8-38) and (8-39). When this is done, and the terms are rearranged, the series can be written

$$v(x) = b_0 + \frac{b_1 - ja_1}{2}\epsilon^{jx} + \frac{b_2 - ja_2}{2}\epsilon^{j2x} + \cdots + \frac{b_1 + ja_1}{2}\epsilon^{-jx} + \frac{b_2 + ja_2}{2}\epsilon^{-j2x} - \cdots \tag{16-59}$$

Now consider the formulas for $a_n$ and $b_n$, with the trigonometric terms in Eqs. (16-11) replaced by Eq. (16-58). For $n \geq 1$,

$$a_n = \frac{1}{2\pi j}\int_0^{2\pi} v(x)\epsilon^{jnx}\,dx - \frac{1}{2\pi j}\int_0^{2\pi} v(x)\epsilon^{-jnx}\,dx \qquad b_n = \frac{1}{2\pi}\int_0^{2\pi} v(x)\epsilon^{jnx}\,dx + \frac{1}{2\pi}\int_0^{2\pi} v(x)\epsilon^{-jnx}\,dx \tag{16-60}$$

The formula for $b_0$ is unchanged. From Eqs. (16-60)

$$b_n - ja_n = \frac{1}{\pi}\int_0^{2\pi} v(x)\epsilon^{-jnx}\,dx \qquad b_n + ja_n = \frac{1}{\pi}\int_0^{2\pi} v(x)\epsilon^{jnx}\,dx \tag{16-61}$$

It is convenient to define the new coefficient

$$\mathbf{C}_n = \frac{1}{2\pi}\int_0^{2\pi} v(x)\epsilon^{-jnx}\,dx \tag{16-62}$$

in which $n$ is allowed to have positive, negative, or zero values. Comparing the right-hand sides of Eqs. (16-61) and (16-62) gives, for $n \geq 1$,

$$\frac{b_n - ja_n}{2} = \mathbf{C}_n \qquad \frac{b_n + ja_n}{2} = \mathbf{C}_{-n} \tag{16-63}$$

These are the general expressions for all of the coefficients of Eq. (16-59) except for $b_0$. From Eqs. (16-11) and (16-62), $b_0 = \mathbf{C}_0$, so that the series is

$$v(x) = \mathbf{C}_0 + \mathbf{C}_1\epsilon^{jx} + \mathbf{C}_2\epsilon^{j2x} + \mathbf{C}_3\epsilon^{j3x} + \cdots + \mathbf{C}_{-1}\epsilon^{-jx} + \mathbf{C}_{-2}\epsilon^{-j2x} + \mathbf{C}_{-3}\epsilon^{-j3x} + \cdots \qquad (16\text{-}64)$$

Observe that there is no need to evaluate $C_n$ and $C_{-n}$ independently because

$$\mathbf{C}_{-n} = \mathbf{C}_n{}^* \qquad (16\text{-}65)$$

Equation (16-64) is called the *complex form* of the Fourier series. It is really simpler than the trigonometric form, but it has the slight disadvantage of employing complex functions, which cannot easily be graphed.

Even when the trigonometric form is required, it is sometimes convenient first to compute the $\mathbf{C}_n$ coefficients, because the integral of Eq. (16-62) may be simpler than the integrals of Eqs. (16-11). The $a_n$ and $b_n$ coefficients can then be found from Eqs. (16-63) by adding and subtracting them, to give, for $n \geq 1$,

$$\begin{aligned} a_n &= j(\mathbf{C}_n - \mathbf{C}_{-n}) \\ b_n &= (\mathbf{C}_n + \mathbf{C}_{-n}) \end{aligned} \qquad (16\text{-}66)$$

The $c_n$ and $\theta_n$ parameters of Eq. (16-12) can be obtained from the complex $\mathbf{C}_n$ coefficient. From Eq. (16-13) and (16-63), for $n \geq 1$,

$$\begin{aligned} c_n &= \sqrt{a_n{}^2 + b_n{}^2} = 2\sqrt{\mathbf{C}_n\mathbf{C}_n{}^*} = 2|\mathbf{C}_n| \\ \theta_n &= \tan^{-1}\frac{b_n}{a_n} = \tan^{-1}\frac{\mathrm{Re}\,(\mathbf{C}_n)}{-\mathrm{Im}\,(\mathbf{C}_n)} \end{aligned} \qquad (16\text{-}67)$$

Perhaps a more convenient viewpoint is to note that the first equation of (16-13) and Eq. (16-63) combine to give, for $n \geq 1$,

$$c_n\underline{/\theta_n} = j2\mathbf{C}_n \qquad (16\text{-}68)$$

Equation (16-68) provides the same information as the two equations of (16-67). Equations (16-67) and (16-68) are supplemented by $c_0 = \mathbf{C}_0$.

**16-9. Summary.** The nonsinusoidal periodic functions met in engineering practice can be expressed as Fourier series. This is either a series of cosine and sine terms, with frequencies which are integral multiples of the lowest frequency, or a series of exponentials. In either case, formulas are available for the coefficients of the series, as integrals involving the function itself, combined with trigonometric or exponential terms. The trigonometric series is the simpler to interpret, but the exponential form leads to simpler formulas for the coefficients.

In analyzing a function for its Fourier components, it is helpful to heed all symmetries. When the function is symmetrical, some terms are absent from the series and the formulas for the remaining ones are simpler than otherwise.

The effective value of a nonsinusoidal periodic function is easily obtained when its Fourier series is known, being the square root of the sum of the squares of the effective values of the individual harmonic components.

## PROBLEMS

**16-1.** Prove Eqs. (16-3) and (16-7) of the text.

**16-2.** Let $v(x)$ have point symmetry about $x = 0$. Prove that the wave is zero at any multiple of $\pi$ on the $x$ axis, if the period is $2\pi$.

**16-3.** Let $v(x)$ have point symmetry about $x = 0$ and axis symmetry about a point $x = x_a$, and let the period of the wave be $2\pi$.

*a.* Prove that $x_a$ must be an odd multiple of $\pi/2$.

*b.* Prove that the wave also has half-wave symmetry.

**16-4.** Formulas (16-16) of the text are to be proved for each of the symmetries defined in the text. HINTS: (*a*) For point symmetry at the origin use the fact that $v(x) = -v(-x)$. (*b*) For axis symmetry at the origin use the fact that $v(x) = v(-x)$. (*c*) For half-wave symmetry utilize the fact that $v(x) = -v(x + \pi)$.

**16-5.** Assuming $f(t)$ has the following properties:

$$f(t) = f(-t)$$
$$f\left(\frac{T}{4} - t\right) = f\left(\frac{T}{4} + t\right)$$

Prove that the function has the period $T/2$.

**16-6.** Let $i(x)$ be a function having half-wave symmetry. Prove that its Fourier coefficients are given by the formulas

$$a_n = \frac{2}{\pi}\int_A^{A+\pi} i(x)\sin nx\,dx \qquad n \text{ odd}$$
$$b_n = \frac{2}{\pi}\int_B^{B+\pi} i(x)\cos nx\,dx \qquad n \text{ odd}$$

where $A$ and $B$ are arbitrary constants. It is not necessary to prove that $n$ is odd, since this fact is established in the text.

**16-7.** If a function $f(x)$ has point symmetry at the origin and half-wave symmetry, prove that formulas for its Fourier coefficients can be written

$$a_n = \frac{4}{\pi}\int_0^{\pi/2} f(x)\sin nx\,dx \qquad n \text{ odd}$$
$$b_n = \frac{4}{\pi}\int_0^{\pi/2} f(x)\cos nx\,dx \qquad n \text{ odd}$$

**16-8.** Let the function $v(t)$ have the period $T$. Prove that the coefficients for its Fourier series can be written

$$a_n = \frac{2}{T}\int_0^T v(t) \sin \frac{2n\pi t}{T} dt$$

$$b_n = \frac{2}{T}\int_0^T v(t) \cos \frac{2n\pi t}{T} dt$$

NOTE: In the following problems it may be convenient to use theorems that are stated in the above problems. Once proved, they may be regarded as material of the text and may be used in the following. In the problems which follow, when a series is asked for, it is understood that four nonzero harmonics are to be found, including the constant term and the fundamental.

**16-9.** Five wave shapes are illustrated in Fig. P16-9. In each case write the form of the series, but do not evaluate the coefficients. However, omit those terms you will expect to be zero, as dictated by symmetry conditions.

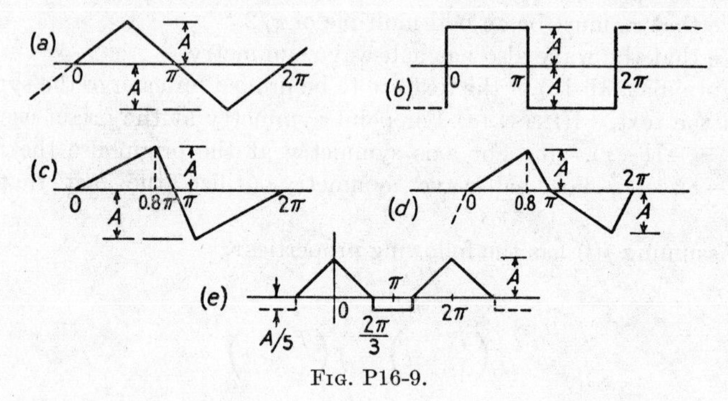


FIG. P16-9.

**16-10.** The wave shape obtained from a half-wave rectification of a sinusoidal wave is shown in Fig. P16-10$a$.

*a.* Obtain the series for the wave, with the axis in the position shown, expressing it is a function of $x$.

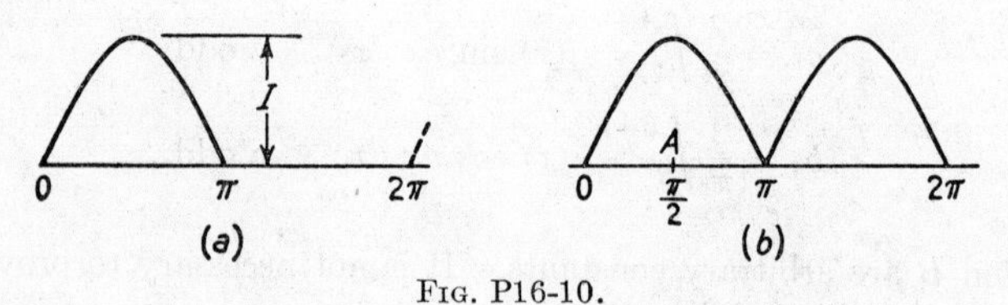


FIG. P16-10.

*b.* Express the series as a function of time if the frequency of the wave is 60 cps.

*c.* From the results of part $a$ obtain the series for the full-wave rectified wave shown in Fig. P16-10$b$.

*d.* Determine the Fourier series for wave ($b$) as a function of $y$, where $y$ is measured along the $x$ axis but with the zero of $y$ at pint $A$.

**16-11.** Obtain the series for the wave shown in Fig. P16-9$c$.

**16-12.** Obtain the series for the wave shown in Fig. P16-9*d*.

**16-13.** Obtain the series for the wave shown in Fig. P16-9*e*.

**16-14.** The graphical representation of a succession of dots and dashes in a code signal is shown in Fig. P16-14. Obtain the Fourier series for this signal, including the constant term, giving eight terms.

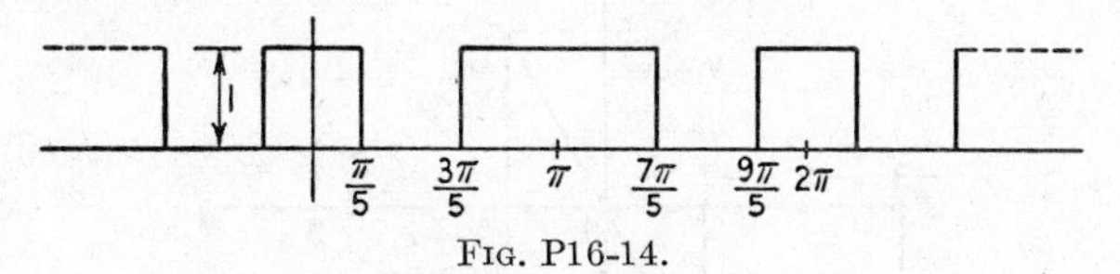


FIG. P16-14.

*a.* Express the series in terms of the variable $x$, which has the period $2\pi$.

*b.* Express the series in terms of the variable $t$, if the repetition rate of each pair of one dot and one dash is 1 sec.

**16-15.** Two wave trains consisting of a series of dots are shown in Fig. P16-15. The one shown at (*b*) is similar to the one shown at (*a*), except for the inclusion of an additional pulse of smaller magnitude between the other two.

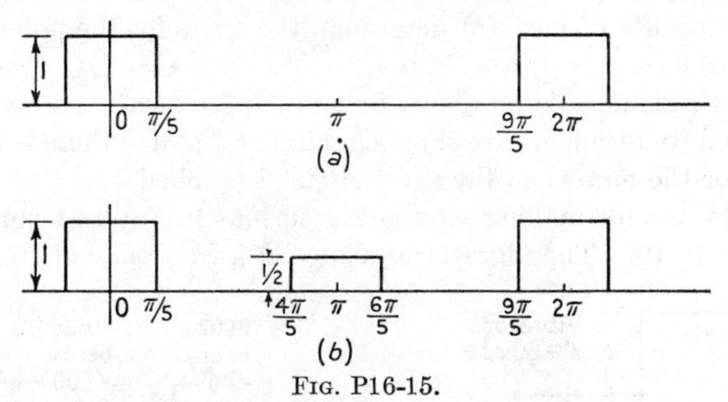


FIG. P16-15.

*a.* Obtain the Fourier series for the wave shown at (*a*).

*b.* Use the results obtained in part *a* to get the Fourier series for the wave shown at (*b*).

**16-16.** The Fourier series for the triangular wave of Fig. 16-5 is given in the text. Use this result to obtain the Fourier series for the wave shown in Fig. P16-16.

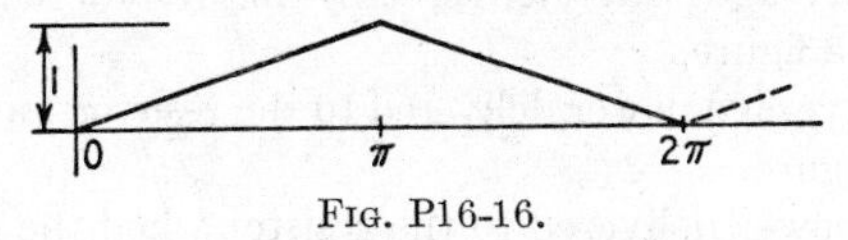


FIG. P16-16.

**16-17.** Use the series for the triangular wave of Fig. 16-5 to obtain the series for the wave shown in Fig. P16-17.

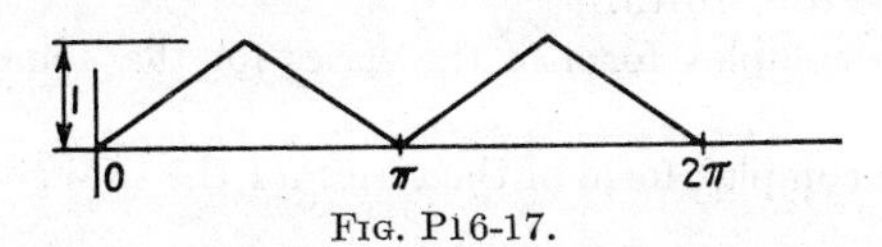


FIG. P16-17.

**16-18.** Let the magnetization curve of an iron core be approximated by the graph of Fig. P16-18. The coil has 200 turns. The current is the sinusoidal function $i = 3 \sin 377t$.

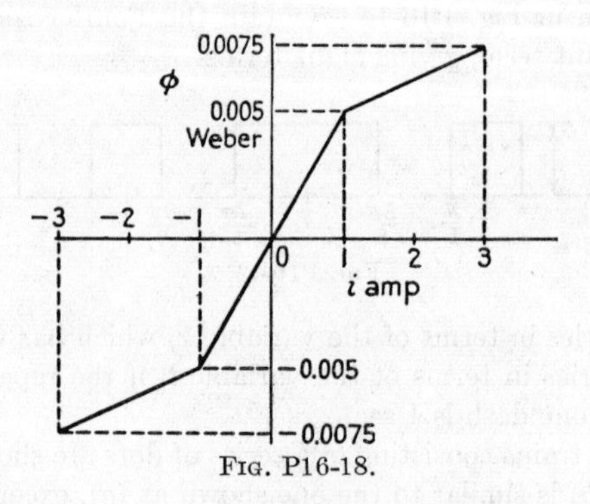


Fig. P16-18.

*a.* Obtain the series for the flux $\phi$ as a function of time.

*b.* From the results of part (*a*) determine the series for the potential induced by the changing flux.

*c.* If the coil resistance is 50 ohms, find the approximate average power loss in the coil, when its terminals are short-circuited. Assume there is no change in the equation for the flux when the short circuit is applied.

**16-19.** A vibrator for making alternating current from direct current is illustrated in Fig. P16-19. The vibrator oscillates at a frequency of 60 cps.

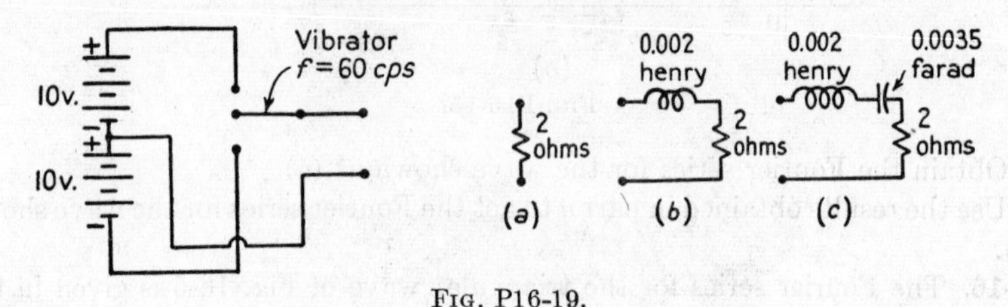


Fig. P16-19.

*a.* Determine the average power delivered by this system to a resistor of 2 ohms, as shown at (*a*) of the figure.

*b.* Determine the average power delivered to the resistor-inductor combination shown at (*b*) of the figure.

*c.* Determine the power delivered to the resistor when the load is a series circuit of $R$, $L$, and $C$, as shown at (*c*) in the figure.

**16-20.** Plot the spectra of the currents delivered to the various loads specified in the three cases of Prob. 16-19.

**16-21.** Obtain the complex form of the series for the square wave shown in Fig. 16-4.

**16-22.** Obtain the complex form of the series for the triangular wave shown in Fig. 16-5.

## QUESTIONS

**16-1.** How is the constant term in a Fourier series related to the average value of the wave?

**16-2.** Suppose a function is not periodic but that Fourier coefficients are computed for it, taking it over the interval from 0 to $T$. To what extent will the series represent the given function?

**16-3.** If a wave has point symmetry about the origin, what terms are absent from its series?

**16-4.** If a wave has axis symmetry about the origin, what terms are absent from its series?

**16-5.** If a wave has half-wave symmetry, what terms are absent from its series?

**16-6.** The three types of symmetry have different effects on the series for a wave. For which one of them is the effect independent of the position of the origin?

**16-7.** When a wave has symmetry, certain terms are zero and the nonzero terms can be computed by integrating over less than the full period. Suppose an attempt is made to compute one of the coefficients which should be zero by integrating over the reduced range. Will the correct value be obtained in all cases?

**16-8.** Each harmonic component of a Fourier series can be symbolically represented by a sinor. Furthermore, each of these sinors can be expressed as a complex number. How are these complex numbers related to the coefficients of the complex form of a Fourier series?

**16-9.** Is it possible first to evaluate the coefficients for the complex series of a wave and then to write the series in trigonometric form?

**16-10.** Is it ever possible to add a harmonic frequency component to a sinusoidal wave and thereby to reduce its effective value?

# APPENDIX A

## CALCULATION OF CIRCUIT PARAMETERS

In Sec. 2-13 it is pointed out that it is actually impossible to have pure resistance, inductance, or capacitance, except under direct-current conditions. However, in many practical situations the frequency is low enough to permit distributed effects to be neglected. For these conditions, within the limits of certain other approximations to be pointed out, it is possible to obtain formulas for the resistance, inductance, and capacitance of circuit elements from their physical properties and dimensions. A few such formulas are given in this appendix. When shapes are more complex than the ones considered here, additional formulas will be found in the literature. However, in many cases the simplest approach is to make laboratory measurements on physical samples.

In this elementary discussion no consideration is given to power losses in the magnetic and electric fields, due to hysteresis in magnetic and dielectric materials.

**A-1. Resistance.** For a conductor of uniform cross section and a length which is much larger than any cross-sectional dimension, as in Fig. A-1,

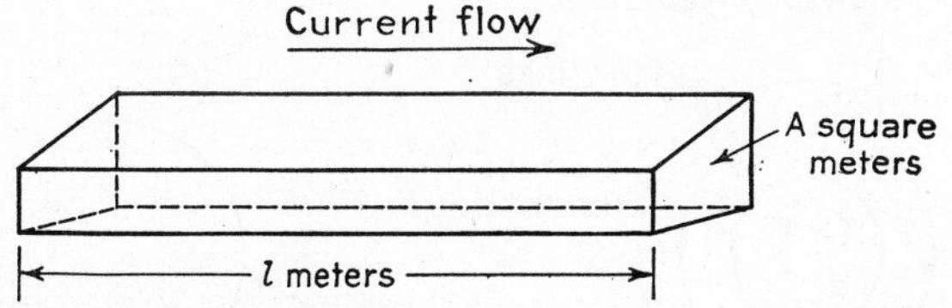


FIG. A-1. Dimensions pertinent to the computation of resistance of a conductor.

the resistance for direct current is

$$R = \rho \frac{l}{A} \tag{A-1}$$

where $l$ = conductor length, m
$A$ = conductor cross-sectional area, sq m
$\rho$ = resistivity, ohm-m

A table of values of $\rho$ for a variety of materials is given in Table A-1.

When a conductor carries an alternating current its resistance is increased because the current is not uniformly distributed across the conductor area. This effect is not to be confused with the increase of

TABLE A-1

| Material | $\rho_{20}$ at 20°C, in units of $10^{-8}$ ohm-m | $\alpha$ Temperature coefficient at 20°C |
|---|---|---|
| Aluminum | 2.828 | 0.0049 |
| Copper | 1.724 | 0.00393 |
| Iron | 9.8 | 0.006 |
| Nickel | 10.0 | 0.005 |
| Silver | 1.629 | 0.00381 |
| Tin | 11.5 | 0.0042 |
| Zinc | 5.9 | 0.0035 |
| Brass | 7.5 | 0.002–0.007 |
| Nichrome | 650 | 0.0002 |
| Advance | 295 | 0 |
| Manganin | 290 | ±0.00001 |
| Ohmax | 1,000 | −0.00035 |
| German silver | 185 | 0.00027 |

At temperature $t$°C the resistivity is

$$\rho = \rho_{20}[1 + \alpha(t - 20)]$$

impedance of a closed circuit due to inductive reactance. The situation may be qualitatively understood by referring to Fig. A-2 which shows the cross section of a conducting loop. The current produces the magnetic field which is indicated by dotted circles. The loop is assumed to

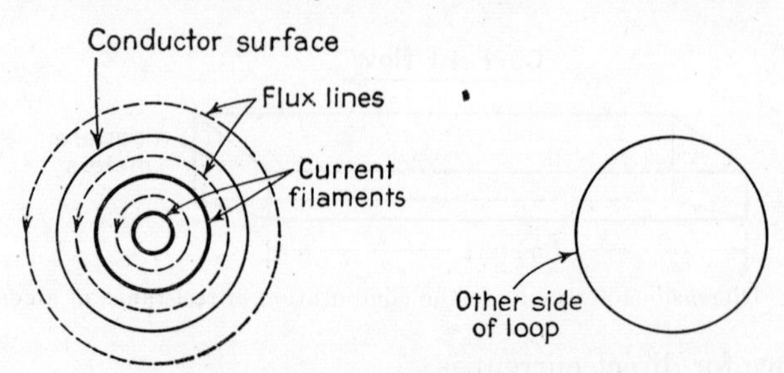
Conductor surface
Flux lines
Current filaments
Other side of loop
Current filaments and flux lines are exactly circular only when other side of loop is infinitely remote

FIG. A-2. Example of flux and current within a conducting wire.

have a large diameter so that the magnetic flux will not be appreciably distorted by the return conductor on the other side. It is convenient to think of the current as being made up of numerous concentric filaments of current flowing perpendicular to the paper. The two heavy circles in Fig. A-2 are cross sections of such current filaments. Since there is flux within the conductor itself, there is more flux encircling the small filament in the center than encircles the larger filament near the outside. This results in a higher reactance for the closed loop formed by the inside current filament compared with an outside filament. Consequently, under a-c conditions there is a weakening of the current in the central part of the conductor.

This crowding of current to the outside is, in effect, the same as a reduction of conductor cross section, and hence it increases the resistance. The phenomenon is called *skin effect.* The amount of increase in resistance caused by skin effect increases with frequency and is a function of the size and shape of the conductor cross section. In some cases the effect is quite negligible and in others it is very important. A coil of fine wire may show no appreciable skin effect at 60 cps, but a tuning coil in a radio transmitter at $10^6$ cps may have a very appreciable amount of skin effect.

There is no intention of going deeply into the subject of skin effect in this appendix. The following graph and formula should be adequate for many engineering calculations.* Consider a wire of the following dimensions:

$d$ = diameter, m
$\rho$ = resistivity on direct current, ohm-m
$\mu$ = permeability of material of wire (= 1 for nonmagnetic materials)
$f$ = frequency, cps

and define the parameter

$$w = \pi d \sqrt{\frac{0.2\mu f}{\rho}} \times 10^{-3} \qquad \text{(A-2)}$$

For an isolated conductor (or, practically, the conductor in a large loop, as in Fig. A-2) the ratio of resistance for sinusoidal alternating current at frequency $f$ to the direct-current resistance is given as a function of $w$ in Fig. A-3. Observe that eventually the curve is nearly proportional to frequency. The straight-line portion of the curve (curve $B$) is expressed by the equation

$$\frac{R_{ac}}{R_{dc}} = 160 \sqrt{\frac{\mu f}{\rho}} \times 10^{-6} \qquad \text{(A-3)}$$

The lower frequency limit for the validity of Eq. (A-3) may be taken as occurring when $w = 3$. For copper Eq. (A-2) gives a frequency limit

$$f_c = \frac{9}{\pi^2 d^2} \frac{1.72}{0.2} \times 10^4 = \text{(say)}\ \frac{8 \times 10^4}{d^2}$$

* See F. E. Terman, "Radio Engineers' Handbook," pp. 30, 35, McGraw-Hill Book Company, Inc., New York, 1943.

These results are restricted to the case of an isolated conductor of circular cross section. However, they give an indication of order of magnitude for noncircular shapes, provided the deviation is not too great. For example, Fig. A-3 may be expected to be quite good for conductors of square cross section, but not good for a thin strip, since the latter deviates widely from a circle. For coils, in which the conductors cannot be regarded as isolated, the above results apply only as an approximation.*

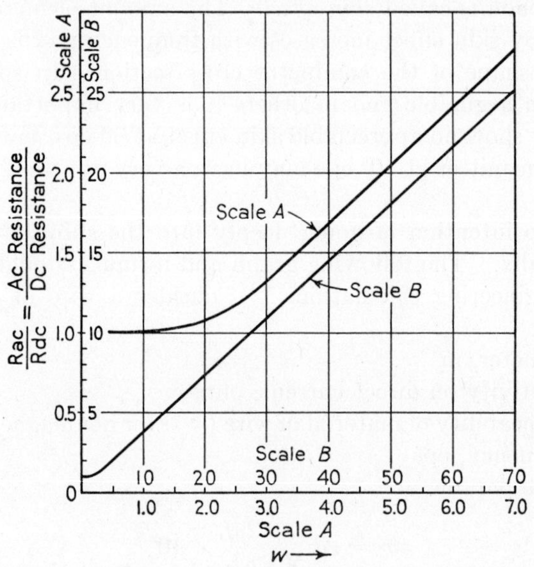


FIG. A-3. Skin effect in a round isolated conductor.

**A-2. Inductance.** In Chaps. 2 and 5 the inductance of a coil is given as the multiplying parameter $L$ by which the rate of change of current is multiplied to give the potential difference at its terminals, if its resistance were zero. Owing to skin effect, the current distribution in the conductor of a coil is a function of the rate of change of current, and this would cause the inductance to be a function of the rate of change of current. In fact, the equation for the potential due to inductance would be more accurately written

$$v = \frac{d(Li)}{dt} \tag{A-4}$$

However, in linear circuit analysis it is assumed that $L$ is a constant. To consider $L$ as a constant means that rates of change of current must be confined to sufficiently small values. Consider the equation

* For a treatment of the coils with closely spaced turn, see Terman, "Radio Engineers' Handbook," p. 77, McGraw-Hill Book Company, Inc., New York, 1943.

$$v = L \frac{di}{dt} \tag{A-5}$$

for which the reference conditions are shown in Fig. (A-4). In Eq. (A-5) $L$ is in henrys, $v$ is in volts, and $i$ is in amperes.

Although Eq. (A-5) is used to define inductance, it is not convenient for use directly in obtaining formulas for inductance from the physical properties of a coil. For deriving inductance formulas it is sometimes convenient to use energy considerations. For example, consider the loop of wire shown in Fig. A-4. By some external means a current $I$ is caused to flow in the loop. In the process of creating this current, Eq. (A-5) is obeyed. Let $T$ be the time required to bring the current from zero to $I$. The energy, in joules, supplied to the coil (omitting energy dissipated in its resistance) is

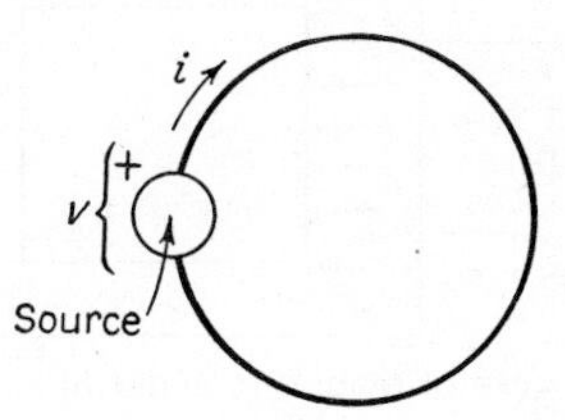

FIG. A-4. Reference conditions for Eq. (A-5).

$$W_m = \int_0^T iv\, dt = L \int_0^T i \frac{di}{dt}\, dt = L \int_0^I i\, di = \frac{LI^2}{2} \tag{A-6}$$

The energy $W_m$ is stored in the magnetic field created by the current $I$. From magnetic-field considerations it can be proved that the energy stored in a magnetic field is given by

$$W_m = \frac{10^7}{8\pi} \int \frac{B^2}{k_m}\, d\tau \qquad \text{(A-7)*}$$

where $k_m$ is the *permeability* of the medium (= 1 for vacuum), $d\tau$ is an element of volume in cubic meters, $B$ is flux density in webers per square meter, and the integration is carried out through all space. For a small number of simple geometrical shapes formulas can be obtained for $B$ and the integral of Eq. (A-7) can be evaluated. The inductance is then given by

$$L = \frac{2W_m}{I^2} \qquad \text{henrys} \tag{A-8}$$

In situations where it is possible to define a magnetic circuit to which most of the flux is confined, as in Fig. A-5, the flux linkage viewpoint exemplified by Eq. (2-33) is often convenient. In Fig. A-5 the core is of high-permeability magnetic material, so that a negligible amount of flux is found in the surrounding space. This condition makes it relatively

* In Eq. (A-7) it is implied that $k_m$ is a constant with respect to variations of $B$. That is, ferromagnetic media which become magnitically saturated are excluded.

easy to find $B$ within the coil and then to find its integral over the area (the total flux).

Assume that there is a current $i$ flowing in the coil, and that the current takes an increment $di$. The potential difference $v$ due to the changing current is given by Eq. (A-5) and also by

$$v = N\frac{d\phi}{dt} \tag{A-9}$$

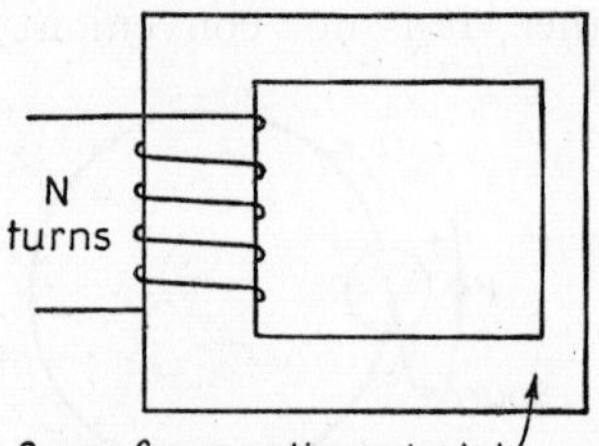


FIG. A-5. A magnetic circuit provided by a core of magnetic material.

Equating Eqs. (A-5) and (A-9) gives

$$L\frac{di}{dt} = N\frac{d\phi}{dt} \tag{A-10}$$

from which it follows that

$$L = N\frac{d\phi}{di} \quad \text{henrys} \tag{A-11}$$

where $\phi$ is in webers and $i$ is in amperes. Equation (A-11) states that the self-inductance of a coil is proportional to the rate of change in flux linkages with respect to the current that produces the flux. It is essentially the same as Eq. (2-33), except that it deals with increments of flux and current, and that $N\phi$ replaces $\int B\,dA$.

Formulas have been derived for coils of many shapes and are available in the literature.* A few examples are given here. The formulas given are good for computations requiring engineering accuracy, at frequencies which are low enough to make skin effect have negligible effect on the inductance. This does not mean, however, that the formulas are applicable only if there is no skin effect at all. Resistance is affected by skin effect at lower frequencies than inductance is affected, and so a resistance correction may be required at the same time that the given formulas for inductance are reasonably accurate.

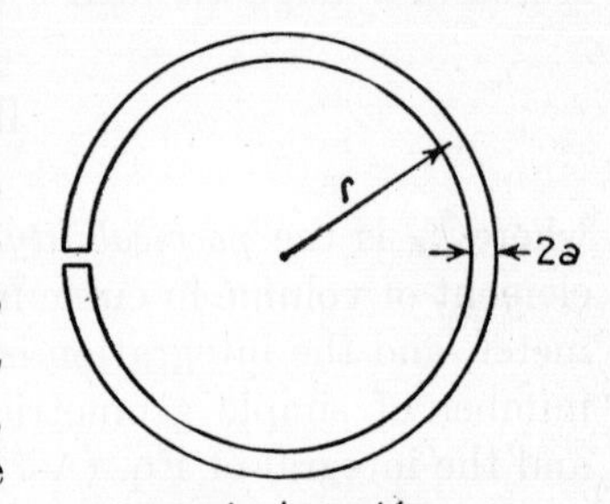


FIG. A-6. Dimensions of a single turn.

1. *Single circular turn in air.* For the single circular turn of Fig. A-6, at low frequencies, the inductance is approximately

$$L = 4\pi r\left(\ln\frac{8r}{a} - \frac{7}{4}\right) \times 10^{-7} \quad \text{henrys} \tag{A-12}$$

The dimensions $a$ and $r$ are in meters.

* See F. E. Terman "Radio Engineers' Handbook," pp. 47–109, McGraw-Hill Book Company, Inc., New York, 1943.

2. *Single-layer solenoid in air.* For the single-layer solenoid of Fig. A-7 the inductance at low frequencies, in henrys, is approximately

$$L = K_s d N^2 \qquad \text{(A-13)}$$

where $K_s$ is a function of the ratio of the diameter to length of the coil, and $d$ is the coil diameter in meters. $K_s$ is given graphically in Fig. A-8.

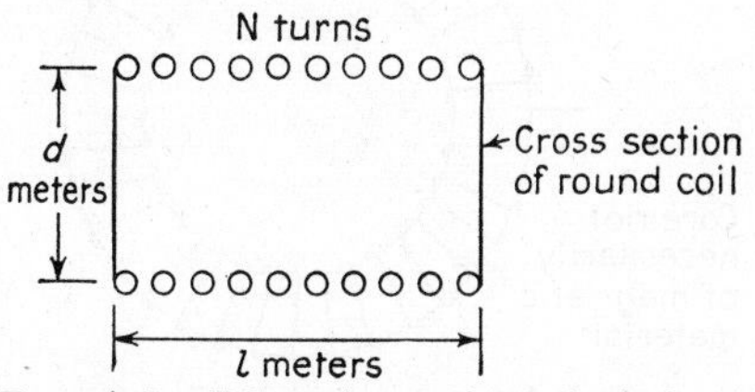


FIG. A-7. Dimensions of a single-layer solenoid.

3. *Coil with a uniform magnetic circuit.* Typical examples of coils with well-defined uniform magnetic circuits are shown in Figs. A-9 and A-10. In the case of Fig. A-9 the magnetic circuit is well-defined whether or not it is made of ferromagnetic material, because the arrangement of the winding causes most of the flux to be confined inside the coil. If

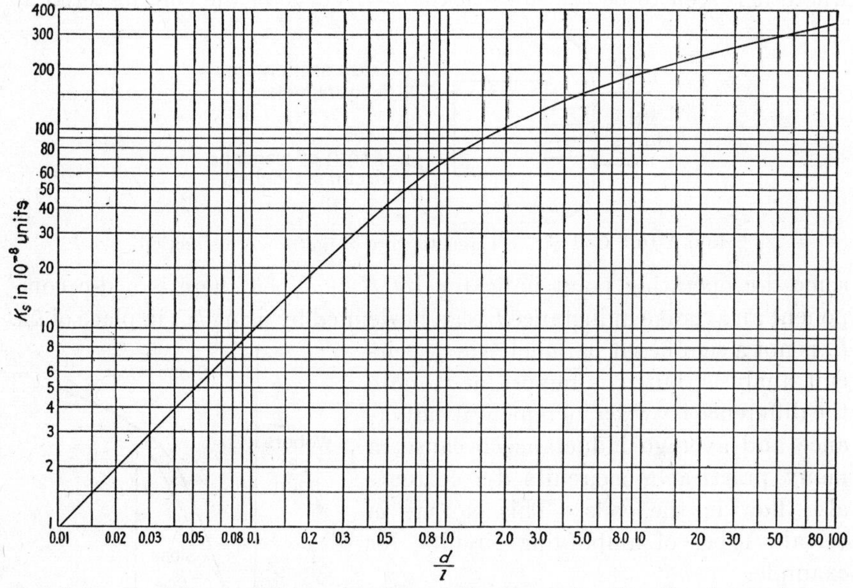


FIG. A-8. $K_s$ of Eq. (A-13) as a function of diameter-to-length ratio of a single-layer solenoid.

the magnetic core were not present in Fig. (A-10), this case would fall in classification (2). For calculations of engineering accuracy it is usually permissible to neglect the leakage flux which is not in the core, and then Fig. A-10 falls in the same classification as Fig. A-9.

Equation (A-11) is convenient for coils in this classification. From the properties of magnetic circuits it is known that a current increment $di$

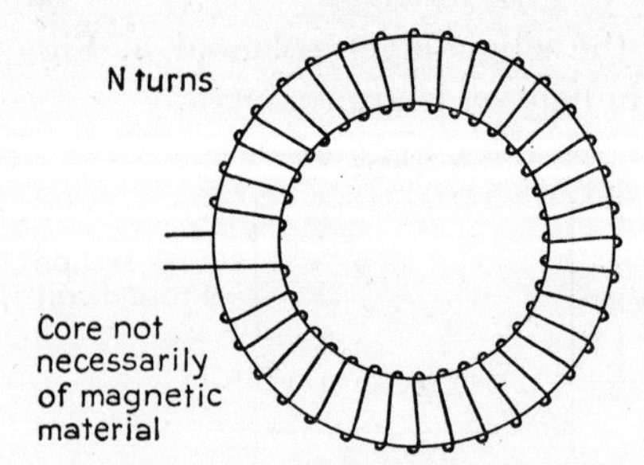

FIG. A-9. A toroidal coil.

produces a flux increment

$$d\phi = \frac{4\pi k_m AN\,di}{l} \times 10^{-7} \quad \text{webers} \tag{A-14}$$

where $k_m$ is the *incremental permeability* (= 1 in vacuum), $A$ is the cross-sectional area of the magnetic circuit perpendicular to the flux in square meters, and $l$ is the length of the magnetic circuit in meters. From Eq. (A-11) it follows that

$$L = \frac{4\pi k_m AN^2}{l} \times 10^{-7} \quad \text{henrys} \tag{A-15}$$

The meaning of the incremental permeability $k_m$ is given in Fig. A-11, where it is seen to be the slope of the $B$-$H$ curve of the core material at

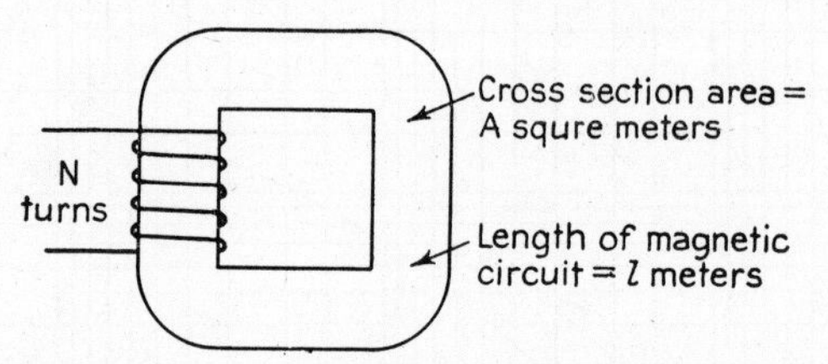

FIG. A-10. Coil with a magnetic core of uniform cross section.

some d-c operating point indicated by $H_0$. When there is a d-c component an average inductance $L_a$ can be defined by using $k_{ma}$ in place of $k_m$. $L_a$ is not a significant parameter in a-c circuit analysis, but it is important to note the difference between incremental inductance and average inductance because in many practical a-c circuits d-c currents also flow in the coils. This is true in certain types of amplifying circuits, for example.

A typical curve showing how incremental permeability varies with the d-c component of magnetizing force is given in Fig. A-12. It should be understood that when saturation is encountered, $L$ is a linear parameter only for a-c currents which are small enough so that the slope of the $B$-$H$ curve does not change appreciably between the positive and negative swings of the a-c

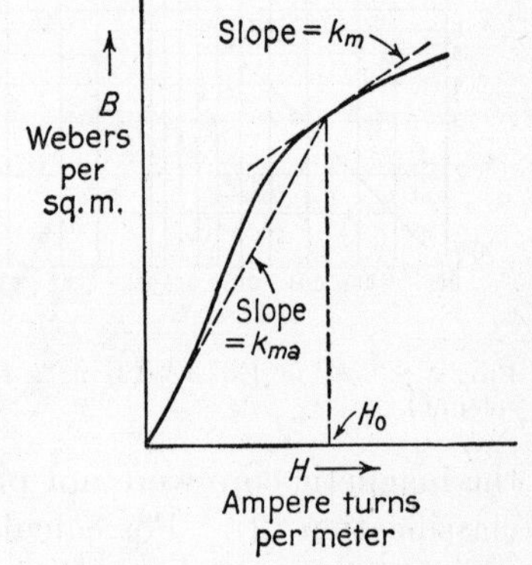

FIG. A-11. Typical magnetization curve of a ferromagnetic material.

component. It is also to be realized that no consideration has been given to hysteresis.

Because of the large changes in $k_m$ with variations of flux density in ferromagnetic materials, any attempt at tabulation of values of $k_m$ is likely to be misleading. For accurate calculations it is necessary to refer to data on the magnetic properties of specific materials. In general, however, it may be said that values of $k_m$ up to $10^5$ can be obtained.

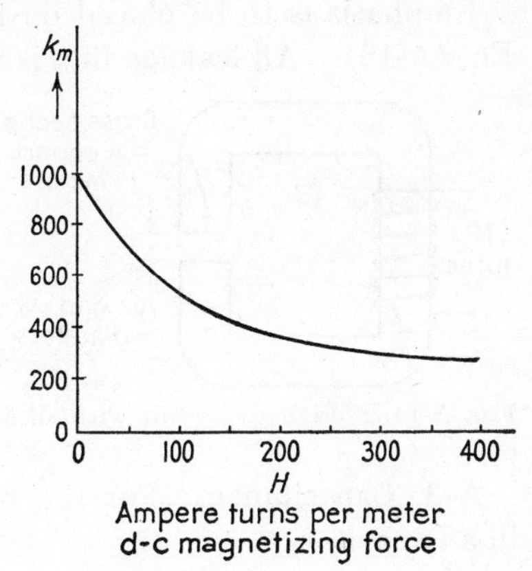


FIG. A-12. Typical curve of incremental permeability $k_m$ for silicon steel, as a function of d-c magnetizing force.

4. *Coil with a nonuniform magnetic circuit.* The case shown in Fig. A-5 cannot be treated by Eq. (A-15) because there is no single cross-sectional area. The relationship between flux and current must be found for the particular magnetic circuit by assuming a sequence of values of $\phi$ and computing the corresponding ampere-turns required to produce that flux. A curve similar to Fig. A-13 can then be obtained, and the inductance is

$$L = \mathcal{P}N^2 \tag{A-16}$$

where $\mathcal{P}$ is the slope of the curve of Fig. A-13 at the d-c operating point. $\mathcal{P}$ is called the *incremental permeance* of the magnetic circuit. It is measured in henrys. In similarity with case (3), the d-c inductance would be obtained by using an average permeance $\mathcal{P}_a$, as defined in Fig. A-13.

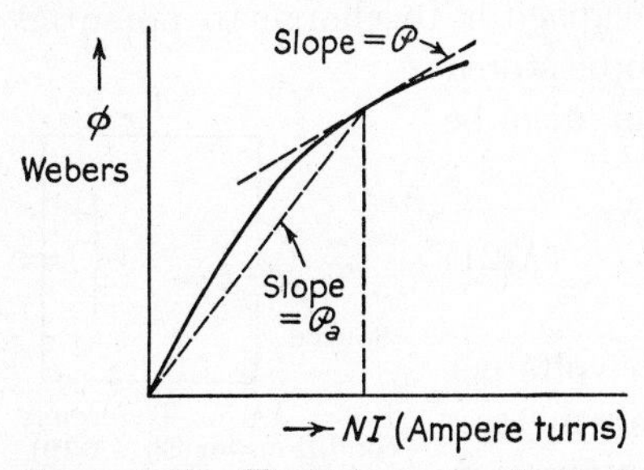


FIG. A-13. Typical magnetization curve of a magnetic circuit.

5. *Coil having a magnetic circuit with an air gap.* If there is an air gap in a core of very high permeability magnetic material, the permeance of the magnetic circuit may sometimes be taken as that of the air gap alone. For example, consider Fig. A-14, which shows a core with an air gap of cross section $A$ sq m and length $l$ m. The permeance of the air gap is approximately (neglecting fringing of flux)

$$\mathcal{P} = \frac{4\pi A}{l} \times 10^{-7} \qquad \text{henrys} \tag{A-17}$$

so that the inductance is approximately

$$L = \frac{4\pi AN^2}{l} \times 10^{-7} \qquad \text{henrys} \tag{A-18}$$

Emphasis is to be placed on the approximations that are involved in Eq. (A-18). All leakage flux is neglected, and it is further assumed that the permeance of the iron path is so high that all of the ampere-turns of the coil are effective in creating flux in the air gap. If these assumptions are not justified, as may be judged from a magnetization curve of the core in specific cases, then Fig. A-14 is placed in classification (4).

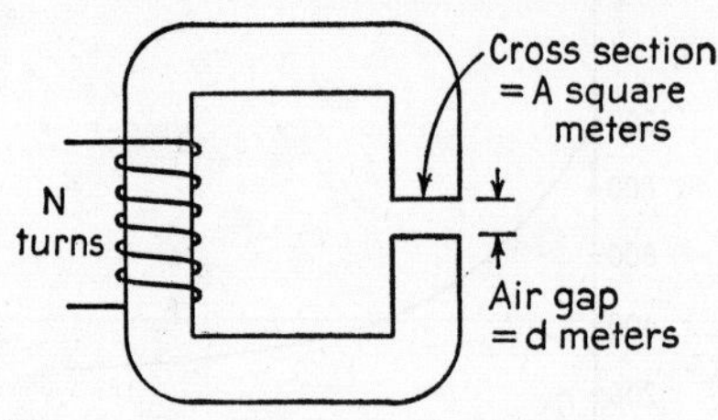


Fig. A-14. Magnetic circuit with an air gap.

**A-3. Capacitance.** For the reference conditions shown in Fig. A-15, in a capacitor

$$i = C\frac{dv}{dt} \tag{A-19}$$

where $C$ is in farads, $v$ is in volts, and $i$ is in amperes. While the capacitor is being charged to a potential difference $V$, the energy going into the charge separation, in joules, is

$$W_e = \int_0^T vi\,dt = C\int_0^T v\frac{dv}{dt}\,dt = C\int_0^V v\,dv = \frac{CV^2}{2} \tag{A-20}$$

where $T$ is the time required for the capacitor to charge to potential difference $V$. The energy $W_e$ is said to be stored in the electric field. This energy can also be given by

$$W_e = \frac{10^{-9}}{72\pi}\int k_e \mathcal{E}^2 d\tau \tag{A-21}$$

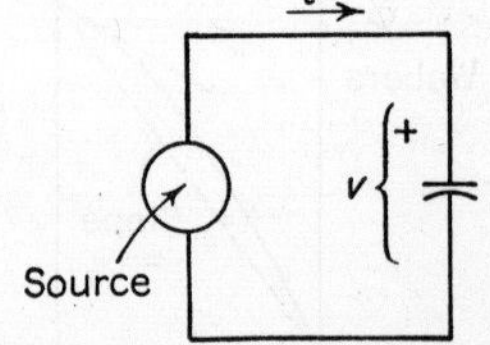


Fig. A-15. Reference conditions for Eq. (A-19).

where $\mathcal{E}$ is the electric field intensity in volts per meter, $d\tau$ is an element of volume in square meters, and $k_e$ is the *dielectric constant*. The integration is carried out for all space. In those simple geometrical cases for which Eq. (A-21) can be evaluated, the capacitance can be calculated from

$$C = \frac{2W_e}{V^2} \tag{A-22}$$

$C$ can also be computed from Eq. (2-34).

Formulas for a few simple geometrical shapes are given below. Formulas for more complicated arrangements can be found in the literature.*

1. *Parallel plates.* For the arrangement shown in Fig. A-16, if fringing of the electric field at the edges is neglected, the capacitance between the plates is

$$C = \frac{k_e A}{36\pi l} \times 10^{-9} \quad \text{farads} \quad \text{(A-23)}$$

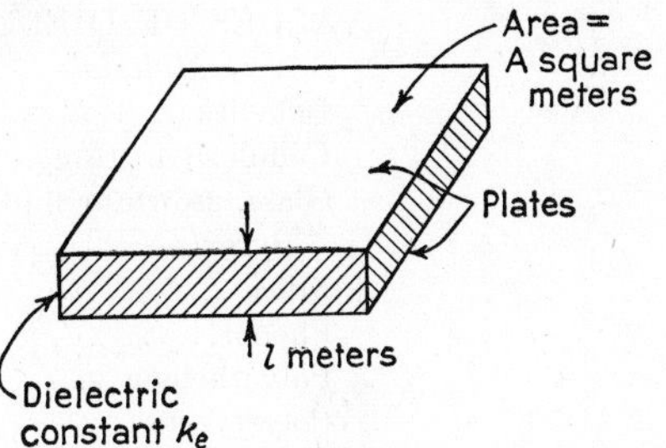


FIG. A-16. Dimensions of a parallel-plate capacitor.

Equation (A-23) also applies for multiple-place capacitors if $A$ is interpreted as the combined cross section of all the dielectric slabs.

2. *Concentric spheres.* Let two concentric spheres have radii $r_2$ and $r_1$ (where $r_2 > r_1$) in meters, and let the space between them be filled with a material of dielectric constant $k_e$. The capacitance between the spheres is

$$C = \frac{k_e r_1 r_2}{9(r_2 - r_1)} \times 10^{-9} \quad \text{farads} \quad \text{(A-24)}$$

3. *Concentric cylinders.* Consider two concentric cylinders which are very long in comparison with their diameters. They are separated by a material of dielectric constant $k_e$. The capacitance between them is

$$C = \frac{k_e}{18 \ln (r_2/r_1)} \times 10^{-9}$$

farads per meter of length (A-25)

where $r_2$ is the radius of the larger cylinder and $r_1$ is the radius of the smaller one.

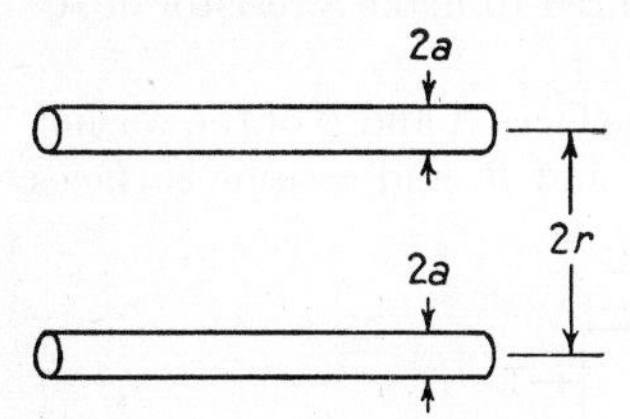


FIG. A-17. Two "infinitely long" parallel cylinders.

4. *Parallel cylinders.* Two long identical cylinders for which the separation is much larger than the cylinder diameter are shown in Fig. A-17. The capacitance between them is approximately

$$C = \frac{27.7 k_e}{\ln (2r/a)} \times 10^{-12} \quad \text{farads per meter of length} \quad \text{(A-26)}$$

This formula is quite accurate if $r > 5a$.

* See F. E. Terman, "Radio Engineers' Handbook," pp. 109–126, McGraw-Hill Book Company, Inc., New York, 1943.

Some tabulated values of dielectric constant $k_e$ are given in Table A-2. In most cases of materials which are compounds the dielectric constant depends on the proportions of the various constituents, and so rather

TABLE A-2
VALUES OF DIELECTRIC CONSTANT $k_e$

| *Material* | $k_e$ |
|---|---|
| Bakelite | 4.5–5.5 |
| Cellulose nitrate | 11.4 |
| Glass, crown or flint | 6.2–7.0 |
| Pyrex | 4.5 |
| Mica | 7.0–7.3 |
| Phenol | 5.5 |
| Polyethelene | 2.26 |
| Polystyrene | 2.56 |
| Porcelain | 6.2–7.5 |
| Rubber | 2.4–3.0 |
| Neoprene | 6.7 |
| Benzene | 2.15 |
| Petroleum oils | 2.2 |
| Ethyl alcohol | 25 |
| Methyl alcohol | 31 |
| Distilled water | 81 |

wide variations may be found in tabulated values. When accuracy is needed, the published data for a specific material should be consulted.

## PROBLEMS

**A-1.** What length of Advance wire would be required to make a resistor of $10^6$ ohms, if its diameter is 0.002 in.?

**A-2.*** Find a formula for the resistance between the faces $A$ and $B$ of the washer shown in Fig. PA-2. Neglect the space between $A$ and $B$, and assume surfaces $A$ and $B$ to be constant-potential surfaces.

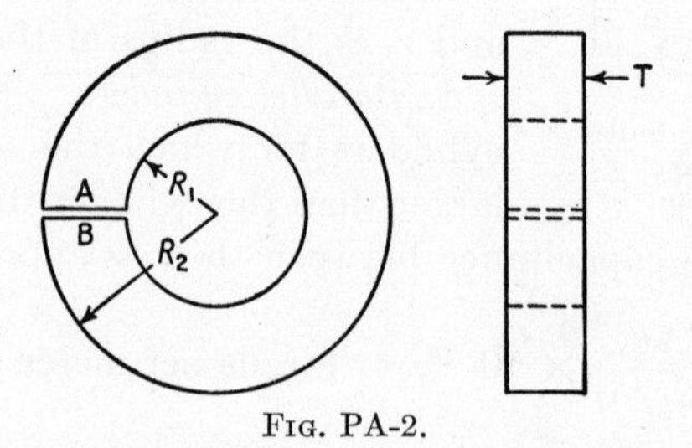


FIG. PA-2.

* In the problems marked with an asterisk the fundamental formula is applied to a suitably chosen integration element, and then integrated over the volume.

**A-3.*** Figure PA-3 shows a dielectric cylinder which occupies the space between two concentric conducting cylinders. The dielectric has a finite resistivity $\rho$. Obtain a formula for the resistance between the conducting cylinders.

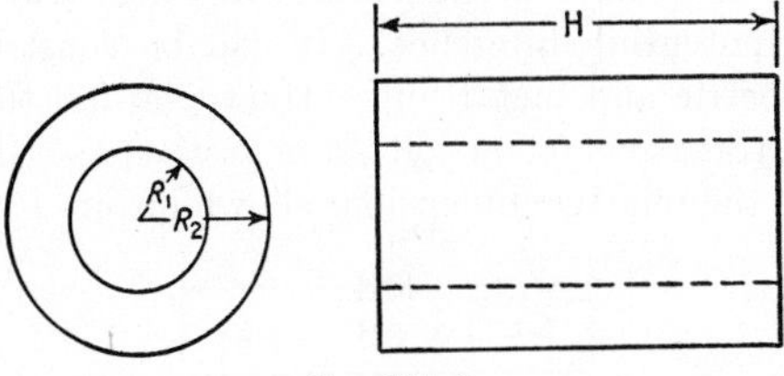


FIG. PA-3.

**A-4.** Eighty turns of No. 20 wire form a single layer on a 2-in.-diameter cylindrical nonmagnetic core. Assume insulation and irregularities cause the spacing between coils to have an average value of 0.004 in. Compute the inductance of this coil.

**A-5.** Obtain approximate resistances for the coil of Prob. A-4 at direct current and at frequencies of $10^3$ and $10^5$ cps, if the wire is copper.

**A-6.** An inductor is constructed in the form of a toroid, as shown in Fig. PA-6. Assume the ratio of radii $R_2/R_1$ is small enough so that the magnetic circuit can

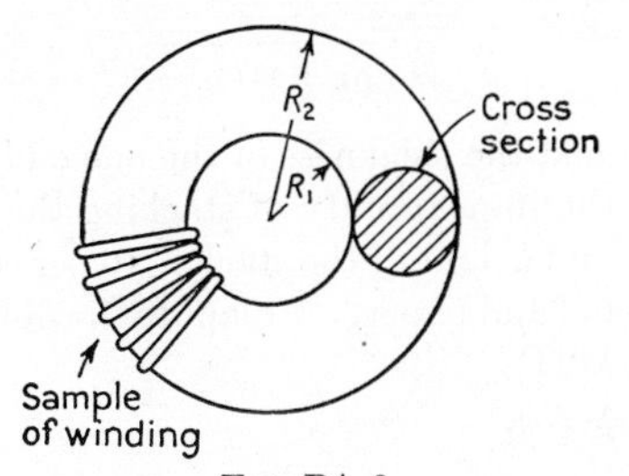


FIG. PA-6.

be given an average length $\pi(R_1 + R_2)$. Let the spacing between turn centers on the inside of the toroid be $W$. Obtain a formula for the coil inductance as a function of $W$, $R_1$, and $R_2$.

**A-7.** An inductor is constructed like Fig. PA-6 with an iron core for which $k_m = 600$. The coil is wound with No. 20 wire. Assume the effective wire diameter is increased by 20 per cent to obtain the turn spacing. Let $R_2/R_1 = 1.3$. Use the assumption stipulated in Prob. A-6 to compute the dimensions of a core to obtain an inductance of 1 henry.

**A-8.*** Obtain a formula for the inductance of the arrangement shown in Fig. PA-6 as a function of $R_1$, $R_2$, and $W$, without using an average circumference for the core.

**A-9.** An audio-frequency transformer has a silicon steel core of 1 sq cm uniform cross-sectional area and a length of 14 cm. The primary coil has 3,500 turns and carries a d-c current of 15 ma. What is the incremental inductance of this coil for a small a-c component superimposed on the d-c?

**A-10.** An air capacitor is made up of 15 stacked plates, with alternate plates connected together. Their separation is 0.5 mm and each has an area of 8 sq cm. Compute the capacitance, neglecting fringing of the electric field.

**A-11.** A capacitor is to have a capacitance of 0.1 $\mu$f and be capable of withstanding 500 volts potential difference. It will be constructed of a series of layers of paper dielectric and metal foil. The metal-foil thickness is 0.004 cm. Assume a dielectric strength of 5,000 volts/mm for the paper, and a value $k_e = 5.5$. The stack is to have the relative dimensions shown in Fig. PA-11. In computing

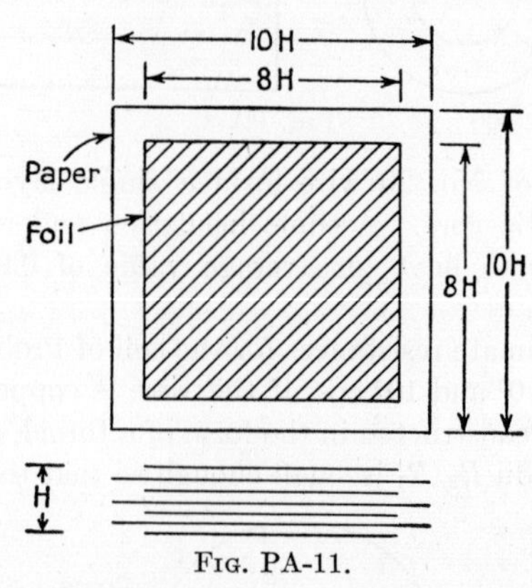


FIG. PA-11.

the dimensions of the stack, the thickness of the one odd plate at the end may be neglected. Because of the impossibility of stacking the plates with perfect contact, assume that the actual height of the stack is 10 per cent greater than the sum of the thicknesses of the foil and paper. Compute the dimensions of the capacitor.

**A-12.*** Derive Eq. (A-24).

**A-13.*** Derive Eq. (A-25).

# APPENDIX B

# D-C NETWORK ANALYSIS

**B-1. Introduction.** In a sense a d-c circuit can be considered a special case of an a-c circuit, for which the frequency is zero, but there are advantages to considering d-c circuit analysis as a separate entity. The purpose of this Appendix is to present the essential features of d-c circuit analysis in a manner that will supplement the more complete treatment of the a-c case in the text, particularly as presented in Chaps. 10 and 11. This Appendix is not a review of introductory electrical engineering; it is confined solely to d-c network theory. It is assumed that the reader is familiar with the concepts of potential difference, current, power, the usual sources of d-c electrical energy (batteries and generators), and the rudiments of electrical measurements.

**B-2. Resistance and Conductance.** Resistance and conductance are numerical parameters that make it possible to express a proportionality between the potential difference across a resistor and the current through it. For Fig. B-1 the proportionality, which is Ohm's law, can be written in either of the two forms

$$\begin{aligned} V &= RI \\ I &= GV \end{aligned} \qquad \text{(B-1)}$$

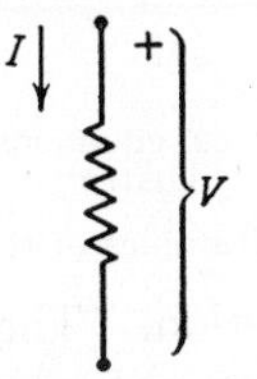

FIG. B-1. Usual reference conditions for a resistor.

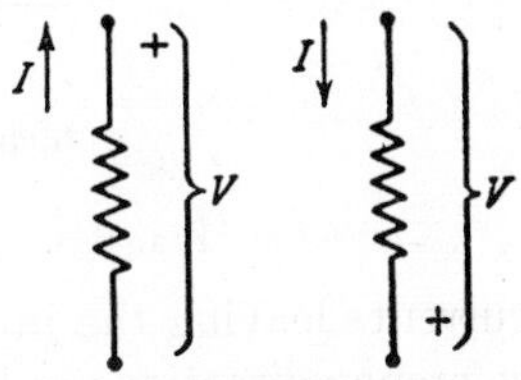

FIG. B-2. Reference conditions leading to a negative sign in the equation for Ohm's law.

$R$ is the resistance of the resistor, in ohms, and $G$ is its conductance, in mhos, if $V$ is in volts and $I$ is in amperes. This discussion deals only with *linear* elements, meaning that, for a given resistor, $R$ and $G$ are constants. The two forms of Eq. (B-1) are both given because in some cases $R$ is the natural parameter to use and in other cases $G$ is more convenient. $R$ and $G$ are related by

$$R = \frac{1}{G} \qquad \text{(B-2)}$$

It is instructive to note how the *reference polarity* of a potential difference and the *reference direction* of a current affect the equation relating $V$ and $I$ for a resistor.* For both cases illustrated in Fig. B-2 the equations

* $V$ and $I$ are algebraic variables. For example, in Fig. B-1 the current need not

of proportionality are

$$V = -RI$$
$$I = -GV \tag{B-3}$$

**B-3. Kirchhoff's Laws.** The two Kirchhoff laws are discussed at some length in Sec. 5-2 of the text. In this Appendix the laws are stated and illustrated with examples.

1. *Kirchhoff's Law for Currents.* At any *node* (*junction*) in a network the sum of the currents entering the junction is equal to the sum of the currents leaving the junction. The current directions to be used are the reference directions indicated by arrows on a circuit diagram.

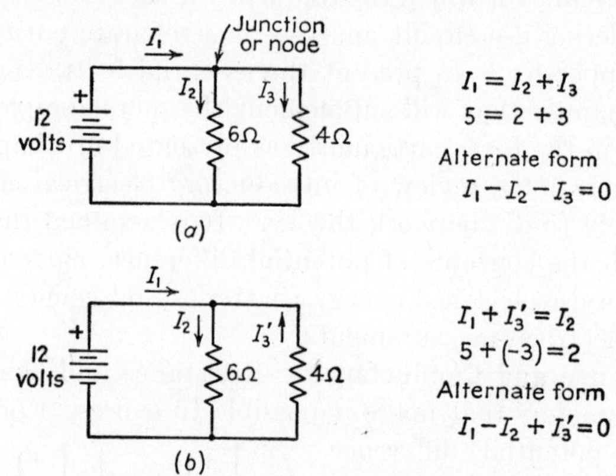


FIG. B-3. Examples of the Kirchhoff law for currents.

Kirchhoff's current law is an expression of the fundamental law of conservation of electrical charge. Two examples of the law are given in Fig. B-3. In each case the law is written for the literal variables, and also for the numerical case illustrated. Note that each equation can be written with zero on one side of the equality sign, as in the alternate forms given.

2. *Kirchhoff's Law for Potential Differences.* When traveling continuously in one direction around a closed *loop* of a network the sum of the potential rises is equal to the sum of the potential drops. The polar-

be in the direction of the arrow, and if it is not $I$ becomes a negative quantity. The direction of the arrow is called the *reference direction* for the current. Also in Fig. B-1, the potential difference need not have the polarity shown, and if the actual polarity is different $V$ will be algebraically negative. The polarity shown on the diagram is called the *reference polarity*. Each $V$ and $I$ symbol used in network analysis must have a reference polarity or direction specified for it, usually by suitable marking on a circuit diagram. For additional information see Sec. 2-6 of the text.

ities to be used in determining whether a potential difference is a rise or a drop are the reference polarities indicated by marks on the diagram.

Kirchhoff's potential law is an expression of the fundamental law of conservation of energy, because potential difference is really a measure of work done in moving a unit test charge between two points. Two examples of Kirchhoff's potential law are given in Fig. B-4. In each case the law is given in literal form, and also for the numerical case illustrated. Note that each equation can be written with zero on one side of the equality sign, as shown in the alternate forms.

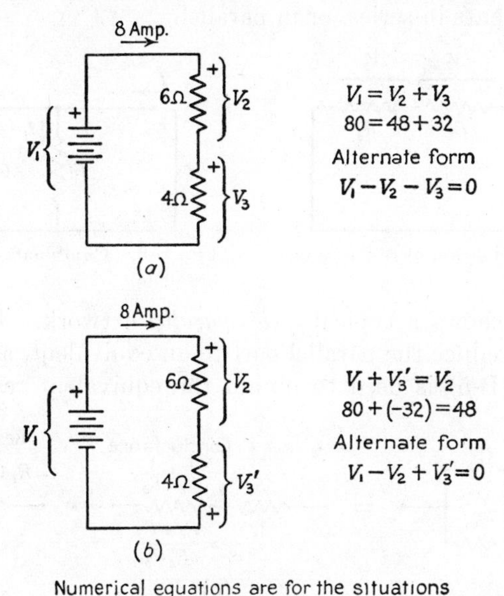


Numerical equations are for the situations illustrated in the diagrams

FIG. B-4. Examples of the Kirchhoff law for potential differences.

The examples of Figs. B-3 and B-4 illustrate that the algebraic equations used to express Kirchhoff's laws have forms which depend on the reference conditions. In the analysis of d-c circuits reference conditions are usually chosen to coincide with actual polarities and current directions, when they are known; otherwise the references are chosen arbitrarily, usually to give a minimum number of negative signs in the equations.

**B-4. Equivalent Resistance and Conductance for Two-terminal Passive Networks.** *A two-terminal passive d-c network* is one that contains nothing but resistors. For Fig. B-5, which is called a *series* connection of resistors, Kirchhoff's potential law gives

$$V = V_1 + V_2 + V_3 = (R_1 + R_2 + R_3)I \tag{B-4}$$

The resistance $R$ of the combination is the ratio $V/I$; thus

$$R = R_1 + R_2 + R_3 \tag{B-5}$$

For the *parallel* circuit of Fig. B-6 Kirchhoff's current law gives

$$I = I_1 + I_2 + I_3 = (G_1 + G_2 + G_3)V \tag{B-6}$$

The equivalent conductance $G$ is the ratio $I/V$, giving

$$G = G_1 + G_2 + G_3 \tag{B-7}$$

Equations (B-5) and (B-7) can of course be extended to apply to any number of elements in series, or in parallel.

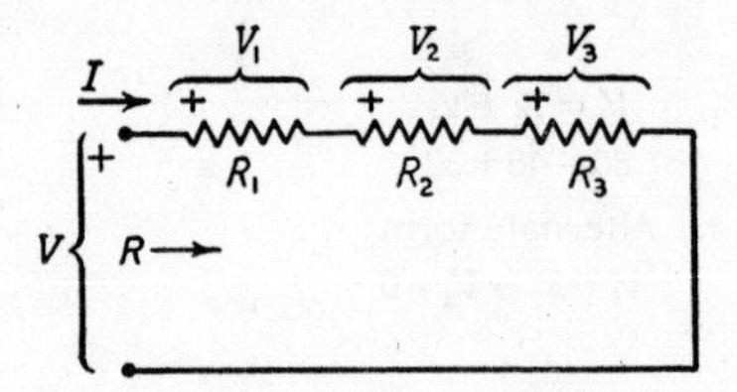


Fig. B-5. Combination of resistors in series.

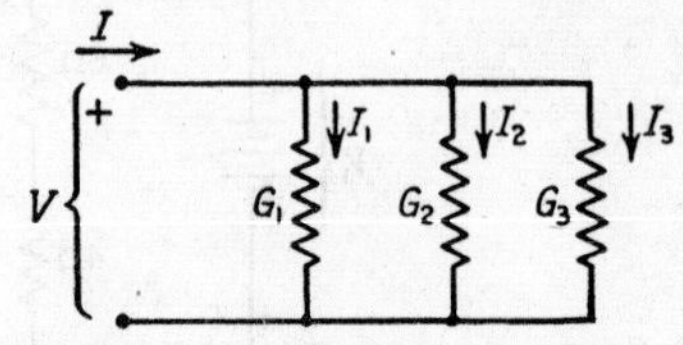


Fig. B-6. Combination of resistors in parallel.

Figure B-7a shows a typical *series-parallel* network. Equation (B-7) can be used to reduce the parallel part to an equivalent, as shown at (*b*), and then Eq. (B-5) is used to obtain the equivalent resistance of the

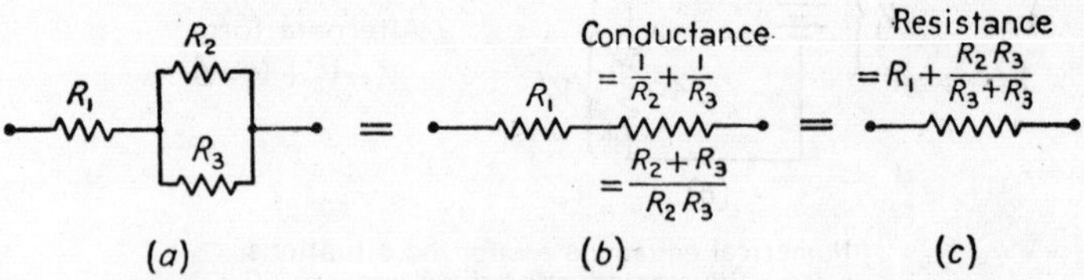

Conductance $= \frac{1}{R_2} + \frac{1}{R_3}$ $= \frac{R_2 + R_3}{R_2 R_3}$

Resistance $= R_1 + \frac{R_2 R_3}{R_3 + R_3}$

(*a*) (*b*) (*c*)

Fig. B-7. Reduction of a series-parallel combination of resistors.

Conductance $= \frac{1}{R_1} + \frac{1}{R_2 + R_3} = \frac{R_1 + R_2 + R_3}{R_1(R_2 + R_3)}$

Resistance $= \frac{R_1(R_2 + R_3)}{R_1 + R_2 + R_3}$

(*a*) (*b*) (*c*)

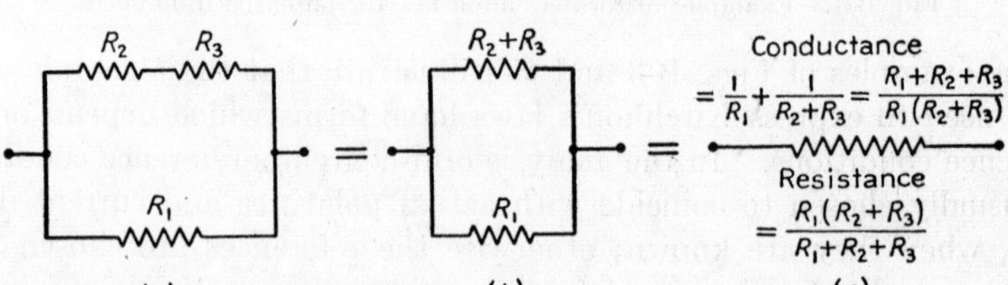

Fig. B-8. Reduction of a parallel-series combination of resistors.

complete network, as shown at (*c*). The appropriate formulas are given in the figure. A similar treatment is used on the *parallel-series* network of Fig. B-8.

The procedure outlined in Figs. B-7 and B-8 can be used as long as the necessary sequence of series and parallel combinations can be found.

When using such a procedure it is important to indicate at each stage whether an expression is for resistance or conductance, because both may arise from time to time in the process. In some cases it is convenient to use $1/R$ for $G$ (or $1/G$ for $R$) to avoid introducing too many symbols. In other cases it is sometimes warranted to use $G_2$ for $1/R_2$, etc.

Figure B-9 shows a bridge network for which the resistance cannot be found by the above method. This case can be handled by several methods, one of which is described in the following section.

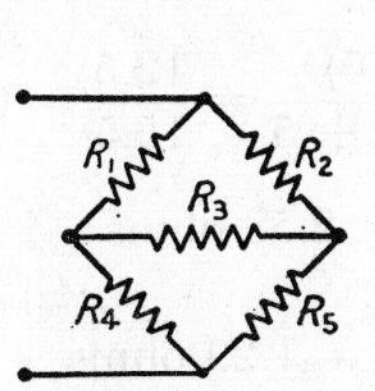


FIG. B-9. A bridge circuit; a case where reduction is not possible by series-parallel or parallel-series combinations.

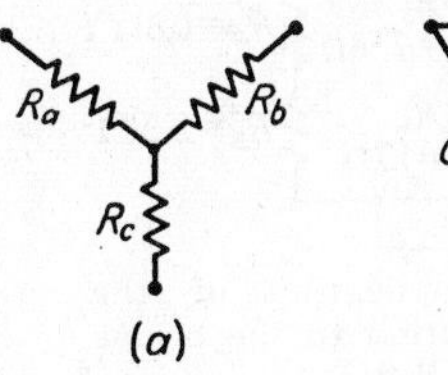


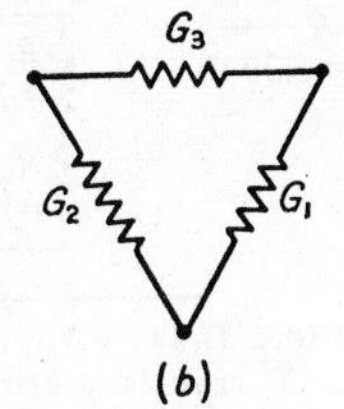


FIG. B-10. T and Π (Y and Δ) networks.

**B-5. T–Π and Π–T (Y–Δ and Δ–Y) Transformation.** Consider the pair of three-terminal networks shown in Fig. B-10. It can be demonstrated that both networks will exhibit identical behavior, when connected into any network, if the $R$'s and $G$'s are related by the formulas*

$$
\begin{aligned}
G_1 &= \frac{R_a}{R_aR_b + R_bR_c + R_cR_a} = \frac{G_bG_c}{G_a + G_b + G_c} \\
G_2 &= \frac{R_b}{R_aR_b + R_bR_c + R_cR_a} = \frac{G_cG_a}{G_a + G_b + G_c} \\
G_3 &= \frac{R_c}{R_aR_b + R_bR_c + R_cR_a} = \frac{G_aG_b}{G_a + G_b + G_c}
\end{aligned}
\tag{B-8}
$$

and

$$
\begin{aligned}
R_a &= \frac{G_1}{G_1G_2 + G_2G_3 + G_3G_1} = \frac{R_2R_3}{R_1 + R_2 + R_3} \\
R_b &= \frac{G_2}{G_1G_2 + G_2G_3 + G_3G_1} = \frac{R_3R_1}{R_1 + R_2 + R_3} \\
R_c &= \frac{G_3}{G_1G_2 + G_2G_3 + G_3G_1} = \frac{R_1R_2}{R_1 + R_2 + R_3}
\end{aligned}
\tag{B-9}
$$

* One way to derive these formulas is first to prove that a sufficient condition for the two networks to behave identically in all situations is to have them exhibit identical resistances between corresponding pairs of terminals, when the networks are free of any externally connected network. Equations (B-8) and (B-9) are obtained when expressions for these resistances are equated and simplified. Equations (B-8) and (B-9) can also be proved directly from four-terminal-network theory (see LePage and Seely, "General Network Analysis," McGraw-Hill Book Company, Inc., New York, 1952, p. 155.)

As an aid in remembering these formulas, note that if subscripts 1, 2, and 3 correspond respectively to $a$, $b$, and $c$, then corresponding branches in the two circuits are in opposite positions with respect to the centers of the networks.

Consider Fig. B-9 for the numerical case: $R_1 = 8$, $R_2 = 2.5$, $R_3 = 5$, $R_4 = 1.7$, $R_5 = 3.3$ ohms. By using the $\Delta$ to Y transformation the network can be put in the form shown in Fig. B-11, for which the numerical values are

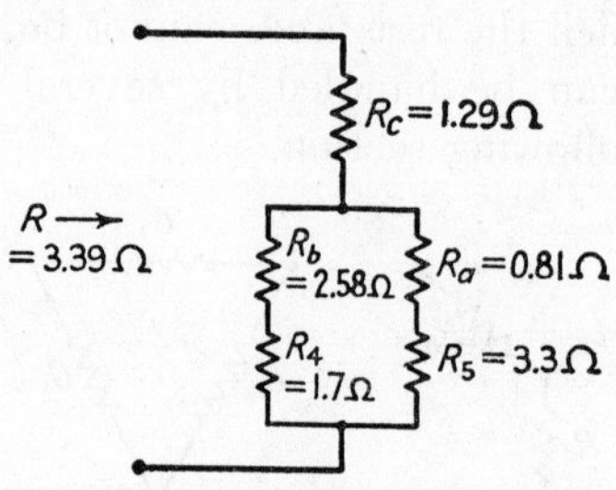


FIG. B-11. Application of the $\Delta$–Y transformation to the bridge network of Fig. B-9.

$$R_a = \frac{(2.5)(5)}{8 + 2.5 + 5} = \frac{12.5}{15.5} = 0.81 \text{ ohm}$$

$$R_b = \frac{(5)(8)}{15.5} = 2.58 \text{ ohms}$$

$$R_c = \frac{(8)(2.5)}{15.5} = 1.29 \text{ ohms}$$

From Sec. B-4 the resistance of the series-parallel circuit of Fig. B-11 is

$$R = 1.29 + \frac{1}{(1/4.28) + (1/4.11)} = 1.29 + \frac{1}{0.234 + 0.243}$$

$$= 1.29 + \frac{1}{0.477} = 1.29 + 2.10 = 3.39 \text{ ohms}$$

**B-6. Equivalent Circuits for Batteries and Generators.** Imagine an experiment conducted on a battery or a generator, as shown in Fig. B-12.

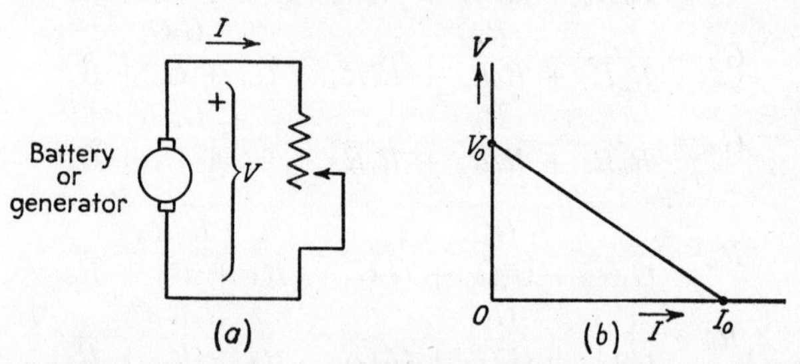


FIG. B-12. Relationship between current and potential difference for a linear source.

The resistor is varied, and readings of $I$ and $V$ are taken and plotted on a graph, as in Fig. B-12$b$. In many cases the graph will be a straight line, or at least so nearly so that it may be considered straight. A generator or battery which does give a straight-line graph is called a *linear source*. It is the only type of source admitted in linear circuit analysis. From analytic geometry, by introducing the intercepts $V_0$ and $I_0$ and slope $-R_0$ the equation for the line can be written

$$V = V_0 - R_0 I \tag{B-10}$$

or

$$I = I_0 - \frac{1}{R_0} V \tag{B-11}$$

Equation (B-10) is recognized as also representing Fig. B-13*a* in which the battery symbol represents a *potential source* of value $V_0$. That is, if $V_0$ and $R_0$ are known it is possible to construct, on paper at least, a circuit which is equivalent to the actual source. Also, the circuit of Fig. B-13*b* is described by Eq. (B-11), and so it follows that Fig. B-13*b* is another equivalent circuit. In Fig. B-13*b* the circle represents a current source of value $I_0$.

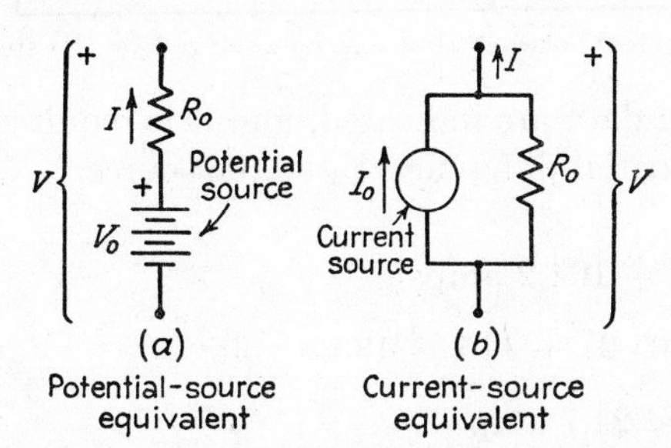


FIG. B-13. Potential-source and current-source equivalents of a linear source.

The significant fact about the equivalent circuits of Fig. B-13 is that they include an *internal resistance* $R_0$ combined with either a *potential source* or a *current source.* The potential difference of the potential source is the open-circuit potential of the actual source, and the current source is the short-circuit current of the actual source. Figure B-13*a* is called the *potential-source equivalent,* and Fig. B-13*b* is called the *current-source equivalent.* (It must be noted that in the usage of this text the symbol consisting of alternate long and short parallel lines represents a d-c potential source, and not a physical battery.) In the case of a separately excited generator, $R_0$ is very nearly the resistance measured between the armature terminals when the machine is not running. In circuit analysis it is possible to assume that the parameters of the equivalent circuits are known, and so the networks can be set up with batteries and generators replaced by equivalent circuits in either of the forms of Fig. B-13.

The reader is warned that neither equivalent circuit necessarily provides an accurate picture of what goes on inside the source, although one equivalent may be closer than the other. For example, the power loss in $R_0$ in Fig. B-13*a* is more nearly the power loss in an actual battery than is the power loss in $R_0$ in Fig. B-13*b*. The two circuits are equivalent to each other and to the original source only with respect to the relationship between $V$ and $I$ at their terminals.

**B-7. Solution of Networks by Step-by-step Methods.** In some cases the given information is in such a form that a solution of a network can be obtained by a series of steps, in the course of which there is never more than one unknown quantity. As a typical example consider Fig.

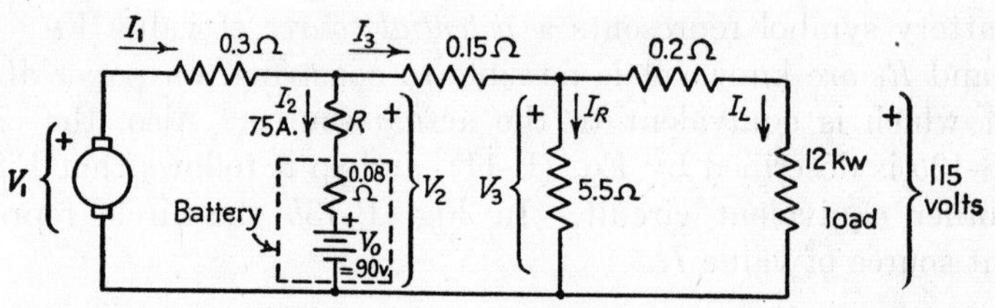


FIG. B-14. A typical network that can be analyzed by the step-by-step method.

B-14. The given data are indicated, and it is required to find the value of $R$ and the potential difference $V_1$ at the source.

$$I_L = \frac{12{,}000}{115} = 104.2 \text{ amps}$$
$$V_3 = (0.2)(104.2) + 115 = 135.8 \text{ volts}$$
$$I_R = \frac{135.8}{5.5} = 24.7 \text{ amps}$$
$$I_3 = 104.2 + 24.7 = 128.9 \text{ amps}$$
$$V_2 = (0.15)(128.9) + 135.8 = 155.1 \text{ volts}$$
$$R = \frac{155.1 - (0.08)(75) - 90}{75} = \frac{59.1}{75} = 0.788 \text{ ohms} \qquad (Ans.)$$
$$I_1 = 75 + 128.9 = 203.9 \text{ amps}$$
$$V_1 = (0.3)(203.9) + 155.1 = 216.3 \text{ volts} \qquad (Ans.)$$

**B-8. Solution of Networks by the Method of Branch Currents.** Figure B-15 will be used to illustrate the several methods that are available for solving networks which cannot be solved by the step-by-step method. Perhaps it is unusual for so many branches to include potential sources, but the potential sources are included in this illustrative example to lend generality to the development.

The language of network analysis uses the terms *branch*, *node* (or *junction*), and *loop* (or *mesh*). A branch is a resistor or a source (sometimes it is any two-terminal section between two nodes), and a node is a point of connection between two or more branches, such as point $B$ or point $G$ (which is really the entire bottom line since it is assumed to be a zero resistance connection). A loop is any closed path which may be traced out along branches of the network.

The aim is to find values for each of the five currents, if the resistances and potential differences of the sources are given. In the branch-current

method the number of nodes at which three or more branches join is counted, and a Kirchhoff current equation is written for each of them, less one, as follows:
For node $B$:

$$I_1 - I_2 - I_4 = 0$$

For node $C$: (B-12)

$$I_2 - I_3 - I_5 = 0$$

A Kirchhoff potential equation is written for each loop of a set of *independent* loops. (An independent set is rather difficult to define. For

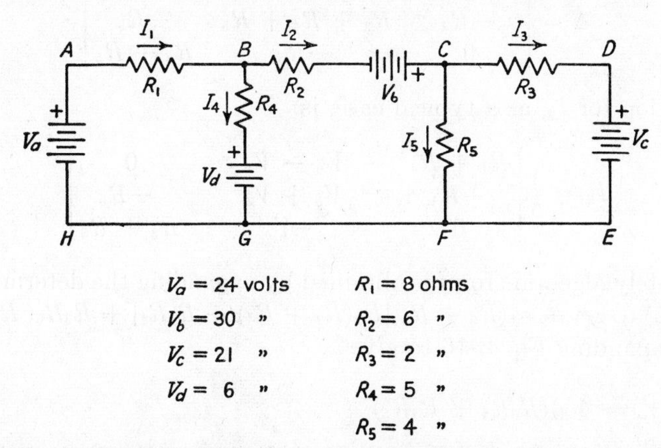


FIG. B-15. A typical network that can be analyzed by the branch-current method.

an elementary treatment it is sufficient to define an independent set of loops as those loops which give a sufficient number of *independent* equations.) Figure B-15 has six loops, but only three that are independent. As an aid in writing the equations it is recalled that when a potential across a resistor is written $RI$, the reference polarity is indicated by a positive sign at the tail end of the current arrow (that is, the reference polarity is a drop in the direction of the current reference direction).
For loop $HABG$:

$$-V_a + R_1 I_1 + R_4 I_4 + V_d = 0$$

For loop $GBCF$:

$$-V_d - R_4 I_4 + R_2 I_2 - V_b + R_5 I_5 = 0 \qquad \text{(B-13)}$$

For loop $FCDE$:

$$-R_5 I_5 + R_3 I_3 + V_c = 0$$

Equations (B-13) can be simplified by eliminating two currents, say $I_4$ and $I_5$, by observing that Eqs. (B-12) can be written $I_4 = I_1 - I_2$ and $I_5 = I_2 - I_3$. After substituting these expressions for $I_4$ and $I_5$ into

Eqs. (B-13), and rearranging terms, three equations in three unknowns are obtained, as follows:

$$\begin{aligned} (R_1 + R_4)I_1 \quad & -R_4 I_2 & &= V_a - V_d \\ -R_4 I_1 + (R_2 + R_4 + R_5)I_2 & & -R_5 I_3 &= V_b + V_d \\ & -R_5 I_2 + (R_3 + R_5)I_3 & &= -V_c \end{aligned} \qquad \text{(B-14)}$$

One way to solve these equations is by the use of determinants.* To do so define the determinant

$$\Delta = \begin{vmatrix} R_1 + R_4 & -R_4 & 0 \\ -R_4 & R_2 + R_4 + R_5 & -R_5 \\ 0 & -R_5 & R_3 + R_5 \end{vmatrix} \qquad \text{(B-15)}$$

The solution for $I_2$, as a typical case, is

$$I_2 = \frac{1}{\Delta} \begin{vmatrix} R_1 + R_4 & V_a - V_d & 0 \\ -R_4 & V_b + V_d & -R_5 \\ 0 & -V_c & R_3 + R_5 \end{vmatrix} \qquad \text{(B-16)}$$

A completely algebraic form is obtained by expanding the determinant of Eq. (B-15) to get $\Delta = (R_3 + R_5)[R_2(R_1 + R_4) + R_4R_1] + R_3R_5(R_1 + R_4)$, and by expanding Eq. B-16 to give

$$\begin{aligned} I_2 &= \frac{1}{\Delta}[(V_a - V_d)(R_3R_4 + R_4R_5) \\ &\quad + (V_b + V_d)(R_1R_3 + R_1R_5 + R_3R_4 + R_4R_5) - (V_c)(R_1R_5 + R_4R_5)] \\ &= \frac{1}{\Delta}[V_a(R_3R_4 + R_4R_5) + V_b(R_1R_3 + R_1R_5 + R_3R_4 + R_4R_5) \\ &\quad - V_c(R_1R_5 + R_4R_5) + V_d(R_1R_3 + R_1R_5)] \end{aligned} \qquad \text{(B-17)}$$

Equation (B-17) will be referred to at a later time. Meanwhile it should be noted that Eq. (B-16) is in itself a solution, because it indicates how a numerical solution should be obtained. For example, directly from Eq. (B-16),

$$I_2 = \frac{\begin{vmatrix} 13 & 18 & 0 \\ -5 & 36 & -4 \\ 0 & -21 & 6 \end{vmatrix}}{\begin{vmatrix} 13 & -5 & 0 \\ -5 & 15 & -4 \\ 0 & -4 & 6 \end{vmatrix}} = \frac{2{,}808 - 1{,}092 + 540}{1{,}170 - 208 - 150} = \frac{2{,}256}{812} = 2.78 \text{ amps}$$

* Of course, the three simultaneous equations can be solved by other methods which, however, are less compact.

**B-9. Superposition and Helmholtz-Thévenin and Norton Theorems.** 1. *Superposition.* The main purpose in writing Eq. (B-17) out in detail is to make it possible to observe that

$$I_2 = I_{2a} + I_{2b} + I_{2c} + I_{2d} \tag{B-18}$$

where

$$I_{2a} = \frac{R_3R_4 + R_4R_5}{\Delta} V_a$$

$$I_{2b} = \frac{R_1R_3 + R_1R_5 + R_3R_4 + R_4R_5}{\Delta} V_b \tag{B-19}$$

etc.

The significant point about Eq. (B-19) is that $I_{2a}$ would be the current in $R_2$ if all sources except $V_a$ were zero (that is, replaced by short circuits), $I_{2b}$ would be due to $V_b$ acting alone, and so forth. Equation (B-18) shows that the actual current can be considered as the sum of component currents due to each of the sources acting alone. Although this proof is given for a specific network, it can be proved for the general case and could also be extended to include current sources. However, when a current source is removed it is replaced by an open circuit.

Superposition is not a very useful theorem for calculation, but it is often useful in theoretical analysis for predicting how a network will behave when only one of several sources undergoes a change. It is important to note that we are dealing with linear networks, which means that each $R$ has a constant value no matter what the value or direction of the current. It cannot be said that superposition holds in nonlinear circuits, such as circuits which include vacuum tubes, transistors, or similar devices.

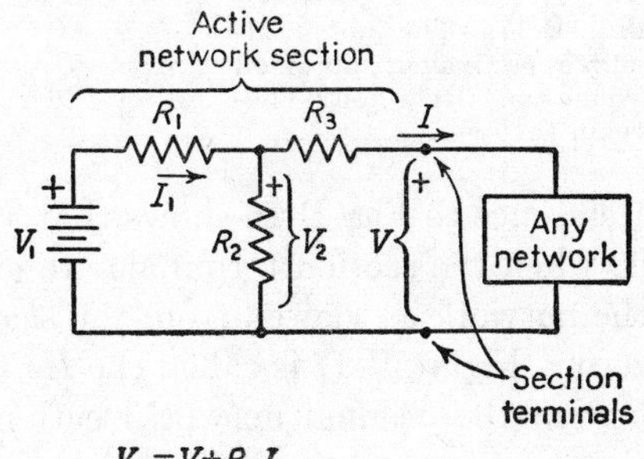


$$V_2 = V + R_3 I$$

$$I_1 = I + \frac{V + R_3 I}{R_2}$$

$$V_1 = R_1\left(I + \frac{V + R_3 I}{R_2}\right) + V + R_3 I$$

$$V_1 = I\left(R_1 + R_3 \frac{R_1 + R_2}{R_2}\right) + V\left(\frac{R_1 + R_2}{R_2}\right)$$

FIG. B-16. Illustration of the Helmholtz-Thévenin theorem.

2. *Helmholtz-Thévenin Theorem.* Consider the network shown in Fig. B-16, in which the network section labeled "Active Network Section" (an active network being one that includes sources) is to be simplified. The section shown is to be regarded as a typical example for demonstrating how an active two-terminal network can be replaced by a simplified network. Since the contents of the rectangle are not given,

$I$ and $V$ cannot be found. However, a relationship does exist between $I$ and $V$. To obtain this relationship assume temporarily that $V$ and $I$ are known, so that the step-by-step solution can be carried out as indicated in the figure, finally arriving at an expression for $V_1$. The relationship has more meaning for the immediate purpose if it is solved for $V$, to give

$$V = V_1 \frac{R_2}{R_1 + R_2} - I\left(R_3 + \frac{R_1 R_2}{R_1 + R_2}\right) \tag{B-20}$$

To repeat, $I$ and $V$ must satisfy Eq. (B-20), and any network section obeying this equation will be equivalent to the original section. Such a network has previously been considered and is given in Fig. B-17. It is, of course, necessary to define $V_0$ and $R_0$ to have the values

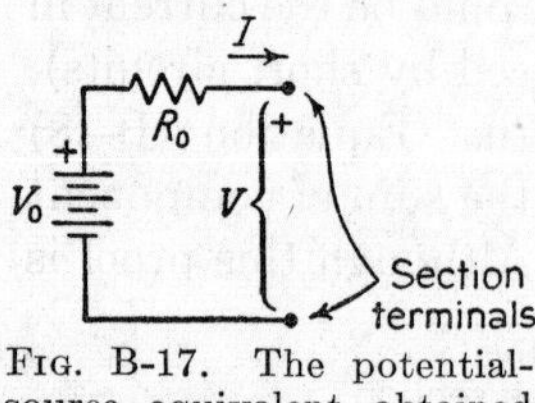

FIG. B-17. The potential-source equivalent obtained from the Helmholtz-Thévenin theorem.

$$V_0 = V_1 \frac{R_2}{R_1 + R_2} \tag{B-21}$$

$$R_0 = R_3 + \frac{R_1 R_2}{R_1 + R_2} \tag{B-22}$$

Reference to Fig. B-16 shows that $V_0$ is the value of $V$ when $I = 0$ (that is, when the section terminals are open), and that $R_0$ is the resistance of the network as viewed from the section terminals when $V_1$ is reduced to zero. Figure B-17 is called the *Helmholtz-Thévenin* (or *Thévenin*) equivalent of the original network section. The theorem can be extended to the most general case where the section can have any number of sources and any combination of resistors.* It is only necessary to be able to find the potential across the section terminals on open circuit and the resistance of the section, viewed from its terminals, when all sources have been reduced to zero (potential sources replaced by short circuits and current sources replaced by open circuits).

The Helmholtz-Thévenin theorem is particularly useful when the replaced portion is of fairly simple form, so that not too many auxiliary calculations are required to find $V_0$ and $R_0$, and also when the network represented by the rectangle is relatively simple, so that the final network is simple. Figure B-15 can be used as an illustration. The Helmholtz-Thévenin theorem is to be used to find $I_2$. The network can be viewed as it is redrawn in Fig. B-18*a*, suggesting that the theorem may be used twice. The relatively simple calculations shown in the figure lead to Fig. B-18*b*, from which the solution for $I_2$ is

* A more general treatment is given in Sec. 11-5.

$$I_2 = \frac{12.91 + 30 - 14}{3.07 + 6 + 1.33} = \frac{28.91}{10.4} = 2.78 \text{ amps}$$

which agrees with the value obtained in Sec. B-8. This same formula would be obtained by applying the Helmholtz-Thévenin theorem to the entire network outside the dotted rectangle.

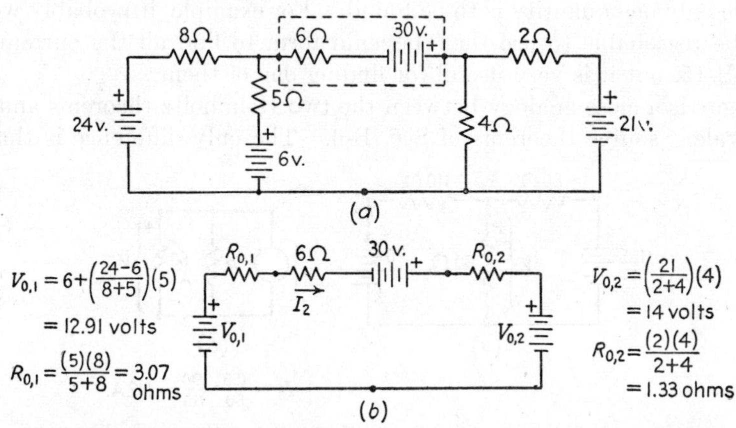


FIG. B-18. Solution of a network by the Helmholtz-Thévenin theorem.

3. *Helmholtz-Norton Theorem.* In Sec. B-6 it was shown that Fig. B-13*b* can be the equivalent of Fig. B-13*a*. However, it was also shown that Fig. B-17, which is identical in form to Fig. B-13*a*, can replace the network section. It follows that the network section of Fig. B-16 can be replaced by the equivalent section shown in Fig. B-19. This is the *Helmholtz-Norton* equivalent. $I_0$ is the current that will flow in the terminals of the original network section if the section terminals are shorted together, and $R_0$ is the resistance of the section between these terminals with all sources reduced to zero.

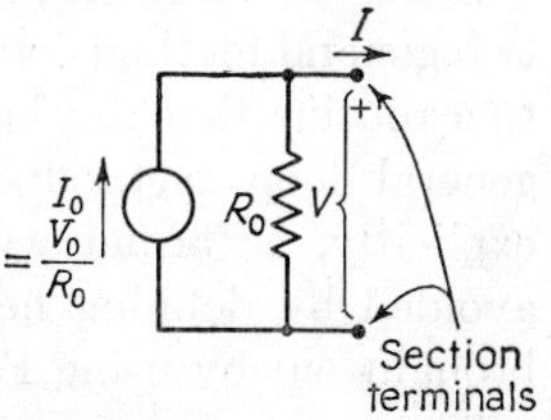

FIG. B-19. The current-source equivalent obtained from the Helmholtz-Norton theorem.

Figure B-15 could be used to illustrate the Helmholtz-Norton theorem, but for this particular case the procedure would be quite lengthy, and so Fig. B-20 is offered as an illustrative example. The potential difference $V$ in Fig. B-20*a* is to be determined. The entire network except the 60-ohm resistor is viewed as the network section to be replaced by the Norton equivalent. The calculation of $I_0$ and $R_0$ is carried out in the figure. Parenthetically it should be noted that the superposition theorem is used in finding $I_0$, since $I_0$ is viewed as being the sum of two components:

$^{155}\!/_{80}$ due to the source on the left, and $-^{90}\!/_{110}$ due to the source on the right. The required solution is obtained from Fig. B-20*b* as

$$V = 1.12 \frac{(60)(46.3)}{60 + 46.3} = 29.3 \text{ volts}$$

The two Helmholtz theorems are particularly useful in many cases where only one quantity is to be found. For example, it probably would not be reasonable to use the Thévenin form to find all the currents in Fig. B-15, but it is very useful for finding one of them.

There is a close analogy between the two Helmholtz theorems and the equivalent source theorems of Sec. B-6. The only difference is that in

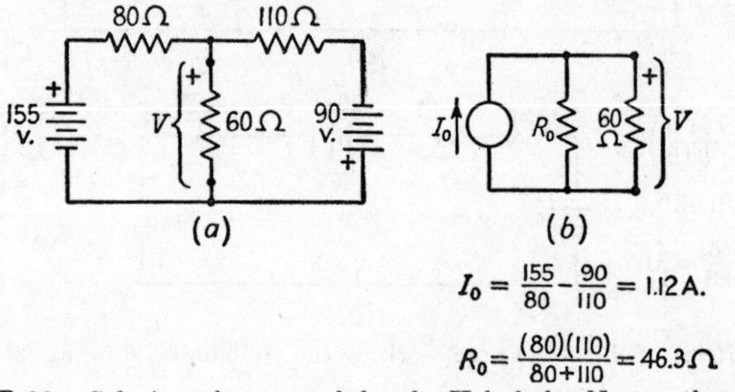


FIG. B-20. Solution of a network by the Helmholtz-Norton theorem.

Sec. B-6 a potential-source or current-source equivalent is set up for a single device (a battery or generator), but in the Helmholtz theorems any two-terminal active network, including any number and types of sources is replaced by a potential-source or current-source equivalent.

**B-10. General Network Analysis Using Loop Currents.** There are two general methods of circuit analysis in which the procedure is reduced to a routine that can be applied by following a few simple rules. In the general loop method only the Kirchhoff potential equations appear explicitly, a formal writing of the Kirchhoff current equations being avoided by defining fictitious *loop currents*. How this comes about is brought out by using Fig. B-15 as an example.

The network is repeated in Fig. B-21, with three curved arrows included to represent fictitious loop currents. Each loop current is imagined to flow on the contour of the loop in which it is drawn. The current in a branch between two loops is then the algebraic sum of the currents in the loops shared by the branch. For example, the current with reference direction downward in $R_4$ is $I_1 - I_2$. This is the same as the first of Eq. (B-12), showing that such a combination of loop currents is an expression of Kirchhoff's current law. In this way the current law is introduced implicitly, rather than explicitly as in Eqs. (B-12).

With the introduction of the concept of loop currents it is convenient to make a distinction between two kinds of branches. A branch which is shared by two or more loops is called a *common* branch, and a branch that is in one loop only is an *external* branch. In the loop analysis it is also convenient to define a branch in a restricted sense, as the sum of all elements in series between two nodes at which three or more branches join. For example, in Fig. B-21, if $R_5$ were replaced by two resistors in series, the combination would still constitute a single branch, in this viewpoint.

For the loop analysis all sources must be presented as potential-source equivalents, as is the case in Fig. B-21. Any current source appearing

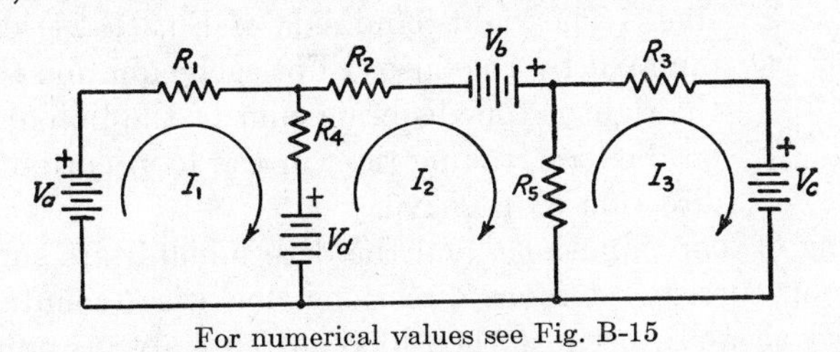


For numerical values see Fig. B-15

FIG. B-21. A network set up for solution by the loop-current method.

in the original network can be combined with a small portion of the network (usually a shunt resistor), and then this combination can be converted to potential-source equivalent.* Therefore, the general loop method is applicable to all networks, sometimes after suitable modifications. Returning to Fig. B-21, a Kirchhoff potential equation is written for each loop, just as was done in Eqs. (B-13). Writing the sum of the potential drops equal to the sum of the potential rises, in the clockwise direction, yields

$$\begin{aligned} R_1I_1 + R_4(I_1 - I_2) + V_d &= V_a \\ R_4(I_2 - I_1) + R_2I_2 + R_5(I_2 - I_3) &= V_b + V_d \\ R_5(I_3 - I_2) + R_3I_3 + V_c &= 0 \end{aligned} \qquad \text{(B-23)}$$

or, in rearranged form,

$$\begin{aligned} (R_1 + R_4)I_1 \qquad -R_4I_2 \qquad\qquad &= V_a - V_d \\ -R_4I_1 + (R_2 + R_4 + R_5)I_2 \qquad -R_5I_3 &= V_b + V_d \\ -R_5I_2 + (R_3 + R_5)I_3 &= -V_c \end{aligned} \qquad \text{(B-24)}$$

Equations (B-24) are identical with Eqs. (B-14), so the determinantal method of solving them is the same as presented in Eqs. (B-15) to (B-17).

* Cases can arise where a single current source must first be replaced by two or more current sources before the conversion to a potential-source equivalent is possible. Such cases are described in Sec. 11-12 of the text.

It is instructive to note that the determinant $\Delta$ of Eq. (B-15) can be written from an inspection of the network when viewed in the light of a loop analysis. Each element of the determinant is the summation of all resistances common to the loops corresponding to the row and column which the element occupies. If the row and column numbers are identical the summation is taken with a positive sign, and with a negative sign if they are different. The negative sign appears because loop current reference directions are in opposition in each common branch. If loop currents are chosen so as to be in the same direction in some common branches, corresponding elements in the determinant are positive. The right-hand side of Eq. (B-24) can be formulated by rule also. For each equation the term on the right is the algebraic sum of the potential sources on the loop, taking rises in the loop current reference direction as positive.

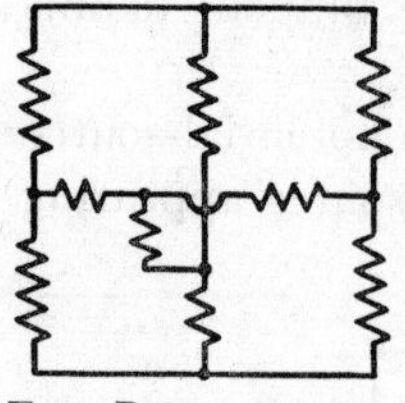

FIG. B-22. Example of a nonflat network.

The writing of loop equations, and the determinant, are simplified by having all loop current reference directions clockwise (counterclockwise would do just as well), because then loop currents always oppose in the common branches. This can always be done with a network that can be drawn in two dimensions, a so-called flat network. A network requiring three dimensions, which must therefore exhibit a crossing of two branches when an attempt is made to draw it in two dimensions, is called a nonflat network. In a nonflat network there will always be at least one branch shared by more than two loop currents, and therefore it follows that at least two of them must be in the same direction. Figure B-22 is an example of a nonflat network.

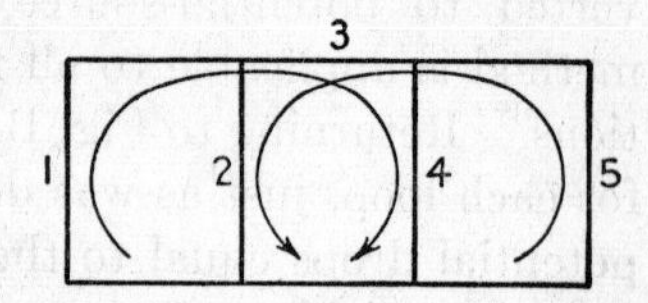


FIG. B-23. Example of a network with insufficient loop currents.

When writing loop equations care must be exercised to be sure that the loop currents occupy the set of independent loops. With the restricted definition of a branch used in this section the set of independent loops are those for which each branch is in at least one loop and for which no two branch currents are the same.* For example, in Fig. B-23 two loops serve to pass through all branches, but the current is the same in branches 1 and 4, and it is the same in branches 2 and 5, and so these two loops do not form an independent set. In a nonflat network it is sometimes difficult to determine the number of independent loops. How-

* By introducing the restricted definition of a branch (see p. 421) this statement can be regarded as a definition of a set of independent loops, which is perhaps slightly more satisfying than the one given on p. 415.

ever, it is always possible to count the number of branches $N_B$ and the number of nodes $N_N$, and from these the number of independent loops $N_L$ can be computed from the equation

$$N_L = N_B - (N_N - 1) \tag{B-25}$$

which is stated without proof

**B-11. General Network Analysis Using Node Potentials.** The node method of analysis is based on the Kirchhoff current equations, which appear explicitly for each node of the network, less one. One node is chosen as a *datum* node, and the variables appearing in the equations are the potentials of the other nodes with respect to the datum node. No current equation is written for the datum node.

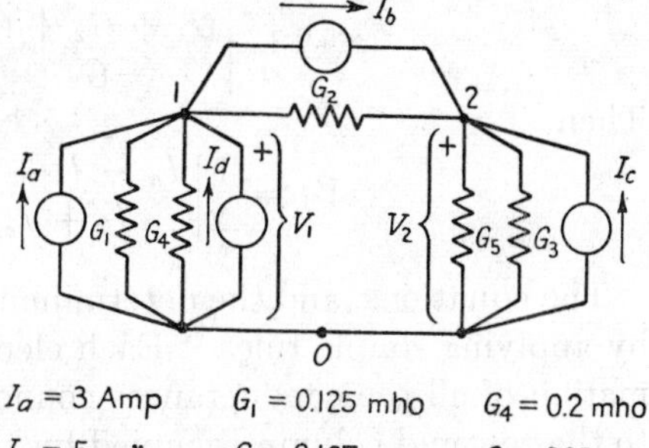


FIG. B-24. A network set up for solution by the node-potential method.

In order to be analyzed by the general node method all sources should be current sources. Any potential source appearing in the original network can be combined with a small portion of the network (usually a series resistor), and then this combination can be converted to a current-source equivalent.* Therefore, the general node method is applicable to all networks, in some cases after suitable modifications. For example, when the sources of Fig. B-15 or Fig. B-21 are changed in this way Fig. B-24 is the result. The new network has only two nondatum nodes, and hence two equations are sufficient for a solution for the node potentials $V_1$ and $V_2$. The datum junction can be chosen at will. A branch between two nondatum junctions is called a *common* branch, and a branch connected to the datum junction is called an *external* branch. Although fewer equations are obtained in this case, the solution for a specific answer is not necessarily simpler than the loop analysis, because the two methods lead to different quantities in the solution.

Note that the total current leaving node 1, through all resistors, is $V_1(G_1 + G_4) + (V_1 - V_2)G_2$. (The Kirchhoff potential law is tacitly employed in writing $V_1 - V_2$ for the potential difference across $G_2$.) With

* Cases can arise where a single potential source must first be replaced by two or more potential sources before the conversion to a current-source equivalent is possible. Such cases are described in Sec. 11-12 of the text.

this idea, the Kirchhoff current equations can be written for junctions 1 and 2, as follows:

$$\begin{aligned}(G_1 + G_4)V_1 + G_2(V_1 - V_2) + I_b &= I_a + I_d \\ (G_3 + G_5)V_2 + G_2(V_2 - V_1) &= I_b + I_c\end{aligned} \tag{B-26}$$

These equations can be transposed, to have the following form,

$$\begin{aligned}(G_1 + G_2 + G_4)V_1 \qquad\qquad -G_2V_2 &= I_a - I_b + I_d \\ -G_2V_1 + (G_2 + G_3 + G_5)V_2 &= I_b + I_c\end{aligned} \tag{B-27}$$

and a solution is available by applying Cramer's rule. For example, if

$$\Delta = \begin{vmatrix} G_1 + G_2 + G_4 & -G_2 \\ -G_2 & G_2 + G_3 + G_5 \end{vmatrix} \tag{B-28}$$

Then

$$V_1 = \frac{1}{\Delta}\begin{vmatrix} I_a - I_b + I_d & -G_2 \\ I_b + I_c & G_2 + G_3 + G_5 \end{vmatrix} \tag{B-29}$$

The equations, and the determinant, can be obtained from the network by applying simple rules. Each element of the determinant is the summation of all the conductances connected to the junctions corresponding to the row and column occupied by the element. If the row and column numbers are identical the summation is taken with a positive sign, and if the row and column numbers are different the sign is negative. This negative sign is a consequence of choosing to put all reference-polarity positive signs at the nondatum nodes. Since this can always be done, even with a nonflat network, the junction analysis can always have negative elements in all positions of the determinant except on the main diagonal. In writing the equations in the form of Eq. (B-27) the rule to be followed on the right-hand side is that the source currents coming together at a junction should be summed algebraically, with those entering the junction taken as positive.

For the numerical values given in Fig. B-24 the solution of the network is

$$\Delta = \begin{vmatrix} 0.492 & -0.167 \\ -0.167 & 0.917 \end{vmatrix} = 0.451 - 0.028 = 0.423$$

$$V_1 = \frac{\begin{vmatrix} -0.8 & -0.167 \\ 15.5 & 0.917 \end{vmatrix}}{0.423} = \frac{-.733 + 2.580}{.423} = \frac{1.847}{.423} = 4.36 \text{ volts}$$

$$V_2 = \frac{\begin{vmatrix} 0.492 & -0.8 \\ -0.167 & 15.5 \end{vmatrix}}{0.423} = \frac{7.62 - .13}{0.423} = \frac{7.49}{0.423} = 17.68 \text{ volts}$$

In order to provide a check with previous solutions, the current $I_2$ of Fig. B-15 can be found from the knowledge of $V_1$ and $V_2$. The branch through which $I_2$ flows can be drawn, as in Fig. B-25, with the potential across it known from the formula $V_1 - V_2$, as indicated. The current is

$$I_2 = \frac{30 + V_1 - V_2}{6} = \frac{30 - 13.32}{6} = \frac{16.68}{6} = 2.58 \text{ amps}$$

in agreement with the value obtained by two other methods. In this example the node method is perhaps the simpler. However, as is demonstrated by Example 11-5 in Chap. 11, the node analysis is sometimes more complicated.

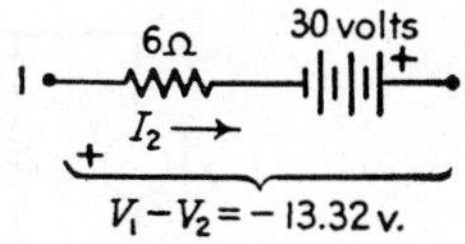

FIG. B-25. Branch between nodes 1 and 2, in its original form.

**B-12. Reciprocity.** The principle of reciprocity is described here in terms of two specific examples, but it is applicable to any linear network having only one source. As the first example, consider Fig. B-26 in which two branches are singled out and labeled $A$ and $B$. First let a potential source $V$ be placed in branch $A$ and the current determined in branch $B$, as shown in Fig. B-26$a$. Then let the potential source be placed in branch $B$ and the current determined in branch $A$. The *reciprocity theorem* states that the current $I$ will be the same in both cases. In the use of the reciprocity theorem the current $I$ will have the same sign, as well as magnitude, in the two cases if the polarity of the source bears the same relation to the current reference direction in both

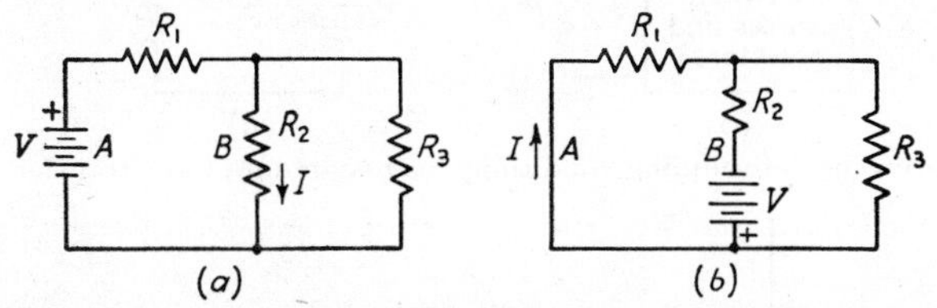


FIG. B-26. Example of reciprocity between a potential source and a current response.

cases. That is, when the source is in branch $B$ its polarity is such that the current reference direction previously in branch $B$ is from minus to plus through the source. The same situation holds for branch $A$.

The reciprocity theorem also applies to a network having a single current source, as illustrated in Fig. B-27. Let the current source be across branch $A$ and let the potential be determined across branch $B$, as shown in Fig. B-27$a$. Then let the current source be placed across branch $B$ and the potential difference be determined across branch $A$. The reciprocity theorem states that the potential difference $V$ is the same in both cases. $V$ will have the same sign if the reference polarity and current directions are as in Fig. B-27*b*. For example, when the source is across branch *B* its current points toward the node that was labeled with the positive reference-polarity sign when *V* was measured across that branch. Branch *A* is treated similarly.

These two forms of the reciprocity theorem can be proved for more general cases. The form illustrated by Fig. B-26 is proved by using the

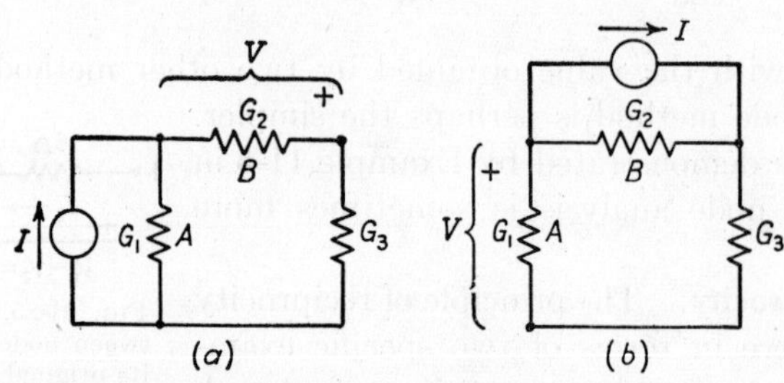


FIG. B-27. Example of reciprocity between a current source and a potential response.

loop analysis, and the form shown in Fig. B-27 is proved by the node method. In each case, the proof depends upon the fact that the determinant of the network equations is symmetrical about its main diagonal. The theorem is not true for a nonlinear network.

**B-13. Maximum Power Transfer.** Suppose a resistor is to absorb power from an active network, which may be represented by the rectangle

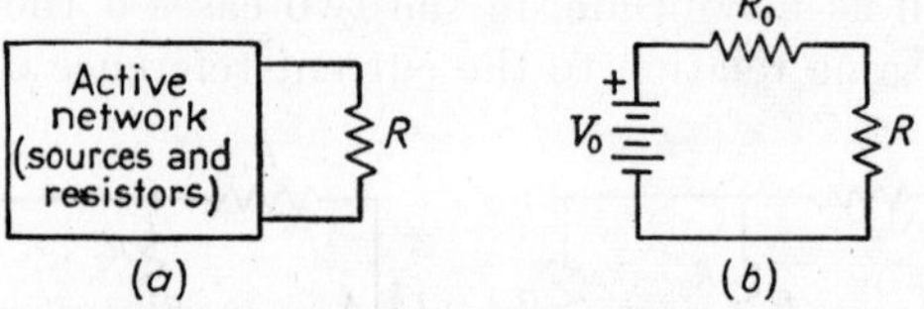


FIG. B-28. Setup for determining conditions for maximum-power transfer to a resistor.

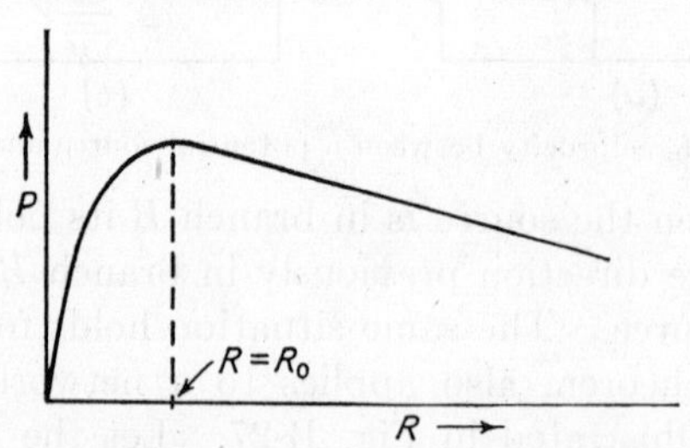


FIG. B-29. Variation of power delivered to *R* in Fig. B-28, as a function of *R*.

of Fig. B-28*a*. If the resistor *R* has its value varied the power it absorbs will vary in the manner shown in Fig. B-29. The value of *R*, at which the power is a maximum, is found by replacing the rectangle by its Thévenin equivalent, as shown in Fig. B-28*b*. $V_0$ and $R_0$ can be considered known, since they can be found by the techniques of Sec. B-9.

The power delivered to $R$ is

$$P = \frac{V_0^2 R}{(R_0 + R)^2} \tag{B-30}$$

and to make it a maximum its derivative with respect to $R$ is set equal to zero. Thus the value of $R$ for maximum power is the solution of the equation

$$\frac{dP}{dR} = V_0^2 \frac{(R_0 + R)^2 - 2R(R_0 + R)}{(R_0 + R)^4} = 0 \tag{B-31}$$

which gives

$$R = R_0 \tag{B-32}$$

**B-14. Summary.** In circuit analysis a network is broken down into parts for which the law relating the potential difference and the current is known. If a d-c network section is passive, meaning that it is composed completely of resistances, it can be reduced to an equivalent resistance. If a section of the network is active it can be replaced by one of the Helmholtz equivalents. In fact, the Helmholtz equivalent networks degenerate into equivalent resistance when the network section which they represent becomes passive.

A complete network solution is obtained by applying the two Kirchhoff laws to the combinations of the various sections making up the network. In many specific cases a step-by-step method of analysis leads to a solution most quickly. However, for more general situations, and for the derivation of various properties of networks in general, the general loop and node methods are available. Many theorems about network behavior can be proved using the general methods, of which the reciprocity theorem is typical. Additional theorems are given in Chap. 11.

The analysis of a d-c circuit is formally the same as for an a-c network. Therefore, the material of Chap. 11 may be considered as supplementary to this Appendix. Finally, it is to be kept in mind that the procedures and conclusions presented here apply only to linear systems, which eliminate devices such as vacuum tubes and transistors.

The two general methods do not do exactly the same job, because the solution of one is in terms of loop currents, and the solution of the other is in terms of node potentials. Therefore, although one method will sometimes be simpler to carry out, it may not necessarily be the simpler method for finding a specific current or potential difference.

## PROBLEMS

**B-1.** Find the equivalent resistance of the network shown in Fig. PB-1 if the dotted resistor is omitted.

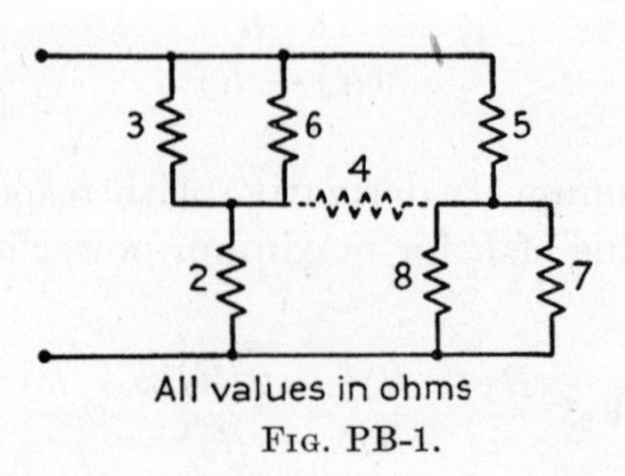


FIG. PB-1.

**B-2.** Find the equivalent resistance of the network of Fig. PB-1 if the dotted resistor is included.

**B-3.** Figure PB-3 shows an arrangement for obtaining a wide range of resistance values. Each of the five double-throw switches may be in an up, down, or

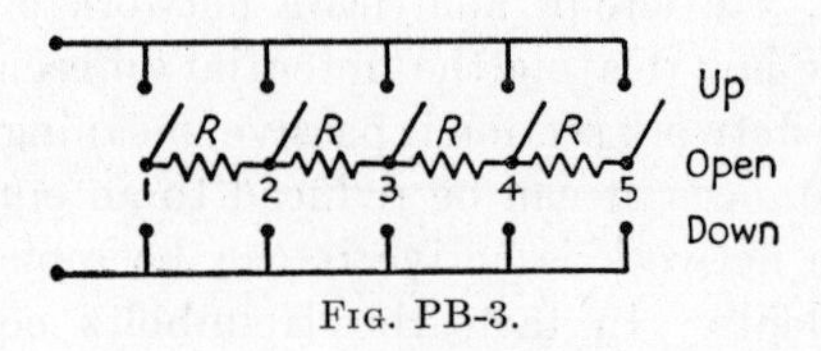


FIG. PB-3.

open position. For each of the four cases listed below determine the resistance of the combination.

| Switch No. | Case | | | |
|---|---|---|---|---|
| | *a* | *b* | *c* | *d* |
| 1 | Up | Up | Down | Up |
| 2 | Down | Up | Open | Down |
| 3 | Up | Down | Up | Open |
| 4 | Down | Down | Down | Up |
| 5 | Up | Open | Up | Down |

**B-4.** In Fig. PB-3 suppose each resistor has a value of 20 ohms. What is the power dissipated in each resistor for each of the switch combinations specified in Prob. B-4.

**B-5.** Use the formulas for a Y–Δ transformation to find the equivalent resistance of Fig. B-9.

**B-6.** Use the Y–Δ transformation to find a Δ equivalent for the three-terminal network of Fig. PB-6. Also use the Δ–Y transformation to find a Y equivalent of the original network. Points labeled *A*, *B*, and *C* are the network terminals.

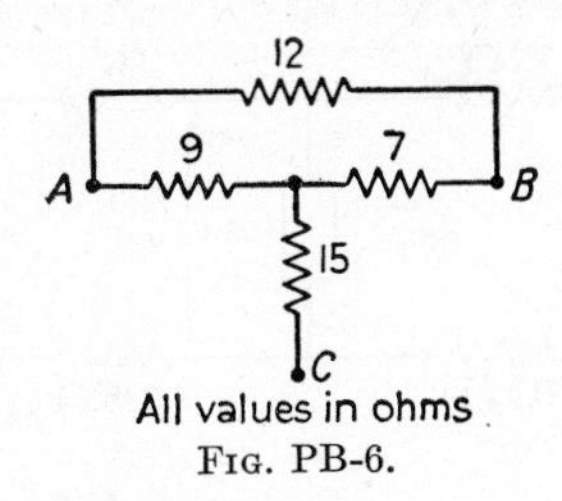


FIG. PB-6.

**B-7.** The system of potential sources shown in Fig. PB-7 is connected first to Fig. B-10$a$ and then to Fig. B-10$b$. By actually obtaining the appropriate alge-

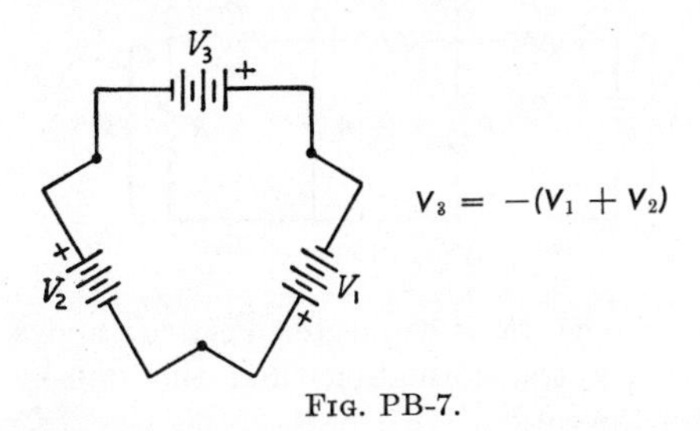


FIG. PB-7.

braic expressions, prove that if the two networks are equivalent the sum of the $R^2I$ power dissipation is the same in each network.

**B-8.** Find $V_1$ in Fig. B-14, but first replace the T section to the right of the battery branch by an equivalent Π.

**B-9.** Figure PB-9 shows a resistor network designed to provide proper potentials at the electrodes of a vacuum tube. These potentials are to have the values

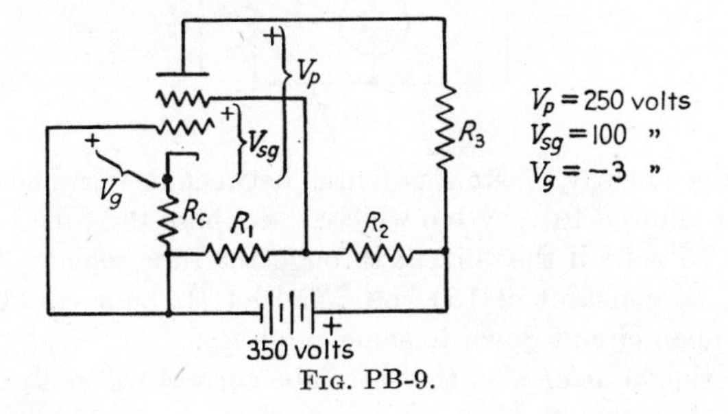


FIG. PB-9.

indicated in the figure, and it is further known that for these conditions the plate current $I_p = 4$ ma and the screen grid current $I_{sg} = 0.8$ ma. There is no current in the control grid circuit, so that the sum of $I_p$ and $I_{sg}$ flows in $R_c$. Find values of the four $R$'s, with the stipulation that the power dissipated in the combination of $R_1$ and $R_2$ shall be 6 watts.

**B-10.** In Fig. PB-10 determine values of $V_1$ and $V_2$ so that each source will supply the same power, and determine that power.

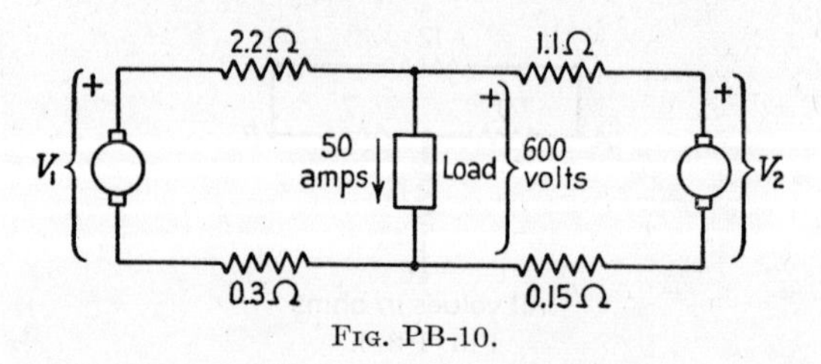


FIG. PB-10.

**B-11.** Use a step-by-step method of solution to find an expression for the ratio of potentials $V_2/V_1$ for Fig. PB-11.

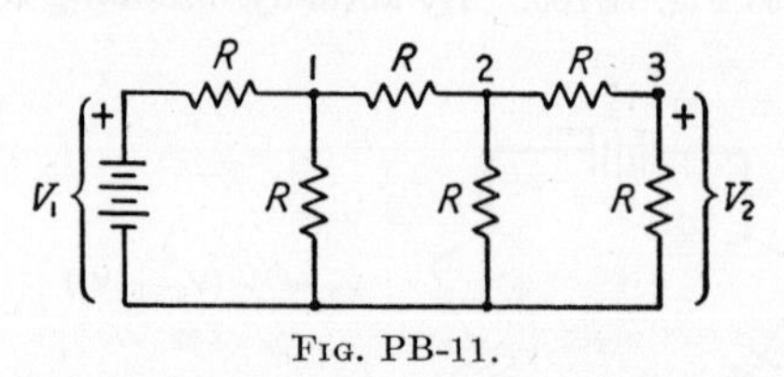


FIG. PB-11.

**B-12.** Suppose a resistance $2R$ is connected between nodes 1 and 3 in Fig. PB-11. Use the necessary transformations and the step-by-step method to obtain an expression for the ratio $V_2/V_1$.

**B-13.** PB-13 shows the circuit used to obtain a regulated potential difference by means of a gas electronic tube. The tube, represented by the circle, has the

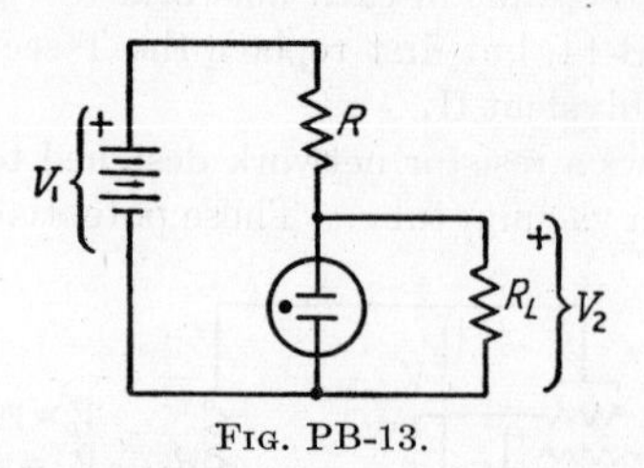


FIG. PB-13.

property of having a nearly constant potential between its terminals, if the current through it is not allowed to vary too widely. Suppose the tube potential difference remains at 75 volts if the current through the tube remains between 5 and 30 ma. Let $V_1$ be constant at 150 volts, and let $R_L$ be a variable load which may vary from open circuit down to some value $R_m$.

*a.* Determine the value of $R$ so that the tube current will not exceed 30 ma.

*b.* Determine the value $R_m$.

*c.* What will be the maximum power dissipated in $R$?

**B-14.** Suppose the circuit of Fig. PB-13 is to be used to stabilize the potential difference across a fixed load resistor of 3,000 ohms, against variations of the source potential $V_1$. The minimum value of $V_1$ is 100 volts.

*a.* What value should $R$ have if the current in the tube is not to be less than 5 ma?

*b.* What will be the largest permissible value for $V_1$?

**B-15.** In Fig. B-14 suppose $R = 0.5$ ohm, and assume the resistance of the load is independent of the potential difference across it. If the battery current is 75 amp as indicated, what is the value of $V_1$, and what is the power delivered to the lighting load?

**B-16.** In Fig. B-14 suppose $R = 0.5$ ohm, and suppose the resistance of the load is independent of the potential difference across the load. In this case the current through the battery is to be adjusted to zero.

*a.* What value should $V_1$ have to make the battery current zero?

*b.* Suppose $V_1 = 2{,}000$ volts, to what value should the 0.3-ohm resistor be changed in order to make the battery current zero?

**B-17.** Figure PB-17 illustrates the "Edison three-wire system" of transmitting power. Find the values for $V_1$ and $V_2$ for the conditions indicated.

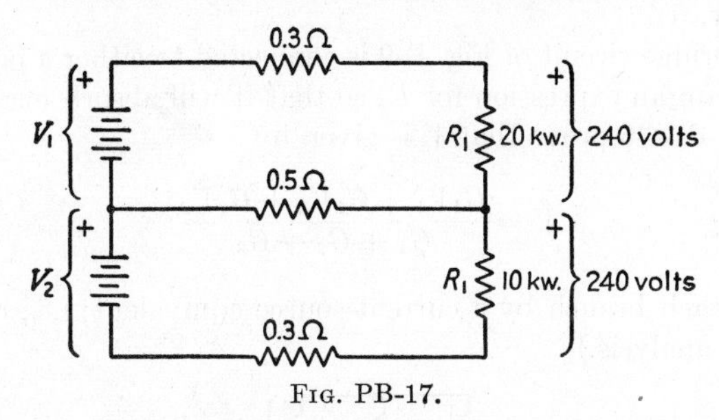


FIG. PB-17.

**B-18.** Suppose $V_1 = V_2 = 320$ volts in Fig. PB-17, and that the load resistances $R_1$ and $R_2$ have the same values as in Prob. B-17. Determine the power dissipated in each of the load resistors.

*a.* Solve using the Y–Δ transformation.

*b.* Solve using the branch-current method of solution.

**B-19.** Solve Prob. B-18 using the general method of loop currents.

**B-20.** Suppose a potential source of potential $V$ is connected between the terminals of the bridge circuit of Fig. B-9.

*a.* Use the general method of loop currents to obtain an expression for the current through $R_3$.

*b.* Prove that this current is zero if $R_1R_5 = R_2R_4$.

**B-21.** Do Prob. B-20 using the Helmholtz-Thévenin theorem.

**B-22.** Do Prob. B-20 using the Helmholtz-Norton theorem.

**B-23.** Use the Helmholtz-Thévenin theorem to determine $I_5$ in Fig. B-15. (*Hint:* apply the theorem twice.)

**B-24.** Use the Helmholtz-Norton theorem to determine $I_4$ in Fig. B-15. (HINT: use Thévenin's form of the theorem, and superposition, in finding the Norton equivalent.)

**B-25.** Check the superposition theorem on the current in $R_1$ of Fig. PB-17 for the conditions stipulated in Prob. B-18.

**B-26.** Use a general loop method of analysis to do Prob. B-11.

**B-27.** Use a general loop method of analysis to do Prob. B-12.

**B-28.** Use a general node method of analysis to do Prob. B-11.

**B-29.** Use a general node method of analysis to do Prob. B-12.

**B-30.** Use a general node method of analysis to do Prob. B-18.

**B-31.** Suppose a current source of strength $I$ is connected between the terminals of the bridge network of Fig. B-9. Use the general node method of analysis to obtain an expression for the potential difference across resistor $R_3$. What conditions on $R_1$, $R_2$, $R_4$, and $R_5$ will cause this potential difference to be zero?

**B-32.** Check the reciprocity theorem for a potential source and a current response, taking the current through the right-hand resistor in Fig. PB-11.

**B-33.** Carry out a proof of the theorem for maximum-power transfer using a current-source equivalent to represent the active network in Fig. B-28*a*.

**B-34.** In Fig. PB-11 suppose the last resistor on the right has a different value from the others. Call it $R'$. Obtain an expression for $R'$ such that it will absorb maximum power.

**B-35.** If the bridge circuit of Fig. B-9 is connected to either a potential or current source, obtain an expression for $R_3$ so that it will absorb maximum power.

**B-36.** In Fig. PB-36 prove that $V$ is given by

$$V = \frac{G_1V_1 + G_2V_2 + G_3V_3}{G_1 + G_2 + G_3}$$

(Hint: replace each branch by a current-source equivalent; *i.e.*, reduce the network for a node analysis.)

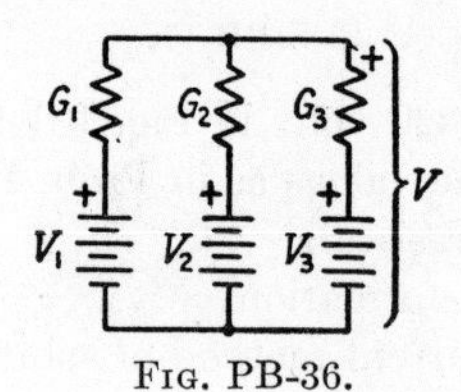


Fig. PB-36.

**B-37.** Verify the reciprocity theorem for Fig. B-26.

**B-38.** Verify the reciprocity theorem for Fig. B-27.

# APPENDIX C

## SOME TRIGONOMETRIC IDENTITIES

$\sin^2 x + \cos^2 x = 1$

$\sin (x + y) = \sin x \cos y + \cos x \sin y$

$\sin (x - y) = \sin x \cos y - \cos x \sin y$

$\cos (x + y) = \cos x \cos y - \sin x \sin y$

$\cos (x - y) = \cos x \cos y + \sin x \sin y$

$\sin 2x = 2 \sin x \cos x$

$\cos 2x = 2 \cos^2 x - 1 = 1 - 2 \sin^2 x$

$$\sin \frac{x}{2} = \sqrt{\frac{1 - \cos x}{2}} = \frac{1}{2}(\sqrt{1 + \sin x} - \sqrt{1 - \sin x})$$

$$\cos \frac{x}{2} = \sqrt{\frac{1 + \cos x}{2}} = \frac{1}{2}(\sqrt{1 + \sin x} + \sqrt{1 - \sin x})$$

$\sin^2 x = \frac{1}{2}(1 - \cos 2x)$

$\cos^2 x = \frac{1}{2}(1 + \cos 2x)$

$\sin x \sin y = \frac{1}{2}[\cos (x - y) - \cos (x + y)]$

$\cos x \cos y = \frac{1}{2}[\cos (x - y) + \cos (x + y)]$

$\sin x \cos y = \frac{1}{2}[\sin (x - y) + \sin (x + y)]$

$$\sin x + \sin y = 2 \sin \left(\frac{x + y}{2}\right) \cos \left(\frac{x - y}{2}\right)$$

$$\sin x - \sin y = 2 \cos \left(\frac{x + y}{2}\right) \sin \left(\frac{x - y}{2}\right)$$

$$\cos x + \cos y = 2 \cos \left(\frac{x + y}{2}\right) \cos \left(\frac{x - y}{2}\right)$$

$$\cos x - \cos y = -2 \sin \left(\frac{x + y}{2}\right) \sin \left(\frac{x - y}{2}\right)$$

$\sin^2 x - \sin^2 y = \sin (x + y) \sin (x - y)$

$\cos^2 x - \cos^2 y = -\sin (x + y) \sin (x - y)$

$\cos^2 x - \sin^2 y = \cos (x + y) \cos (x - y)$

# REFERENCES


## INTRODUCTORY TEXTS

DAHL, O. G. C., "Electric Circuits—Theory and Applications," McGraw-Hill Book Company, Inc., New York, 1928.

EE STAFF, MIT, "Electric Circuits," John Wiley & Sons, Inc., New York, 1943.

FRAZIER, R. H., "Elementary Electric-circuit Theory," McGraw-Hill Book Company, Inc., New York, 1945.

KERCHNER, R. M., and G. F. CORCORAN, "Alternating Current Circuits," 2d ed., John Wiley & Sons, Inc., New York, 1950.

KNIGHT, A. R., and G. H. FETT, "Introduction to Circuit Analysis," Harper & Brothers, New York, 1943.

LAWRENCE, R. R., "Principles of Alternating Currents," McGraw-Hill Book Company, Inc., New York, 1935.

REED, M. B., "Alternating Current Circuit Theory," Harper & Brothers, New York, 1948.

TANG, K. Y., "Alternating Current Circuits," 2d ed., International Textbook Company, Scranton, Pa., 1951.

VAIL, C. R., "Circuits in Electrical Engineering," Prentice-Hall, Inc., New York, 1950.

## ADVANCED TEXTS

Topics of particular interest are indicated in parentheses.

CLARKE, E. W., "Circuit Analysis of A-C Power Systems," John Wiley & Sons, Inc., New York, 1943. (Polyphase.)

GUILLEMIN, E. A., "Communication Networks," Vols. I, II, John Wiley & Sons, Inc., New York, 1931, 1935. (General, Vol. II: filters.)

LECORBEILLER, P., "Matrix Analysis of Electric Networks," John Wiley & Sons, Inc., New York, 1950. (General.)

LEPAGE, W. R., and S. SEELY, "General Network Analysis," McGraw-Hill Book Company, Inc., New York, 1952. (General.)

MALTI, M. G., "Electric Circuit Analysis," John Wiley & Sons, Inc., New York, 1930. (General.)

PIERCE, G. W., "Electric Oscillations and Electric Waves," McGraw-Hill Book Company, Inc., New York, 1920. (General.)

SAH, A. P., "Dyadic Circuit Analysis," International Textbook Company, Scranton Pa., 1939. (Polyphase.)

SHEA, T. E., "Transmission Networks and Wave Filters," D. Van Nostrand Company, Inc., New York, 1929. (Filters.)

TERMAN, F. E., "Radio Engineers' Handbook," Sec. 3, McGraw-Hill Book Company, Inc., New York, 1943. (General.)

WEINBACH, M. P., "Alternating Current Circuits," The Macmillan Company, New York, 1933. (General.)

## TEXTS OF HISTORICAL INTEREST

BEDELL, F., "Alternating Currents," W. J. Johnston Company, New York, 1893.
STEINMETZ, C. P., "Alternating Current Phenomena," W. J. Johnston Company, New York, 1897.

# INDEX

J



K



L



M

Q



R